S0-AAI-613

CALCIPHYLAXIS

'Tis strange—but true; for truth is always strange.

BYRON: *Don Juan*

HANS SELYE

CALCIPHYLAXIS

THE UNIVERSITY OF CHICAGO PRESS

Library of Congress Catalog Card Number: 62-13922
The University of Chicago Press, Chicago & London
The University of Toronto Press, Toronto 5, Canada

© *1962 by The University of Chicago. All rights reserved*
Published 1962. Composed and printed by
The University of Chicago Press, Chicago, Illinois, U.S.A.
Color Atlas printed in Canada

Foreword

It is given to very few investigators in modern medicine to discover a new phenomenon, to describe it, and to characterize it. This Dr. Selye has done by his introduction of calciphylaxis as an entirely new biologic concept—one sure to have an impact on medicine comparable to that of the author's earlier concept of stress.

Pathologic calcification in soft tissues has long been known, but little has been known about its mechanisms or its predisposing factors. Dr. Selye has shown, in a series of brilliant experiments, that tissues may be made sensitive to calcification; this sensitization he has named "calciphylaxis." During the period of sensitivity calcification may be induced by one of a number of challengers, any of which by itself may be quite without effect. The important, heretofore unrecognized feature in calciphylaxis is the sequence of, first, sensitization and, then, challenge. The challenge itself may be as harmless as plucking a few hairs, pinching the skin, or administering such a common and seemingly innocuous substance as the white of an egg.

In introducing this phenomenon under the name "calciphylaxis," Dr. Selye has also made use of a number of related but also new concepts. Of these, the most original is that of vital mordants. He thinks of the challenging agents utilized in his experiments as attracting calcium as histologic mordants attract dyes, and to him the vital mordant is the equivalent of a challenging agent. The characteristics of calciphylaxis are: (1) the calcifier, or systemic sensitizing agent; (2) the challenger, or vital mordant; (3) the adjuvant, or topical activator of the vital mordant, which potentiates the action of subthreshold amounts of the challenger; and (4) the critical period, which must elapse between treatment with the sensitizer and with the challenger. Since all these, with the exception of the adjuvant, must be specifically interrelated, both in time and in space, to result in the reaction that constitutes calciphylaxis, it is not surprising that the phenomenon has hitherto gone undetected.

Another feature of calciphylaxis is its selectivity. While the sensitivity itself is always systemic, the end result may be either a local or a topical appearance of calcification at the point of application of the challenger, or it may, depending upon the time-and-space relationships above referred to, be caused to appear in such diverse but predetermined locations as the pancreas, the spleen, the salivary

v

glands, the lacrimal glands, the Kupffer cells of the liver, the uterus, or the thyroid or the parathyroid glands. In its specificity calciphylaxis bears a certain resemblance to other hypersensitivity reactions, such as the tuberculin reaction, classical anaphylaxis, and the Arthus phenomenon. In other respects, however, calciphylaxis differs, especially since there is no evidence of immune-body formation and thus of an antigen-antibody response.

Dr. Selye is careful to point out that it remains to be shown whether there are any phenomena in human physiology or pathology that correspond to the experimentally induced calciphylactic responses. He does, however, propose to explore the possible connections between calciphylaxis and the collagen diseases, such as dermatomyositis, lupus erythematosus, mysotis ossificans, and sarcoidosis. Other analogies suggest themselves to him and no doubt will receive attention. In the meantime he has observed and placed on record a whole chain of new biologic phenomena; these are certain to receive much attention in the years to follow publication of this book.

FRANKLIN C. McLEAN

CHICAGO, ILLINOIS
February 1962

Preface

Calciphylaxis is a special kind of hypersensitivity reaction which hitherto escaped attention, presumably because both its manifestations and the mechanism of its production are quite unlike those of other biologic responses.

Factors conducive to soft-tissue calcification have held a singular interest for me ever since, at the age of nineteen, I published my first paper on hypervitaminosis D. In retrospect it is difficult to see how I could have missed noticing calciphylaxis during the subsequent thirty-five years of planned effort; yet it is only some nine months ago that in the course of work done conjointly by our group we stumbled upon the key to it by accident. My only excuse for this blindness to a phenomenon which was clearly within my reach all this time is the well-known difficulty of seeing the wholly unexpected and accepting the improbable.

We are not prepared to think of a mammal as an animal which—like snakes or crabs—could cast off its skin and grow a new one. We have no reason to look for selective calcification in the parathyroids or the carotid body after an intravenous injection of ferrous chloride. There is nothing in our past experience to suggest that the subcutaneous injection of insulin on the back could produce circumscribed, symmetrical calcification of the cheeks or that a single dose of a histamine discharger might elicit widespread calcification throughout the skin and skeletal musculature. It is perhaps even more unexpected that three to five days after discontinuation of parathyroid hormone treatment (but not at an earlier time!) a single dose of serotonin would produce extensive and often fatal necrotizing muscular lesions without calcification. Yet—as we shall see—all these and many other equally unusual changes can be elicited with great regularity in the calciphylactically sensitized organism under certain well-defined conditions.

Calciphylactic hypersensitivity depends upon the administration or endogenous production of a *sensitizing calcifier* (e.g., vitamin-D compounds, parathyroid hormone) and of a *challenger* (e.g., metallic salts, mastocyte depletors, albumen); in addition usually a *"critical period"* must elapse between sensitization and challenge. If these conditions are fulfilled, the manifold calciphylactic syndromes can be obtained very consistently; yet they are not likely to occur accidentally because their production depends upon treatment with certain agents under strictly defined conditions of dosage, timing, route of administration, etc. Besides, calciphylaxis is readily prevented by seemingly incidental factors (e.g., stress, dietary ingredients).

Little is known as yet about the biologic significance of calciphylaxis, but the phenomenon appears to be essentially a defense reaction which—as many other homeostatic responses, including serologic immunity and the General Adaptation Syndrome—may become pathogenic under certain circumstances. It remains to be seen to what extent calciphylaxis plays a role in physiology and pathology and whether it can be used for therapy.

The purpose of this monograph is to facilitate further research on calciphylaxis by summarizing what we have learned about it in the laboratory and co-ordinating these data with comparable observations in clinical medicine. To accomplish this, the book must be not only a text but also an atlas and a fairly complete source of references.

Accordingly, our material has been subdivided as follows:

Chapter i is a general introduction. It briefly *characterizes calciphylaxis* and presents a *color atlas* of its most striking morphologic changes. This is followed by an outline of the *history* of calciphylaxis, a *glossary* of definitions and a section on general *methodology*.

Chapter ii deals with *topical calciphylaxis* induced by the direct application of challengers to the target area.

Chapter iii is devoted to *systemic calciphylaxis* elicited by the effects of challengers at a distance from the site of their application.

Chapter iv describes the factors that influence *susceptibility to calciphylaxis* (e.g., site of challenge, critical period, diet, stress, hormones, nervous stimuli, etc.).

Chapter v deals with the so-called *direct calcifiers*, substances that cause calcification upon contact with tissues without the necessity of sensitization. We have no proof that the action of direct calcifiers is related to calciphylaxis, but the lesions are sufficiently similar in the two cases to warrant conjoint study.

Chapter vi represents a detailed review of all those spontaneous *diseases of man* that in our opinion are sufficiently similar to certain experimental calciphylactic syndromes to warrant re-examination from this new point of view.

Chapter vii is frankly labeled *"Speculations"*; it can make no pretense at offering definitive explanations. However, while the other sections are virtually limited to the factual description of observations, here we shall attempt to interpret our data as best we can and to consider their possible meaning for biology and medicine. Such a strict division of fact and fancy is particularly necessary in the case of this monograph since the complexity and novelty of its subject may readily give rise to confusion between a definitely established observation and its yet unproven interpretation.

Perhaps the most difficult decision in connection with this book was not how but when to write it. My monograph *Stress* appeared fourteen years after the first publication on *A Syndrome Produced by Various Noxious Agents.* The present volume goes to press three decades after the first paper on *A Condition Simulating Human Scleroderma in Rats Injected with Parathyroid Hormone,* but barely nine months have passed since we thought of writing this book, and it is scheduled to be published within three months. This pace raised a number of technical problems for author and publisher alike.

During these critical months almost the entire staff of our Institute has been engaged in research on calciphylaxis, and new syndromes still come to light continuously. In addition, as the original publications on calciphylaxis began to appear, many readers called our attention to papers on similar lesions in man which should be mentioned in connection with the experimental syndromes. Such additional information was introduced in the galley proofs, but it meant inserting many photographs and references between the already consecutively numbered ones and this had to be done by adding letters to the corresponding numerals. These complications might have been avoided had we taken another three decades to develop the concept and write this book, but during this time no doubt new observations would have brought in further complications—and possibly even the author's energy might have run out. Besides, it is precisely while a field is developing that a co-ordinated description of its already established parts can do most to guide its logical systematic development.

ACKNOWLEDGMENTS

It is a pleasant duty to thank Professor F. C. McLean for the interest he has taken in this book. The lectures he has delivered as a Claude Bernard Visiting Professor at the University of Montreal have been the stimulus for many of our experiments on calciphylaxis, and it is owing to his intercession that arrangements could be made with the university press of his alma mater for the rapid and extremely competent publication of this work. I am particularly grateful to him also for having critically read the manuscript and for consenting to write the Foreword.

I would also like to take this opportunity to express my heartfelt gratitude to Sister Adrian Marie Hofstetter and Doctors M. Cantin, J.-M. Dieudonné, G. Gabbiani, G. Gentile, S. Grasso, T. Ishii, P. Jean, P. Mendell, L. Mikulaj, N. Padmanabhan, P. Prioreschi, R. Strebel, B. Tuchweber, J. Vašků and R. Veilleux, who assisted me in many of the original experiments that form the subject matter of this volume.

My special thanks are due to Mrs. E. Staub and Miss M. MacKay (who edited the manuscript), Mr. G. Ember and Mrs. Thérèse Peternell (the librarians of our Institute, who helped to collect the literature and prepared the Index), Mr. K. Nielsen and Miss M. Barath (who prepared the histologic slides and photographic illustrations), as well as to the Misses L. Côté, A. Dunn, and N. Mathieu and Mrs. L. Shapkin (for the extraordinary care and devotion with which they prepared the typescript and read the proofs).

I would also like to thank my publishers, the University of Chicago Press, for the special attention they have given to all details of manufacture and design.

The original experimental work that forms the basis of this volume was subsidized by: The Gustavus and Louise Pfeiffer Research Foundation, who also underwrote the rather considerable expenses of the Color Atlas; the National Heart Institute (Grant No. H-6182), the National Institute of Arthritis and Metabolic Diseases (Grant No. A-1641), the National Institute of Neurological Diseases and Blindness (Grant No. B-2037), U.S. Public Health Service; the Canadian Arthritis and Rheumatism Society; the Medical Research Council of Canada (Consol. Gr. No. 11); the U.S. Army Medical Research and Development Command, Office of the Surgeon General, Contract No. DA-49-193-MD-2039; and the "Fondations Joseph Rhéaume."

H. S.

UNIVERSITÉ DE MONTRÉAL
January 1962

Contents

CHAPTER I
GENERALITIES

BRIEF CHARACTERIZATION OF CALCIPHYLAXIS 1

The Calcifier (Systemic Sensitizing Agent) 2

The Challenger (Vital Mordant) 4

The Adjuvant (Topical Activator of Challenger) 5

The "Critical Period" 5

Comparison of Calciphylaxis with Classical (Immunologic) Allergic Reactions 6

Comparison of Calciphylaxis with Other Connective-Tissue Reactions . . 6

Summary 8

HISTORY 8

DEFINITIONS AND TERMINOLOGY 13

COLOR ATLAS OF EXPERIMENTAL CALCIPHYLAXIS (*following p. 16*)

METHODOLOGY 17

Classification of Material 17

Labeling of Illustrations 17

Choice of Experimental Animal 18

The Production of Calciphylaxis 19

Evaluation of Lesions 30

CHAPTER II
TOPICAL CALCIPHYLAXIS

TOPICAL CALCIPHYLAXIS IN THE SKIN 37

The Various Forms of Cutaneous Calcinosis 37

Sensitizers 47

Challengers 48

Critical Period 54

Adjuvants 55

TOPICAL CALCIPHYLAXIS IN TISSUES OTHER THAN THE SKIN 63

CHAPTER III
SYSTEMIC CALCIPHYLAXIS

A. THE CALCIPHYLACTIC SYNDROMES 83

Generalities 83

Calciphylactic Syndromes Produced after Sensitization by DHT 85

Calciphylactic Syndromes Produced after Sensitization by Vitamin D_3 . . 212

Calciphylactic Syndromes Produced after Sensitization by Parathyroid Hormone 213

Calciphylactic Syndromes Produced after Sensitization by Nephrectomy . 227

Calciphylactic Syndromes Produced after Sensitization by NaAST . . . 235

Calciphylactic Syndromes Produced after Sensitization by Esophageal and Gastric Fistulas 239

Calciphylactic Syndromes Produced after Sensitization by Other Means . . 240

B. THE METACALCIPHYLACTIC SYNDROMES 241

Inflammation, Sclerosis, and Hyalinization 241

Ectopic Osteogenesis 242

Osteitis Fibrosa and Osteosclerosis 242

Other Lesions 249

CHAPTER IV
FACTORS INFLUENCING SUSCEPTIBILITY
TO CALCIPHYLAXIS

Generalities 250

Site of Challenge 250

Critical Period 252

Diet 257

Stress 261

Hormones 275

Nervous Stimuli 282

Renal Lesions 282

Gastric and Esophageal Fistulas 283

Drugs 284

Age and Sex 289

Species 292

CHAPTER V
DIRECT CALCIFIERS

$KMnO_4$ 298

Other Salts 305

Calcium Salts 314

Organ-Specific Direct Calcifiers 317

CHAPTER VI
CLINICAL IMPLICATIONS

Generalities 318

The Calcinoscleroses 318

Acrodermatitis Chronica Atrophicans 320

Acrosclerosis 321

Adiponecrosis Neonatorum 321

Anetoderma Erythematodes 321

Arteriosclerosis 325

Bone Diseases in General 325

Buerger's Disease 326

Calcinosis 326

Calcinosis of the Adrenals 327

Calcinosis of Bursae 327

Calcinosis of the Choroid Plexus 328

Calcinosis Cutis 328

Calcinosis of the Ear 330

Calcinosis of the Gallbladder 331

Calcinosis of Intervertebral Discs 331

Calcinosis of the Joints 331

Calcinosis of the Lung 334

Calcinosis of the Nose 336

Calcinosis of the Ovary 338

Calcinosis of the Pancreas 338

Calcinosis of the Pericardium 338

Calcinosis of the Pineal Body 338

Calcinosis of the Pleura 339

Calcinosis of the Scrotum 339

Calcinosis Segmentalis Congenita 340

Calcinosis of the Spleen 340

Calcinosis of the Thyroid 340

Calcinosis Universalis 340

Calcinosis of the Uterus 341

Calculi 341

Chondrodystrophia Calcificans Congenita Punctata 342

Collagen Diseases in General 343

Congenital Ectodermal Defect 345

Dermatofibrosis Lenticularis Disseminata 345

Dermatomyositis 346

Dupuytren's Contracture 354

Ehlers-Danlos Syndrome 354

Heberden's Nodules 356

Hemochromatosis and Hemosiderosis 356

Hyperparathyroidism 356

Hypervitaminosis D 361

Hypoparathyroidism 366

Ichthyosis and Other Types of Hyperkeratosis 367

Impetigo Herpetiformis 367

Keloids 367

Leukoplakia and Kraurosis Vulvae 370

Libman-Sacks Syndrome 370

Lichen Sclerosus 370

Lipocalcinogranulomatosis 371

Lipo-Fibro-Calcareous Myopathy 371

Lupus Erythematosus (Discoid and Disseminated) 373

Mastocytomas and Urticaria Pigmentosa 377

Milia and Epidermal Inclusion Cysts 377

Milk-Alkali Syndrome of Burnett *et al.* 377

Myositis Fibrosa 382

Myositis Ossificans (Circumscribed and Progressive) 382

Necrobiosis Lipoidica Diabeticorum 386

Neurofibromatosis 386

Osler-Rendu-Weber's Syndrome 386

Osteitis Deformans 387

Osteogenesis Imperfecta 387

Osteopetrosis 391

Osteoporosis 391

Osteosis Cutis 391

Panniculitis 392

Pemphigus 392

Periarteritis Nodosa 392

Poikiloderma Vasculare Atrophicans 393

Progeria 393

Pseudohypoparathyroidism 395

Pseudoxanthoma Elasticum 395

Psoriasis 395

Raynaud's Syndrome 396

Reiter's Syndrome 396

Renal Disease 397

Rheumatoid Arthritis 399

Rheumatic Fever 400

Rheumatoid Spondylitis 400

Romberg's Disease 401

Rothmund's Disease 401

Sarcoidosis 401

Scleredema Adultorum Buschke 405

Sclerema Neonatorum 406

Scleroderma 406

The Scleroscleroses 431

Sjögren's Syndrome 431

"Stiff-Man Syndrome" and the "Stiffness-Syndrome" of Guinea Pigs . . . 431

Thrombotic Thrombocytopenic Purpura 433

Topical Tissue Injury 433

Tumors 434

Urticaria 437

Villonodular Synovitis 437

Werner's Disease 437

CHAPTER VII
SPECULATIONS

Generalities 439

Direct Calcification 442

Sensitization 443

Challenge 444

Adjuvation 453

The Critical Period 454

The Latency Period 455

Local Factors 455

Resistance 456

Stress and Hormones 457

The Biologic Significance of Calciphylaxis 460

BIBLIOGRAPHY

BIBLIOGRAPHY 471

INDEX

INDEX 521

Illustrations

FIGURES

1. Technique of gavage 21
2. Technique of subcutaneous injection avoiding backflow 22
3. Technique of intrapedal injection 24
4. Technique of intravenous injection 25
5. "Triple wheal" test produced by DHT + alizarin red s.c. 32
6. Topical effect of FeCl$_3$ upon subcutaneous tissue in the nonsensitized rat . . . 38
7. Topical cutaneous calcinosis produced by DHT + plucking of scalp hair . . . 39
8. Various acute forms of cutaneous calcinosis produced by DHT + plucking of scalp hair 40
9. Bone produced by DHT + FeCl$_3$ s.c. 41
10. Various chronic forms of cutaneous calcinosis produced by DHT + epilation (hair plucking) 42
11. Cutaneous molt produced by DHT + albumen s.c. 43
12. Calciphylactic wheal with central "overchallenge" 44
13. Arborizing skin lesions produced by DHT + Fe-Dex i.p. 45
14. "Arborizing type" of cutaneous calcinosis produced by DHT + pectin s.c. . . . 46
15. Cutaneous calcinosis produced by NaAST + albumen s.c. 48
16. Cutaneous calcinosis produced by DHT + skin traction 55
17. Adjuvation by dextran of cutaneous calcinosis produced by DHT + FeCl$_3$ s.c. . 56
18. Adjuvation by dextran of cutaneous calciphylaxis produced by DHT + FeCl$_3$ s.c. . 61
19. Dental changes produced by DHT + CrCl$_3$ intracarotid 65
20. Dental changes produced by DHT + CrCl$_3$ intracarotid 66
21. Calcification of the lacrimal gland, tongue and skeletal musculature produced by DHT + CrCl$_3$ intracarotid 67
22. Calcification of the tongue produced by DHT + CrCl$_3$ intracarotid 68
23. Ocular changes produced by DHT + CrCl$_3$ intracarotid 68
24. Evolution of calciphylactic changes produced by DHT + CrCl$_3$ intracarotid . . 69
25. Calcification and necrosis in the brain produced by DHT + CrCl$_3$ intracarotid . 69

xvii

26. Unilateral changes in the choroid plexus and Gasserian ganglion produced by DHT + CrCl₃ intracarotid 70

27. Calcinosis of hind limb produced by DHT + CrCl₃ intra-iliac 70

28. Calcification of uterus, ureter and urinary bladder produced by DHT + CrCl₃ intra-iliac 71

29. Rectal, vaginal and urethral calcinosis produced by DHT + CrCl₃ intra-iliac . . 72

30. Calcified granuloma pouch produced by DHT + CrCl₃ topically 73

31. Hepatic calcification and regeneration produced by DHT + FeCl₂ intraportal . . 75

32. Calcification and partial occlusion of portal vein branches produced by DHT + CrCl₃ intraportal 76

33. Hepatic lesions produced by DHT + FeCl₂ intraportal 76

34. Pulmonary calcification produced by DHT + KMnO₄ intratracheal 77

35. Lingual lesions produced by DHT + CrCl₃ intracarotid 78

36. Intense calcinosis and atrophy in the right hind limb musculature produced by DHT + CrCl₃ intra-iliac 79

37. Selective calcinosis of the periductal connective tissue in the submaxillary gland produced by DHT + FeCl₂ intracarotid 80

38. Calcification and necrosis in a Walker tumor transplant produced by DHT + Fe-Dex intratumoral 81

39. Cardiac calcification produced by DHT + albumen i.v. 86

40. Calcification of salivary glands produced by DHT + albumen i.v. 87

41. Pulmonary calcification produced by DHT + albumen i.v. or i.p. 88

42. Intense, diffuse, cutaneous calcinosis produced by DHT + albumen i.v. . . . 89

43. Calcification of the entire abdominal wall produced by DHT + albumen i.p. . . 90

44. Pancreatic calcification produced by DHT + albumen i.p. 90

45. Intense fibrosis with little calcification of the pancreas produced by DHT + albumen i.p. 91

46. Calcification of vessels in the Langerhans' islets produced by DHT + albumen i.p. 91

47. Calcification of periadrenal fat produced by DHT + albumen i.p. 92

48. Calcification of mesenteric vessels produced by DHT + albumen i.p. . . . 92

49. Calcification in the ovary produced by DHT + albumen i.p. 93

50. Calcification in oviduct produced by DHT + albumen i.p. 94

51. Pancreatic fibrosis and giant-cell formation produced by DHT + albumen i.p. . . 95

52. Sclerosis and calcification of the retroperitoneal fat produced by DHT + albumen i.p. 95

53. Calcification of the diaphragm produced by DHT + albumen i.p. 96

54. Calcification and sclerosis of intercostal muscles produced by DHT + albumen i.p. 96

55. Calcification of spleen produced by DHT + CeCl₃ i.v. 99

56. Calcification of the carotid body produced by DHT + CrCl₃ i.v. 101

57. Calcification of the carotid body produced by DHT + CrCl₃ i.v. 102

58. Selective calcification of the parathyroids produced by DHT + CrCl₃ i.v. . . . 103

59. Selective calcification of the parathyroids produced by DHT + CrCl₃ i.v. . . . 104

60. Squamous metaplasia of tracheal epithelium, with submucosal calcification, produced by DHT + CrCl₃ i.v. 105

61. Calcification of the renal pelvis produced by DHT + CrCl₃ i.v. 106

62. Incrustation of the parathyroid stroma produced by DHT + CrCl₃ i.v. 107

63. Calcification of the diaphragm produced by DHT + CrCl₃ i.v. 107

64. Pattern of calcium deposition within a duodenal loop produced by DHT + CrCl₃ i.v. 108

65. Cardiac and pulmonary calcinosis produced by DHT + CrCl₃ i.v. 108

66. Calcinosis of Brunner's glands produced by DHT + CrCl₃ i.v. 109

67. Calcification of the salivary glands produced by DHT + CrCl₂ i.v. 109

68. Calcification of the lacrimal glands produced by DHT + CrCl₂ i.v. 110

69. Calcification of the choroid plexus produced by DHT + CrCl₂ i.v. 110

70. Calcification of the heart, thymus, trachea and lung produced by DHT + CrCl₂ i.v. 111

71. Calcification in the proventriculus and ventriculus produced by DHT + FeCl₂ i.v. 113

72. Pulmonary lesions produced by DHT + FeCl₂ i.v. 113

73. Singular form of mesenteric arteriosclerosis produced by DHT + FeCl₂ i.v. . . 114

74. Pancreatic calcification produced by DHT + Fe-Dex i.v. 115

75. Calcification of the pancreas produced by DHT + Fe-Dex i.v. 116

76. Severe pancreatic sclerosis produced by DHT + Fe-Dex i.p. 119

77. Cutaneous lesions produced by DHT + Fe-Dex i.p. 120

78. Calciphylactic psoriasis produced by DHT + Fe-Dex i.p. 121

79. Calciphylactic psoriasis produced by DHT + Fe-Dex i.p. 122

80. Calciphylactic psoriasis produced by DHT + Fe-Dex i.p. 123

81. Calcification of the uterus produced by DHT + Fe-Dex i.p. 124

82. Calcification of the genital fat and uterus produced by DHT + Fe-Dex i.p. . . 124

83. Comparison of uterine calcification as produced by DHT + Fe-Dex i.p. and by DHT + Fe-OS i.p. 125

83a. "Butterfly and sleeves" syndrome with lingual lesions produced by DHT + Fe-Dex i.v. + insulin s.c. 126

84. Calciphylactic dermatomyositis produced by DHT + Fe-Dex i.v. + PMX s.c. . . 128

85. General appearance of the musculocutaneous lesions produced by DHT + Fe-Dex i.v. + PMX s.c. 129

86. Calcification of cardiac valve produced by DHT + Fe-Dex i.v. + PMX s.c. . . 130

87. Calcification of the mediastinum and esophagus produced by DHT + Fe-Dex i.v. + PMX s.c. 131

88. Mast cell "explosion" and calcification produced by DHT + Fe-Dex i.v. + PMX s.c.   132

89. Typical calciphylactic scleroderma produced by DHT + Fe-Dex i.v. + PMX s.c. .   133

90. Cutaneous calcinosis of the face produced by DHT + Fe-Din i.v.   134

91. Calciphylactic "annular scleroderma" produced by DHT + Fe-Din i.v.   135

92. Evolution of facial lesions produced by DHT + Fe-Din i.v.   137

93. Evolution of pulmonary lesions produced by DHT + Fe-Din i.v.   137

94. Healing of facial lesions produced by DHT + Fe-Din i.v.   138

95. Selective calcification of the renal cortex stroma produced by DHT + Fe-OS i.v. .   139

96. Calcific cholangitis produced by DHT + Fe-OS i.v.   140

97. Calcification of Brunner's glands produced by DHT + Fe-OS i.v.   140

98. Calcification of adrenal nerve produced by DHT + Fe-OS i.v.   141

99. Biliary tract lesions produced by Fe-OS i.v.   142

100. Hemorrhagic pancreatitis with dilatation of the bile duct produced by Fe-OS i.v. .   142

101. Occlusive coronary lesions with myocardial infarction produced by DHT + Fe-OS i.v.   144

102. Arborizing pattern of intestinal calcification produced by DHT + FeSO$_4$ i.v.   .   .   146

103. Thymic calcification produced by DHT + F-COL s.c.   147

104. Thymic calcification produced by DHT + triamcinolone s.c.   148

105. Nodular calcification of the thymus long after treatment with DHT + triamcinolone s.c.   149

106. Calcification of salivary and lacrimal glands produced by DHT + 5HT s.c.   .   .   150

107. Calcification of salivary glands produced by DHT + 5HT s.c.   151

108. Calcification of salivary glands produced by DHT + 5HT s.c.   152

109. Inflammation of the ciliary zonule produced by DHT + 5HT s.c.   153

110. Renal lesion produced by DHT + 5HT s.c.   154

111. Calciphylactic muscular dystrophy produced by DHT +5HT s.c.   155

112. Muscular dystrophy produced by DHT + 5HT s.c.   156

113. Calcification and sclerosis of the hibernating gland produced by DHT + 5HT s.c. .   157

114. Calcification of the tongue produced by DHT + 5HT s.c.   159

115. Corneal lesions produced by DHT + 5HT s.c.   160

116. Calcification of the optic nerve produced by DHT + 5HT s.c.   161

117. Cataract produced by DHT + 5HT s.c.   161

118. Opacity of lens produced by DHT + 5HT s.c.   162

119. Retrolental changes produced by DHT + 5HT s.c.   162

120. Calcification of the salivary gland produced by DHT + 5HT s.c. + IPR i.p.   .   .   163

121. Calcification in the gluteal musculature produced by DHT + 5HT s.c. + IPR i.p.   164

122. Calcification of salivary glands produced by DHT + 5HT s.c. + IPR i.p. . . . 165

123. Calcification of the cornea produced by DHT + 5HT s.c. + IPR i.p. 166

124. Peculiar pattern of cardiac calcification produced by DHT + IPR i.p. 167

125. Papillary nephrocalcinosis produced by DHT + magnesium phosphate p.o. . . 169

126. Pulmonary calcification produced by DHT + Na_2SnO_3 i.v. 171

127. Splenic calcification produced by DHT + Pb-acetate i.v. 172

127a. Papillary and cortical calcinosis produced by DHT + Pb-acetate 172

128. Granular cutaneous calcification in the snout produced by DHT + PMX intrapedal 173

129. Calcification of Peyer's patches produced by DHT + PMX s.c. 174

130. Calcification of the salivary glands produced by DHT + PMX intrapedal . . . 175

131. Calcification of the salivary glands produced by DHT + PMX s.c. 176

132. Calcification of the tongue, pharynx and esophagus produced by DHT + Thorotrast® i.v. 178

133. Calcification of the esophagus produced by DHT + Thorotrast® i.v. 179

134. Cutaneous calcinosis of the face produced by DHT + Thorotrast® i.v. 180

135. Cutaneous calcinosis and epithelial giant-cell formation produced by DHT + Thorotrast® i.v. 181

136. Calcification of the shoulder musculature produced by DHT + Thorotrast® i.v. . 182

137. Calcification of the pancreas produced by DHT + Thorotrast® i.v. 183

138. Splenic calcification produced by DHT + Thorotrast® i.v. 184

139. Articular lesions produced by DHT + Thorotrast® i.v. 185

140. Articular, muscular and perineural lesions produced by DHT + Thorotrast® i.v. . 186

141. Soft tissue calcification produced by DHT + Thorotrast® i.v. 187

142. Lingual calcification produced by DHT + Thorotrast® i.v. 187

143. Nodular calcification in tongue and cheek produced by DHT + Thorotrast® i.v. . 188

144. Evolution of nodular calcification in cheek and esophagus after treatment with DHT + Thorotrast® i.v. 189

145. Healing of perineural and articular lesions produced by DHT + Thorotrast® i.v. . 189

146. Calcification of the knee joint produced by DHT + Thorotrast® i.v. 190

147. Storage of Thorotrast® in phagocytes of bristle roots 191

148. Peritoneal calcification without pancreatic calcinosis produced by DHT + Thorotrast® i.p. 192

149. Cutaneous calcinosis produced by DHT + thallium acetate s.c. + plucking of scalp hair and its prevention by restraint 193

150. Pure cortico-medullary nephrocalcinosis produced by DHT + thallium acetate s.c. 194

151. Islets of calcification in spleen produced by DHT + yolk i.v. 195

152. Calcification of spleen produced by DHT + yolk i.v. 196

153. Calcification of liver produced by DHT + yolk i.v. 196

154. Nephrocalcinosis produced by DHT + yolk i.v. 197

155. Glomerular hyalinization produced by DHT + yolk i.v. 197

156. Calcification of the stomach produced by DHT + yolk i.v. 198

157. Calcification of the gastric mucosa produced by DHT + yolk i.v. 199

158. Evolution of calciphylactic changes produced by DHT + yolk i.v. 201

159. Atypical epithelial proliferations and chronic inflammation in renal pelvis produced by DHT + yolk i.v. 202

160. Calcinosis produced by yolk i.v. alone 202

161. Calcification of omentum produced by DHT + yolk i.p. 203

162. Calcification of a thymic lymph node produced by DHT + yolk i.p. . . . 204

163. Thymic calcinosis produced by DHT + yolk i.p. 205

164. Thymic calcinosis produced by DHT + yolk i.p. 206

165. Splenic calcinosis produced by DHT + yolk i.p. 207

166. Splenic calcinosis produced by DHT + yolk i.p. 207

167. Pulmonary calcinosis produced by DHT + yolk i.p. 208

168. Fully developed cutaneous lesions produced by DHT + yolk i.v. + PMX s.c. . . 209

169. Hepatic calcification and necrosis produced by DHT + ZnCl₂ i.v. 210

170. Vascular lesions produced by DHT + ZnCl₂ i.v. 211

171. Cardiac, thyroid and carotid body calcification produced by parathyroid hormone s.c. + CrCl₃ i.v. 214

172. Calcification of adrenal medulla and choroid plexus produced by parathyroid hormone s.c. + CrCl₃ i.v. 215

173. Muscular dystrophy produced by parathyroid hormone s.c. + Fe-Dex i.v. + PMX s.c. 216

174. Calciphylactic dermatomyositis produced by parathyroid hormone s.c. + Fe-Dex i.v. + PMX s.c. 217

175. Calciphylactic dermatomyositis produced by parathyroid hormone s.c. + Fe-Dex i.v. + PMX s.c. 217

176. Cardiac calcification produced by parathyroid hormone s.c. + Fe-OS i.v. . . . 218

177. Hepatic calcification produced by parathyroid hormone s.c. + Fe-OS i.v. . . . 219

178. Nephrocalcinosis produced by parathyroid hormone s.c. + Fe-OS i.v. 220

179. Calcification of bile ducts and calcifying periarteritis nodosa of hepatic artery produced by parathyroid hormone s.c. + Fe-OS i.v. 221

180. Periarteritis nodosa of hepatic artery produced by parathyroid hormone s.c. + Fe-OS i.v. 222

181. Calcification of adrenal medulla produced by parathyroid hormone s.c. + Fe-OS i.v. 222

182. Changes in ganglion cells of adrenal medulla produced by parathyroid hormone
     s.c. + 5HT s.c. 223

183. Calciphylactic muscular dystrophy produced by parathyroid hormone s.c. + 5HT
     s.c. 225

184. Calciphylactic muscular dystrophy produced by parathyroid hormone s.c. + 5HT
     s.c. 226

185. Cardiac lesion produced by parathyroid hormone s.c. + 5HT s.c. 227

186. Calciphylactic scleroderma with laryngeal, lingual and esophageal lesions produced
     by parathyroid hormone s.c. + Thorotrast® i.v. 228

187. Cutaneous calcinosis and arthritis produced by parathyroid hormone s.c. + Thoro-
     trast® i.v. 229

188. Organ lesions produced by nephrectomy + CrCl₃ i.v. 230

189. Facial calcinosis produced by nephrectomy + Thorotrast® i.v. 232

190. Splenic calcinosis produced by nephrectomy + Thorotrast® i.v. 233

191. Facial calcinosis produced by nephrectomy + Thorotrast® i.v. 233

192. Lingual calcinosis produced by nephrectomy + Thorotrast® i.v. 234

193. Cardiovascular and renal calcinosis produced by NaAST i.p. 235

194. Pancreatic calcinosis produced by NaAST i.p. + Fe-Dex i.v. 237

195. Esophageal calcinosis produced by NaAST i.p. + Fe-Din i.v. 237

196. Cardiac and adrenal lesions produced by NaAST i.p. + Fe-OS i.v. 238

197. Calcinosis of facial skin produced by NaAST i.p. + Thorotrast® i.v. . . . 239

198. Metacalciphylactic lesions produced by DHT + albumen s.c. 243

199. Osteitis fibrosa produced by DHT + Fe-Dex s.c. 244

200. Osteitis fibrosa produced by DHT + Fe-Dex s.c. 244

201. Osteitis fibrosa produced by DHT + Fe-Dex s.c. 245

202. Osteitis fibrosa produced by DHT + Fe-Dex s.c. or albumen s.c. 245

203. Osteitis fibrosa produced by DHT + Fe-Dex s.c. 246

204. Osteitis fibrosa produced by DHT + yolk i.v. 247

205. Prevention by calciphylaxis of lesions produced by DHT + albumen s.c. . . . 248

206. Prevention by calciphylaxis of coronary calcinosis produced by DHT + albumen s.c. 248

207. Squamous metaplasia of bronchial epithelium produced by DHT + Fe-Dex i.v. . 249

208. Cutaneous calcinosis of the limb produced by DHT + Fe-Dex into paw . . . 251

209. Responsiveness of various sites to challenge by PMX after treatment with DHT +
     Fe-Dex 251

210. Cutaneous calcinosis produced by vitamin D₂ + NaH₂PO₄ p.o. 258

211. Pure cortical nephrocalcinosis produced by DHT + calcium acetate p.o. . . . 259

212. Generalized nephrocalcinosis produced by DHT + Na₂HPO₄ p.o. 260

213. Lingual calcinosis produced by DHT + NaH$_2$PO$_4$ p.o. 261

214. Prevention by restraint of pancreatic calcinosis produced by DHT + albumen i.p. 267

215. Prevention by restraint of cutaneous and pancreatic calcinosis produced by DHT + albumen i.p. 268

216. Prevention by restraint of thyroid and parathyroid calcinosis produced by DHT + CrCl$_3$ i.v. 269

217. Prevention by restraint of dermatomyositis produced by DHT + Fe-Dex i.v. + PMX s.c. 270

218. Prevention by restraint of lesions produced by DHT + Fe-Din i.v. 271

219. Prevention by restraint of cutaneous calcinosis produced by DHT + Thorotrast® i.v. 272

220. Prevention by restraint of facial calcification produced by DHT + Thorotrast® i.v. 272

221. Prevention by restraint of facial calcification produced by DHT + Thorotrast® i.v. 273

222. Prevention by restraint of musculocutaneous lesions produced by vitamin D$_3$ i.v. + Fe-Dex i.v. + PMX s.c. 274

223. Prevention by restraint of salivary gland and renal calcification produced by vitamin D$_3$ i.v. + 5HT s.c. 275

224. Prevention by restraint of salivary gland calcification produced by vitamin D$_3$ i.v. + 5HT s.c. 276

225. Prevention of topical calciphylaxis by hypophysectomy 277

226. Prevention by hypophysectomy of calciphylactic dermatomyositis produced by DHT + Fe-Dex i.v. + PMX s.c. 278

227. Papillary nephrocalcinosis produced by hypophysectomy + DHT 279

228. Calcification and sclerosis of preputial glands produced by DHT + lyophilized anterior pituitary powder (LAP) s.c. 280

229. Uterine calcification produced by ovariectomy + DHT + Fe-Dex i.p. 282

230. Prevention by extirpation of superior cervical sympathetic ganglion of carotid body calcification produced by DHT + CrCl$_3$ i.v. 283

231. Cutaneous calcinosis produced by DHT + Fe-Dex s.c. in the hamster 293

232. Cutaneous calcinosis produced by DHT + Fe-Dex s.c. in the mouse 294

233. Pulmonary calcinosis with suppuration and fibrosis produced by DHT + CrCl$_3$ i.v. in the cat 294

234. Calcinosis of carotid bifurcation produced by DHT + CrCl$_3$ i.v. in the cat . . . 295

235. Calcinosis of the carotid body produced by DHT + CrCl$_3$ in the guinea pig . . 295

236. Calcinosis of parathyroid and carotid body produced by DHT + CrCl$_3$ i.v. in the rabbit 296

237. Histologic appearance of calcified wheals produced by KMnO$_4$ s.c. 299

238. Histogenesis of direct calcification produced by KMnO$_4$ s.c. 301

239. Defensive value of calciphylaxis produced by DHT + CrCl$_2$ s.c. 302

240. Protective value of direct tissue calcification produced by ZnCl$_2$ s.c. 303

241. Prevention by hypophysectomy of calcified wheals produced by KMnO₄ s.c. . . 304

242. Age-dependence of the topical response to KMnO₄ s.c. 305

243. Muscular atrophy produced by KMnO₄ intra-iliac 306

244. Muscle lesions produced by KMnO₄ intra-iliac 307

245. Muscular fibrosis produced by KMnO₄ intra-iliac 308

246. Osseous lesions produced by KMnO₄ intra-iliac 309

247. Epiphyseal and osseous lesions produced by KMnO₄ intra-iliac 310

248. Bone absorption produced by KMnO₄ s.c. 311

249. Cutaneous and hepatic calcinosis produced by KMnO₄ s.c. 312

250. Hepatic calcification produced by KMnO₄ s.c. 313

251. Direct calcification produced by CaCl₂ s.c. 314

252. Typical "asbestos-like" muscle calcification produced by DHT + PMX s.c. . . 315

253. Topical muscle calcification produced by DHT + PMX s.c. 316

254. Selective calcification of the renal cortex produced by HgCl₂ s.c. 317

255. Acrosclerosis with arterial lesions 322–323

256. Acrosclerosis 324

257. Calcification and formation of corpora amylacea in choroid plexus of man . . . 328

258. Postphlebitic subcutaneous calcinosis 331

259. Calcinosis of intervertebral disc 332

260. Calcinosis of the joints 333

261. Pulmonary calcinosis in histoplasmosis 335

262. Pulmonary calcinosis in histoplasmosis 336

263. Pulmonary calcinosis in histoplasmosis 337

264. Calcified ovarian dermoid cysts 338

265. Calcinosis of pancreas 339

266. Calcified uterine fibromyomas 341

267. Lithopedion 342

268. Chondrodystrophia calcificans congenita punctata 344–345

269. Dermatomyositis 346

270. Dermatomyositis 347

271. Dermatomyositis 348

271a. Dermatomyositis with generalized calcinosis 349

271b. Dermatomyositis with generalized calcinosis 350

272. Dermatomyositis and calcinosis universalis treated with ACTH 355

273. Hyperparathyroidism conducive to cutaneous calcinosis 358

274. Hyperparathyroidism due to metastasizing parathyroid carcinoma 359

275. Hyperparathyroidism with nephrocalcinosis 360

276. Renal insufficiency with severe calcinosis due to excessive alkali-intake . . . 362–363

277. Hypervitaminosis D 364

278. Calcinosis produced by hypervitaminosis D in man 365

279. Calcinosis produced by hypervitaminosis D in man 365

280. Impetigo herpetiformis with parathyroid tetany after strumectomy 368–369

281. Lipocalcinogranulomatosis in man 372

282. Chronic discoid lupus erythematosus 373

283. Lupus erythematosus disseminatus 375

284. Pulmonary changes in systemic lupus erythematosus 376

285. Urticaria pigmentosa (mastocytosis) 378

286. Milk-alkali syndrome 380

287. Burnett's syndrome due to primary hyperparathyroidism 381

288. Myositis ossificans 383

289. Myositis ossificans 384

290. Myositis ossificans 385

291. Osler-Rendu-Weber's Syndrome with cutaneous amyloidosis 388

292. Osler-Rendu-Weber's Syndrome with cutaneous calcinosis 389

293. Osler-Rendu-Weber's Syndrome with flat angioma-like formations on toes . . . 390

294. Osler-Rendu-Weber's Syndrome with calcinosis of the finger tips 390

295. Pulmonary changes in periarteritis nodosa 394

296. Nephrocalcinosis with osteomalacia 398

297. Sarcoidosis with chronic polymyositis 404

298. Generalized scleroderma 408

299. Trophic disturbances in generalized scleroderma 408

300. Cutaneous lesions in generalized scleroderma 410

301. Scleroderma with calcinosis 411

302. Generalized scleroderma 412

303. Scleroderma with calcinosis 413

304. Roentgen changes in systemic scleroderma 414

305. Esophageal lesions in generalized scleroderma 415

306. Esophageal lesions in generalized scleroderma 416

307. Roentgen changes in systemic scleroderma 417

308. Pulmonary changes in scleroderma 418

309. Pulmonary changes in scleroderma 419

310. Cardiac lesions in generalized scleroderma 420

311. Vascular lesions in generalized scleroderma 420

312. Systemic changes in scleroderma 422

313. Roentgen changes in systemic scleroderma 424

314. Linear scleroderma 425

314a. Scleromyxedema 428–429

315. Sjögren's syndrome associated with scleroderma 432

316. Calcinosis of biliary system 435

317. Circinate cutaneous calcinosis produced by DHT around a Walker tumor transplant 467

318. Extrusion of calcified skin masses following treatment with DHT + Fe-Dex . . 467

TABLES

1. Potency grading in "triple wheal test" 48

2. Potency of substances tested for cutaneous calciphylactic challenging effect . 49–53

3. Effect of various agents upon cutaneous calciphylaxis induced by iron compounds 59–60

4. Effect of various agents upon cutaneous calciphylaxis induced by $CrCl_2$ . . . 62

5. Critical period for various forms of topical calciphylaxis 254

6. Critical period for various forms of systemic calciphylaxis 255–256

7. Effect of stress upon various forms of topical calciphylaxis 263

8. Effect of stress upon various forms of systemic calciphylaxis 265–266

9. Prevention of various calciphylactic responses by PMX (large doses) 285

10. Prevention of various calciphylactic responses by PMX (small doses) 287

11. Production or aggravation of various calciphylactic responses by PMX (small doses) 288

12. Production or aggravation of various calciphylactic responses by PMX (large doses) 290–291

DIAGRAMS

I. Action of calcifiers, challengers, and adjuvants 440

II. Mechanism of siderocalciphylaxis 448

III. Participation of hormones in calciphylaxis 459

Plates in Color Atlas

(*following page 16*)

PLATE I

A.   Cutaneous calcinosis and bone fragility produced in the suckling rat by DHT treatment of its mother.

B.   Topical cutaneous calcinosis produced by DHT + epilation.

C.   Calciphylactic lesion with central "overchallenge."

D, E, F.   Various acute forms of cutaneous calcinosis produced by DHT + epilation.

PLATE II

A.   Acute form of cutaneous calcinosis produced by DHT + plucking of scalp hair.

B.   Acute cutaneous calcinosis produced by DHT + Fe-Dex i.p.

C, D.   Preosseous plaques produced by DHT + albumen s.c.

E.   Intense diffuse cutaneous calcinosis produced by DHT + albumen i.v.

F, G.   Three typical calcified skin plaques in a rat treated with DHT + albumen i.p.

PLATE III

A, B.   Pancreatic calcification produced by DHT + albumen i.p.

C, D.   Calcification of abdominal wall produced by DHT + albumen i.p.

E, F, G.   Calcification of spleen and liver produced by DHT + yolk i.v.

PLATE IV

A, B.   Massive calcification of thyro-parathyroid apparatus produced by DHT + $CrCl_2$ i.v.

C.   Prevention by restraint of thyroid and parathyroid calcinosis produced by DHT + $CrCl_3$ i.v.

D.   Calcification of parathyroid and thyroid stroma produced by DHT + $CrCl_3$ i.v.

E.   Calcification of thyroid and carotid body produced by DHT + $FeCl_2$ i.v.

F.   Calcification of carotid body produced by DHT + $CrCl_3$ i.v.

G.   Calcification of renal pelvis produced by DHT + $CrCl_3$ i.v.

PLATE V

A.	Calcification of choroid plexus produced by DHT + $CrCl_2$ i.v.
B.	Pancreatic calciphylaxis produced by DHT + Fe-Dex i.v.
C, D.	Pancreatic calciphylaxis produced by DHT + Fe-Dex i.p.
E, F.	Calcification of region of Brunner's glands in duodenum produced by DHT + Fe-Dex i.p.

PLATE VI

A.	Calcification of genital fat and uterus produced by DHT + Fe-Dex i.p.
B.	Calcification of pancreas, but not of spleen, produced by DHT + Fe-Dex i.v.
C.	Endometrial calcification produced by DHT + yolk i.p.
D.	Calciphylactic psoriasis produced by DHT + Fe-Dex i.p.
E.	Healing of facial lesions produced by DHT + Fe-Din i.v.
F.	Prevention by restraint of cutaneous and periarticular calcification produced by DHT + Thorotrast® i.v.

PLATE VII

A, B.	General appearance of the musculocutaneous lesions produced by DHT + Fe-Dex i.v. + PMX s.c.
C.	Late stages of cutaneous lesions produced by DHT + Fe-Dex i.v. + PMX s.c.
D.	Calcification of skin and nuchal musculature produced by DHT + Fe-Dex i.v. + PMX s.c.
E, F.	Mast cell "explosion" and calcification produced by DHT + Fe-Dex i.v. + PMX s.c.

PLATE VIII

A.	Auricular type of cardiac calcification produced by DHT + Fe-OS i.v.
B.	Cardiac calcification produced by parathyroid hormone s.c. + Fe-OS i.v.
C, D.	Acute necrosis of duodenum and calcification of choledochus produced by DHT + Fe-OS i.v.
E.	Calcification of papilla of Vater produced by DHT + Fe-OS i.v.
F.	Hepatic calcification produced by parathyroid hormone s.c. + Fe-OS i.v.

PLATE IX

A, C, E.	Periarteritis nodosa of hepatic artery produced by parathyroid hormone s.c. + Fe-OS i.v.
B, D.	Selective calcification of renal cortex stroma produced by DHT + Fe-OS i.v.
F.	Adrenal calcification produced by parathyroid hormone s.c. + Fe-OS i.v.

PLATE X

A.   Calcification of thymus produced by DHT + F-COL s.c.

B.   "Arborizing" pattern of intestinal calcification produced by DHT + $FeSO_4$ i.v.

C.   Calcification of salivary glands produced by DHT + 5HT s.c.

D.   Fully developed cutaneous lesions produced by DHT + yolk i.v. + PMX s.c.

E.   Calciphylactic muscular dystrophy produced by DHT + 5HT s.c.

F.   Calcification and sclerosis of nuchal musculature produced by DHT + 5HT s.c.

PLATE XI

A.   Calciphylactic scleroderma of face and paws produced by DHT + Thorotrast® i.v.

B.   Esophageal calcification produced by nephrectomy + Thorotrast® i.v.

C.   Calcification of tongue, pharynx and esophagus produced by DHT + Thorotrast® i.v.

D.   Nodular calcification of tongue and oral mucosa produced by DHT + Thorotrast® i.v.

E, F.   Chronic esophageal and faucial calcification produced by DHT + Thorotrast® i.v.

G.   Calcareous bursitis of shoulder joint produced by DHT + Thorotrast® i.v.

H.   Facial calcification produced by nephrectomy + Thorotrast® i.v.

PLATE XII

A, B, C, D.   Unilateral calcification of the head produced by DHT + $CrCl_3$ intracarotid.

E.   Calcinosis and atrophy in right hind limb produced by DHT + $CrCl_3$ intra-iliac.

F.   "Phylactic" value of calciphylaxis.

G.   Calcification and necrosis in a Walker tumor transplant produced by DHT + Fe-Dex intratumoral.

PLATE XIII

A, B.   Splenic thrombosis and hepatic necroses produced by DHT + $ZnCl_2$ i.v.

C.   Biliary and duodenal lesions produced by Fe-OS i.v.

D.   Cataract produced by DHT + 5HT s.c.

E.   Granuloma pouch technique for the study of calciphylaxis.

F.   Blood as a calciphylactic challenger.

I
Generalities

BRIEF CHARACTERIZATION OF CALCIPHYLAXIS

Definition.—Calciphylaxis is a condition of induced systemic hypersensitivity in which tissues respond to appropriate challenging agents with a precipitous, though sometimes evanescent, local calcification.

The term was coined in analogy with such designations as anaphylaxis, tachyphylaxis or skeptophylaxis that likewise refer to induced systemic alterations in the body's responsiveness to certain challenging agents. Apparently calciphylaxis is a fundamentally defensive (phylactic) response of inflammation and sclerosis, induced by the selective deposition of calcium in the challenged area. Thereby calciphylaxis can sequestrate a pathogen and increase topical resistance to injury but—like many other basically defensive reactions (e.g., serological immunity)—it can also become the cause of morbid lesions.

We distinguish: (1) *topical calciphylaxis* induced by the direct application of the challenger to the responsive tissue from (2) *systemic calciphylaxis* in which the challenger is distributed throughout the organism (e.g., after intravenous or intraperitoneal administration) and produces a response in diverse tissues for which it has a selective affinity.

Examples.—If a rat (weighing about 100 g.) is given a single oral dose of dihydrotachysterol, or "DHT" (e.g., 1 mg. in 0.5 ml. of corn oil), the subcutaneous injection of as little as 25 μg. of $FeCl_3$ (in 0.2 ml. of water) on the following day elicits a precipitous local deposition of calcium salts during the next two to three days. Macroscopically, this *topical calciphylactic response* is characterized by the appearance of a hard white patch at the site of injection. Histologically, we note calcareous incrustation of dermal and subcutaneous connective-tissue fibers, followed by reactive inflammatory infiltration (in which eosinophils and pseudoeosinophils predominate) and eventually sclerosis.

If under similar circumstances, instead of the subcutaneous application of $FeCl_3$, 1 ml. of a ferric oxide saccharate, or "Fe-OS" (containing 20 mg. of metallic iron), is injected intravenously on the day of sensitization with DHT, a *systemic calciphylactic syndrome* results. Here, calcification occurs predominantly in the left auricular appendage of the heart, the subepicardial layers of the ventricular myocardium, the bile ducts, the duodenum, and the renal cortex. Presumably this

1

distribution is due to the fact that iron when given in this form tends to accumulate selectively in these regions and attracts calcium to them.

As we shall see, there are many other sensitizers, or "systemic calcifiers," that
can replace DHT, and numerous challengers can substitute for $FeCl_3$ or Fe-OS in
the production of such calciphylactic responses; yet, almost invariably the interval
elapsing between the application of the systemic sensitizer and the local challenger
is of decisive importance. In most forms of topical and systemic calciphylaxis that
we tested, the critical period for the most efficacious application of the challenger
is 24–48 hours after sensitization; however, the length of this interval varies, depending upon the sensitizers and the challengers used. Indeed, some types of calciphylaxis can only be obtained by applying the challenger before the sensitizer,
and even the quality of the response (e.g., the distribution of the lesions in systemic calciphylaxis) may depend upon the timing of the two types of pathogens.

Both topical and systemic calciphylaxis are truly pluricausal morbid lesions,
since in themselves neither the sensitizing DHT nor the challenging iron preparations can evoke them.

The Calcifer (Systemic Sensitizing Agent)

Most of the original work on calciphylaxis was performed on animals sensitized
with **DHT** because this happens to be a readily available and extremely active,
calcification-promoting agent. Its actions are essentially those of parathyroid hormone, but, unlike the latter, DHT is a synthetic sterol obtainable in chemically
pure form; hence, this compound helped us to show that sensitization for calciphylactic responses can be achieved by a nonantigenic substance of comparatively simple structure.

We still do not know how calciphylactic sensitization acts, but all sensitizers
tested share with DHT the property of mobilizing calcium and of predisposing for
calcification in general; that is why these agents may also be referred to simply as
calcifiers. However, the nonspecific, "metastatic" calcification caused by a mere
excess of such calcifiers (without the need for any additional treatment with an
exogenous challenger) differs essentially from calciphylaxis in that it occurs only
in certain naturally predisposed sites (e.g., gastric mucosa, cardiovascular system,
kidney). Hence calcification thus produced—e.g., by excessive amounts of parathyroid hormone or DHT alone—offers no possibility of altering the distribution-
pattern of the resulting lesions by directing calcium at will to predetermined sites.

The solvent and route of administration are also of importance in determining
the efficacy of DHT and related compounds. For example, orally administered
DHT is much more efficacious as a calciphylactic sensitizer when given in oil than
in water.[491, 822] Furthermore, if DHT is administered in water, three times the
quantity given orally must be injected intravenously to obtain a comparable degree of sensitization for cutaneous calcinosis. Such high intravenous doses produce

marked nonspecific renal and cardiovascular calcification, so that the technique is not suitable for studies on calciphylaxis.[491]

Among the sensitizers for calciphylaxis examined to date, ***vitamin D₂, vitamin D₃, parathyroid hormone*** and ***sodium acetylsulfathiazole*** (***NaAST***) have proven to be the most effective. Under appropriate conditions of dosage and timing, pretreatment with any of these compounds "conditions" for the induction of a precipitous local calcification of the connective-tissue fibers (with subsequent sclerosis or necrosis) at sites subsequently treated with challengers (e.g., FeCl₃). Of course, when given in very high doses, any of these calcifiers can produce nonspecific calcinosis at the previously mentioned sites of predisposition; but even at much lower doses they sensitize other tissues for calcification under the influence of challenge.

The vitamin-D compounds are close chemical analogues of DHT; like the latter they presumably act directly and not through stimulation of parathyroid-hormone secretion, since they remain effective even after parathyroidectomy. On the other hand, NaAST acts as a calcifier only in the presence of the parathyroids, presumably because it causes renal lesions that result in an increased parathyroid-hormone secretion. The possibility of producing calciphylaxis with this compound shows that this response can be elicited through the stimulation of parathyroid activity by a nephrotoxic agent that has no direct influence upon calcium metabolism.

Thus we have learned to distinguish between ***direct systemic calcifiers*** that sensitize for calciphylaxis in themselves and ***indirect systemic calcifiers*** whose action depends upon a secondary reaction, the increased elaboration of an endogenous sensitizer—parathyroid hormone.

Even various ***surgical interventions*** (e.g., bilateral nephrectomy, ligature of both ureters, obstruction of the pylorus combined with the establishment of a gastric fistula) can produce metastatic calcification at the usual sites of predisposition. Presumably the effect of these operations is mediated through parathyroid stimulation, since it is abolished by parathyroidectomy. Yet, all these interventions are only moderately effective sensitizers, perhaps because they produce intense stress and—as we shall see—an alarm reaction tends to prevent calciphylaxis.

Many drugs can cause "***dystrophic calcification***" by virtue of their destructive action upon certain organs that are naturally predisposed to take up calcium; yet, these drugs do not necessarily sensitize for calciphylaxis. For example, intoxication with HgCl₂ causes severe calcification of the renal tubules directly damaged by the mercury but fails to sensitize other tissues to the calciphylactic action of potent challengers. Apparently there is an essential difference between "dystrophic calcification" and calciphylaxis.

THE CHALLENGER (VITAL MORDANT)

We have already mentioned that some sensitizers act directly, others indirectly (e.g., through parathyroid stimulation). A similar distinction may be made as regards the challengers, or vital mordants. Most challengers act at the site of application; for example, they produce cutaneous calcinosis wherever they are subcutaneously injected in a DHT-sensitized rat. Among these *direct challengers* are salts of iron, chromium, aluminum, manganese, thorium, cerium, zirconium, titanium, and lead; but certain organic compounds (e.g., egg white, egg yolk) and even the mild mechanical trauma of plucking the hair or pinching the skin are also very effective in this respect.

There appears to be no proportionality between the damaging effect of an agent (as judged by its ability to cause necrosis or inflammation) and its mordanting action: many strong inflammatory irritants (e.g., croton oil, bile) and corrosives (e.g., NaOH, HCl) are quite ineffective, while typical challengers produce calciphylactic responses even at dose levels at which, by themselves, they elicit no demonstrable tissue damage.

Many direct challengers that cause topical calciphylaxis upon subcutaneous injection also proved to elicit some form of a systemic calciphylactic syndrome when administered intravenously or intraperitoneally. However, as we shall see, the distribution and structure of the resulting lesions differs greatly, depending upon the particular organ affinities of the various challengers and upon the reactivity of the experimental animal. For example, in rats sensitized with DHT, the intravenous administration of egg white produces an almost selective calcification of the pancreas, while egg yolk causes calcification in the spleen and the Kupffer cells of the liver (presumably because the yolk globules tend to be phagocytosed by the cells of the RES). Both these systemic calciphylactic reactions are, in turn, quite unlike that produced under similar circumstances by Fe-OS, which we have already discussed. Factors affecting the reactivity of the organism (e.g., age, genetic background, hypophysectomy, drugs, stress) can likewise markedly alter the intensity and quality of calciphylactic responses.

Indirect challengers are agents that cause little or no topical calciphylaxis when directly applied to an otherwise receptive site such as the skin of a suitably sensitized animal, but which elicit systemic calciphylactic syndromes when introduced into the general circulation. For example, in the DHT-sensitized rat histamine liberators (e.g., 48/80, dextran, polymyxin, glucocorticoids) cause virtually no local cutaneous calcinosis upon subcutaneous administration, but they can elicit calciphylactic responses in various distant organs if injected intravenously or intraperitoneally. Indeed if sufficiently large amounts of such compounds are injected subcutaneously, systemic calciphylaxis may result even though the site of administration fails to undergo calcification. As a working hypothesis, we assume that mordants of this type act only indirectly through the liberation or activation of some endogenous challenger (e.g., mastocyte granules, iron), but this interpretation has not yet been proven.

THE ADJUVANT (TOPICAL ACTIVATOR OF CHALLENGER)

Certain substances that have little or no vital mordanting action in themselves can enormously increase the activity of threshold doses of topical challengers. For example, in the DHT-sensitized rat, dextran does not act as a vital mordant in itself, but if otherwise ineffective amounts of $FeCl_3$ are injected subcutaneously in dextran solution, severe cutaneous calcinosis results at the challenged site. Unlike dextran, egg white possesses considerable direct challenging potency, but, if high dilutions of albumen (which are in themselves almost ineffective) are subcutaneously injected with equally ineffective traces of $FeCl_3$, the result is again a greatly increased topical calciphylactic response. Here, the dextran and egg white apparently potentiate the action of subthreshold amounts of iron, somewhat as adjuvants can increase the efficacy of antigens.

THE "CRITICAL PERIOD"

It is impossible to reproduce certain calciphylactic phenomena consistently without strictly observing the critical period that must elapse between treatment with sensitizer and challenger. The length of this period is not the same for all forms of calciphylactic responses; indeed, we may obtain qualitatively different reactions by merely altering the time interval between treatment with sensitizer and challenger. For example, if female rats weighing about 200 g. are first given 1.5 mg. of DHT p.o. and 24 hours later 1 ml. of ferric dextran or "Fe-Dex" (= 50 mg. Fe) i.p., they develop intense calcification in the pancreas and retroperitoneal fat. Even the adipose tissue in the mesometrium exhibits a calciphylactic response, but the uterus itself does not react. On the other hand, if the experiment is repeated under otherwise identical conditions except that now the Fe-Dex is given 24 hours before the DHT, the pancreas and adipose tissue fail to react, while the uterus undergoes intense calcification. Numerous other examples illustrating the decisive importance of the critical period will be given when we describe the individual calciphylactic syndromes.

It is not yet clear how minor differences in the timing of the treatment with sensitizer and challenger can so radically change the form of a calciphylactic response. In anaphylaxis, a rest period after sensitization is necessary to allow time for the formation of antibodies before the challenging antigen is applied, but in calciphylaxis we have no evidence of any antigen-antibody reaction. It may be argued that, here, time is required for the absorption of the sensitizer and for the mobilization of calcium from the bones. However, as we have said, some calciphylactic reactions are best elicited by simultaneous treatment with sensitizer plus challenger (e.g., the cardiovascular, renal and biliary-tract lesions induced by DHT +

Fe-OS, i.v.), while others (e.g., uterine calcification after Fe-Dex, i.p. + DHT) are most readily obtained after pretreatment with the challenger.

In view of these facts, it is unlikely that the time-lapse required for the development of any one metabolic change could account for the length of the critical period in all types of calciphylaxis. Many factors may play a role here, for example: (1) the time necessary for the absorption of both sensitizer and challenger, (2) the speed of inactivation or elimination of these agents, and (3) the development of systemic and local adaptive reactions that can selectively affect calciphylaxis in one or more target organs.

COMPARISON OF CALCIPHYLAXIS WITH CLASSICAL (IMMUNOLOGIC) ALLERGIC REACTIONS

Calciphylaxis resembles certain immunologic hypersensitivity reactions (e.g., the tuberculin reaction, the local and general Shwartzman-Sanarelli phenomenon, classical anaphylaxis in the guinea pig, the Arthus phenomenon) in that it likewise depends upon a properly spaced treatment with a sensitizer and a challenger. Infiltration of the target area by eosinophils or plasma cells is also characteristic of both anaphylactic and many calciphylactic reactions.

However, in most other respects the two types of responses are essentially different. Unlike in immunologic hypersensitivity responses, in calciphylaxis: (1) there is no evidence of immune-body formation, (2) the sensitizer and challenger are essentially different substances, and (3) the response is primarily characterized by the local precipitation of calcium salts.

Furthermore, calciphylaxis can be obtained by sensitizers and challengers of known and comparatively simple structure. This fact facilitates the study of the underlying chemical mechanisms, but it does not represent an essential difference between calciphylaxis and immunologic hypersensitivity phenomena, since simple compounds of known structure can act as haptenes.

It would be unjustifiable to disregard a priori as coincidental the many similarities between calciphylaxis, on the one hand, and such reactions as drug allergies, physical allergies, and nonreagenic allergies, on the other, but at present we have no proof of any connection between these phenomena.

COMPARISON OF CALCIPHYLAXIS WITH OTHER CONNECTIVE-TISSUE REACTIONS

Now that we have briefly outlined calciphylaxis and its possible relationship to other hypersensitivity reactions, it may help to consider its nosologic position in relation to certain well-known experimental and clinical connective-tissue reactions, particularly inflammation, wound healing, and the "collagen diseases."

Like *inflammation*, calciphylaxis may be viewed as a reaction to injury; yet, the two types of response are essentially different. As we have said, there is no relationship between the ability of an agent to elicit morphologically detectable signs of injury (e.g., necrosis, cicatrization) or inflammation (e.g., exudation, granuloma formation) and its efficacy as a calciphylactic challenger. Furthermore, inflammation (except for the allergic forms) does not depend upon pretreatment with a sensitizer, nor is it characterized by topical calcification. Yet, calciphylaxis is accompanied by inflammation and—like many other phlogistic responses—it is followed by sclerosis; hence there undoubtedly do exist connections between the two forms of response.

Wound healing is also a reaction to injury, whicn—like calciphylaxis—can be elicited by diverse mechanical or chemical agents and is associated with inflammation and sclerosis (cicatrization). Yet wound healing, like inflammation, does not depend upon any specific sensitization nor is it usually associated with calcification, although calcium deposition and even bone formation occur occasionally in scars.

It will be particularly important to explore the possible connections between calcification and the **collagen diseases.** Cutaneous calciphylaxis has often been compared to the calcifying variety of *scleroderma*. The "sclérodermie calcaire" is a typical systemic connective-tissue disease, which—like calciphylaxis—is characterized by swelling and calcification of collagen fibers, followed by intense sclerosis. Also like calciphylaxis, scleroderma exhibits a particular predilection for the skin, but it affects other organs as well (e.g., the cardiovascular system, the kidney, and the alimentary tract).

Calcification may also occur in other clinical collagen diseases; for example, in *dermatomyositis*, *lupus erythematosus*, *generalized myositis ossificans*, and *sarcoidosis*. Since iron compounds are particularly effective calciphylactic challengers, it is noteworthy that this metal is frequently found in pathologic calcium deposits, while the *"sideroscleroses"* (e.g., Gamna corpuscles) exemplify connective-tissue proliferations associated with iron precipitation in human pathology.

All these observations suggest that calcium and iron may act as important stimulants of connective-tissue proliferation not only in experimental animals but also in man. It is true that (with the exception of calcifying scleroderma, calcareous bursitis, and calcinosis universalis) calcification is never as constant or as intense in human pathology as in typical experimental calciphylaxis, but this difference may not be fundamental. Even experimental calciphylactic reactions may be primarily characterized by hyalinization. For example, *periarteritis nodosa* can be produced (especially in the hepatic and pancreatic arteries of the rat) by sensitization with small doses of parathyroid hormone followed by the intravenous administration of Fe-OS. Here there may be no demonstrable calcium in the affected vessels (von Kóssa technique), although the media is intensely infiltrated with PAS-positive material and the adventitia shows advanced inflammatory changes. A slight and evanescent topical calcium deposition might play a pathogenic role in these lesions but it is impossible to prove this, either in the experimental model or in clinical periarteritis nodosa. Even if detectable amounts of calcium should accumulate within the vessel wall at an early stage, they are no longer demonstrable by the time the morbid changes are fully developed.

Calciphylactic periarteritis nodosa is structurally indistinguishable from the vascular changes produced by excess NaCl in rats sensitized (or "conditioned") by mineralocorticoids. The latter lesion is also a proliferative connective-tissue response that depends upon conjoint treatment with a sensitizer and a challenger; furthermore, the sensitizer (like DHT) is a steroid and the challenger (like so many of the calciphylactic mordants) a metallic salt. In this connection it is also noteworthy that sensitization with DOC augments the inflammatory potential, so that mechanical and chemical irritants elicit excessive connective-tissue responses; for example, in the DOC-pretreated rat, the pulse-pressure may suffice to produce periarteritis nodosa, and mild chemical irritants injected into the paw elicit excessive arthritic reactions.

Of course, such parallelisms may be purely coincidental. They are mentioned here only in order to suggest possible future avenues for research concerning the relationships between this new type of tissue response and the known forms of experimental and clinical derangements in tissue reactivity.

Summary

Calciphylaxis is defined as a condition of hypersensitivity in which—especially during a "critical period" after sensitization by a systemic calcifying factor (e.g., vitamin-D compounds, parathyroid hormone)—topical treatment with certain challengers (e.g., egg white, egg yolk, metallic salts) causes an acute local calcinosis followed by inflammation and sclerosis.

In suitably sensitized (e.g., DHT-treated) rats, such calciphylactic reactions can also be elicited selectively at predetermined sites (e.g., in the skin, muscles, joints, pancreas, bile ducts, uterus, spleen, RES-cells, lung, trachea, thyroid, parathyroid, carotid body, Brunner's glands, salivary glands, and lacrimal glands) by intravenous administration of challenging agents that exhibit a particular affinity for certain organs.

As a working hypothesis, it is assumed that in calciphylaxis the challenging agents act somewhat like mordants in that they prepare tissues for the uptake of calcium.

It remains to be shown whether calciphylaxis plays a part in human physiology or pathology.

HISTORY

In 1927, while still a medical student, I embarked upon my research career by purchasing a few elderly rats from the janitor of our pathology department and poisoning them with irradiated ergosterol, a preparation that had just become available at that time. Overdosage with this synthetic ***vitamin-D preparation produced widespread metastatic calcification in adult rats*** (particularly in the cardiovascular system, kidneys, lungs, and intestine), but only minor changes in the skeleton. However, the young of rats so treated during pregnancy or lactation responded to vitamin D (received through the milk or placenta) with an altogether different syndrome. In them, the usual soft-tissue calcification was negligible, but multiple spontaneous fractures occurred as a consequence of bone absorption; simultaneously the skin—especially the scalp—lost its elasticity and adhered to the subjacent tissues, so that the animals became *"hidebound."* These facts were duly (though somewhat haltingly) reported to the *Verein Deutscher Ärzte in Prag* on October 26, 1928, in what happened to be my first lecture. The essence of this work was published the next year.[806, 811] Since the offspring of the vitamin-D treated mothers also suffered from malnutrition and dehydration, little importance was attached to the skin lesions at that time in comparison with the more striking and evidently specific skeletal changes (Plate I, *A*).

Soon afterward I chanced to see *a patient in whom multiple organ calcifications occurred in combination with a parathyroid adenoma, nephritis, and colitis.* The calcium deposits were very similar to those induced in adult rats with vitamin D and were thought to result from excessive endogenous parathyroid-hormone secretion. It seemed that, here, parathyroid stimulation might have represented a homeostatic hormonal reaction, an attempt to rectify the derangement caused by damage to the organs normally concerned with the absorption and excretion of calcium and phosphate. This supposition could not be proven at that time and we had to consider alternative interpretations also, but our case appeared to throw a new light upon Virchow's classical concept of "metastatic calcification" as a consequence of renal disease. We thought that, in uremia, calcification could be largely mediated through the parathyroids as a consequence of a *"pathogenic adaptive reaction,"*[807] the type of derangement that we would now call a "disease of adaptation."

In 1932 it was noted that, *in the rat, parathyroid hormone can produce a cutaneous calcinosis with sclerosis* resembling the calcifying type of scleroderma.[809] This observation has been repeatedly confirmed[3, 70, 454, 588, 589, 880] without, however, adding much to our understanding of the underlying mechanism. Still, I began to suspect that an increased parathyroid activity—such as occurs as an adaptive response to derangements in calcium metabolism—may participate in the pathogenesis of collagen diseases.[810]

It was not until twenty-five years later that we succeeded in reproducing *similar lesions in rats treated with DHT,* a vitamin-D derivative that closely imitates the actions of parathyroid hormone.[819] However, the cutaneous lesions produced either by parathyroid extract or by DHT could not serve as practical models of disease, because they were invariably accompanied by high mortality and developed only inconstantly in newborn rats on the scalp and neck (and not where we wanted to induce them).

Nevertheless these observations induced numerous surgeons to *remove the parathyroids in an effort to cure scleroderma.* The results were quite inconstant, but, allegedly, sometimes marked improvement did occur.[2, 55, 67, 69, 92, 94, 95, 96, 169, 177, 223, 226, 231, 293, 329, 330, 333, 357, 369, 444, 445, 447, 475, 503, 557, 560, 582, 584, 585, 586, 587, 588, 589, 621, 622, 691, 705, 730, 734, 910, 962, 990]

One group of surgeons pointed out that, although scleroderma improved greatly following parathyroidectomy, similar ameliorations were noted in patients in whom they could not find the glands. However, even this result was ascribed to incidental trauma to the parathyroids.[3]

In view of what we have learned since about the importance of "conditioning factors" in the determination of adaptive hormonal reactions,[813, 831] we felt that further work on our experimental model of calcareous scleroderma would be rewarding if the technique could be perfected, perhaps by the use of some local sensitizing agent.

Topical trauma proved to cause local calcification and sclerosis in certain internal organs of DHT-treated rats.[820] This finding was of special interest to us, because a survey of the literature had shown that clinical scleroderma likewise tends to develop at sites of local injury.[810] Further experiments then revealed that cutaneous calcinosis with sclerosis can also be consistently produced at will in predetermined skin regions—even in adult rats—if the selected area is lightly traumatized (e.g., by epilation) during a *"critical period"* of DHT-treatment[858] (Plate I, *B*). Presumably, our failure to obtain consistent results in the early experiments was due to the fact that cutaneous lesions developed only where we accidentally traumatized the skin while holding the rats by the nape of the neck for injection. Newborn animals may have been especially sensitive merely because their hairless, tender skin is particularly subject to injury during handling. Be this as it may, now we had a reliable technique permitting the consistent production of cutaneous calcinosis at any desired point of the skin surface, in rats of different age groups and without having to give near-lethal doses of parathyroid hormone or DHT.

The perfection of this simple test represented a turning point in our studies: with its help we made more progress during the next six months than we had during the preceding thirty-two years. The way was now opened for a systematic analysis of the particular qualities that a local challenger must have to produce cutaneous calcinosis in the suitably sensitized animal.

One of the first facts revealed by this new technique was that there is *no proportionality between the local damaging effect and the challenging potency of a topical trauma.* For example, mere plucking of the hair or slight pinching of the skin sufficed to produce marked cutaneous calcinosis in the DHT-sensitized rat. Conversely, if the skin was severely compressed with a hemostat, no such lesion developed in the directly damaged area, although a calcified "halo" appeared around the compressed stripe[858, 862] (Plate I, *C*).

It then turned out that not only traumatic interventions but numerous **chemical agents can act as challengers** and cause cutaneous calcinosis in sensitized animals: subcutaneous injections of many metallic salts (e.g., those of iron, chromium, aluminum, copper, lead, cerium, zirconium, manganese, silver, and tin) as well as egg white and egg yolk were soon shown to be highly effective in this respect as judged by tests on DHT-pretreated rats.[478, 479, 830] It is noteworthy that so many metallic salts proved to be effective challengers, while only very few organic compounds exhibited this potency; indeed it remains to be seen whether even these act directly or merely by activating some endogenous challenger (e.g., metals pre-existent in the body).* Bones and skin possess a particular affinity for metals, and the possible relationship between this property and the predisposition for calcification may be a fruitful subject for future study.

Certain organic compounds such as dextran and gelatin—though themselves devoid of direct challenging potency—can act as topical **adjuvants** of challengers. For example, in the DHT-sensitized rat, otherwise subthreshold doses of $FeCl_3$ induce extensive cutaneous calcinosis if injected in a dextran solution. Egg white and egg yolk are active in themselves, but their challenging potency can be greatly augmented by the admixture of trace amounts of iron. Hence, even the activity of native albumen and yolk may be largely dependent upon their normal iron content.[848]

At this point of our study we became interested in the **systemic factors that influence this form of calcinosis.** Probably the most important among these is systemic stress, which—if applied at the proper time—can completely protect the sensitized rat against the induction of calcification by an otherwise active topical challenger.[492, 493, 494, 859] However, unlike in most other instances of such stress-induced "cross-resistance," here the protection is not necessarily mediated through the discharge of ACTH and glucocorticoids, since adrenalectomy does not always prevent the stress-induced protection against calciphylaxis[494] and only certain forms of systemic calciphylaxis (e.g., the calciphylactic dermatomyositis) are effectively inhibited by glucocorticoids.[829a, 857]

Several other systemic factors were found to influence the development of cutaneous calcinosis decisively; thus, hypophysectomy can prevent it,[857] while pretreatment with thallium salts,[859] phosphates, or calcium salts,[830] as well as extensive partial nephrectomy[491, 826] sensitize for it.

* As we shall see, several observations suggest that the process of vital mordanting does not merely depend upon a direct interaction between the challenging metal and calcium. Multiple deposits of the same metal situated in the same animal may attract calcium in one organ and not in another. Furthermore, heavy deposits of active challenging metals (Fe, Cr, Th) may be demonstrable at sites where they normally do produce calcification and yet attract no calcium after hypophysectomy or previous exposure to stress. It is possible, therefore, that the challenging metals must first attract some organic calcifiable material (e.g., mucopolysaccharides) before they can cause calcinosis. Be this as it may, metals evidently play a decisive part in the process of calciphylactic challenge.

Perhaps the greatest stimulus to further studies along these lines was the demonstration that diverse **systemic syndromes of calcification and sclerosis** can be produced after DHT-sensitization by the intravenous or intraperitoneal administration of certain challengers. Thus a single injection of albumen or Fe-Dex into the jugular vein induces calcification and sclerosis predominantly in the pancreas, Fe-OS in the cardiac auricles and bile ducts, thorium preparations in the esophagus, 5HT in the salivary glands, chromium salts in the thyroids and parathyroids, etc.[827, 849]

These findings were mainly responsible for the development of the whole **concept of calciphylaxis** as we see it today. They showed that here we are dealing with a form of altered tissue reactivity that resembles classical immunologic hypersensitivity phenomena in many respects. As we have said before both forms are **allergies** in the original sense of the word (manifestations of altered responsiveness), both depend upon properly spaced treatment with a sensitizer and a challenging agent and both are frequently associated with eosinophilia.

It was the study of the systemic calciphylactic syndromes that also called attention to possible relationships between these experimentally induced derangements of the entire connective-tissue system and the clinical collagen diseases, particularly those characterized by sclerosis and hyalinization. It soon became evident that endogenous metabolites can replace DHT or injected parathyroid hormone as sensitizers for experimental calciphylaxis. For example, pretreatment with NaAST (a compound known to cause renal damage with secondary parathyroid stimulation) sensitizes the rat for a calciphylactic response to subsequent subcutaneous $FeCl_3$-treatment. Here, a drug possessing no direct effect upon calcium metabolism can act as a calciphylactic sensitizer, perhaps by causing renal damage and thereby stimulating parathyroid activity as a secondary, hormonal adaptive response.[827] This possibility gained in likelihood when it was shown that bilateral nephrectomy also sensitizes for calciphylaxis, but not after parathyroidectomy.[829a]

Could certain pathogens act similarly in man, and if so, could they sensitize even for the production of noncalcifying lesions? Calcium deposition sometimes represents only a brief, transient stage in the development of hyalinizing and sclerosing "collagen diseases" in the course of experimental calciphylaxis. For example, after sensitization with parathyroid hormone, periarteritis nodosa of the hepatic arteries can be produced by treatment with Fe-OS without there being any demonstrable calcification in the affected vessels. Furthermore, after priming with parathyroid hormone 5HT causes a severe muscular dystrophy without demonstrable calcinosis.[829a] Apparently, calciphylactic responses are not necessarily associated with a calcium deposition sufficiently severe to be detectable by current histochemical techniques.

On the other hand, as we shall see, the literature reveals many instances of collagen disease (e.g., scleroderma, dermatomyositis, sarcoidosis, myositis ossificans, formation of Heberden's nodules) in which hyalinization and sclerosis are accompanied by marked soft-tissue calcification. This association of sclerosis and calcification is, of course, particularly common in the various forms of chronic cardiovascular disease.

These were the facts that began to direct attention to the possible role of calciphylaxis in human pathology.

DEFINITIONS AND TERMINOLOGY

Now that we have become acquainted with the principle of calciphylaxis, let us try to define a few of its basic concepts. In essence all calciphylactic phenomena depend upon co-ordinated interactions between systemic sensitization and topical challenge, but both these processes are themselves subject to regulation by a variety of activators and inhibitors. The effectiveness of systemic sensitization depends upon the availability of calcium and of substances with which this element is normally combined in vivo (e.g., phosphate, carbonate, mucopolysaccharides). The result of topical challenge is influenced by the many factors that regulate the responsiveness of tissues to local stimulation in general (e.g., inflammation, scar formation, blood supply). Hence, in principle every aspect of calcium metabolism and of tissue reactivity would be germane to our subject, but here we shall attempt to define only those concepts that are specifically concerned with calciphylaxis as such.

Adjuvants of Challengers: Compounds that have little or no challenging action by themselves but greatly increase the activity of direct topical challengers (e.g., dextran, gelatin).

Adjuvants of Indirect Calcifiers: Substances that increase the diverse effects of indirect calcifiers; they can thereby enhance calciphylaxis but they themselves do not sensitize for challengers. (For example, dietary fat supplements increase the calcifying effect of DHT or of parathyroid hormone, but by themselves they do not sensitize for challengers.)

Albumen: The albumen of avian eggs.

Calcifiers: Agents which promote calcification of tissues. We distinguish:

1. *Indirect calcifiers,* which favor calcification in general by virtue of their effects upon systemic calcium metabolism (e.g., DHT, vitamin D_2, vitamin D_3, parathyroid hormone, calcium salts, phosphates, sodium acetylsulfathiazole). At high dose levels they may induce "nonspecific calcinosis" by themselves (i.e., without the aid of challengers or adjuvants), though only in certain predisposed tissues (e.g., the cardiovascular system, kidney, lung, gastrointestinal tract). However, indirect calcifiers can sensitize for calciphylaxis even when they are given in amounts not normally conducive to nonspecific calcinosis.

2. *Direct calcifiers,* which produce topical tissue calcification at the site of administration without previous sensitization (e.g., $KMnO_4$).

Calcinoscleroses: Diseases characterized by excessive connective-tissue formation on the basis of a preceding, often evanescent, topical calcium deposition.

Calcinosis: A generic term to designate any form of morbid soft-tissue calcification. (Cf. also Cutaneous Calcinosis.)

Calciphylactic Dermatomyositis: A musculocutaneous inflammation with calcification induced by calciphylaxis, particularly by siderocalciphylaxis. The term is not meant to imply any fundamental relationship to clinical dermatomyositis.

Calciphylactic Muscular Dystrophy: An experimental disease of the muscles characterized by degenerative and inflammatory changes with comparatively little calcification. The term is not meant to imply any fundamental relationship to the clinical muscular dystrophies.

Calciphylactic Psoriasis: A chronic, scaly dermatosis induced by calciphylaxis. The term is not meant to imply any fundamental relationship to clinical psoriasis.

Calciphylactic Scleroderma: A dermatosis which begins with cutaneous calcinosis and gradually leads to the development of intense sclerosis with disappearance of the cutaneous appendages, flattening of the epidermo-dermal junction line and frequently epidermal atrophy. The term is not meant to imply any fundamental relationship to clinical scleroderma.

Calciphylaxis: A condition of induced systemic hypersensitivity in which tissues respond to appropriate challengers with local calcium deposition. We distinguish:

1. **Topical calciphylaxis** induced by the direct application of the challenger to the responsive tissue;

2. **Systemic calciphylaxis,** in which the challenger is distributed throughout the organism but produces responses only in tissues for which it (or some endogenous product released by it) has a selective affinity.

Challengers: Substances that, following sensitization by an indirect calcifier, cause local calcification where applied or (in the event of systemic administration) in tissues for which these compounds have a particular affinity (e.g., $FeCl_3$, Fe-OS, Fe-Dex, albumen, yolk). We distinguish:

1. **Direct challengers** ("vital mordants"), which are effective locally where they are directly applied or selectively taken up from the blood (e.g., Fe-Dex, $CrCl_3$, yolk);

2. **Indirect challengers,** which have little or no direct effect upon the site of application but apparently act through the liberation of endogenous direct challengers from certain tissues. For example, even in the DHT-sensitized organism, histamine liberators (mastocyte dischargers), such as 48/80 and polymyxin, produce no local calciphylaxis, but they induce granular calcification throughout the derma, presumably by releasing challenging tissue-metabolites from the mast cells. Similarly, the subcutaneous injection of glucocorticoids, such as triamcinolone, produces no local calciphylactic reaction under these conditions, but causes calcification of the thymus, probably through the discharge of direct challengers from thymocytes.

Critical Period: The time interval that must elapse between treatment with a sensitizer and a challenger to yield a calciphylactic response. In most instances, the reaction is maximal if the sensitizer is administered first (e.g., DHT-treatment must precede the subcutaneous injection of albumen to produce cutaneous calcinosis). However, some forms of calciphylaxis are most severe if the challenger is given first (e.g., the most marked and selective uterine calcification occurs if intraperitoneal injection with Fe-Dex is followed by oral treatment with DHT). Only few calciphylactic reactions are best obtained by concurrent treatment with sensitizer and challenger (e.g., the syndrome of auricular and subepicardial calcification accompanied by calcific cholangitis, which is induced by intravenous injection of Fe-OS + oral administration of DHT).

Cutaneous Calcinosis: Calcification of the skin. Most important among its calciphylactically induced experimental variants are: (1) the primarily *fibrous* form initiated by calcium deposition along connective-tissue fibers, which may form solid skin plaques or assume an arborizing (reticular) pattern that follows the course of blood vessels; (2) the primarily *granular* form, which is initiated by the calcification of discharged mastocyte granules, but usually terminates in fiber incrustation and then becomes indistinguishable from the primarily fibrous form.

Dermatomyositis Induced by Calciphylaxis: (Cf. Calciphylactic Dermatomyositis.)

Dex: Dextran.

DHT: Dihydrotachysterol.

Din: Dextrin or British Gum.

Direct Calcifiers: (Cf. Calcifiers.)

Direct Challengers: (Cf. Challengers.)

DOC: Desoxycorticosterone.

DOC-ac: Desoxycorticosterone Acetate.

F-COL: 9a-fluorocortisol.

Fe-Dex: Ferric Dextran (Imposil®, Imferon®).

Fe-Din: Ferric Dextrin (Ferrigen®).

Fe-OS: Ferric Oxide Saccharate (Proferrin®).

Fe-Sol: Ferric Sorbitol (Jectofer®).

5HT: 5-hydroxytryptamine or Serotonin.

Indirect Calcifiers: (Cf. Calcifiers.)

Indirect Challengers: (Cf. Challengers.)

Inhibitors of Challengers: Substances which counteract the effects of challengers directly at the site of administration. For example, topical pretreatment with India ink, strong mechanical trauma, or inflammatory irritants can desensitize a skin area to the calciphylactic effect of an otherwise active challenger subsequently applied to the same region.

Inhibitors of Indirect Calcifiers: Agents that inhibit the calciphylactic, though not necessarily all other, effects of indirect calcifiers (e.g., systemic stress, hypophysectomy).

IPR: Isoproterenol.

Metacalciphylactic Changes: (From the Greek "meta" = with or after.) Changes that accompany or follow calciphylactic reactions without being essential parts of them (e.g., osteitis fibrosa).

Muscular Dystrophy Induced by Calciphylaxis: (Cf. Calciphylactic Muscular Dystrophy.)

NaAST: Sodium Acetylsulfathiazole.

Nonspecific Calcinosis: A type of calcinosis that affects only predisposed tissues (e.g., the cardiovascular system, kidney, lung, gastrointestinal tract). It can be obtained by heavy overdosage with indirect calcifiers (e.g., DHT, parathyroid hormone) without the use of challengers or adjuvants.

Overchallenge: Inhibition of a calciphylactic reaction by treatment with an excess of a challenger. For example, in the DHT-sensitized rat, subcutaneous injection of FeCl$_3$ may produce a "circinate" cutaneous calcinosis in which the central area fails to respond owing to overchallenge, while a calcified ring develops in the periphery where the concentration of the challenger was lower.

PMX: Polymyxin.

Psoriasis Induced by Calciphylaxis: (Cf. Calciphylactic Psoriasis.)

PVP: Polyvinylpyrrolidone.

RES: Reticuloendothelial System.

Scleroderma Induced by Calciphylaxis: (Cf. Calciphylactic Scleroderma.)

SDS: (Cf. Stromal Depot System.)

Siderocalciphylaxis: Hypersensitivity induced by an indirect calcifier and systemic treatment with an iron compound given simultaneously with the challenger (e.g., DHT + Fe-Dex i.v. + PMX s.c. as used for the production of calciphylactic dermatomyositis).

STH: Somatotrophic Hormone.

Stromal Depot System (SDS): A system of various stromal elements especially capable of storing particulate matter either by phagocytosis (within giant cells, fibroblasts, and vascular endothelia) or by extracellular deposition (on connective-tissue fibers, discharged mastocyte granules, etc.). The collagenous and vascular elements of the skin, lung, joints, esophagus, and pancreas are particularly active parts of the SDS, but many other organs (e.g., the stroma of the salivary glands, Brunner's glands, the thyroparathyroid apparatus) likewise belong to this system. The SDS is of special interest in connection with calciphylaxis because many challengers (and subsequently calcium) are selectively taken up by certain portions of this system, while others are deposited in the phagocytes of the RES.

Systemic Calciphylaxis: (Cf. Calciphylaxis.)

Systemogenic Calcification: A calcinosis which is primarily due to systemic metabolic factors. This term is used instead of such older designations as "metastatic calcification" or "calcium gout."

Topical Calciphylaxis: (Cf. Calciphylaxis.)

Topogenic Calcification: A calcinosis which is primarily due to local changes. This term is used instead of the less precise designation "dystrophic calcification."

Vital Mordants: (Cf. Challengers.)

Yolk: The yolk of avian eggs.

48/80: Condensation product of p-methoxyphenylmethylamine with formaldehyde. A histamine and mastocyte discharger.

Color Atlas
of Experimental Calciphylaxis

The following plates comprise 84 colored photographs selected to illustrate some of the most typical calciphylactic responses. They are meant to act as a pictorial complement of the preceding descriptive general characterization of calciphylaxis.

Up to now this new field has been explored primarily from the morphologic point of view, hence it was felt that the most helpful introduction to it would be a visual review of the principal observations upon which the concept of calciphylaxis is based.

No effort will be made here to interpret our findings but great care has been taken to label each photograph (or list references to previously published descriptions) so as to clearly identify the procedure used to obtain the illustrated change. The style of the labels is self-explanatory, but a complete description of it will be found on pages 17 and 18.

The author is particularly grateful to the Gustavus and Louise Pfeiffer Research Foundation for their generous Grant to defray the cost of this Color Atlas.

PLATE I

A: Cutaneous calcinosis and bone fragility produced in the suckling rat by DHT treatment of its mother. Ten-day-old suckling rat. Typical patch of hairless, calcified, indurated and edematous skin on head. Severe deformation of front paws is due to multiple spontaneous bone fractures. Lesions developed without intentional challenge, although accidental trauma may have played a role.

B: Topical cutaneous calcinosis produced by DHT+epilation. Rat sensitized with DHT and challenged by plucking hair over scalp and back. Typical appearance of calcified skin wheals in epilated areas.

C: Calciphylactic lesion with central "overchallenge." Halo of cutaneous calcinosis surrounding each of three linear hemostat pinches. Directly traumatized area itself remains unaffected.

D, E, F: Various acute forms of cutaneous calcinosis produced by DHT+epilation. *D:* Beginning calcification of slightly swollen dermal collagen fibers. Pronounced parakeratosis with calcification in most superficial layer of exfoliating skin. *E:* In this form of acute cutaneous calcinosis the very pronounced calcification of dermal connective tissue reaches deep into the corium, but avoids hair follicles. *F:* Skin region adjacent to that shown in "E." Here there is selective calcification of the hair follicles (especially in deep stratum), while the connective tissue is spared. (D, E, F, von Kóssa×110.)

A, after Selye,[819] courtesy of Williams and Wilkins Co. (J. Invest. Dermat.); **B,** after Selye et al.,[858] courtesy Proc. Soc. Exper. Biol. and Med.; **C, D, E, F,** after Selye and Nielsen,[862] courtesy of Akadémiai Kiadó Budapest (Acta Morphol. Acad. Sc. Hungar.)

PLATE I

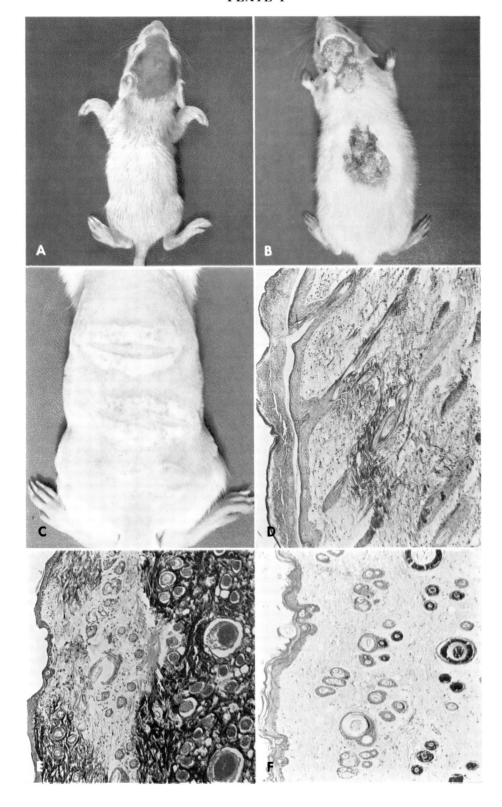

PLATE II

A: Acute form of cutaneous calcinosis produced by DHT+plucking of scalp hair.
One normal and one disintegrating mastocyte (near upper margin) with mastocyte granules diffusely distributed throughout tissue in this region. Elastic fibers have undergone selective calcification. Mastocyte granules (particularly in the mastocytes themselves) stained distinctly purple with hematoxylin-phloxine counterstain. (von Kóssa×490.) Mast cells and granules were identified on adjacent sections by metachromatic staining with cresyl violet and elastic fibers by the phosphotungstic-elastica stain.

B: Acute cutaneous calcinosis produced by DHT+Fe-Dex i.p. Rat (200 g.♀): DHT (2 mg. p.o.) 1st day + Fe-Dex (1 ml.=50 mg. Fe, i.p.) 2d day; killed 5th day. Beginning calcification and swelling of dermal collagen fibers. (Celestin blue × 420.)

C, D: Preosseous plaques produced by DHT+albumen s.c. Rat (100 g.♀): DHT (1 mg. p.o.) 1st day + albumen (50%, 5 ml. s.c.) 2d and 3d day; killed 32d day. *C:* Formation of preosseous plaques in subcutaneous adipose tissue. Fat cells have disappeared, but their outlines remain clearly visible owing to demarcation by PAS-positive material and invasion by connective tissue elements. *D:* Section through abdominal musculature underneath site of albumen injection. Formation of intensely PAS-positive, preosseous plaques surrounded by sclerotic connective tissue and numerous osteoclast-like giant cells. (PAS × 120.)

E: Intense diffuse cutaneous calcinosis produced by DHT+albumen i.v. Rat (100 g.♀): DHT (1 mg. p.o.) 1st day + albumen (50%, 5 ml. i.v.) 2d and 3d day; killed 29th day. Particularly intense generalized cutaneous calcinosis leading to gradual detachment of large hard skin plaques.

F, G: Three typical calcified skin plaques in a rat treated with DHT+albumen i.p.
On ventral aspect sharply delimited plaques over xiphoid process and along costal margin. Plaques are visible also from the back.

A, after Selye and Nielsen,[862] courtesy of Akadémiai Kiadó Budapest (Acta Morphol. Acad. Sc. Hungar.)
F, G, after Selye et al.,[849] courtesy Proc. Soc. Exper. Biol. and Med.

PLATE II

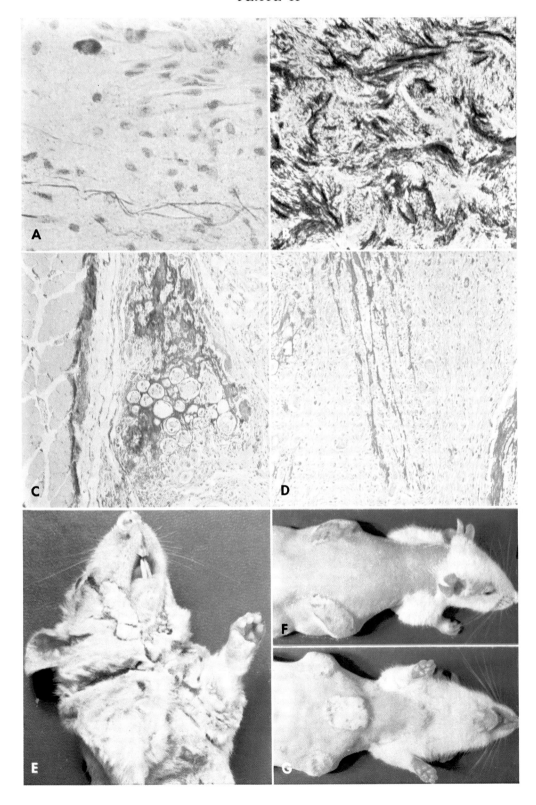

PLATE III

A, B: Pancreatic calcification produced by DHT+albumen i.p. Rat (100 g. ♀): DHT (1 mg. p.o.) 1st day + albumen (50%, 5 ml. i.p.) 2d day; killed 6th day. Extensive calcification of pancreatic stroma with secondary degenerative and inflammatory changes in parenchyma. Despite extraordinary intensity of calcification, the mineral deposits are dustlike and show no tendency to form solid masses. (A von Kóssa, B celestin blue, × 120.)

C, D: Calcification of abdominal wall produced by DHT+albumen i.p. Rat (100 g. ♀): DHT (1 mg. p.o.) 1st day + albumen (50%, 5 ml. i.p.) 2d day; killed 6th day. Two consecutive sections through entire abdominal wall in costovertebral angle. Laminated calcium deposits are visible throughout thickness of preparation from subperitoneal muscle layer (bottom) up to epidermis. Note excellent correspondence of calcified areas, as demonstrated by von Kóssa *(D)* and celestin blue *(C)* stains, except that latter dye impregnates only peripheral margins of calcified regions. (× 35.)

E, F, G: Calcification of spleen and liver produced by DHT+yolk i.v. Two rats (100 g. ♀): DHT (1 mg. p.o.) 1st day + yolk (50%, 5 ml. i.v.) 2d day; killed 4th day. *E:* Spleen of rat treated with DHT alone (left) shows no sign of calcium deposition, while that of animal given combined treatment is heavily calcified. *F:* Section through adjacent spleen. *G:* In the liver, calcium deposition affects Kupffer cells and some connective tissue fibers along walls of sinusoids. (F celestin blue × 35; G von Kóssa × 120.)

E, F, G, after Selye,[827] courtesy Allergie u. Asthma

PLATE III

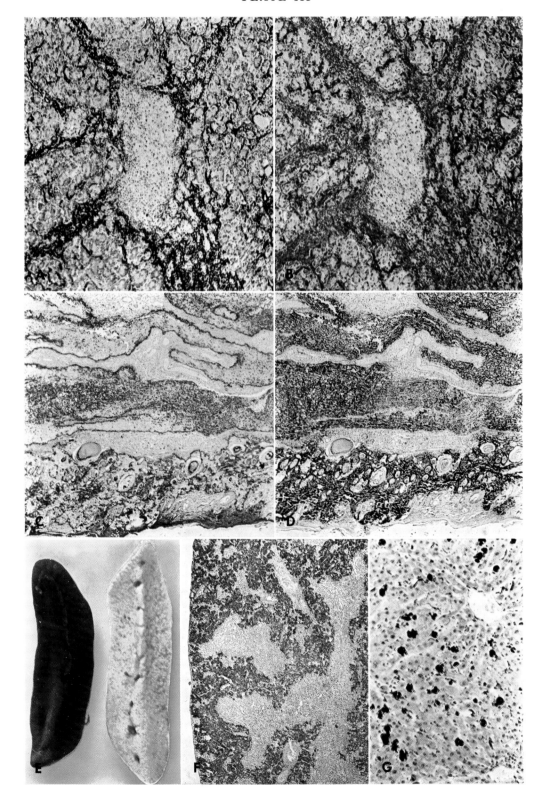

PLATE IV

A, B: Massive calcification of thyro-parathyroid apparatus produced by DHT+CrCl₂ i.v.
Two rats (100 g.♀): DHT (1 mg. p.o.) 1st day + (A) CrCl₂ (3.3 mg. in 0.35 ml. water,
i.v.) 2d day; killed 6th day. *A:* In animal given combined treatment, both thyroid and
parathyroid (arrow) are heavily calcified and hence white. *B:* DHT-treatment without
challenge by CrCl₂ leaves thyro-parathyroid apparatus unchanged.

C: Prevention by restraint of thyroid and parathyroid calcinosis produced by DHT+
CrCl₃ i.v. Two rats (100 g.♀): DHT (1 mg. p.o.) 1st day + CrCl₃ (6 mg. in 2 ml. water, i.v.)
2d day + (right) restraint (24 hours) 1st day; killed 6th day.

D: Calcification of parathyroid and thyroid stroma produced by DHT+CrCl₃ i.v.
Rat (100 g.♀): DHT (1 mg. p.o.) 1st day + CrCl₃ (10 mg. in 1 ml. water, i.v.) 2d day;
killed 5th day. Intense calcium incrustation of stroma in the parathyroids, accompanied by
less pronounced calcification of thyroid stroma. (von Kóssa × 400.)

E: Calcification of thyroid and carotid body produced by DHT+FeCl₂ i.v. Rat
(100 g.♀): DHT (1 mg. p.o.) 1st day + FeCl₂ [4 injections (1, 2, 3 and 3 mg.) each in
1 ml. water, i.v.] throughout 2d day (to avoid toxicity of sudden overdosage); killed 6th
day. Completely calcified thyro-parathyroid apparatus (near left margin) and carotid body in
bifurcation just underneath origin of occipital artery (center of field). Wavy white lines
correspond to uncalcified nerves.

F: Calcification of carotid body produced by DHT+CrCl₃ i.v. Rat (100 g.♀): DHT
(1 mg. p.o.) 1st day + CrCl₃ (10 mg. in 1 ml. water, i.v.) 2d day; killed 6th day. Carotid
body (shown in bifurcation) with complete calcification of stroma; adjacent superior cervical
sympathetic ganglion (lower part of field) reveals no trace of calcification. (von Kóssa × 35.)

G: Calcification of renal pelvis produced by DHT+CrCl₃ i.v. Rat (200 g.♀): CrCl₃
(20 mg. in 1 ml. water, i.v.) 1st day + DHT (2 mg. p.o.) 2d day; killed 9th day. Intense
calcium infiltration of submucosa in renal pelvis. The papilla remains free of calcium, but two
arteries in the perirenal fat are mildly calcified. (von Kóssa × 35.)

F, after Selye and Dieudonné,[837] courtesy of Biochem. e Biol. sper.

PLATE IV

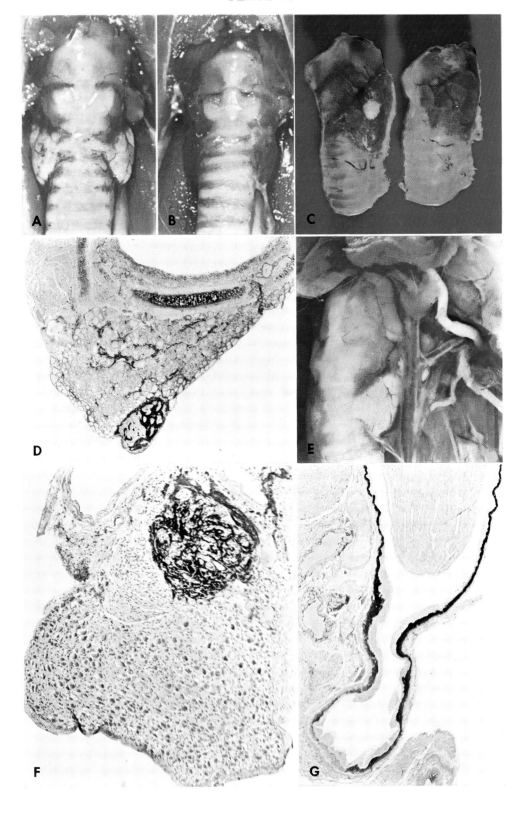

PLATE V

A: Calcification of choroid plexus produced by DHT+CrCl₂ i.v. Rat (100 g.♀):
DHT (1 mg. p.o.) 1st day + CrCl₂ (3.5 mg. in 0.35 ml. water, i.v.) 2d day; killed 6th day.
Extensive calcification of blood vessels in choroid plexus of third ventricle. The epithelial cells
themselves have not undergone calcification and appear to be free of any noticeable damage
from the intense calcium deposition in the adjacent vessels. (von Kóssa × 120.)

B: Pancreatic calciphylaxis produced by DHT+Fe-Dex i.p. Rat (100 g.♀): DHT
(1 mg. p.o.) 1st day + Fe-Dex (1 ml.=50 mg. Fe, i.p.) 3d day; killed 6th day. Ferrification
(blue) and calcification (black) of pancreatic stroma. (Prussian blue + von Kóssa × 420.)

C, D: Pancreatic calciphylaxis produced by DHT+Fe-Dex i.p. Rat (100 g.♀): DHT
(1 mg. p.o.) 1st day + Fe-Dex (1 ml.=50 mg. Fe, i.p.) 3d day; killed 9th day. *C:* Intense
calcification of pancreas with compression of duodenum and consequent dilatation of stomach.
Spleen normal. *D:* Untreated control for comparison with "C."

**E, F: Calcification of region of Brunner's glands in duodenum produced by DHT+
Fe-Dex i.p.** Rat (200 g.♀): DHT (2 mg. p.o.) 1st day + Fe-Dex (1 ml.=50 mg. Fe, i.p.)
2d day; killed 6th day. Massive calcium deposition in stroma of Brunner's glands. (Two
consecutive sections: E von Kóssa, F celestin blue, × 120.)

A, after Selye and Dieudonné,[836] courtesy Zhur. Nevropath. i. Psikhiat.

PLATE V

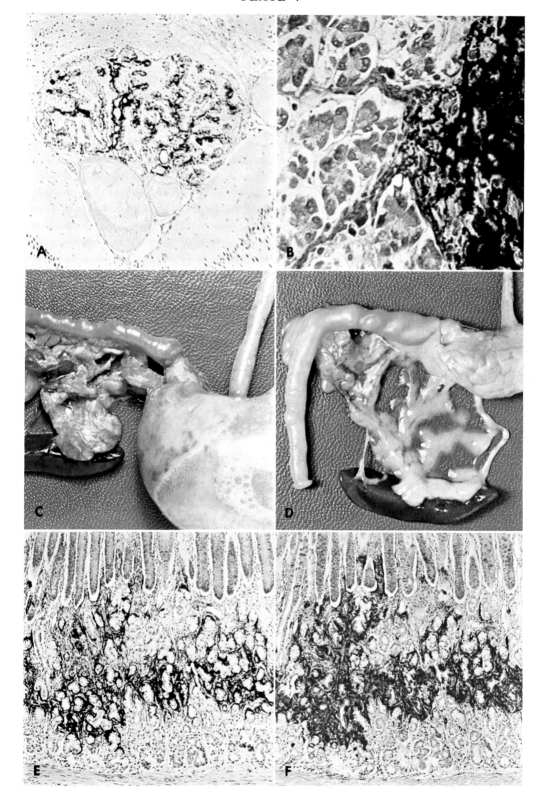

PLATE VI

A: Calcification of genital fat and uterus produced by DHT+Fe-Dex i.p. Two rats (200 g.♀): Fe-Dex (1 ml.= 50 mg. Fe, i.p.) 1st day + DHT (2 mg. p.o.) 2d day; killed 9th day. Fresh specimen. *Left:* Heavy calcification in the uterus, which assumes "gooseneck" appearance; no calcification of sexual fat. *Right:* Intense calcification of sexual fat; no calcium deposition in uterus. (It is not yet known why, under the influence of the same treatment, the calcification is virtually limited to the sexual fat in some animals and to the uterus in others.)

B: Calcification of pancreas, but not of spleen, produced by DHT+Fe-Dex i.v. Rat (100 g.♀): DHT (1 mg. p.o.) 1st day + Fe-Dex (1 ml.=50 mg. Fe, i.v.) 3d day; killed 6th day. Intense calcification (black) of pancreatic stroma with still uncalcified iron granules (blue) in lower left portion of field. Dense iron granules (blue) in adjacent spleen fail to cause calcification. (Prussian blue + von Kóssa × 120.)

C: Endometrial calcification produced by DHT+yolk i.p. Rat (200 g.♀): DHT (2 mg. p.o.) 1st day + yolk (50%, 10 ml. i.p.) 2d day; killed 6th day. Uterine calcification is uncommon under these conditions; when it does occur, it usually affects only endometrial stroma, as shown here. (von Kóssa × 100.)

D: Calciphylactic psoriasis produced by DHT+Fe-Dex i.p. Rat (200 g.♀): Fe-Dex (1 ml.=50 mg. Fe, i.p.) 1st day + DHT (2 mg. p.o.) 2d day; killed 12th day. Calcium infiltration with marked scaling of skin. Reticular pattern of nodules clearly visible through skin surface (near lower margin of picture). Removal of scales (by gentle scratching along midline over lower thoracic regions) caused diffuse surface bleeding corresponding to Auspitz' sign in psoriasis.

E: Healing of facial lesions produced by DHT+Fe-Din i.v. Rat (100 g.♀): DHT (1 mg. p.o.) 1st day + Fe-Din (0.35 ml.=7 mg. Fe, i.v.) 2d day; photographed 60th day. Lips and ears had undergone widespread calcinosis during first two weeks after challenge. Here, two months later, large portions of the calcified right lip are becoming detached and begin to be cast off (as they were in corresponding portion on left, where hyperemic scar now replaces shed skin).

F: Prevention by restraint of cutaneous and periarticular calcification produced by DHT+Thorotrast® i.v. Two rats (120 g.♀): DHT (1 mg. p.o.) 2d day + Thorotrast® (0.6 ml. i.v.) 3d day + (left) restraint (17 hours) 1st and 3d day; killed 7th day. Pronounced calcification produced by combined treatment is prevented by restraint.

PLATE VI

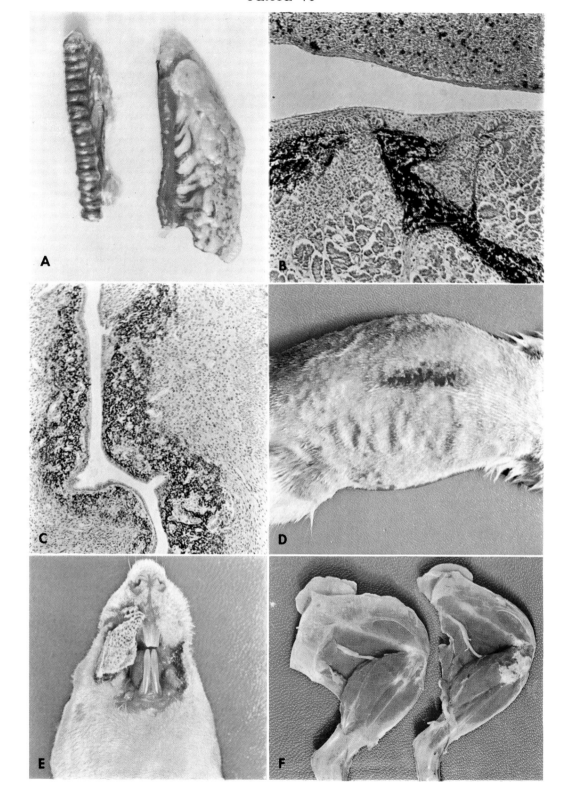

PLATE VII

A, B: General appearance of the musculocutaneous lesions produced by DHT+Fe-Dex i.v.+PMX s.c. *A:* Rat treated with DHT + PMX (left) shows just detectable lesions in skin of head and neck. Treatment with DHT + PMX + Fe-Dex (right) induces pronounced inflammation and calcification of skin, particularly that covering cranial half of body. *B:* Same two rats (position reversed to facilitate comparison of the more severe skin lesions) with skin split along midline of dorsum and reflected to sides; here lesions in subcutis and musculature are especially obvious.

C: Late stages of cutaneous lesions produced by DHT+Fe-Dex i.v.+PMX s.c. Rat (100 g.♀): DHT (1 mg. p.o.) 1st day + Fe-Dex (1 ml.=1 mg. Fe, i.v.) 3d day + PMX (2 mg. in 0.2 ml. water, s.c. in flank region) 3d day; photographed 20th day. Extensive cutaneous calcinosis and inflammation; beginning detachment of affected skin area around shoulders and forelimbs. Intensity of lesions decreases in cranio-caudal direction.

D: Calcification of skin and nuchal musculature produced by DHT+Fe-Dex i.v.+PMX s.c. Rat (100 g.♀): DHT (1 mg. p.o.) 1st day + Fe-Dex (1 ml.=1 mg. Fe, i.v.) 2d day + PMX (2 mg. in 0.2 ml. water, s.c.) 2d day; died 5th day. Fresh specimen. Section through neck showing cervical spinal cord with characteristic butterfly pattern (lower central portion of field). Calcium deposition (white lines) in skin and all fascial planes of nuchal musculature.

E, F: Mast cell "explosion" and calcification produced by DHT+Fe-Dex i.v.+PMX s.c. Two stages in the calcification of discharged mast cell granules. Uncalcified granules are purple, small and regular *(E)*; upon calcification they become larger and coalesce into black clumps *(F)*. (von Kóssa + methylene blue × 1000.)

A, B, E, F, after Selye et al.,[843] courtesy Canad. M.A.J.

PLATE VII

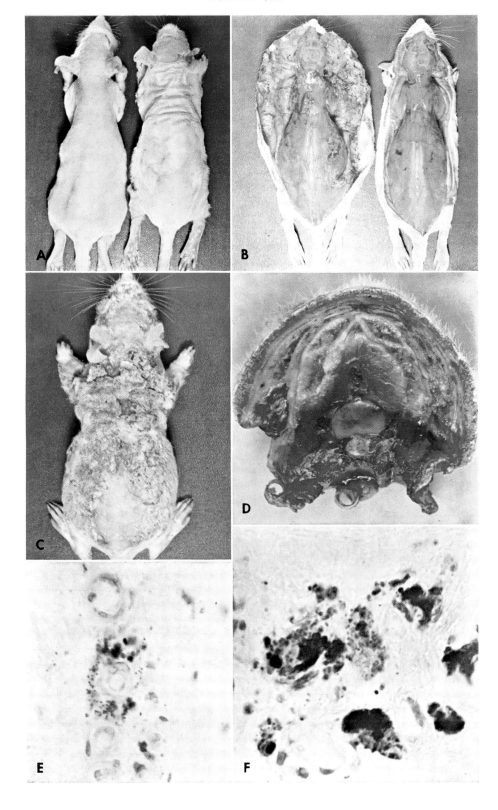

PLATE VIII

A: Auricular type of cardiac calcification produced by DHT+Fe-OS i.v. Rat (100 g.♀):
DHT (1 mg. p.o.) 1st day+Fe-OS (1 ml.=20 mg. Fe, i.v.) immediately after DHT, 1st
day; killed 7th day. Intense calcification of left auricular appendage and of subepicardial
layer of left ventricle around major coronary vein (the vein itself remains unaffected).

B: Cardiac calcification produced by parathyroid hormone s.c.+Fe-OS i.v. Rat (100
g.♀): parathyroid hormone (100 units in 1 ml. water), s.c.)×1 on 1st day,×3 on 2d day+Fe-OS
day+Fe-OS (1 ml.=20 mg. Fe, i.v.) 2d and 3d day; killed 4th day. Pronounced calcification,
especially in connective tissue and muscle fibers of left auricle. (von Kóssa × 35)

**C, D: Acute necrosis of duodenum and calcification of choledochus produced by DHT+
Fe-OS i.v.** Two rats (200 g.♀). *C:* Untreated control for comparison. *D:* DHT (1.5 mg. p.o.)
1st day+Fe-OS (1 ml.=20 mg. Fe, i.v.) 1st day; killed 4th day. Intense hemorrhagic necrosis
of entire duodenal loop. The pancreatic duct is greatly dilated and surrounded by whitish,
calcified masses. The ampulla of Vater is functionally obstructed, thereby causing marked
retention icterus.

E: Calcification of papilla of Vater produced by DHT+Fe-OS i.v. Rat (100 g.♀):
Fe-OS (1 ml.=20 mg. Fe, i.v.) 1st day+DHT (1.5 mg. p.o.) 2d day; killed 4th day.
Section through duodenum at level of papilla of Vater. Intense calcium deposition, especially
in connective tissue surrounding the ampulla. (von Kóssa × 35.)

F: Hepatic calcification produced by parathyroid hormone s.c.+Fe-OS i.v. Rat (100
g.♀): parathyroid hormone (100 units in 1 ml. water, s.c.) × 1 on 1st day, × 3 on 2d and 3d
day+Fe-OS (1 ml.=20 mg. Fe, i.v.) 2d and 3d day; killed 4th day. Calcification of all
hepatic veins, but not of portal veins and arteries. Calcification is also clearly visible in Kupffer
cells as well as in some connective-tissue fibers around sinusoids. (von Kóssa × 120.)

A, C, D, after Selye,[827] courtesy Allergie u. Asthma

PLATE VIII

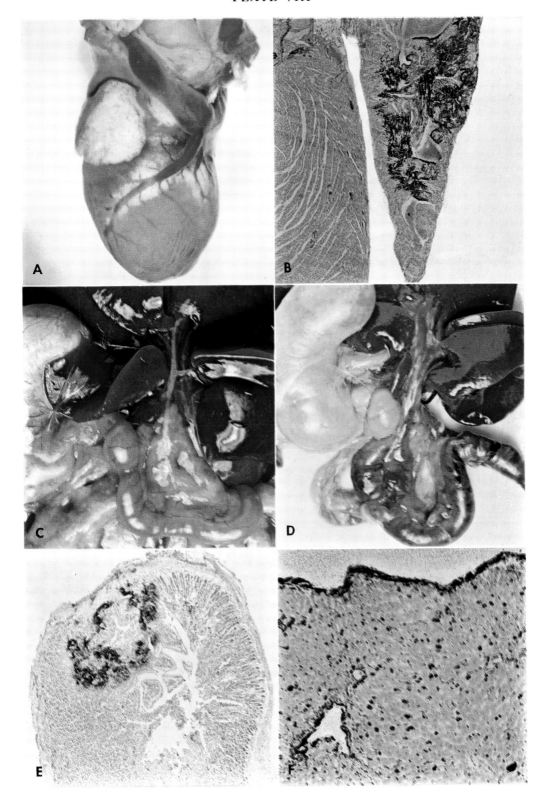

PLATE IX

A, C, E: Periarteritis nodosa of hepatic artery produced by parathyroid hormone s.c.+Fe-OS i.v. Rat (200 g. ♀): parathyroid hormone (200 units in 2 ml. water, s.c. × 2) 1st day + Fe-OS (1 ml. = 20 mg. Fe, i.v. × 2) 1st day; died 4th day. Acute periarteritis nodosa with intense hyalinization of intima and media as well as inflammatory changes throughout arterial wall. Three consecutive sections using different stains. *A:* Intensely PAS-positive hyaline material. *C:* No detectable trace of calcium on von Kóssa-stained section. *D:* Celestin blue reveals infiltration by unidentified material exhibiting tinctorial properties of calcifying tissue. (× 120.)

B, D: Selective calcification of renal cortex stroma produced by DHT+FeOS i.v. Rat (100 g. ♀): Fe-OS (1 ml. = 20 mg. Fe, i.v.) 1st and 2d day + DHT (1.5 mg. p.o.) 2d day; killed 6th day. Calcium deposition is sharply limited to stroma of the renal cortex and some glomerular loops. Medullary rays remain unaffected. (B celestin blue, D von Kóssa × 120.)

F: Adrenal calcification produced by parathyroid hormone s.c.+Fe-OS i.v. Rat (100 g. ♀): parathyroid hormone (100 units in 1 ml. water, s.c.) × 1 on 1st day, × 3 on 2d day + Fe-OS (1 ml. = 20 mg. Fe, i.v.) 2d and 3d day; killed 4th day. Intense calcification, especially in stroma of medulla and in juxtamedullary cortical sinusoid walls. (von Kóssa × 120.)

D, E, after Grasso and Selye,[401] courtesy of Oliver & Boyd Ltd. (J. Path. and Bact.)

PLATE IX

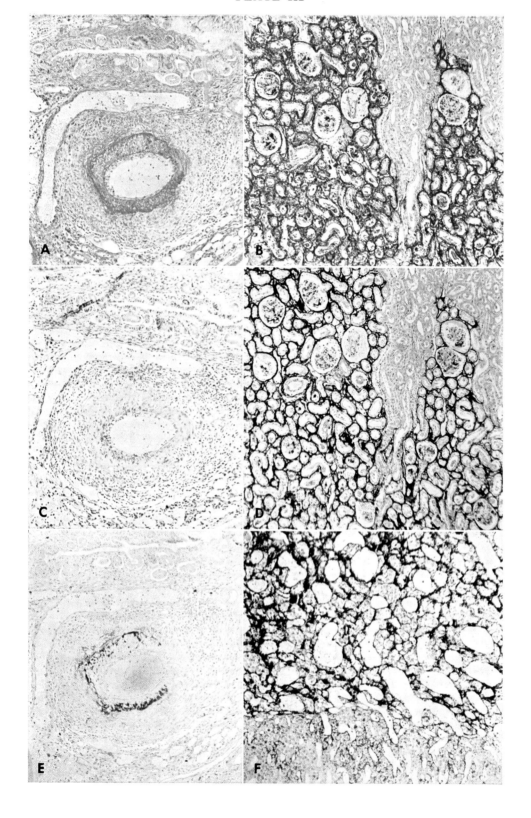

PLATE X

A: Calcification of thymus produced by DHT+F-COL s.c. Two rats (100 g. ♀): DHT (1 mg. p.o.) 1st day + (left) F-COL (2 mg. microcrystal suspension in 0.2 ml. water, s.c.) 2d day; killed 6th day. Heavily calcified thymus of animal given combined treatment *(right)* compared with normal thymus of control rat *(left)*. (Thymus is shown here in its normal location, with trachea, lungs and heart as background.)

B: "Arborizing" pattern of intestinal calcification produced by DHT+FeSO₄ i.v. Rat (200 g. ♀): DHT (2 mg. p.o.) 1st day + FeSO₄ (3 injections in aqueous solution of 2 mg. in 0.2 ml., 4 mg. in 0.4 ml., and 6 mg. in 0.6 ml., i.v.) 2d day; killed 5th day. Lacelike pattern of calcification follows blood vessel arborization in this small-intestinal segment.

C: Calcification of salivary glands produced by DHT+5HT s.c. Rat (100 g. ♀): DHT (1 mg. p.o.) 1st day + 5HT (3 mg. in 0.5 ml. water, s.c. × 2) 2d day; killed 7th day. Calcified salivary glands with calcified regional lymph nodes and cervical hibernating-gland tissue (white masses caudad from salivary glands) after ablation of skin.

D: Fully developed cutaneous lesions produced by DHT+yolk i.v.+PMX s.c. Rat (100 g. ♀): DHT (1 mg. p.o.) 1st day + yolk (25%, 2 ml. i.v.) 2d day + PMX (2 mg. in 0.2 ml. water, s.c. in flank region) 2d day; photographed 6th day. Skin lesions very similar to those of "dermatomyositis" produced by DHT+Fe-Dex i.v.+PMX s.c., their intensity also decreasing gradually in cranio-caudal direction. ("Michel" clip in right inguinal region indicates site of yolk injection into femoral vein.) Here calcinosis selectivity avoids lips.

E: Calciphylactic muscular dystrophy produced by DHT+5HT s.c. Rat (200 g. ♀): DHT (2 mg. p.o.) 1st day + 5HT (5 mg. in 0.5 ml. water, s.c. × 2) 3d day; killed 6th day. Whitish discoloration of affected superficial *(left)* and deep *(right)* musculature of hind limbs.

F: Calcification and sclerosis of nuchal musculature produced by DHT+5HT s.c. Rat (100 g. ♀): DHT (1 mg. p.o.) 1st day + 5HT (5 mg. in 0.5 ml. water, s.c. × 2) 3d day; died 7th day. Focus of dustlike calcium deposition with intense sclerosis in nuchal musculature. (von Kóssa × 400.)

A, after Selye and Padmanabhan,[863] courtesy J. Endocrinol.; **C,** after Selye and Gentile,[839] courtesy of Springer Verlag (Naturwissenschaften)

PLATE X

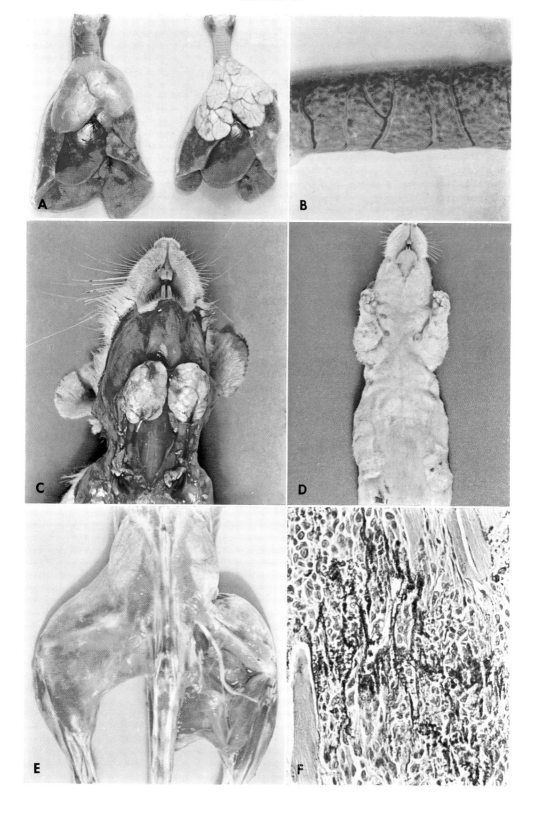

PLATE XI

A: Calciphylactic scleroderma of face and paws produced by DHT+Thorotrast® i.v. Rat (100 g.♀): DHT (1 mg. p.o.) 1st day + Thorotrast® (1 ml. i.v.) 2d day; killed 6th day.

B: Esophageal calcification produced by nephrectomy+Thorotrast® i.v. Rat (220 g.♀): DOC (5 mg/day in 0.2 ml. water, s.c.) 1st-9th day + Thorotrast® (1.25 ml. i.v.) 4th day + bilateral nephrectomy 5th day; died 9th day. Advanced calcinosis involving entire submucosa except immediate surroundings of vessels and nerves. (von Kóssa × 35.)

C: Calcification of tongue, pharynx and esophagus produced by DHT+Thorotrast® i.v. Two rats (100 g.♀): DHT (1 mg. p.o.) 1st day + (right) Thorotrast® (1 ml. i.v.) 2d day; killed 6th day. Pronounced calcium deposition at root of tongue, on both sides of glottis and along entire length (except most cranial portion) of esophagus is noted only in rat *(right)* receiving Thorotrast®.

D: Nodular calcification of tongue and oral mucosa produced by DHT+Thorotrast® i.v. Rat (200 g.♀): DHT (2 mg. p.o.) 1st day + Thorotrast® (1.25 ml. i.v.) 2d day; photographed 31st day. White nodules of calcification at tip of tongue and over oral mucosa, particularly the inner surface of lower lip. (Exulcerated focus near hemostat.)

E, F: Chronic esophageal and faucial calcification produced by DHT+Thorotrast® i.v. Rat (100 g.♀): DHT (1 mg. p.o.) 1st day + Thorotrast® (0.3 ml. i.v.) 2d day; killed 60th day. Nodular foci of calcification in fauces and esophagus. *E:* Mucosal aspect of esophagus. Numerous calcified nodules in middle portion and at top, near fauces (left). Polyplike foci of calcification around glottis and in soft palate which is reflected to the right (right). *F:* Loupe magnification of same specimen.

G: Calcareous bursitis of shoulder joint produced by DHT+Thorotrast® i.v. Rat (200 g.♀): DHT (2 mg. p.o.) 1st day + Thorotrast® (1 ml. i.v.) 2d day; killed 15th day. Intense calcification of periarticular tissues around humero-scapular joint. Minor calcium deposits in elbow region.

H: Facial calcification produced by nephrectomy+Thorotrast® i.v. Rat (230 g.♀): DOC (5 mg/day in 0.2 ml. water, s.c. was given to prolong life after nephrectomy) 1st-10th day + bilateral nephrectomy 7th day + Thorotrast® (1.25 ml. i.v.) 7th day; died 10th day. Intense calcification of perineurium of facial nerve bundle. (von Kóssa × 120.)

A, C, after Selye et al.,[845] courtesy Brit. M.J.

PLATE XI

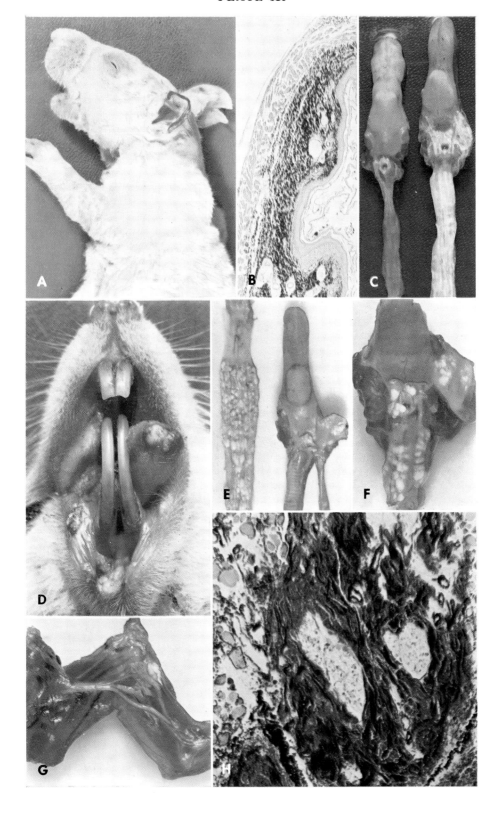

PLATE XII

A, B, C, D: Unilateral calcification of the head produced by DHT+CrCl₃ intracarotid.
(A, B, D) Rat (270 g. ♀): DHT (3 mg. p.o.) 1st day + CrCl₃ (1.5 mg. in 2 ml. water, into left common carotid artery) 2d day; died 16th day. *A:* Intact right side of head. *B:* Heavily calcified face and tongue on left side. *C:* Rat (300 g. ♀): DHT (3 mg. p.o.) 1st day + CrCl₃ (0.5 mg. in 2 ml. water, into left common carotid artery) 2d day; killed 6th day. Calcification of stroma and blood vessels, as well as pronounced atrophy of muscles and intralingual salivary glands, are all sharply limited to left side (left half of picture) of tongue. (von Kóssa ×35.) *D:* Thyro-parathyroid apparatus with heavy calcification, especially in parathyroid on injected side.

E: Calcinosis and atrophy in right hind limb produced by DHT+CrCl₃ intra-iliac. Rat (100 g. ♀): DHT (1 mg. p.o.) 1st day + CrCl₃ (1 mg. in 2 ml. water, into right common iliac artery) 2d day; killed 60th day. Intense atrophy and multiple foci of calcification in musculature of right hind limb. Note isolated calcified plaque in subcutaneous tissue near right knee.

F: "Phylactic" value of calciphylaxis. Two rats (110 g. ♀): DHT (1 mg. p.o.) 1st day + "granuloma pouch" produced by s.c. injection of 25 ml. air (under dorsal skin) 2d day + croton oil (10%, 0.5 ml. in olive oil, injected into air sac) 7th day + (right) yolk (10%, 5 ml. injected into air sac) 2d day; photographed 12th day. *Left:* Otherwise untreated control shows large area of dry necrosis in skin of croton-oil-injected pouch. *Right:* In the air sac pretreated with yolk there is mild calciphylaxis with little visible calcification but the necrosis is completely prevented.

G: Calcification and necrosis in a Walker tumor transplant produced by DHT+Fe-Dex intratumoral. Rat (100 g. ♀): Walker tumor (implant into thigh) 1st day + DHT (1 mg. p.o.) 16th day + Fe-Dex (1 ml. = 100 μg. Fe, direct intratumoral infiltration, twice) 18th day; killed 22d day. Tumor showed partial liquefaction with extensive calcium deposition. Calcium is visible not only in stroma but in the neoplastic cells themselves, especially along the borderline between necrotic and still viable tumor tissue. (Celestin blue, ×170)

PLATE XII

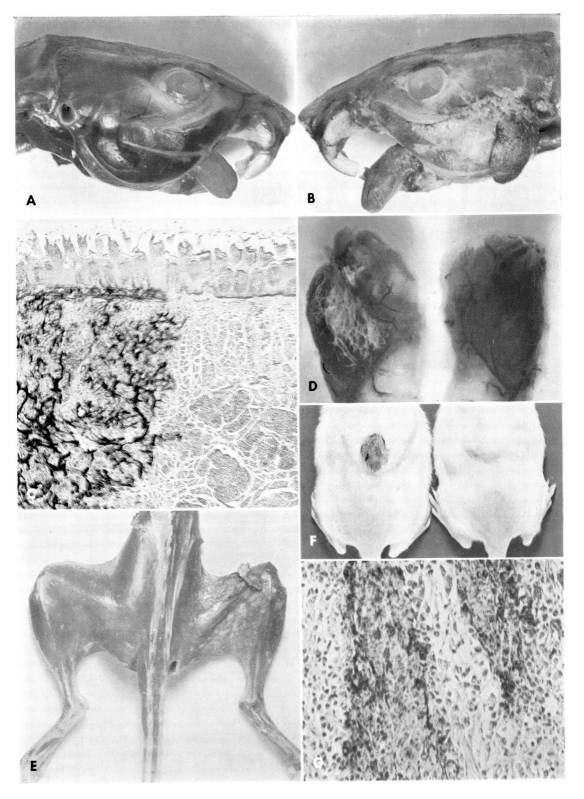

PLATE XIII

A, B: Splenic thrombosis and hepatic necroses produced by DHT+ZnCl₂ i.v. Rat (100 g. ♀): DHT (1 mg. p.o.) 1st day + ZnCl₂ (2.5 mg. in 1 ml. water, i.v. × 2) 2d and 4th day; killed 5th day. *A:* Multiple large light patches of necrosis in liver. Spleen greatly enlarged, hard and almost completely necrotic as consequence of thrombosis in splenic veins. *B:* Thrombotic occlusion of the splenic vein as it courses through the pancreas. Adjacent artery intact. (PAS × 120.)

C: Biliary and duodenal lesions produced by Fe-OS i.v. Rat (200 g. ♀): Fe-OS (1 ml. = 20 mg. Fe, i.v.) 1st and 3d day; killed 7th day. Intense dilatation of the extrahepatic bile ducts with brown discoloration and dilatation of duodenum. There is no trace of calcification since the animal was not calciphylactically sensitized to the iron. (Cf. Plate VIII, *C, D.*)

D: Cataract produced by DHT+5HT s.c. Rat (100 g. ♀): DHT (1 mg. p.o.) 1st day + 5HT (5 mg. in 0.5 ml. water, s.c.) 2d day; photographed under anesthesia 60th day. Clouding of the lens, mydriasis and intense hyperemia of the iris.

E: Granuloma pouch technique for the study of calciphylaxis. Rat (100 g. ♀): DHT (1 mg. p.o.) 1st day; on 2d day 25 ml. air was injected under the shaved dorsal skin, this being followed immediately by the injection of CrCl₃ (100 μg. in 5 ml. water) into the air sac so formed; killed 7th day. After careful removal of the dorsal skin the calcinosis is seen to creep upwards along each of the regularly spaced neurovascular trunks that ascend into the wall of the air sac from the intercostal spaces. The wall of such a granuloma pouch is sufficiently thin to be used as a connective-tissue spread for histologic study.

F: Blood as a calciphylactic challenger. Rat (100 g. ♀): 2 ml. of its own fresh blood (taken from jugular and injected immediately under the dorsal skin) 1st and 10th day + DHT (1 mg. p.o.) 20th day; killed 25th day. Prior to sensitization, time was allowed for liberation of iron from hemoglobin. Since many iron preparations have no sharp critical period even late sensitization was expected to be effective. Multiple calcified (dark blue) foci with necrotic (light blue) centers in giant-cell containing granuloma. On top cutaneous muscle. Without sensitization blood injected s.c. exhibits little or no calcification, but calciphylactic nature of this lesion is questionable since calcinosis does not affect collagen fibers of host and is largely limited to the injected blood itself. (Celestin blue × 120.)

PLATE XIII

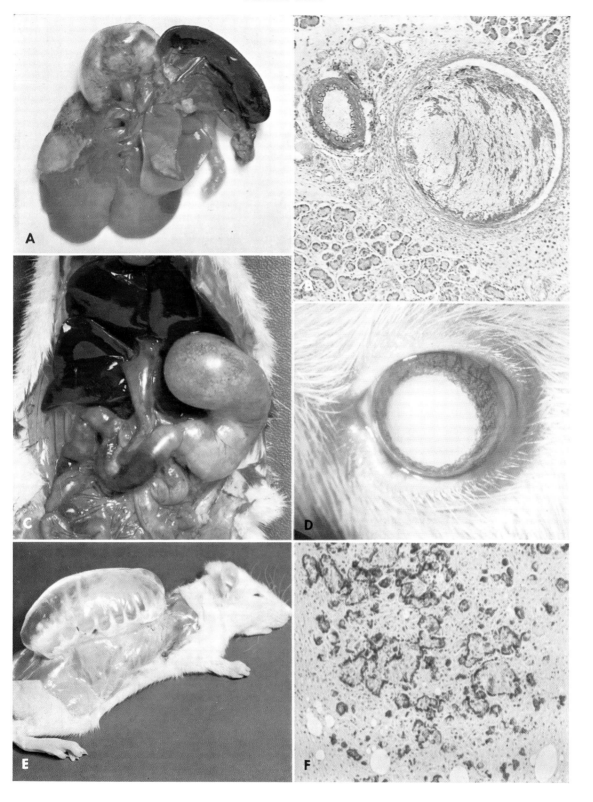

Color inserts printed in Canada

METHODOLOGY

This book is designed to correlate many unpublished observations with previously reported data; therefore, it will have to give more attention to technical details than is customary in medical monographs.

Special procedures employed only for the study of particular problems of calciphylaxis will be discussed later, in the corresponding sections.

CLASSIFICATION OF MATERIAL

For a detailed plan of our classification the reader is referred to the Table of Contents. However, there are many transitional forms between the calciphylactic syndromes, and identical organ lesions can be produced by different means; hence no one system of classification can provide us with nonoverlapping categories. In principle it would be possible to systematize these syndromes on the basis of either their structural characteristics or the agents used to produce them, but in practice (especially now, when we are just beginning to understand the complexities of this new field) it seems advisable to refer both to the evocative agents and to the resulting structural changes in our classification. Even so, many cross references between sections will be needed wherever there is an important overlap.

Most forms of calciphylaxis exhibit rather characteristic, gross morphologic features clearly distinguishable on fresh specimens by inspection with the naked eye or loupe. Thorough familiarity with these lesions is indispensable, because their distribution pattern throughout the body is often of greater diagnostic value than the fine microscopic structure of individual foci. Besides, in systematic investigations on a very large scale, only a limited number of representative specimens from each experimental group can be examined microscopically and even the choice of fixatives for these must be guided by some idea of the histologic changes that can be expected. Furthermore, in discussing various morbid lesions, it is impractical to identify them by a full description of all their characteristics each time they are mentioned. Hence, depending upon the topic to be discussed, we shall designate the calciphylactic syndromes either by their most striking microscopic features (e.g., "salivary gland calciphylaxis," "calciphylactic muscular dystrophy") or by the combination of agents most suited to elicit them (e.g., the "DHT + 5HT type").

LABELING OF ILLUSTRATIONS

Since this book is meant to serve not only as a text but also as an atlas of the calciphylactic lesions, great care has been taken to illustrate every important observation by one or more instructively labeled photographs. In the case of previously published material a brief title with the bibliographic reference will suffice, but hitherto unpublished photographs will be fully described. For the sake of conciseness we used the following procedure:

The species, approximate body weight, and sex are always indicated but—as in the text itself—the body weight of rats is approximated to the closest ten grams to avoid unnecessary complication of the legends by the separate description of each specimen depicted in the plate. The dosage of the drugs employed is given in micrograms, milligrams, or, in the case of electrolytes, in millimols, special mention being made of the route of administration (p.o. = per os, s.c. = subcutaneously, i.p. = intraperitoneally). The legend also indicates whether the individual dose was given once (e.g., 1 mg/day), or several times (e.g., 2 × 2 mg/day), daily. The kind and amount of solvent are likewise mentioned except in the case of DHT, which—unless otherwise indicated—was given in 0.5 ml. corn oil by stomach tube.

For example, the legend for Figure 67 is intended to explain that the four salivary gland pictures shown are two different photographs of the same two glands. They come from two female rats, both of which weighed 100 g. (± 10 g.) at the beginning of the experiment. Both rats were given 1 mg. of DHT in 0.5 ml. corn oil by stomach tube (according to the standard technique described on p. 21) on the first day of the experiment. The animal whose salivary gland is shown on the right side of each picture was given no other treatment, while the one whose gland is shown on the left received—in addition to the DHT—two individual doses of 2.5 mg. of $CrCl_2$ in 0.25 ml. of water intravenously on the second day. Neither of the rats succumbed to this treatment; they were killed for autopsy on the sixth day. Figure 67*A* is a photograph of the glands in the fresh condition, while Figure 67*B* shows them after staining with silver nitrate.

All this information is condensed as follows:

Two rats (100 g. ♀): DHT (1 mg. p.o.) 1st day + (left) $CrCl_2$ (2.5 mg. in 0.25 ml. water, i.v. ×2) 2d day; killed 6th day. *A* fresh, *B* $AgNO_3$-stained, specimens.

The number of rats in each group (of which the illustrated specimens are examples) is not mentioned in the legends, but as we shall see, all our experiments were performed on groups of 10–50 animals and only statistically significant results are illustrated by photographs.

It was felt that using this procedure a maximum of information could be conveyed without encumbering the legends with irrelevant details.

Choice of Experimental Animal

The rat was selected as our routine test animal. For the studies described in this monograph we have regularly required between 1,000 and 1,400 rats per week during the last year; this fact in itself limited our choice of the standard species to be employed. With the possible exception of the mouse—which is less sensitive to most forms of calciphylaxis and does not lend itself well to many of the standard surgical interventions—no purebred laboratory mammal other than the rat would have been available in such numbers. To demonstrate that calciphylaxis is not peculiar to the rat, we repeated the fundamental observations in other species, but all our conclusions are based on observations checked in the rat so as to make them intercomparable. As a further safeguard all calciphylactic syndromes were reproduced in female Sprague-Dawley rats bred under strict supervision at the Holtzman farms (Madison, Wisconsin, U.S.A.) and rigidly matched as regards body weight. All animals were maintained on "Purina Laboratory Chow."

As far as we have been able to establish, most of the calciphylactic syndromes can also be obtained in males, but the age (or weight) of the animal considerably alters its responsiveness: certain organ lesions (e.g., those produced after DHT-sensitization by Fe-Dex in the uterus or by Fe-OS in the biliary tract) are much more readily elicited in fully grown than in immature rats, while the reverse is true of other lesions (e.g., the cutaneous calcinosis produced by topical challenge). Hence we had to use animals of different weights, depending upon the purpose of a particular study, but for the sake of uniformity two standard body weight ranges were selected, namely 100 g. and 200 g. (with a maximum deviation from the mean of 10 g.).

Each experimental group consisted of no less than 10, and often up to 50, animals. The mean body weight given in the text and legends is approximated to the closest 10 g., and unless there is a special reason to do otherwise, only the initial body weights are listed.

THE PRODUCTION OF CALCIPHYLAXIS

In our introductory outline we have already mentioned a few examples showing how topical and systemic calciphylaxis can be produced; others will be given later, in the sections devoted to each type of calciphylaxis. Here we shall merely discuss generally applicable techniques and list the various sensitizers, challengers, and adjuvants, indicating the manner in which they are employed.

Topical calciphylaxis.—The most suitable site for the study of topical calciphylaxis is the ***skin*** because of its great sensitivity and easy accessibility. Hence we usually test agents for possible direct challenging potency by a standardized *subcutaneous assay* technique:

Ten 100 g. female rats are prepared by removing the hair over the entire back with electric clippers on the day prior to the experiment; since the animals have not yet been sensitized, incidental cutaneous trauma inflicted during this procedure cannot act as a challenger. On the first day of the experiment the animals receive 1 mg. of DHT in 0.5 ml. corn oil by stomach tube. For this purpose the animal is held steady with the left hand by the loose skin of the nape of the neck and gently pressed against the table, while with the right hand a soft urethral catheter (No. 8) is introduced into the esophagus to a depth of about 5 cm. When an oily solution of DHT is aspirated into the syringe, some of it adheres to the outside of the catheter making it sufficiently slippery for introduction. As soon as the catheter is in place, pressure (with the right hand) on the piston of the syringe delivers the fluid directly into the stomach (Fig. 1).

Twenty-four hours later the compound to be tested is injected at various standard concentrations *subcutaneously*, usually at three points along the midline of the back according to the "triple wheal test" technique (p. 31). To obtain perfect discoid skin patches the test fluid must be deposited as a regularly formed subcutaneous bleb. It is advisable either to anesthetize the rat lightly or to have an assistant hold it firmly for the injections. The needle is first pushed through 2–3 cm. of loose subcutaneous connective tissue, then into the dense derma and eventually back into the subcutis where the material is deposited. Reflux is thus prevented by the valvelike action of the derma (Fig. 2).

Intracutaneous injection is often even more effective in producing topical calciphylaxis, but it can be used only for compounds having a negligible topical irritating effect.

The results of both the subcutaneous and the intracutaneous tests are evaluated by measuring the mean diameter of each wheal (Fig. 5, p. 32).

Topical calciphylaxis can also be produced by mere *plucking of the hair or compression of the skin with a hemostat* during the critical period. In rats sensitized by DHT, this time usually corresponds to the second or third day (Fig. 12, p. 44).

Topical calciphylaxis can also be produced in **internal organs** by the direct application of challengers to the target tissues. The technique to be followed is essentially the same as for skin tests, except that during the critical period the challenger is injected into the site selected for testing (e.g., peritoneum, pleura, kidney, thymus, or spleen). Experiments of this type have been performed to determine the calciphylactic reactivity of various organs in response to direct challenge, but for a quantitative assay these tests do not lend themselves as well as skin tests because of:

1. unequal spreading of the challenger in most internal organs,
2. comparative paucity and unequal distribution of the connective tissue, which is most sensitive to calciphylaxis,
3. comparative inaccessibility of most internal targets,
4. impossibility of following the progress of the lesions during life.

Systemic calciphylaxis.—Calciphylactic syndromes with lesions in various organs can be produced by the systemic administration of challengers during the critical period. As previously stated, here the *age* of the test animal is an important factor: some calciphylactic syndromes are better obtained in young, others in adult, rats. Therefore both 100 g. and 200 g. rats were employed; the former, though already quite resistant to various toxic agents, are still actively growing, while the latter have reached a virtual growth plateau. These differences in growth potential probably play an important role in calciphylaxis, since the responsive-

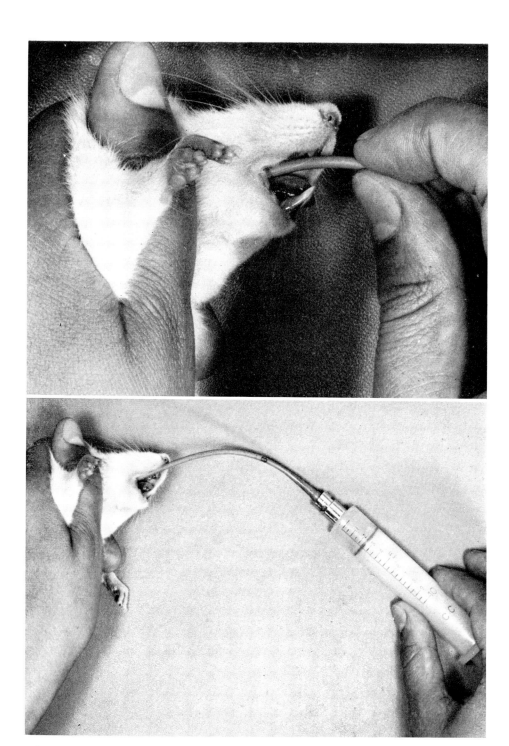

Fig. 1. Technique of gavage. Introduction of catheter (*top*) and injection of fluid from attached syringe (*bottom*).

(After Selye, [823] courtesy Charles C Thomas Publ., Springfield, Ill.)

ness of the bones to agents that influence growth and calcification as well as the calcium requirements are much greater during the period of active growth.

In analyzing any one calciphylactic syndrome, we must first determine its particular ***critical period***; some changes are best obtained if the challenger is administered after, others if it is given simultaneously with or even before, the sensitizer. To establish the optimum time-relations we usually perform preliminary experi-

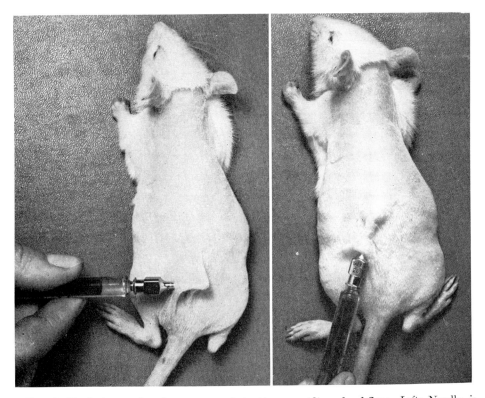

Fig. 2. Technique of subcutaneous injection avoiding backflow. *Left:* Needle is pushed through loose connective tissue into basal layer of dense derma. *Right:* After traversing derma, needle is pushed back into subcutis where injection fluid is deposited. Reflux is prevented by valvelike action of pierced, dense, dermal layer.

ments in which the challenger is given at different times before and after sensitization. In describing such experiments, the day on which the sensitizer (DHT, vitamin D_3, parathyroid hormone) is administered will be considered day 1. The preceding days are indicated as "−" (minus), the following days as "+" (plus); accordingly, there is no day −1 or +1 (day 1 being considered as "−" during its first, and "+" during its second twelve hours). In this manner, our days +2, +3, etc. correspond to what is generally designated as the 2d, 3d, etc. day of an experiment and the corresponding "+" and "−" days are equidistant from day 1.

The procedures for **sensitization** to systemic calciphylaxis need not be discussed, since they are the same as those described in the preceding section on "Topical Calciphylaxis," but let us now consider some of the most generally applicable techniques for the systemic administration of challengers or adjuvants.

The **route of administration** of all the evocative agents (sensitizers, challengers, adjuvants) likewise plays a decisive role; for example, among the sensitizers, DHT is best administered by mouth, parathyroid hormone subcutaneously, and NaAST intraperitoneally. Similarly, some challengers (e.g., Fe-OS) must be given intravenously; others (e.g., PMX, 48/80, 5HT) subcutaneously, intraperitoneally or, even better, into a paw, to be maximally effective. These differences may depend upon the absorption and distribution rates of various agents; some compounds act best if they flood the circulation suddenly, others if they are slowly absorbed from the site of application.

Such differences are quite obvious even when the active ingredient of various challengers is the same. For example, $FeCl_3$ is very slowly absorbed and distributed throughout the body following subcutaneous or intraperitoneal administration, Fe-OS somewhat more quickly, and Fe-Dex most rapidly. The ability of these three compounds to spread directly through the connective tissue from the site of administration increases in the same order. Incidentally, the reverse is true of the intravenous toxicity of these iron preparations, $FeCl_3$ being the most, and Fe-Dex least, toxic.

The calciphylactic challenging potency of the Fe atom also largely depends upon the **carrier substance** to which it is attached. For example, as we shall see, in DHT-sensitized rats the maximum dose of Fe tolerable by the intravenous route produces no organ-specific lesions if given as $FeCl_3$, predominantly thyroparathyroid and carotid body calcification if given as $FeCl_2$, cardiac and biliary tract lesions if given as Fe-OS, and pancreatic changes if given as Fe-Dex. These variations in the toxicity and organ affinity of the Fe-containing challengers may result from their different absorption and spreading rates.

Subcutaneous injections present no special problem, but to insure against possible loss by backflow, it is well to use the "dermal valve technique" as outlined in connection with the production of topical calciphylactic skin lesions (Fig. 2; cf. also p. 20).

For **intraperitoneal injections** it is best to use No. 25 needles whose tips have been blunted on a stone to protect against the very real danger of delivering the fluid into an intestinal loop. Here it is also advisable to make a "tissue valve" in order to prevent backflow; this is readily accomplished by pushing the needle forward in the subcutis for some distance before entering the peritoneum.

Certain challengers (e.g., dextran, PMX) are especially active upon **injection into the paw** (Fig. 3). Incidentally, this route of administration has also been found to be particularly efficacious in producing generalized anaphylactoid reactions with dextran in the rat.[815] The singular potency of such injections may be due to the excellent lymphatic supply of the paw or to its unusually high inflammatory potential, which could facilitate the absorption of challengers or result in the local production of activators.

For *intravenous injection* the rat is anesthetized with ether and tied to an operating board; the hair over the throat is removed with clippers. After exposing the jugular vein through a small skin incision, a needle is introduced into the vessel through the pectoral musculature (Fig. 4). Rigid observance of this technique is especially important with challengers that could cause severe topical calciphylaxis

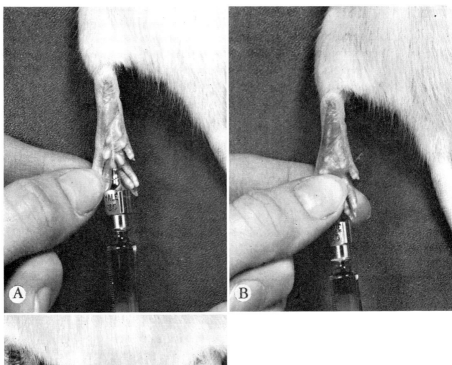

Fig. 3. Technique of intrapedal injection. *A:* The needle is inserted under the plantar aponeurosis. *B:* During injection backflow is prevented by slight pressure (with left thumb) upon the injection point. Then material is pushed away from needle prick by gentle massage with the thumb, to prevent backflow. *C:* Appearance of paw after injection, to show even distribution of (colored) fluid.

(e.g., Fe-Dex) or inhibit blood coagulation and thereby predispose to hematoma formation (e.g., Fe-OS) if the needle prick were not completely closed. If repeated intravenous injections eventually damage the vessel walls, the contralateral jugular and both femoral veins may also be used. It must be remembered, however,

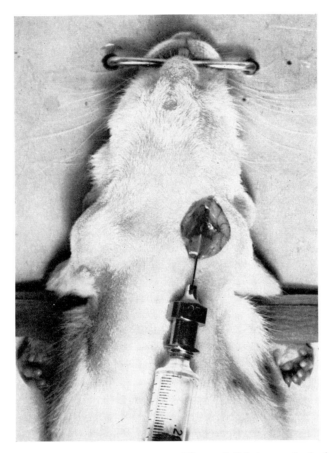

Fig. 4. Technique of intravenous injection. The rat is lightly anesthetized with ether and fastened to operating board. Small skin incision exposes jugular vein near its entry into thorax. Needle (No. 27 gauge) traverses strip of pectoralis major muscle before entering the vein. Muscular channel thus formed acts as valve and prevents backflow. Single "Michel" clip will suffice to close this wound.

that when injected into the femoral vein many challengers (e.g., Fe-Dex, Fe-Din) are more toxic than if introduced through the jugular vein. The cause of this difference is hitherto unexplained.

Sensitizers, Challengers, and Adjuvants.—Here we shall list only those frequently employed evocative agents that require some special comment:

Sensitizers:

DHT. Dihydrotachysterol (Calcamin®, Dr. A. Wander, S.A., Bern, Switzerland) is the most commonly used calciphylactic sensitizer. For this purpose the pure crystals may be dissolved in corn oil to make a stable solution (usually 1 mg. of DHT in 0.5 ml.) which can be kept at 0° C almost indefinitely.

Vitamin D_2. Has been used in the form of "Dry vitamin D_2" (Roche, Montreal, Canada), which contains 850,000 U.S.P. units/g. Like DHT, it is usually administered orally in corn oil.

Vitamin D_3. Vi-Dé 3 Hydrosol® (Dr. A. Wander, S.A., Bern, Switzerland) is an aqueous solution containing 15 mg. of vitamin D_3 (= 600,000 I.U.) in each vial of 1.5 ml. It can be injected intravenously.

Parathyroid hormone. Para-Thor-Mone® (Eli Lilly and Co., Indianapolis, U.S.A.) is an aqueous extract of bovine parathyroids containing no less than 100 U.S.P. units (20 Collip units)/ml. To safeguard against gradual loss of potency, the vials sometimes contain more than the stated number of units. The preparation is fairly stable if kept in the cold. In this text the term "units" refers to U.S.P. units.

NaAST. Sodium acetylsulfathiazole or 4'-(2-thiazolylsulfamoyl)-, 4'-Sodium Derivative (Lederle Laboratories, American Cyanamid Co., Pearl River, U.S.A.) is usually given as a single intraperitoneal injection of 50–150 mg. in 1 ml. water. The compound is eliminated mainly through the kidney and presumably sensitizes for calciphylaxis because of the renal block induced by the massive precipitation of NaAST crystals in the collecting tubules. The resulting serious disturbances in calcium metabolism (with massive calcification of the aorta, heart, kidney, and gastric mucosa) resemble the syndrome of intoxication with parathyroid hormone, DHT or vitamin D.

Surgical interventions. Under certain circumstances sensitization for calciphylaxis can be achieved by complete or partial nephrectomy, ligature of both ureters, or the establishment of gastric or salivary fistulas. These techniques have been described elsewhere.[823]

Direct Challengers:

Thorotrast®. A 24–26% stabilized colloidal thorium dioxide preparation containing 25% aqueous dextrin as a stabilizer and 0.15% methyl parasept as a preservative. It is dispensed as a contrast medium for roentgenography (Testagar and Co., Detroit, U.S.A.). In the study of calciphylaxis it can act as a local challenger (e.g., after s.c. injection), but following systemic (e.g., i.v.) administration it produces a generalized calciphylactic syndrome with predominantly facial and esophageal lesions.

Fe-OS. Saccharated ferric oxide or Proferrin® (Merck, Sharp and Dohme, Philadelphia, U.S.A.) is a stable iron preparation suitable for intravenous use. It contains saccharated ferric oxide N.F. VII 66.7 mg. (= 20 mg. Fe), thimerosal, N.F. 0.04 mg. and NaOH U.S.P. (to pH 10.9)/ml. water. Occasional vials in which a sediment is noted should not be used. Intravenous injections must be given very slowly to avoid acute toxicity.

Fe-Dex. Ferric dextran is distributed as Imferon® (= 50 mg. Fe/ml.) for human and as Imposil® (= 75 mg. Fe/ml.) for veterinary use (Benger Ltd., Holmes Chapel,

England). In these preparations iron is present as ferric hydroxide in complex with a low molecular weight dextran fraction. 0.5% phenol is added as a preservative. pH 5.8.

Fe-Din. A ferric dextrin, Ferrigen® or Astrofer® (= 20 mg. Fe/ml., Astra, Södertälje, Sweden). pH 7.4.

Fe-Sol. Jectofer® (= 50 mg. Fe/ml., Astra, Södertälje, Sweden) is an iron-sorbitol-citric acid complex prepared in the presence of dextrin. pH 7.5.

Electrolytes: All electrolytes used were of the highest available purity-grade; for the sake of precision we shall list them here together with their chemical formulas (indicating the water of crystallization) and the name of the supplier. The following list includes all electrolytes tested for possible direct challenging effect irrespective of whether they were found to be active or inactive.

NAME	FORMULA	MANUFACTURER
Ammonium sulfate	$NH_4(SO_4)_2$	Merck
Aluminum ammonium sulfate	$AlNH_4(SO_4) \cdot 12H_2O$	Merck
Aluminum chloride	$AlCl_3 \cdot 6H_2O$	Merck
Aluminum nitrate	$Al(NO_3)_3 \cdot 9H_2O$	Fisher
Aluminum potassium sulfate	$AlK(SO_4)_2 \cdot 12H_2O$	Anachemia
Barium chloride	$BaCl_2 \cdot 2H_2O$	Merck
Bismuth chloride	$BiCl_3$	Fisher
Cadmium chloride	$CdCl_2 \cdot 2\frac{1}{2}H_2O$	Merck
Calcium acetate	$Ca(CH_3 \cdot COO)_2 \cdot H_2O$	Fisher
Calcium chloride anhydrous	$CaCl_2$	Fisher
Calcium chloride dihydrate	$CaCl_2 \cdot 2H_2O$	Baker
Cerous chloride	$CeCl_3 \cdot 7H_2O$	Fisher
Cesium chloride	$CsCl$	Fisher
Chromium chloride	$CrCl_3 \cdot 6H_2O$	Merck
Chromium nitrate	$Cr(NO_3)_3 \cdot 9H_2O$	Fisher
Chromium oxide	Cr_2O_3	Anachemia
Chromium sulfate	$Cr_2(SO_4)_3 \cdot 15H_2O$	Fisher
Chromous chloride	$CrCl_2$	Fisher
Cobalt chloride	$CoCl_2 \cdot 6H_2O$	Fisher
Cupric chloride	$CuCl_2 \cdot 2H_2O$	Fisher
Cupric nitrate	$Cu(NO_3)_2 \cdot 3H_2O$	Analar
Cupric sulfate	$CuSO_4 \cdot 5H_2O$	Merck
Cuprous chloride	$CuCl$	Fisher
Ferric ammonium sulfate	$FeNH_4(SO_4)_2 \cdot 12H_2O$	Mallinckrodt
Ferric chloride	$FeCl_3 \cdot 6H_2O$	Fisher
Ferric nitrate	$Fe(NO_3)_3 \cdot 9H_2O$	Fisher
Ferric oxide	Fe_2O_3	Fisher
Ferrous ammonium sulfate	$Fe(NH_4)_2(SO_4)_2 \cdot 6H_2O$	Fisher
Ferrous chloride	$FeCl_2 \cdot 4H_2O$	Fisher

NAME	FORMULA	MANUFACTURER
Ferrous gluconate	$Fe[CH_2OH(CHOH)_4CO_2]_2 \cdot 2H_2O$	Montreal Pharmacy
Ferrous lactate	$Fe(C_3H_5O_3)_2 \cdot 3H_2O$	Montreal Pharmacy
Ferrous sulfate	$FeSO_4 \cdot 7H_2O$	Fisher
Gallium nitrate	$Ga(NO_3)_3 \cdot 8H_2O$	Delta Chemicals
Gallium sulfate	$Ga_2(SO_4)_3 \cdot 16H_2O$	Montreal Pharmacy
Gold sodium thiomalate	$C_4H_3AuNa_2O_4S$	Poulenc
Indium chloride	$InCl_3$	Montreal Pharmacy
Iridium tetrachloride	$IrCl_4$	Brickman
Lanthanum chloride	$LaCl_3 \cdot 7H_2O$	Fisher
Lead acetate	$Pb(CH_3 \cdot COO)_2 \cdot 3H_2O$	Merck
Lead chloride	$PbCl_2$	Fisher
Lead nitrate	$Pb(NO_3)_2$	Fisher
Lithium chloride	$LiCl$	Baker
Magnesium chloride	$MgCl_2 \cdot 6H_2O$	Merck
Manganese chloride	$MnCl_2 \cdot 4H_2O$	Fisher
Mercuric acetate	$Hg(CH_3 \cdot COO)_2$	Merck
Mercuric sulfide black	HgS	Delta Chemicals
Nickel chloride	$NiCl_2 \cdot 6H_2O$	Fisher
Niobium pentachloride	$NbCl_5$	Delta Chemicals
Palladium chloride	$PdCl_2 \cdot 2H_2O$	Fisher
Palladium nitrate	$Pd(NO_3)_2$	Fisher
Platinic potassium chloride	PtK_2Cl_6	Delta Chemicals
Potassium bromide	KBr	Anachemia
Potassium chlorate	$KClO_3$	Fisher
Potassium chloride	KCl	Fisher
Potassium chromate	K_2CrO_4	Fisher
Potassium dichromate	$K_2Cr_2O_7$	Baker
Potassium ferricyanide	$K_3Fe(CN)_6$	Merck
Potassium ferrocyanide	$K_4Fe(CN)_6$	Fisher
Potassium iodate	KIO_3	Merck
Potassium iodide	KI	Baker
Potassium manganate	K_2MnO_4	B.D.H.
Potassium perchlorate	$KClO_4$	Fisher
Potassium periodate	KIO_4	Eastman Kodak
Potassium permanganate	$KMnO_4$	Fisher
Potassium sulfate	K_2SO_4	Mallinckrodt
Potassium tellurate	$K_2TeO_4 \cdot 3H_2O$	Delta Chemicals
Potassium thiocyanate	$KSCN$	Merck
Rubidium chloride	$RbCl$	Anachemia
Silver acetate	$AgCH_3 \cdot COO$	Fisher
Silver nitrate	$AgNO_3$	Fisher
Silver sulfate	Ag_2SO_4	Fisher
Sodium acetate	$NaCH_3 \cdot COO$	Fisher
Sodium arsenate dibasic	Na_2HAsO_4	B.D.H.

NAME	FORMULA	MANUFACTURER
Sodium arsenite	$NaAsO_2$	Brickman
Sodium bicarbonate	$NaHCO_3$	Merck
Sodium carbonate	Na_2CO_3	Anachemia
Sodium chloride	$NaCl$	Brickman
Sodium citrate	$Na_3C_6H_5O_7 \cdot 2H_2O$	McArthur Co.
Sodium manganate	$Na_2MnO_4 \cdot 3H_2O$	Fisher
Sodium molybdate	Na_2MoO_4	Fisher
Sodium nitrate	$NaNO_3$	Baker
Sodium nitrite	$NaNO_2$	Analar
Sodium oxalate	$Na_2C_2O_4$	Fisher
Sodium perchlorate	$NaClO_4$	Fisher
Sodium permanganate	$NaMnO_4$	Fisher
Sodium phosphate dibasic anhydrous	Na_2HPO_4	Merck
Sodium phosphate mono-basic	$NaH_2PO_4 \cdot H_2O$	Fisher
Sodium selenite	Na_2SeO_3	B.D.H.
Sodium stannate	$Na_2SnO_3 \cdot 3H_2O$	Fisher
Sodium sulfate	Na_2SO_4	Mallinckrodt
Sodium thiosulfate	$Na_2S_2O_3 \cdot 5H_2O$	Fisher
Sodium vanadate	$NaVO_3 \cdot 4H_2O$	Fisher
Stannous chloride	$SnCl_2 \cdot 2H_2O$	Brickman
Strontium chloride	$SrCl_2 \cdot 6H_2O$	Fisher
Thallium acetate	$Tl(CH_3 \cdot COO)$	Fisher
Thallium chloride	$TlCl$	Fisher
Thorium chloride	$ThCl_4$	Fisher
Thorium nitrate	$Th(NO_3)_4 \cdot 4H_2O$	Fisher
Thorium oxide	ThO_2	Fisher
Titanium tetrachloride	$TiCl_4$	Canlab
Titanium trichloride	$TiCl_3$	Canlab
Vanadyl sulfate	$VOSO_4 \cdot 2H_2O$	Fisher
Zinc chloride	$ZnCl_2$	Fisher
Zirconium oxychloride	$ZrOCl_2 \cdot 8H_2O$	Fisher

Physical agents. Plucking of hair, crushing of skin with a hemostat.

Indirect Challengers:

48/80. A condensation product of p-methoxyphenylmethylamine with formalin (Burroughs Wellcome and Co., Montreal, Canada). This is a histamine discharger and mastocyte depletor. For calciphylaxis experiments in the rat, we usually administer 2–3 mg. in 0.2 ml. water s.c. or by injection into the paw, which elicits a marked anaphylactoid reaction. Like PMX (see below), 48/80 presumably acts by liberating endogenous challengers from the mast cells.

PMX. Polymyxin B Sulphate (Burroughs Wellcome and Co., Montreal, Canada) is an antibiotic which also acts as a histamine discharger and mastocyte depletor. In the study of systemic calciphylaxis, it is usually administered at the dose of 2–3 mg. in 0.2 ml. water, s.c. or by injection into the hind paws. At this dose it produces a pronounced anaphylactoid reaction in the rat. In siderocalciphylactically sensitized rats 0.1–10 μg. of PMX s.c. suffice to produce topical calcinosis.

5HT. 5-hydroxytryptamine, serotonin, 5-hydroxy-3-(β-aminoethyl) indole is usually employed for calciphylaxis experiments in the rat, as the creatinine sulfate, at the dose of 2–5 mg. in 0.5 ml. water, given s.c., i.p. or into the paw. It presumably causes submaxillary-gland calcification by liberating endogenous challengers from these glands. Its action on skeletal muscle may be direct.

Glucocorticoids. After sensitization steroids of this group (e.g., cortisol, fluorocortisol) cause selective calcification in the thymus, presumably because they liberate endogenous challengers from disintegrating thymocytes.

Adjuvants:

Dextran. Dextran (M.W. $\approx$ 75,000) is distributed as a 6% solution stabilized by 5.7% sorbitol N.F., as a 12% solution in isotonic NaCl (Abbott Laboratories, North Chicago, U.S.A.). In the study of calciphylaxis, it can act both as an adjuvant and as an indirect challenger. It may be given s.c., i.v., or i.p. and produces anaphylactoid reactions with mastocyte depletion in the rat.

Dextrin. British gum or starch gum (Difco Labs, Detroit, U.S.A.) is a polysaccharide $[(C_6H_{10}O_5)n \times H_2O]$ prepared by incomplete hydrolysis of starch.

Pectin. Pectin N.F. (Sunkist Growers, Inc., Ontario, California, U.S.A.) is a purified preparation of polygalacturonic acid methyl ester.

Gelatin. Gelatin (granular) U.S.P. (Fisher Scientific Co., Montreal, Canada) is a protein and amino-acid mixture obtained by boiling skin, tendons, ligaments, bones, etc. with water.

PVP. Polyvinylpyrrolidone or Subtosan® (Poulenc Ltd., Montreal, Canada) is a histamine discharger commonly marketed as a 37% solution.

Plasma. Lyophilized human blood plasma (Connaught Medical Research Laboratories, Toronto, Canada).

C.S.A. Chondroitinsulfuric acid (Delta Chemical Works, Inc., New York, U.S.A.). Specially purified preparations were kindly supplied by Dr. Karl Meyer, N.Y.

EVALUATION OF LESIONS

Macroscopic observations.—Topical calciphylactic lesions lend themselves well for quantitative, or at least semiquantitative, evaluation on the basis of macroscopic criteria. In general, the *mean diameter* of the wheal is measured. With a direct calcifier (e.g., $KMnO_4$), which tends to produce sharply delimited and almost perfectly circular wheals, this form of measurement is fairly accurate since the diameter is uniform and well definable. Wheals elicited by challengers following sensitization are usually less regular, especially when the challengers are mixed with certain adjuvants; hence here the selection of a certain diameter as representative of the mean is more subjective.

For greater accuracy and particularly in the event of small wheals that do not penetrate into the derma, it is best to kill the animal and to measure the wheals on the subcutaneous surface after removal of the skin.

If the wheals are well circumscribed but have a very irregular contour, only *planimetric* measurements can give accurate results.

The limitation imposed by the use of any of these techniques of measurement is the tendency of certain calciphylactic skin lesions to develop irregular contours. *Staining of the calcified tissue* does not help measurement appreciably because wherever calcium is deposited it can be readily seen by naked eye inspection. However, particularly for the black-and-white photographic reproduction of certain lesions, defatting of the alcohol-formol fixed specimen with acetone and subsequent staining with the von Kóssa technique is recommended. This procedure proved particularly helpful in the visibilization of the diffuse, reticular type of cutaneous calcinosis ("calciphylactic psoriasis") that is obtained, for example, by Fe-Dex i.p. after sensitization with DHT (Fig. 13, p. 45).

Diffuse lesions of the type just mentioned can only be gauged very roughly in terms of an *arbitrary four-grade scale.* We can readily distinguish: 0 = no lesion, 1 = just visible, 2 = moderate, and 3 = maximal, lesion.

Whenever great accuracy is not required but many determinations must be made rapidly, this arbitrary scale can be used even for the gauging of well circumscribed skin wheals. Scales with more than four grades should be avoided since they give a false impression of a greater accuracy than can be thus achieved. The four-grade scale has the advantage of minimizing the errors of subjective appraisal. The total absence of lesions (Grade 0) as well as the presence of just visible (Grade 1) or maximal (Grade 3) changes is rarely subject to great individual variations in assessment by different investigators; all other intensities are then placed in the only remaining category (Grade 2), within which further subdivisions of intensity would be difficult to make with precision.

A somewhat greater accuracy may be achieved, however, by the *"triple wheal test"* (Fig. 5) performed as follows:

100 g. female Holtzman rats are sensitized by the oral administration of 1 mg. of DHT in 0.5 ml. of corn oil in the usual manner 24 hours after shaving the skin over the back. On the following day the potential challenger is given in three concentrations in the proportion of 1:10:100 (e.g., 1, 10, and 100 mg.) at three points. The weakest concentration is injected between the shoulder blades, the strongest over the sacrum and the intermediate one at about the level of the first lumbar vertebra along the midline of the back (always s.c. in 0.2 ml. of water under ether anesthesia as described on p. 20). At least 10 rats should be used for each triple dose test starting with the strongest tolerable concentrations: in the case of fluids 1, 10, 100%; in the case of solids usually 0.2, 2, 20 mg. If this amount produces signs of systemic toxicity or local necrosis, 1/10 or even 1/100 of the previously used strongest tolerable dose is employed as the highest concentration in a subsequent test. Thus a broad dose range can be assayed on a decimal scale under strictly comparable conditions.

To safeguard against accidental variations in the sensitivity of the test animals or the efficacy of the sensitizing treatment, an additional standard wheal can be made under a patch of shaved abdominal skin using 25 μg. of FeCl$_3$ in 0.2 ml. of water. This normally induces very constant and reproducible calciphylactic wheals with a mean diameter of 8 ± 0.3 mm. Animals in which such a control (FeCl$_3$) wheal differs from the expected mean by more than 2 mm. are eliminated. The disadvantage of this type of check is that even minute amounts of absorbed iron may influence reactivity to the unknown chal-

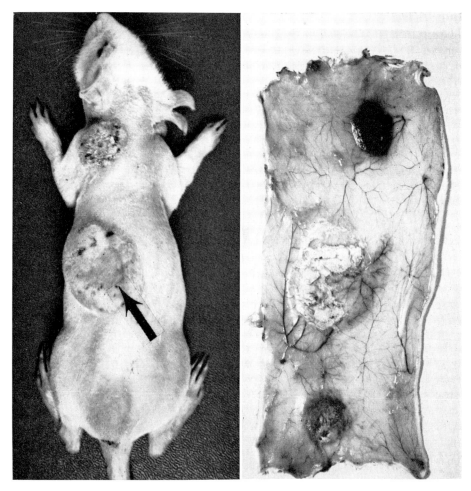

Fig. 5. "Triple wheal" test produced by DHT + alizarin red s.c. Rat (100 g. ♀): DHT (1 mg. p.o.) 1st day + alizarin red (0.2, 2, 20 mg. s.c. in shoulder, upper lumbar, and sacral region, respectively) 2d day; killed 7th day. *Left:* Appearance of the three wheals in living animal. Smallest dose causes massive calcification, medium dose circinate lesion (around noncalcified center marked by arrow), highest dose induces no calcification owing to overchallenge. *Right:* Skin of same animal viewed from subcutis. (Alizarin was used here as challenger because its color makes injection site visible even when no reaction is elicited.)

lenger injected at a distance on the back. Hence, particularly important findings thus obtained should be rechecked without the use of FeCl₃. In any event, rats which show more than barely visible traces of cardiac or renal calcification under these circumstances must be eliminated as hyperreactors, since normally 1 mg. of DHT does not produce pronounced, macroscopically visible lesions in the heart, the vessels, or the kidney.

The triple wheal test (often performed on several dose levels, each consisting of three wheals with the challenger given in the proportion of 1:10:100) is then evaluated as indicated in Table 1 (p. 48).

Histologic observations.—The most commonly employed histologic techniques for the study of calciphylaxis are those in current use for the demonstration of calcium (e.g., von Kóssa, alizarin, celestin blue) mastocyte granules (e.g., toluidine blue, methylene blue, cresyl violet, celestin blue), collagen fibers (van Gieson, PAS), elastic fibers (Weigert), fibrin (phosphotungstic acid), hyalin, so-called "neutral mucopolysaccharides" (PAS), mucoid materials (mucicarmine) and general histologic structure (hematoxylin-phloxine, PAS). Most of these are standard techniques, hence we may limit ourselves here to a description of some new procedures that were developed especially for this study.

For all of these, ***fixation in alcohol-formol*** proved to be most satisfactory. The fixation of specimens for the demonstration of calcium deposition in soft tissues has received little attention until quite recently, except for the fact that acid-containing solutions should be avoided. Even today, in human pathology the fixative most commonly used for this purpose is neutral formalin. Extensive studies performed in our Institute clearly showed the superiority of alcohol and alcohol-formol over neutral formalin; if even minute amounts of calcium are to be preserved, for example, in the experimental cardiopathies.[821, 823] For routine purposes, a solution containing 80 parts of absolute alcohol and 20 parts of 10% formalin (neutralized with CaCO₃) is recommended. Neutral formalin fixation is unsuitable since, for example in some experimental cardiopathies, it yields a positive reaction only when there are macroscopically visible massive calcium deposits.[746]

The ***celestin blue*** technique for the staining of calcified tissues has been described elsewhere.[823, 862] In solid blocks of calcification this technique tends to stain only the border line between the calcified and the surrounding tissue. Only very recent, minute calcium deposits are massively stained with celestin blue; this fact suggests that perhaps affinity for this dye is a sign of beginning, or at least still progressing, calcification. In any event, the technique has the great advantages that it does not blur fine structures and it imparts a very striking, dark violet color even to tissues containing so little calcium that they are not or only indistinctly stained with the von Kóssa procedure. Furthermore, the silver impregnation that forms the basis of the von Kóssa technique renders heavily calcified regions so brittle that they tend to break up into irregular clumps, from which dustlike granules "bleed" into the surroundings. The celestin-blue technique does not have any of these disadvantages, but it is less specific than the von Kóssa procedure because it also stains mastocyte granules very intensely and nuclei hair follicles, degenerating muscle cells and several other structures less intensely (Fig. 44).

The following four techniques which proved particularly useful in the study of calciphylactic lesions have been developed for this purpose by Mr. Kai Nielsen.

The von Kóssa plus van Gieson technique is especially suited for the simultaneous demonstration of calcium and the normal connective-tissue elements, particularly collagen fibers. Various routine techniques may be used as long as the sections are treated for 5 min. with 0.2% gold chloride (after Moffat[664]) following completion of the von Kóssa reaction. The procedure used in our laboratory is as follows:

Fixation in alcohol-formol, dehydration in dioxane, paraffin embedding; deparaffinize and bring sections to water.

1. Rinse in several changes of distilled water.
2. Place in 5% silver nitrate for 10 min. in subdued light, then expose to ultraviolet light for 15 min.
3. Rinse in distilled water.
4. Treat with 0.5% sodium thiosulfate for 5 min.
5. Wash in running water.
6. Tone in 0.2% gold chloride for 5 min.
7. Wash.
8. Stain in Weigert's iron hematoxylin for 30 min.
9. Wash in running water for 5 min.
10. Stain 5 min. in solution of saturated picric acid 190 ml., 1% acid fuchsin 30 ml.
11. Rinse briefly in distilled water, dehydrate in two changes of 95% alcohol, followed by absolute alcohol, clear in xylol, mount.

The von Kóssa plus PAS technique shows calcium and connective-tissue structures, particularly hyalin material, concurrently:

1. The von Kóssa technique is carried out as outlined above, including gold toning. Then proceed as follows:
2. 0.5% periodic acid 15 min.
3. Rinse in several changes of distilled water.
4. Schiff reagent 20 min.
5. Sulfurous water, three changes 3 min. in each.
6. Running water 10 min.
7. Stain in Ehrlich's hematoxylin diluted ten times with distilled water for 15 min.
8. Running water 10 min.
9. Pass through 50% and 70% alcohol and stain for 25 sec. in 0.5% aurantia in 70% alcohol.
10. Dehydrate in three changes of dioxan. Clear in xylol, mount.

The von Kóssa plus methylene blue technique proved invaluable in our studies on the relationship between mastocyte degranulation and calcification. On the same slide, it can demonstrate uncalcified metachromatic mastocyte granules as well as their gradual incrustation with calcium and the imbibition of connective-tissue fibers with metachromatic mastocyte granule material and calcium:

1. The von Kóssa technique is carried out as above, but omitting gold toning.
2. Stain 8 min. in the following mixture: methylene blue 0.5 g., distilled water 2,000 ml., lactic acid 1 ml.

3. Rinse briefly in distilled water.
4. Dehydrate in 2 changes of 95% alcohol followed by two changes of absolute alcohol. Clear in xylol, mount.

The celestin blue technique for calcification in tissue is a slight modification of our previously published method.[862]

1. Alcohol-formol fixation, dioxane dehydration, paraffin embedding.
2. Bring sections to water as usual.
3. Treat sections for 30 min. in following solution: 1% aluminum and potassium sulfate 90 ml. plus 10 ml. of 1 in 100 solution of ammonium hydroxide.
4. Rinse in water 1 min.
5. Stain for 30 min. in following solution: celestin blue B—0.2 g., 50% alcohol 500 ml.; this solution should be made up daily.
6. Rinse in 50% alcohol, followed by distilled water.
7. Counterstain lightly with phloxine.
8. Dehydrate, clear and mount in the usual manner.

Alkaline phosphatase.—Tissues are fixed in cold acetone and the above procedure is carried out beginning at step 3 after the cobalt chloride in Gomori's method for alkaline phosphatase. In this case both the enzyme and preformed phosphates appear blue.

The ***interpretation*** of the results obtained with various "calcium stains" is difficult because none of these techniques are truly specific tests for calcium. The *von Kóssa* technique stains inorganic phosphate and thereby reveals the presence of calcium-phosphate-containing precipitates, such as hydroxyapatite. Although in the tissues precipitates of inorganic phosphates are almost invariably combined with calcium, this is not always the case; besides, various materials other than phosphates (e.g., carbonates, oxalates, oleates) can stain with the von Kóssa technique. This can be shown, for example, on "gelatin models" in which artificial precipitates are produced. It has been concluded that the von Kóssa stain "is a specific test neither for calcium nor for phosphate. The test affords only an admirable pictorial demonstration of a deposit of inorganic material which is, in fact, in most instances composed of calcium phosphate or carbonate."[175]

Alizarin is a nearly specific stain for calcium which can also be used as a vital dye. It reacts with recently deposited calcium phosphate or carbonate but often fails to stain old deposits. This fact, and the comparative difficulty of obtaining uniform results with any of the modifications of the alizarin technique, limits its practical utility.[175]

Pathologists often assume that calcium is present in basophilic tissues which stain with *hematoxylin*. However, not all calcium deposits take up basic dyes and not all amorphous or granular basophilic deposits represent calcium. Hematoxylin does not stain calcium as such, but rather the matrix in which calcification is apt to occur. The reaction often depends on the presence of iron or of some organic material in the ground substance of bone, cartilage or pathologically altered tissues, which if mordanted with aluminum or chromium, stain deeply with hematoxylin.[175]

The frequent association of calcium and iron deposits in tissues will be discussed later.

The so-called *"basophilic degeneration"* and *"fuchsinophilic degeneration"* of cardiac muscle as well as *mucinous degeneration* and the deposition of certain polysaccharides in various tissues may also be related to calcification and iron deposition. The fact that many polysaccharides and mucinous substances can act as adjuvants in calciphylaxis may explain such a relationship, but this topic has been dealt with at length in another publication.[823]

Chemical observations.—Up to now we have only rarely used routine chemical methods (e.g., blood calcium or phosphate determination) for the assessment of calciphylactic lesions. Evidently the determination of calcium or inorganic phosphorus in the directly challenged skin would give a more quantitative basis for the estimation of mineral deposits in topical calciphylactic lesions than our routine tests that are based on morphologic criteria. However, calcification is not necessarily the best index of a calciphylactic reaction. Besides, in most of the studies performed during this initial stage, exact quantitation of the lesions was far less important than the screening of the many combinations of evocative agents that had to be tested to give at least some tentative picture of the mechanism, significance, and applicability of this new reaction form.

On the other hand, future research will have to keep in mind that only accurate chemical determinations can give us quantitative data concerning the numerous metabolic problems that are raised by the concept of calciphylaxis, for example: (1) the quantitative relationships between the challengers (e.g., iron, chromium, mucopolysaccharides) that appear to act as mordants and the amount of calcium or phosphate that they can attract; (2) the shifts of calcium and phosphate from the skeleton into soft tissues prepared by challengers; (3) the effect of calciphylaxis upon calcium and phosphate absorption and excretion; (4) the possible participation of endogenous adjuvants (e.g., mucopolysaccharides, iron); (5) the fundamental chemical mechanisms responsible for the development and healing of calciphylactic lesions, etc.

II

Topical Calciphylaxis

TOPICAL CALCIPHYLAXIS IN THE SKIN

THE VARIOUS FORMS OF CUTANEOUS CALCINOSIS

The basic technique for the production of cutaneous calcinosis and the gross characteristics of the resulting lesions have already been discussed. Suffice it to reiterate that such lesions are produced whenever appropriate sensitization by a systemic calcifier (e.g., DHT, parathyroid hormone, NaAST) is followed by treatment of the skin with a direct challenger (e.g., $FeCl_3$, $CrCl_3$, albumen, physical injury). By itself the typical challenger produces no calcification (Fig. 6), but when given after appropriate sensitization, the resulting lesion is grossly characterized by precipitous calcium deposition with subsequent inflammation and sclerosis of the skin (Figs. 7, 8; Plate I, *D, E, F*). The intimate structure of the local reaction depends upon experimental conditions, and three basic types—the "solid," "reticular," and "granular" variants—can be distinguished with many transitional forms between them.

A. The solid form.—The most intense and at the same time most common type of topical cutaneous calciphylaxis begins to be detectable about 48 hours after treatment with the challenger. It is macroscopically characterized by an initially painful edema of the derma and subcutis at the site of challenge and is transformed into a hard, whitish, roughly discoid patch during the subsequent two or three days. In the course of the following two to three weeks this lesion may develop in one of two possible directions.

If comparatively small amounts of the challenger are applied to the deep strata of the subcutis, the inflammation soon subsides and a fairly well demarcated *calcified plate* is formed. This hard plaque is surrounded by loose connective tissue and thereby completely separated from the derma. It may remain in the subcutis for many weeks or even months without causing any obvious signs of local irritation (Fig. 7).

Histologically, such plates consist initially of *calcium incrustated collagen fibers and fat cells* with fragmentation and calcification of the *elastic fibers* while the mastocytes discharge their granules[858, 862] (Fig. 8; Plate II, *A, B*). As the lesion matures, some of the calcium is absorbed, but most of it is built into the structure of smaller preosseous tissue plates, which apparently develop as a direct consequence of calcium deposition. These plates possess a strongly ***PAS-positive matrix,*** formed about the connective-tissue fibers and between the fat cells. The fat cells themselves are gradually replaced by fibrous connective tissue and histiocytes. Then the fibrocytes within this matrix assume the appearance of osteocytes, while, especially at the edges of the ***preosseous spicules, multinuclear giant cells*** appear which are indistinguishable from osteoclasts. These giant cells eventually remove the small partitions within the PAS-positive, calcified matrix, while adipose and hemopoietic cells invade the resulting larger spaces. Thus the tissue assumes most of the characteristics of true bone, but unlike the latter, it remains strongly PAS positive, contains only abortive bone canaliculi, and shows no lamellation (Plate II, *C, D*).

Only exceptionally did we find ***true lamellated bone*** with hemopoietic marrow and a PAS-negative, solidly calcified matrix with typical osteocyte canaliculi under these conditions. True bone induction succeeded much more regularly when we injected challengers into subcutaneous air sacs (pneumoderma technique) and then introduced a glass tube as a "tissue scaffolding" into this challenged cavity.

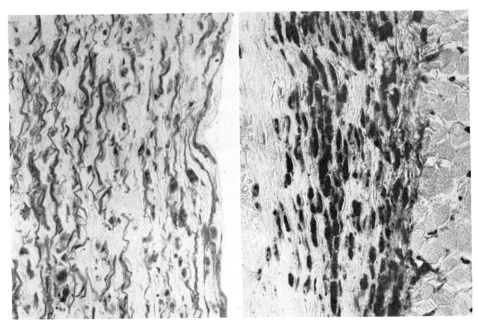

Fig. 6. Topical effect of FeCl₃ upon subcutaneous tissue in the nonsensitized rat. *Left:* Iron impregnation of collagen fibers and of some histiocytes in FeCl₃-injected connective tissue. *Right:* In more peripheral region of same FeCl₃ injection site, iron impregnation is limited to the cytoplasm of fibroblasts and to some phagocytes, while collagen fibers remain unaffected. (Prussian blue, ×350.)

[After Selye *et al.*, [830] courtesy Williams & Wilkins Co. (J. Inv. Dermat.).]

It will be recalled that even mere implantation of these "tissue scaffoldings" suffices for bone induction,[860] but the combination of this technique with the provocation of a topical calciphylactic reaction appears to yield more constant results (Fig. 9).

The development of the lesions is quite different whenever, during the initial stages, more than traces of calcification occur in the derma itself. In this case, the calcified region *exulcerates* and is eventually cast off while underneath it a new skin develops, which may or may not contain hair and sebaceous glands (the rat possesses no sweat glands) depending upon the thickness of the eliminated layer. Apparently, some vestiges of hair follicles and sebaceous glands must remain in situ to permit regeneration.

By following its histogenesis, this artificial cutaneous molt could be traced to an intense epithelial proliferation separating the calcified (necrotic and subse-

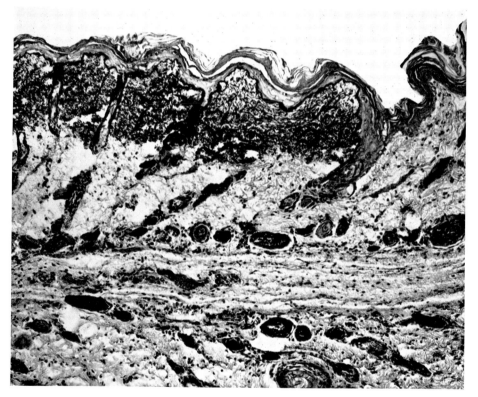

Fig. 7. **Topical cutaneous calcinosis produced by DHT + plucking of scalp hair.**
Rat sensitized with DHT and challenged by plucking hair over scalp and back. Histologic appearance of typical calcified skin wheal in epilated area. Calcium deposition is limited to subepithelial connective-tissue fibers of sharply circumscribed region. (von Kóssa, ×135; cf. Plate I, *B*.)

(After Selye *et al.*, [858] courtesy Proc. Soc. Exper. Biol. and Med.)

quently rejected) skin plate from the subjacent healthy tissue. At the edges of the
focus this proliferating, new epithelium is derived from an ***ingrowth of adjacent
epidermal cells*** under the calcified necrotic plate. However, if the destruction
does not go too deep, epithelial remnants, especially around the hair follicles, also
contribute to the formation of a new, complete epidermal covering. Consequently,
before the old skin is cast off it is often possible to recognize two parallel plates of
epidermis, one on the surface undergoing necrosis and one which runs parallel to it
underneath the dying derma (Fig. 10).

A virtually complete ***cutaneous molt*** can be obtained in DHT-sensitized rats
if, during the critical period, their entire skin surface is infiltrated with solutions of
albumen or Fe-Dex. In such experiments care must be taken not to interfere with
locomotion, food ingestion, and excretion, by leaving the head, ano-genital region,
and extremities untouched. Under these circumstances almost the entire skin surface (including the hair and the sebaceous glands) turns into a hard carapace

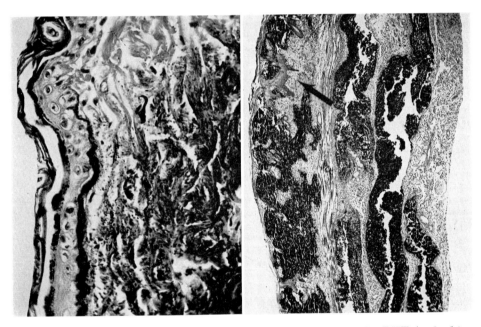

**Fig. 8. Various acute forms of cutaneous calcinosis produced by DHT + plucking
of scalp hair.** *Left:* Beginning calcification of dermal collagen fibers. Celestin blue stain clearly
shows that—in addition to diffuse calcium deposition—regular, round or oval granules of lime
salts appear within the collagen fibers. Additional calcium deposits are seen along basement
membrane of epidermis. (×350). *Right:* Extensive, subcutaneous calcareous masses separated
from calcified dermal patch by cutaneous muscle layer. At one point (arrow) epidermis grows
deep into derma and turns around edge of calcified region about to be exfoliated. (von Kóssa,
×22; cf. Plate I, *D, E, F.*)

[After Selye and Nielsen, [862] courtesy Akadémiai Kiadó Budapest (Acta Morphol. Acad.
Sc. Hungar.).]

which is subsequently cast off and replaced by new skin. Among the rats so treated, some happened to have accidental scars in the infiltrated region, which were cast off together with the old skin; interestingly, the new skin underneath showed no evidence of comparable scar formation. This artificially induced molt has been compared to the process of exuviation that normally occurs only at lower levels of phylogenesis (e.g., in reptiles, crustaceans, and insect larvae)[844] (Fig. 11).

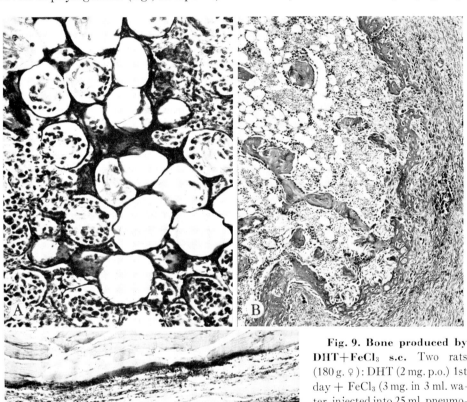

Fig. 9. Bone produced by DHT+FeCl₃ s.c. Two rats (180 g. ♀): DHT (2 mg. p.o.) 1st day + FeCl₃ (3 mg. in 3 ml. water, injected into 25 ml. pneumodermal sac) 1st day + (A and B) "tissue scaffolding" (glass tube 30 mm. diameter, 20 mm. axis, introduced into pneumoderma) 6th day; killed 50th day. Formation of preosseous, intensely PAS-positive, calcified matrix in subcutaneous fat tissue. Round spaces originally occupied by adipose cells are now invaded by hemopoietic and connective tissue in one focus (A), while in adjacent region (B) true bone, cartilage and hemopoietic bone marrow have formed, on animal's back within area surrounded by glass tube. In rat without glass tube implant, base of the FeCl₃-treated air sac contains only PAS-positive, calcified, preosseous plaques (C), which show no tendency to become transformed into true bone. (PAS, A ×310, B, C ×90.)

(After Selye and Veilleux.[866a])

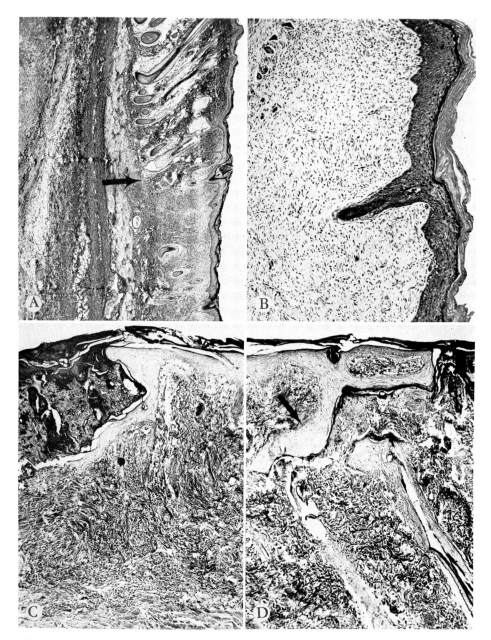

Fig. 10. Various chronic forms of cutaneous calcinosis produced by DHT + epilation (hair plucking). *A:* Borderline between healthy and sclerosed skin during period of healing. In the affected region (below arrow) there is dense connective tissue, but sebaceous glands are absent, hair follices rare, and the epidermis is thickened. (Fuchsin, ×28.) *B:* Calcium is no longer visible in dense connective tissue of this healing patch. Only few calcified granules remaining in foreign-body giant cells near upper left corner. (von Kóssa, ×80.) *C:* Advanced exulceration with beginning epithelialization of wound surface. The normal collagen fibers (center) stained red, while the swollen, degenerating fibers (edge of field) took on yellowish tinge. (Fuchsin, ×80.) *D:* Here, the necrosis progresses farther in depth than on the surface. The epidermis turns around edge of ulcer, following borderline between healthy (superficial) and necrotic (deep) tissue. Consequently, strata of newly formed (arrow) epithelium are reversed. (Fuchsin, ×80.)

[After Selye and Nielsen,[862] courtesy Akadémiai Kiadó Budapest (Acta Morphol. Acad. Sc. Hungar.).]

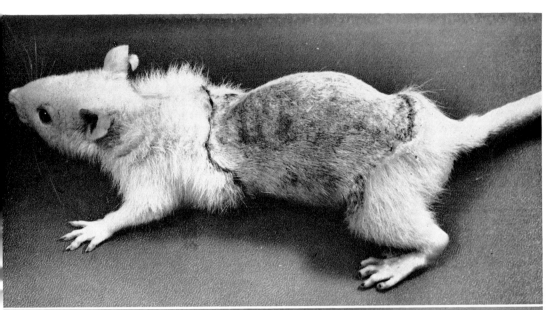

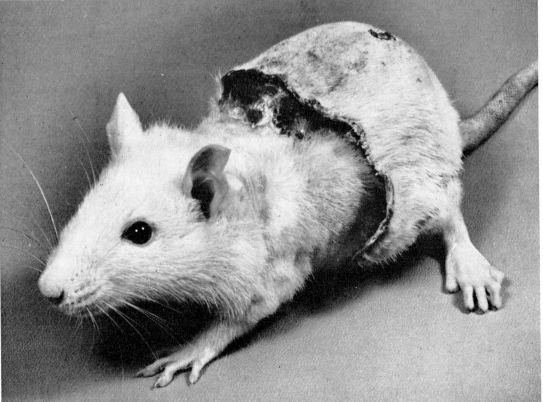

Fig. 11. Cutaneous molt produced by DHT + albumen s.c. Rat (100 g. ♀): DHT (1 mg. p.o.) 1st day + albumen (50%, 10 ml. s.c. infiltration of entire body surface, except head, ano-genital region and extremities) 2d day; killed 25th day. *Top:* Complete circular skin carapace formed by cutaneous calcinosis of infiltrated region (photographed 18th day). *Bottom:* Rat exuviates its old integument and emerges with new skin on 24th day.

(After Selye *et al.*,[844] reprinted from *Science* by permission.)

Usually calciphylactic cutaneous wheals of the solid type are essentially uniform throughout the affected region; however, sometimes they exhibit a **circinate** aspect, owing to lack of response in the center of the patch. Such circinate lesions are obtained, for example, when the skin of the sensitized animals is treated with excessively strong chemical or mechanical challengers (e.g., several mg. of $FeCl_3$ or crushing with a hemostat). Under these circumstances, the skin apparently becomes irresponsive owing to overstimulation ("overchallenge") at the center of the challenged area and only the less intensely affected peripheral margin responds (Fig. 12; Plate I, C). If we assume that calciphylaxis depends largely upon the discharge of some histogenous storage product (e.g., mast-cell granules), it is conceivable that such excessive stimulation is inactive merely because the reactive substrate is too rapidly discharged and removed from the tissues to capture calcium. This process may also explain why pretreatment of the skin with a strong stimulus applied prior to calciphylactic sensitization induces a topical resistance to the same or even to other challengers applied to the same area after sensitization. Thus, here we are dealing not only with specific but also with nonspecific

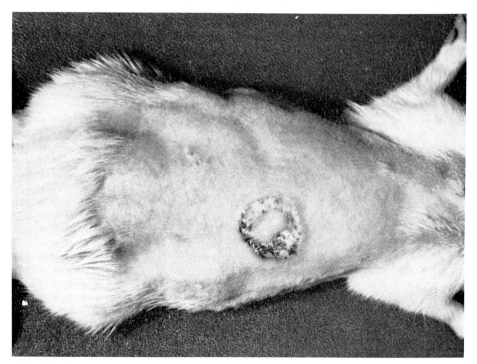

Fig. 12. Calciphylactic wheal with central "overchallenge." Circinate cutaneous cal-cinosis on margin of skin patch infiltrated with 10% yolk. Central area remains unaffected. (Cf. Plate I, C.)

[After Selye and Nielsen,[862] courtesy Akadémiai Kiadó Budapest (Acta Morphol. Acad. Sc. Hungar.).]

"cross-resistance" of the target area as previously defined.[825] (Cf. also Figs. 208, 209.)

B. The reticular form.—Certain challengers (e.g., pectin) tend to produce a cutaneous calcinosis of the **reticular type.** Here the affected area is not solidly calcified, but only along arborizing and anastomosing strands, which form a more or less dense network. Such lesions are less rigid than the solid wheals and do not tend to result in the exfoliation and replacement of entire large skin areas. Instead, there is usually intense scaling with subsequent formation of disseminated, small, surface defects as the scales are cast off. As judged from the animal's behavior, the reticular type of cutaneous calcinosis appears to cause itching and pain, especially in the acute stage. This dermatosis somewhat resembles psoriasis both in its aspect and in that even gentle removal of the scales results in diffuse surface bleeding (reminiscent of Auspitz' sign in clinical psoriasis) (Fig. 13; Plate VI, *D*).

Histologically, the reticular, arborizing distribution of the lesions corresponds

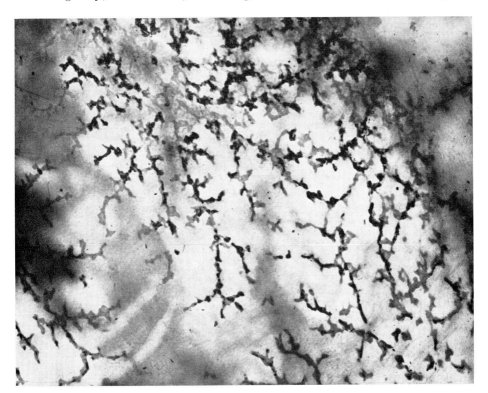

Fig. 13. Arborizing skin lesions produced by DHT + Fe-Dex i.p. Rat (200 g. ♀): Fe-Dex (1 ml. = 20 mg. Fe, i.p.) 1st day + DHT (2 mg. p.o.) 2d day; killed 12th day. Loupe magnification of defatted, von Kóssa-stained specimen (viewed from subcutaneous surface) shows arborizing pattern of nodules along course of vessels. (Cf. Plate VI, *D.*)

to the course of blood vessels, perhaps because the cutaneous mast cells, which appear to play an important role in calciphylaxis, predominate in perivascular tissue. This reticular cutaneous calcinosis, like the solid variant, depends primarily upon calcium incrustation of connective-tissue fibers; however, unlike in the solid type, here the fiber incrustation is discontinuous. It is limited to fairly regularly spaced foci which correspond to the points where the section plane cuts across the arborizing ramifications (Fig. 14).

C. The granular form.—A predominantly granular, cutaneous calcinosis is obtained when histamine dischargers (e.g., PMX, 48/80), Fe-Din, or Thorotrast® are used as challengers. In the acute stage the skin is usually hyperemic and edematous. Histologically, the outstanding characteristic is the widespread discharge and subsequent calcification of mastocyte granules throughout the affected region (Plate VII, *E, F*). At a later stage, either the granules may be absorbed, giving rise only to transient inflammatory phenomena, or calcification may progress toward

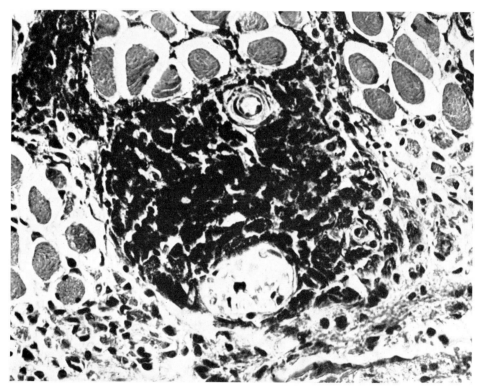

Fig. 14. "Arborizing type" of cutaneous calcinosis produced by DHT + pectin s.c. Rat (100 g. ♀): DHT (1 mg. p.o.) 1st day + pectin (3% in 0.2 ml. water, s.c.) 2d day; killed 7th day. Cross section through one branch of macroscopically visible, white, arborizing pattern. Calcium is deposited in connective tissue surrounding uncalcified artery (top) and nerve (bottom) just below cutaneous muscle. (von Kóssa, ×465.)

the solid type through the gradual incrustation of connective-tissue fibers with calcium. As far as can be judged from histologic sections, both the uncalcified mastocyte material and the calcium that is precipitated around the discharged metachromatic granules tend to diffuse between the connective-tissue fibrils and participate in their gradual calcification. When this process is completed, the resulting lesion becomes indistinguishable from the primarily solid cutaneous calcinosis with collagen fiber incrustation.

Of course, all three of these macro- and microscopically distinct forms of cutaneous calcinosis—the solid, reticular, and granular variants—could result from essentially the same fundamental mechanism: the discharge and subsequent calcification of mastocyte granules. Depending upon the speed and intensity of this process, the lesions may consist of: (1) primarily solid plaques of incrustated fibers (solid variant), (2) fiber incrustations limited to the vicinity of the blood vessels where mastocytes are numerous (reticular variant), (3) calcification primarily affecting only the discharged mastocyte granules themselves (granular variant), though secondarily the fibers usually also become involved. As the lesions spread, both the reticular and the granular variants may turn into the solid form.

A fourth form, the **superficial, macular, scaly dermatosis** (which tends to appear, for example, during the second week of the calciphylactic syndrome induced by DHT + $CrCl_3$ i.v.) need not be discussed here since we have not yet succeeded in eliciting it by topical calciphylaxis.

SENSITIZERS

The systemic calcifiers used to sensitize animals for topical cutaneous calcinosis are the same as those employed to produce systemic calciphylactic reactions in internal organs, e.g., **DHT, vitamin D_2, vitamin D_3, parathyroid hormone, NaAST**.[327] Among these, DHT proved to be the most useful because of its high potency and ready availability. NaAST is least effective, presumably because it acts too slowly through the progressive production of an obstructive nephropathy and the consequent stimulation of parathyroid hormone secretion (Fig. 15). The gradual development of these changes interferes with the induction of a sharply delimited peak of sensitivity, or critical period, such as is necessary for the obtention of clear-cut calciphylactic reactions. Besides, effective doses of NaAST cause considerable stress with eventual death from uremia, and stress tends to prevent the development of calciphylaxis. However, the fact that a compound such as NaAST—which influences calcium metabolism only through the intermediary of the kidney and the parathyroids—can nevertheless sensitize for calciphylaxis suggests that various other agents (e.g., microbes, allergens, drugs, spontaneous renal diseases) could also act indirectly by stimulating the production of **endogenous calcifiers.**

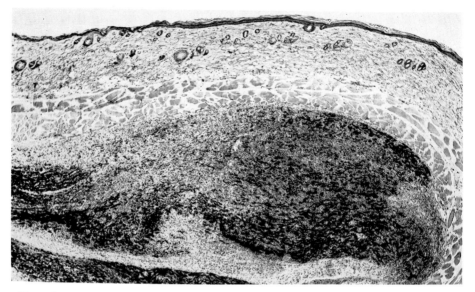

Fig. 15. Cutaneous calcinosis produced by NaAST + albumen s.c. Rat (200 g. ♀):
NaAST (150 mg. in 0.5 ml. water, i.p.) 1st day + albumen (50%, 3 ml. s.c. on belly) 11th day;
killed 14th day. Calcification with particularly intense fibrous tissue proliferation in subcutis.
(von Kóssa, ×40.)

CHALLENGERS

A very large number of potential challenging agents have been tested with the
"triple wheal technique" (p. 31) under standard conditions.[479, 827, 866a] Table 1 lists
the potency grades and Table 2 the results of the relevant tests.

Although these assays furnished us with a very large number of data, they supplied only little information concerning the particular characteristics that an agent

TABLE 1

POTENCY GRADING IN "TRIPLE WHEAL TEST"
(As Used in Table 2)

Grade*	mg.† in 0.2 ml. H_2O
0	>200
1	200
2	20
3	2
4	0.2
5	0.02 or less

* The grade reflects the minimum amount of a substance that
gives a measurable reaction. E.g., a reaction obtainable at no less
than 20 mg. is graded 2. In cases of very weak or very strong reactions (with a diameter of less than 10 mm. or more than 20 mm.)
the corresponding grade is preceded by the signs < or >, respectively.

† For the purpose of this semi-quantitative grading, 1 mg. of
solids is considered equivalent to 1/1000 ml. of fluids, irrespective
of specific gravity.

TABLE 2

POTENCY OF SUBSTANCES
TESTED FOR CUTANEOUS CALCIPHYLACTIC CHALLENGING EFFECT

Substances	Dose Range Tested (mg.)*	Potency
Body constituents and tissue extracts:		
Allantoic fluid (rat)	2– 200	0
Anterior pituitary, lyophilized	0.2– 20	<2
Bile (ox)	0.2– 20	<2
Bone marrow extract (calf)	0.5– 50	<2
Brain extract (calf)	1– 100	<2
Cartilage extract (calf)	0.25– 25	0
Crystalline extract (calf)	0.5– 50	0
Duodenal extract (calf)	1– 100	0
Embryo extract (rat)	1– 100	0
Gastric extract (calf)	0.25– 25	<2
Gastroduodenal extract (rat)	1– 100	0
Globin	0.02– 2	0
Hemoglobin	0.02– 2	0
Liver extract (calf)	1– 100	<2
Nucleus pulposus extract (calf)	0.25– 25	0
Ovary, lyophilized	0.2– 20	0
Posterior pituitary, lyophilized	0.002– 0.2	0
Renal extract (calf)	0.5– 50	<2
Spleen extract (calf)	0.5– 50	0
Sweat (horse)	2– 200	0
Synovial fluid (calf)	2– 200	0
Urinary bladder extract (calf)	1– 100	0
Vitreous humor extract (calf)	1– 100	0
Wharton's jelly (calf)	0.2– 20	0
Wharton's jelly, lyophilized	0.2– 20	>2
Plasma	0.2– 20	>2
Carbohydrates and related compounds:		
Carboxymethylcellulose	0.12– 12	0
Carrageenin	0.2– 20	0
Dextran	0.12– 12	0
Glucose	0.2– 20	0
Glycogen	0.2– 20	0
Heparin	2– 200(U)	0
Pectin	0.2– 20	<2
Starch soluble	0.2– 20	0
Exudates collected from granuloma pouches produced by:		
Carrageenin	2– 200	0
Croton oil	2– 200	0
Glass spiral	2– 200	0
Glass tube	2– 200	0
Ivalon sponge	2– 200	0
Kaolin	2– 200	0
MRLS tumor	2– 200	0
Walker tumor	2– 200	0
Hormones:		
Adrenaline	0.001– 0.1	0
Desoxycorticosterone acetate	0.02– 2	0
Estradiol	0.02– 2	0
Fluoro-cortisol	0.02– 2	0
Histamine	2– 20	0
Methyl-testosterone	0.02– 2	<3
17α-Ethyl-19 nortestosterone	0.02– 2	<3
Noradrenaline	0.001– 0.1	0
Oxytocin	0.02– 2(U)	0
Parathyroid hormone	0.001– 0.1	0
Progesterone	0.02– 2	0
5HT (Serotonin)	0.02– 2	0
Triamcinolone	0.02– 2	0
Vasopressin	0.01– 1(U)	0

* All doses are given in mg. except where otherwise indicated, e.g., unit (U).

TABLE 2—*Continued*

Substances	Dose Range Tested (mg.)*		Potency
Metallic compounds and electrolytes:			
$AgCH_3COO$			(W)†
$AgNO_3$			(W)
$AlCl_3$			(W)
$AlK(SO_4)_2$	0.2–	20	<4
$AlNH_4(SO_4)_2$	0.2–	20	3
$Al(NO_3)_3$			(W)
Aurothioglucose	0.1–	10	0
Aurothiomalate, sodium	0.02–	2	3
$BaCl_2$			(0)
$BiCl_3$			(W)
$Ca(CH_3COO)_2$			(0)
$CaCl_2$			(0)
$CdCl_2$			(M)
$CeCl_3$			(M)
$CoCl_2$			(W)
$CrCl_2$			(S)
$CrCl_3$			(S)
CrO_3			(W)
CsCl			(0)
$Cu(CH_3COO)_2$			(W)
$CuCl_2$			(W)
$Cu(NO_3)_2$			(W)
$CuSO_4$			(W)
$FeCl_2$			(M)
$FeCl_3$			(M)
Fe-Dex (Fe-dextran)	0.02–	15	5, G‡
$Fe(NH_4)(SO_4)_2$			(M)
$Fe(NO_3)_3$			(M)
Fe-OS (Fe-oxide saccharated)	0.04–	4	<5
Ferric albuminate	0.2–	20	3
Ferritin	0.01–	1	0
Ferrous gluconate	0.002–	0.2	>4
Ferrous lactate	0.002–	0.2	<5
$FeSO_4$			(S)
$FeSO_4(NH_4)_2SO_4$			(S)
$Ga(SO_4)_3$	0.2–	20	4
$Ga(SO_4)_3$	0.002–	0.2	<4
$Hg(CH_3COO)_2$			(M)
Hg-sulfide (black)	0.2–	20	<2
$InCl_3$	0.2–	20	4
$InCl_3$	0.002–	0.2	4
$IrCl_4$	0.2–	20	0
KBr			(0)
KCl			(0)
$KClO_3$			(0)
$KClO_4$			(0)
K_2CrO_4			(0)
$K_2Cr_2O_7$			(0)
$K_3Fe(CN)_6$			(0)
$K_4Fe(CN)_6$			(0)
KI			(0)
KIO_3			(0)
KIO_4			(0)
$KMnO_4$	0.02–	2	5
K_2MnO_4	0.02–	2	>3
KSCN			(0)
K_2SO_4			(0)
$LaCl_3$			(M)
LiCl			(0)
$MgCl_2$			(0)
$MnCl_2$			(0)
$NaAsO_2$			(0)
$Na_2B_4O_7$			(0)

† Figures in brackets refer to other series of experiments [479,829a] graded according to a different scale. These are to be interpreted as follows: 0 = no reaction, W = weak reaction, M = medium reaction, S = strong reaction.

‡ Expressed in mg. of Fe. Generalized reaction at highest dose level.

TABLE 2—*Continued*

Substances	Dose Range Tested (mg.)*		Potency
$NaCH_3COO$			(0)
Na-citrate	0.2–	20	0
NaCl	0.2–	20	0
Na_2CO_3			(0)
Na-oxalate	0.1–	10	0
Na_2HAsO_4			(0)
$NaHCO_3$			(0)
NaH_2PO_4			(0)
Na_2MoO_4			(0)
$NaNO_2$			(0)
$NaNO_3$			(0)
Na-pyruvate	0.2–	20	0
Na_2SeO_3			(0)
Na_2SnO_3			(W)
Na_2SO_3			(0)
$Na_2S_2O_3$			(0)
Na_2SO_4			(0)
$NaVO_3$			(0)
Na_2WO_4			(0)
$(NH_4)_2SO_4$			(0)
$NiCl_2$			(0)
OsO_4			(0)
$Pb(CH_3COO)_2$			(M)
$PbCl_2$			(M)
$Pb(NO_3)_2$			(M)
$PdCl_2$			(W)
$Pd(NO_3)_2$	0.2–	20	0
PtK_2Cl_6			(W)
RbCl			(0)
$SnCl_2$			(W)
$SrCl_2$			(0)
$TiCl_3$			(M)
$TiCl_4$			(M)
$TlCH_3COO$	0.02–	2	0
TlCl			(0)
$UO_2(CH_3COO)_2$			(0)
$VOSO_4$			(W)
$ZnCl_2$			(M)
$ZrOCl_2$			(M)
Microbial products:			
Esch. coli lipopolysaccharide (Difco)	0.02–	2	0
Pseudomonas polysaccharide (Piromen)	0.002–	2	0
Westphal. lipopolysaccharide	0.02–	2	0
Yeast, brewer's	0.2–	20	0
Zymosan	0.2–	20	0
Mucilages:			
Gastric mucin	0.2–	20	0
Gum arabic	0.2–	20	0
Gum British (dextrin)	0.2–	20	2
Gum Indian (ghatti)	0.2–	20	0
Gum kino	0.2–	20	0
Gum tragacanth	0.2–	20	2
Mucopolysaccharides:			
Chondroitin sulfuric acid (crude)	0.02–	20	<3
Chondroitin sulfate A	0.02–	2	0
Chondroitin sulfate B	0.02–	2	0
Chondroitin sulfate B (Na-salt)	0.02–	2	0
Chondroitin sulfate C (Na-salt)	0.02–	2	<3
Chondroitin sulfuric acid	0.2–	20	<3
Heparitin sulfate	0.02–	2	0
Na-hyaluronate	0.02–	2	0
Keratosulfate	0.02–	2	0

TABLE 2—*Continued*

Substances	Dose Range Tested (mg.)*	Potency
Physical agents:		
Plucking of hair		(S)
Crushing of skin (hemostat)		(S)
Traction on skin		(M)
Cold (general)		0
Cold (local)		0
Cutaneous incision		0
Desiccation, local (high frequency current)		0
Heat (general)		0
Ultraviolet rays (general)		G
X-rays (local)		0
X-rays (general)		0
Radiopaque substances:		
Chloriodized oil (Iodochlorol®)	2– 200	0
Diatrizoate methylglucamine (Renografin®)	2– 200	<1
Ethiodized oil (Ethiodol®)	2– 200	0
Ethyl iodophenylundecylate (Myodil®)	2– 200	0
Iodipamine methylglucamine (Cholografin®)	2– 200	0
Propyliodone (Dionosil®)		0
Sodium acetrizoate (Urokon®)	2– 200	0
Sodium diatrizoate (Hypaque®)	2– 200	0
Sodium diprotrizoate (Miokon®)	2– 200	<1
Thorium dioxide (Thorotrast®)	2– 200	2
Miscellaneous:		
Acetic acid	0.2– 20	0
Acetylsalicylic acid	0.2– 20	<2
Allyl alcohol	0.02– 2	0
Allyl amine	0.04– 4	0
Allyl isothiocyanate	0.04– 4	0
Aloe (black)	0.2– 20	<3
Aloe (yellow)	0.4– 40	0
Aloin	0.2– 20	0
Aminoacetonitrile (AAN)	0.2– 20	<2
Apresoline®	0.02– 2	0
Bradykinin	0.00002– 0.002	0
Chlorophyll	0.2– 20	0
Colloidal carbon	0.2– 20	0
Croton oil	0.05– 5	0
Ethanol	0.12– 12	0
Formalin	0.04– 4	0
Gelatin	0.2– 20	0
Glycerin	0.12– 12	0
α-Globulin	0.02– 2	0
β-Globulin	0.02– 2	0
γ-Globulin	0.2– 20	0
Hematoporphyrin	0.2– 20	3
Kaolin	0.2– 20	0
Lycopodium	0.2– 20	0
Mustard oil	0.04– 4	0
Mustard powder	0.2– 20	<3
Phenylbutazone	0.2– 20	0
Phosphomolybdic acid	0.2– 20	0
Phosphotungstic acid	0.2– 20	0
Phyltone	0.2– 20	<3
Polymyxin	0.02– 2	3
Polyvinylpyrrolidone	0.05– 5	0
Salicylic acid	0.2– 20	0
Tannic acid	0.02– 2	0
Tween 80	0.2– 20	2
48/80	0.02– 2	3

TABLE 2—*Continued*

Substances	Dose Range Tested (mg.)*	Potency
Dyes:		
Alizarin	0.2– 20	0
Alizarin red	0.2– 20	4
Celestin blue	0.2– 20	0
Congo red	0.2– 20	<2
India ink	0.2– 20	0
Isamine blue	0.2– 20	<3
Kernechtrot	0.2– 20	0
Trypan blue	0.2– 20	0
Eggs and egg constituents:		
Whole egg:		
Carp	0.2– 20	3
Cod	0.2– 20	2
Pickerel	0.2– 20	3
Pike	0.2– 20	3
Embryonated (pheasant)	0.2– 20	<2
Powder (domestic hen)	0.2– 20	2
Albumen:		
Golden pheasant	0.2– 20	<2
Domestic goose	0.2– 20	0
Canada goose	0.2– 20	<2
White Pekin goose	0.2– 20	0
Domestic duck	0.2– 20	0
Wood duck	0.2– 20	<2
Colombian tree duck	0.2– 20	<2
European shell duck	0.2– 20	0
Mute swan	0.2– 20	<2
Grass-parakeet	0.1– 10	0
Domestic hen	0.2– 20	<2
Yolk:		
Golden pheasant	0.2– 20	>2
Domestic goose	0.2– 20	>2
Canada goose	0.2– 20	2
White Pekin goose	0.2– 20	<4
Domestic duck	0.2– 20	<4
Wood duck	0.2– 20	<3
Colombian tree duck	0.2– 20	3
European shell duck	0.2– 20	2
Mute swan	0.2– 20	>2
Grass-parakeet	0.2– 20	<2
Domestic hen	0.2– 20	0
Powder (domestic hen)	0.2– 20	2
Ovomucoid	0.2– 20	0
Ovomucoid in NaCl	0.2– 20	<3
Albumen powder (domestic hen)	0.2– 20	<3
Enzymes:		
Bromelin	0.02– 2	0
Hyaluronidase	0.02– 2	0
Papain	0.02– 2	0
Pepsin	0.02– 2	0
Streptokinase-dornase	20–2000(U)	0
Trypsin	0.02– 2	0

must have in order to act as a calciphylactic challenger. However, the following conclusions appear to be compatible with the facts observed up to now:

1. There is no manifest relationship between the ability of a compound to produce *local tissue damage* (as manifested by inflammation or necrosis) and its challenging potency; some highly irritating or corrosive compounds (e.g., croton oil, mustard powder, phototungstic acid) are ineffective, while many agents which elicit virtually no signs of tissue injury (e.g., plucking of the hair, Fe-Dex) are nevertheless highly efficacious challengers. Inflammatory exudates produced by various means are inert.

2. Both organic and inorganic materials can act as challengers, but most of the highly potent compounds are *metals* (e.g., $KMnO_4$ and salts of Fe, Cr). Curiously, no monovalent metallic cation possesses challenging potency; this may suggest that the phenomenon of chelation plays a part here.

3. Among the *organic compounds,* some tissue extracts, methyltestosterone, 17*a*-ethyl-19 nortestosterone and pectin possess moderate challenging potency, while virtually all egg products tested (both albumen and yolk of avian eggs and whole fish eggs) were definitively active. The iron content of eggs is comparatively high; hence, it is possible that here the organic constituents merely act as adjuvants for iron, especially since—as we shall see—the addition of even minute amounts of iron to egg white greatly augments its challenging power.

5HT and triamcinolone gave negative results, and histamine dischargers (e.g., 48/80, polymyxin) were only slightly active in the triple wheal test upon direct application to the cutaneous connective tissue. Yet, all these agents are highly potent in producing calciphylactic responses in distant organs: 5HT causes calcinosis in salivary glands and muscles, triamcinolone in the thymus, histamine dischargers in skin and muscles. We ascribe these remote effects to indirect challenging potencies, presumably mediated through the liberation of endogenous challengers by compounds which have no challenging effect themselves.

4. Various comparatively mild *physical agents* (e.g., plucking of the hair, pinching of the skin, or traction upon the derma) can produce local calciphylactic responses in the DHT-sensitized rat (Fig. 16; Plate I, *B, C*); here the actual challenging material must of necessity be endogenous.

CRITICAL PERIOD

The critical period for the induction of topical cutaneous calciphylaxis has not yet been determined for every systemic calcifier and every challenging agent. However, in our first preliminary experiments performed with DHT p.o. or vitamin D_3 i.v., maximum receptivity to challenge developed within 24 to 48 hours[491, 824, 827, 858] after treatment with the sensitizer (cf. also p. 252 ff.).

For example, in different groups of rats (100 g. ♀) tested at intervals Fe-Dex (0.2 ml. = 10 μg. Fe, s.c.) was fully efficacious in producing cutaneous calcinosis on the 1st, 2d, and 3d, but not on the 4th day, after sensitization with DHT (1 mg. p.o.). Essentially similar observations were made in an experiment in which a single group of rats (100 g. ♀) was first sensitized with vitamin D_3 (2 mg. in 0.2 ml. water, i.v.) on the 1st day and then repeatedly challenged with Fe-Dex (10 μg. in 0.2 ml. water, s.c. at various sites). Minimal cutaneous calciphylactic wheals were produced by injection on the 1st day, very marked lesions on the 2d and 3d day, but no response on the 4th day. Apparently here—as in the case of sensitization with DHT—the critical period reaches a maximum between the 2d and 3d day.

ADJUVANTS

Generalities.—The efficacy of various calciphylactic challengers can be greatly enhanced if they are administered in a solution containing certain adjuvants. For example, if a DHT-sensitized rat is challenged by as little as 1 μg. of $FeCl_3$, no macroscopically detectable cutaneous calcinosis results; however, if the same

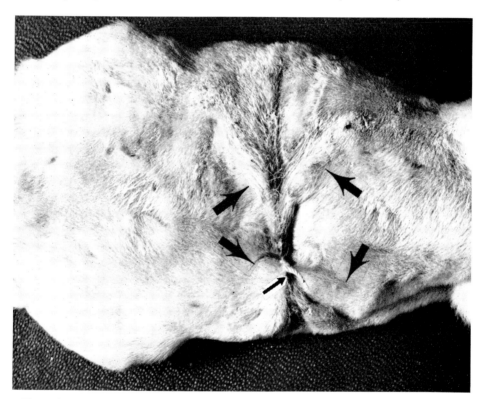

Fig. 16. Cutaneous calcinosis produced by DHT + skin traction. Rat (100 g. ♀): DHT (1 mg. p.o.) 1st day + skin traction [white thread ligature fastened to sides, meeting ends tied under xiphoid (small arrow)] 2d day; killed 5th day. Hard, calcified streaks developed along cutaneous traction lines (large arrows).

amount of FeCl₃ is injected in a 6 per cent dextran solution, it produces a large calciphylactic plaque[848] (Fig. 17).

Dextran itself—like gelatin and many other compounds—is a *pure adjuvant* in that it does not act as a challenger after sensitization with DHT. However, there are numerous compounds (e.g., albumen, pectin, dextrin) which can act both

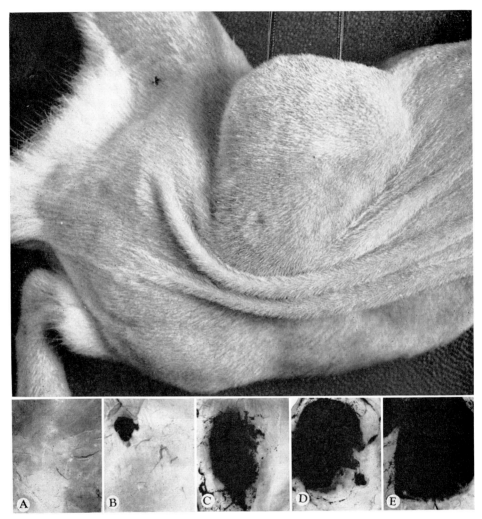

Fig. 17. Adjuvation by dextran of cutaneous calcinosis produced by DHT + FeCl₃ s.c. *Top:* Typical calciphylactic skin patch at site where 25 μg. FeCl₃ (in 0.2 ml. 6% dextran) was injected s.c. 24 hours after DHT sensitization. *Bottom:* Underside of skin following fixation in alcohol-formol and blackening of calcified skin areas with AgNO₃. All animals (100 g. ♀) were sensitized with DHT (1 mg. p.o.) and, 24 hours later, subcutaneously challenged with 0.2 ml. 6% dextran without iron (*A*) or containing FeCl₃: 1 μg. (*B*), 10 μg. (*C*), 25 μg. (*D*), and 100 μg. (*E*).

(After Selye *et al.*,[848] courtesy Rev. All. and Appl. Immunol.)

as challengers and as adjuvants. Following suitable sensitization, these **challenger-adjuvants** can produce calciphylactic wheals by themselves, but even when given at dose levels at which they are virtually inactive, they enhance the effect of typical challengers (e.g., $FeCl_3$, $CrCl_2$) to an extent that often cannot be accounted for by mere summation.

In both the forms of adjuvation just mentioned, the adjuvant is mixed with the challenger but this is not always necessary. Under certain conditions it is possible to obtain a kind of **localizing adjuvation** which concentrates the calciphylactic action of a systemically applied challenger upon a given point. Low doses of certain compounds (e.g., albumen, dextran), though ineffective in rats sensitized by DHT only, can produce topical calciphylaxis at the site of injection if they are administered simultaneously with an intravenous dose of soluble iron, e.g., Fe-Dex. This preparation by a calcifier and iron is what we call **siderocalciphylactic** sensitization.[842]

It remains questionable, however, whether the challenging potency of adjuvants in this iron-enforced type of calciphylaxis actually depends upon their adjuvant effect. Extremely small doses of many otherwise inert or only slightly active compounds (e.g., histamine, polymyxin, 48/80, $KMnO_4$) cause severe topical calcification at the site of injection if they are administered to DHT-sensitized rats concurrently with a comparatively small intravenous dose of Fe-Dex. Most of these compounds which act as challengers in the siderocalciphylactically (DHT + Fe) sensitized rat are ineffective as local adjuvants in the calciphylactically (DHT) sensitized animal in that they do not potentiate the effect of challengers when mixed with the latter.[842]

These observations suggested possible mechanisms through which endogenous sensitizers and challengers might produce a state of calciphylactic hypersensitivity during which even very mild local stimulation may induce disproportionately intense topical responses. For example, an in itself ineffective, topically formed substance with potential challenging activity could cause focal lesions by localizing the effect of, or actually attracting a blood-borne challenger. Such a pathogenic mechanism is at least theoretically conceivable since all ingredients of the siderocalciphylactic situation could be supplied from endogenous sources (e.g., parathyroid hormone as a sensitizer, iron as a blood-borne challenger and the regional release of mastocyte granules as the topical localizing stimulus).

Compounds that increase or localize the activity of challengers.—Many compounds were screened for this type of activity in two series of experiments.

In the first series (Table 3) $FeCl_3$ (25 μg. in 0.2 ml. water, s.c.) acted as a topical, and Fe-Dex (1 ml. = 1 mg. Fe, i.v.) as a systemic, challenger. In the second series (Table 4) only $CrCl_2$ (15 μg. in 0.2 ml. water, s.c.) was used for topical challenge. All these compounds were invariably given to rats (100 g. ♀) 24 hours after the customary sensitization (1 mg. of DHT p.o.). Whenever adjuvants and challengers were to be tested for local synergism, the usual dose of $FeCl_3$ or $CrCl_2$ was dissolved in the adjuvant solution

so that the total volume remained 0.2 ml. When challengers and potential adjuvants
were thus mixed, this is indicated in the Tables by bracketing them together.

In most instances the calciphylactic wheals were sufficiently well delimited to
permit a fairly accurate measurement of their mean diameter, but there were two
exceptions: PMX and 48/80 did not produce typical calciphylactic wheals in the
skin or the subcutaneous tissue, but caused calcification of the subjacent muscle
fibers. This resulted in "asbestos-like," fibrous plaques whose mean diameter could
nevertheless be measured and expressed as usual in mm. However, pectin elicited
diffuse "arborizing" calcium depositions around the dermal blood vessels; the outlines of these lesions were too indistinct to permit a reasonably accurate measurement and hence in this case we applied our arbitrary four-grade scale of 0–3
(p. 31).

Table 3 lists the data obtained with *FeCl₃* as a topical, and *Fe-Dex* as a systemic, challenger. It will be noted that under our experimental conditions neither
gelatin (Group 2) nor dextran (Group 5) exhibited any inherent challenging potency, although when mixed with FeCl₃ (Groups 3 and 6) both these substances
produced calciphylactic wheals which were significantly larger than those elicited
by the same amount of FeCl₃ alone (Group 1, Fig. 18). In fact, dextran (Group 7)
and to a lesser extent gelatin (Group 4) even succeeded in producing calciphylactic
reactions at the site of injection when iron was supplied in the form of Fe-Dex
only through the blood stream.

Albumen possesses some local challenging effect of its own (Groups 8 and 10);
when mixed with FeCl₃ this action is greatly enhanced (Groups 9 and 11). But this
synergism may be due to mere summation, since FeCl₃ + albumen gave calciphylactic wheals whose diameter was not much larger than the sum of the wheals
produced by FeCl₃ alone and albumen alone. Essentially similar, though less pronounced, synergisms were noted with some of the other compounds listed in Table
3, but many of them failed to enhance the challenging effect of iron.

Special attention should be given to the mastocyte and histamine dischargers
PMX and 48/80 (Groups 38, 41). Preliminary experiments had shown that these
compounds are comparatively ineffective in producing calciphylactic wheals in
rats sensitized only by DHT in the usual manner. On the other hand, when large
doses (2 mg.) of mastocyte dischargers are given—as was the case in the present
experiments—they produce circinate calcifying lesions around, but not at, the site
of injection; presumably these compounds act only in regions into which they
diffuse at a comparatively low concentration. At the injection site itself they
caused only calcification in the cutaneous and subjacent muscle fibers, thereby inducing "asbestos-like" patches of a fibrous aspect. This effect was not significantly
changed by the admixture of FeCl₃, but the calcifying action of the latter was suppressed. Consequently, here the FeCl₃ remained visible at the overchallenged injection site as a brown spot and was not replaced by white, chalky calcium deposits

TABLE 3

Effect of Various Agents upon Cutaneous Calciphylaxis Induced by Iron Compounds

(After Selye *et al.*[842])

Group	Number of Rats	Treatment*	Calciphylactic Wheal (Diameter in mm.)
1..........	52	$FeCl_3$	7.9 ± 0.5
2..........	25	Gelatin 6%	0
3..........	13	[$FeCl_3$+Gelatin]	22.5 ± 0.2
4..........	18	Fe-Dex+Gelatin	2.9 ± 1.3
5..........	24	Dextran 12%	0
6..........	14	[$FeCl_3$+Dextran]	21.6 ± 3.7
7..........	19	Fe-Dex+Dextran	19.4 ± 2.7
8..........	10	Albumen 5%	5.1 ± 1.3
9..........	10	[$FeCl_3$+Albumen]	16.2 ± 1.2
10..........	15	Albumen 10%	9.3 ± 2.3
11..........	10	[$FeCl_3$+Albumen]	19.1 ± 1.7
12..........	20	Fe-Dex+Albumen	18.3 ± 1.6
13..........	8	Yolk 5%	8.7 ± 2.3
14..........	10	[$FeCl_3$+Yolk]	13.1 ± 2.9
15..........	8	Yolk 10%	16.8 ± 2.0
16..........	10	[$FeCl_3$+Yolk]	19.1 ± 1.8
17..........	19	Fe-Dex+Yolk	14.5 ± 1.7
18..........	10	Dextrin 3%	7.9 ± 2.3
19..........	10	[$FeCl_3$+Dextrin]	13.0 ± 1.1
20..........	18	Dextrin 6%	10.9 ± 2.5
21..........	8	[$FeCl_3$+Dextrin]	14.5 ± 3.4
22..........	10	Fe-Dex+Dextrin	21.1 ± 2.8
23..........	9	C.S.A. 1 mg.	9.5 ± 2.9
24..........	10	[$FeCl_3$+C.S.A.]	15.7 ± 2.0
25..........	22	C.S.A. 2 mg.	13.5 ± 1.8
26..........	15	[$FeCl_3$+C.S.A.]	19.3 ± 1.1
27..........	18	Fe-Dex+C.S.A.	13.3 ± 2.0
28..........	19	Plasma 6%	8.8 ± 1.7
29..........	10	[$FeCl_3$+Plasma]	13.8 ± 1.9
30..........	10	Fe-Dex+Plasma	4.7 ± 2.1
31..........	9	Plasma 12%	22.8 ± 0.8
32..........	9	[$FeCl_3$+Plasma]	29.8 ± 2.7
33..........	9	Fe-Dex+Plasma	16.1 ± 2.3
34..........	23	Pectin 3%	1.9†
35..........	13	[$FeCl_3$+Pectin]	1.9†
36..........	24	Fe-Dex+Pectin	1.7†
37..........	33	PMX 2 mg.	$14.5‡ \pm 0.6$
38..........	20	[$FeCl_3$+PMX]	$16.4‡ \pm 1.2$
39..........	70	Fe-Dex+PMX	(Dermatomyositis)

* In addition to the agents listed in this column, all animals received a single sensitizing dose of DHT, as described in the text.

† Diffuse "arborizing" lesions, arbitrarily graded: 0–3.

‡ "Asbestos-like" muscle calcification.

TABLE 3—*Continued*

Group	Number of Rats	Treatment*	Calciphylactic Wheal (Diameter in mm.)
40..........	35	48/80 2 mg.	15.4‡±0.4
41..........	20	[FeCl₃+48/80]	14.6‡±0.6
42..........	20	Fe-Dex+48/80	(Dermatomyositis)
43..........	22	PVP 37%	0
44..........	14	[FeCl₃+PVP]	0.8±0.3
45..........	17	Fe-Dex+PVP	1.5±1.1
46..........	10	KMnO₄ 5 µg.	5.8±0.4
47..........	10	[FeCl₃+KMnO₄]	7.3±1.6
48..........	19	KMnO₄ 10 µg.	9.3±0.9
49..........	11	[FeCl₃+KMnO₄]	6.8±1.2
50..........	19	Fe-Dex+KMnO₄	16.5±1.3

as is normally the case. PMX or 48/80 given concurrently with intravenous challenge by Fe-Dex (Groups 39 and 42) resulted in the generalized calciphylactic dermatomyositis characteristic of this type of treatment.[843]

KMnO₄ is a "direct calcifier" (p. 13) which—unlike all other compounds of this series—causes calcium deposition at the site of injection even without previous sensitization. It is interesting, therefore, that the calcium deposition induced by KMnO₄ (Groups 46, 48) was not altered by the admixture of FeCl₃ (Groups 47, 49), although it was greatly enhanced by concurrent intravenous challenge with Fe-Dex (Group 50).

Essentially similar results were obtained with *CrCl₂* as a topical challenger (Table 4).

By itself the standard dose of 15 µg. of CrCl₂ produced calciphylactic wheals having a mean diameter of 10.2 mm. under our experimental conditions (Group 1). Although both gelatin (Group 2) and dextran (Group 4) were ineffective by themselves, they enormously enhanced the topical calciphylactic effect of CrCl₂ (Groups 3 and 5). Curiously, PVP, which in itself is likewise ineffective (Group 22), also acted as an adjuvant for CrCl₂ (Group 23); this is noteworthy because the same compound appears to have actually diminished the action of FeCl₃ under similar circumstances (cf. Table 3, Groups 1 and 44).

The possible adjuvant effect of the other compounds tested is more difficult to assess because all of them act as challengers by themselves; hence, it is often dubious whether their ability to augment the CrCl₂ action is due to mere summation of the two actions or to an actual potentiation, such as is characteristic of adjuvation. It is probable, however, that whenever mixtures of two agents elicited wheals as large or larger than the sum of the wheals produced by each agent alone, we are dealing with true adjuvation. Mere doubling of the dose of FeCl₃ raised the diameter of the wheals from 7.9 ± 0.5 to 11.8 ± 2.9 mm., while doubling the dose of $CrCl_2$ raised it from 10.2 ± 0.5 to 17.0 ± 1.8 mm. only; that is, doubling the dose failed to double the effect.

Only in some cases is a true potentiation quite obvious. For example, the calciphylactic wheals produced by combined treatment with $CrCl_2$ + dextrin (Group 11) are significantly larger than the sum of those produced by $CrCl_2$ (Group 1) and

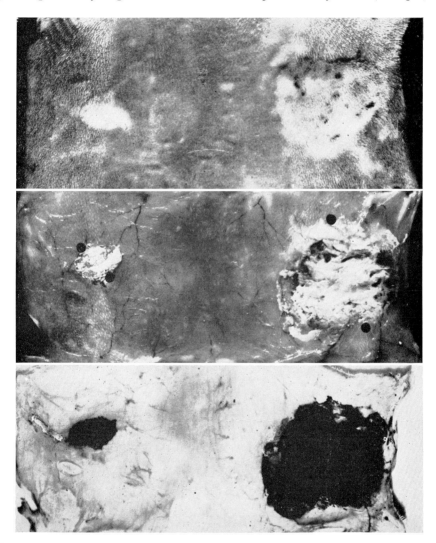

Fig. 18. Adjuvation by dextran of cutaneous calciphylaxis produced by DHT + FeCl₃ s.c. Rat (100 g. ♀): DHT (1 mg. p.o.) 1st day + FeCl₃ [25 µg. in 0.2 ml. water (left) or in 0.2 ml. 12% dextran (right), s.c.] 2d day; killed 11th day. Dorsal skin viewed from surface (*top*), subcutis (*middle*) and subcutis after fixation and staining in AgNO₃ (*bottom*). Diameter of wheals (measured between points indicated by black dots) in middle picture: 8 mm. (left), 22 mm. (right).

[After Selye *et al.*,[342] courtesy S. Karger Basel/New York (Internat. Arch. All.).]

dextrin (Group 10). On the other hand, egg yolk appears to have actually inhibited the calciphylactic action of $CrCl_2$ (Group 9).

Evaluation.—It is obvious that several compounds which by themselves are either inactive or only slightly active can greatly augment the topical calciphylactic action of admixed $FeCl_3$ or $CrCl_2$ in the DHT-sensitized rat. Such an increase in the calciphylactic potency of the challengers could be due to a ***direct effect*** of the adjuvants upon the absorption, spreading, or decomposition of the challenging salts; it could also be an ***indirect effect*** induced by the liberation or

TABLE 4

EFFECT OF VARIOUS AGENTS UPON CUTANEOUS
CALCIPHYLAXIS INDUCED BY $CrCl_2$

(After Selye *et al.* [842])

Group	Number of Rats	Treatment*	Calciphylactic Wheal (Diameter in mm.)
1..........	31	$CrCl_2$	10.2 ± 0.5
2..........	25	Gelatin 6%	0
3..........	10	[$CrCl_2$+Gelatin]	27.9 ± 1.6
4..........	24	Dextran 12%	0
5..........	10	[$CrCl_2$+Dextran]	32.0 ± 1.4
6..........	15	Albumen 10%	9.3 ± 2.3
7..........	10	[$CrCl_2$+Albumen]	21.0 ± 1.9
8..........	16	Yolk 10%	16.8 ± 2.0
9..........	10	[$CrCl_2$+Yolk]	3.9 ± 2.1
10..........	18	Dextrin 6%	10.9 ± 2.5
11..........	10	[$CrCl_2$+Dextrin]	28.2 ± 0.9
12..........	22	C.S.A. 2 mg.	13.5 ± 1.8
13..........	10	[$CrCl_2$+C.S.A.]	17.4 ± 1.8
14..........	19	Plasma 6%	8.8 ± 1.7
15..........	10	[$CrCl_2$+Plasma]	22.2 ± 1.6
16..........	23	Pectin 3%	1.9†
17..........	10	[$CrCl_2$+Pectin]	1.0†
18..........	33	PMX 2 mg.	14.5 ± 0.6
19..........	9	[$CrCl_2$+PMX]	10.2 ± 1.0
20..........	35	48/80 2 mg.	15.4 ± 0.4
21..........	10	[$CrCl_2$+48/80]	13.9 ± 0.5
22..........	22	PVP 37%	0
23..........	10	[$CrCl_2$+PVP]	33.7 ± 2.2
24..........	19	$KMnO_4$ 10 μg.	9.3 ± 0.9
25..........	9	[$CrCl_2$+$KMnO_4$]	14.9 ± 2.4

* In addition to the agents listed in this column, all animals received a single sensitizing dose of DHT, as described in the text.

† Grade (arbitrary scale of): 0–3.

activation of endogenous sensitizing compounds. Inverse effects of the same nature might be responsible for the inhibitory actions of some compounds, e.g., of yolk and $CrCl_2$, both of which produce significantly greater responses by themselves than when given conjointly. At the present time it would be futile to speculate upon each of these possible mechanisms of adjuvation; various compounds may even influence the actions of challengers through different processes.

Particular importance is attached to the singular systemic sensitizing effect of intravenous iron in the DHT-pretreated animal. It is a well-known fact that circulating iron particles tend to localize in inflamed tissue.[162, 649] This mechanism could be responsible for the sensitizing effect of intravenous Fe-Dex in calciphylaxis. Here, the adjuvant (e.g., dextran) produces a mild local inflammation which could attract blood-borne iron to the treated site; the challenger thus localized would then be activated by the adjuvant effect of the same compound (e.g., dextran) that attracted it to the focus.

In any event, it is clear that calciphylactic sensitization by DHT can be so much enhanced through the intravenous injection of Fe-Dex that otherwise inactive compounds produce pronounced local calcium depositions. The extraordinary degree of sensitization that can be obtained by this iron-enforced siderocalciphylaxis is also illustrated by the fact that even pure distilled water suffices to produce large calciphylactic wheals in rats sensitized by DHT + Fe-Dex under the standard conditions of the experiments listed in Table 3. This effect of distilled water presumably depends upon the mastocyte-depleting action of hypotonic solutions; therefore comparatively large amounts must be injected since otherwise the treated focus does not remain hypotonic for long.[837c] On the other hand, as little as 0.1 μg. of 48/80, polymyxin or stilbamidine suffices to produce cutaneous calcified wheals at the site of injection in the siderocalciphylactically sensitized rat, presumably owing to the mastocyte-discharging power of these compounds.[838b]

TOPICAL CALCIPHYLAXIS IN TISSUES OTHER THAN THE SKIN

The skin lends itself especially well to the study of topical calciphylactic reactions because of its great sensitivity and easy accessibility for manipulation and observation. However, localized responses can also be produced by the direct application of various challengers to many other sites. Up to now two techniques have been employed for this type of study:

1. Local application of challengers in the form of solutions or dry powders in and around the target.

2. Introduction of challenger solutions into the blood- or lymph-vessels that enter the target.

Usually this second technique consists in intra-arterial injections. However, selective calciphylactic responses in the liver or heart can be obtained by injecting the challengers into the portal or jugular veins, respectively. Furthermore, if injected intraperitoneally, certain challengers (e.g., albumen) are rapidly removed through the lymphatics to the pleural cavity and the perithymic lymph nodes, where they can produce local calciphylactic reactions.

Only a few model experiments will be discussed here to illustrate the type of change that can be obtained in this manner at various sites. Unless otherwise stated, our remarks shall refer to experiments performed under routine conditions on rats weighing 100 or 200 g. and challenged 24 hours after sensitization by the oral administration of 1 mg. of DHT/100 g. body weight.

Tissues contiguous with skin.—Among the tissues immediately underlying the rat's skin the connective tissue of the *snout*, especially around the roots of the bristles in the upper lip, is most sensitive to the induction of calciphylaxis by the topical application of many challengers (e.g., Fe-Dex, Thorotrast®, albumen). The *eyelids* and the roots (but not the distal portions) of the *external ears* are likewise very sensitive, while the *paws* and *tail* are comparatively refractory.

The *panniculus adiposus* underneath the skin and around the mammary glands, as well as adipose tissue elsewhere (e.g., in the mesentery or the retroperitoneal space) and the so-called "brown fat," or *hibernating glands,* are approximately as sensitive to direct challenge as is the subcutaneous and underlying intermuscular *connective tissue.*

Usually, at any of these sites the topically induced calciphylactic reactions do not differ markedly from those produced by the intravenous application of challengers that happen to have a particular affinity for the same targets. For example, intravenous challenge with very large doses of albumen causes a cutaneous calcinosis which often penetrates deep into the panniculus adiposus and there produces very characteristic changes. Calcium is precipitated between the fat cells, and the latter are subsequently replaced by connective tissue. This process results in a singular, spongy structure with calcified spherules that correspond to the outlines of the original adipose cells and are filled by uncalcified connective-tissue elements. Exactly the same picture is obtained by the direct injection of albumen into adipose tissue (Plate II, *C, D*).

However, *certain challengers which never affect a particular target following systemic treatment can do so when applied directly to it.* For example, $CrCl_3$ given intravenously, be it even in amounts causing fatal systemic calcinosis, does not produce calcification in the face or the conjunctiva, while it is highly effective in this respect if it is injected directly into these areas or into the common carotid artery. Furthermore, several challengers (e.g., $FeCl_2$, $CrCl_3$) can produce pronounced calciphylactic lesions in the striated muscles and connective tissue of a hind limb if injected into the corresponding common iliac artery, although no such changes are obtained after intravenous injection of the highest tolerable amounts.

It is especially noteworthy that when challengers are injected into one ***common carotid*** (Figs. 19–26), or ***common iliac artery*** (Figs. 27, 28, 29), of sensitized rats, the resulting lesions are strictly unilateral. This is in spite of the excellent collateral circulation to the opposite side, which is demonstrated by the virtually complete absence of any functional or morphologic change in the corresponding vascular territory when one of these paired vessels is tied off.

Conversely, ***certain challengers are more effective following systemic than after topical administration.*** For example, the intravenous injection of Thorotrast® to sensitized rats causes intense calcinosis—with subsequent inflammation, sclerosis, and ulceration—in the lips and palpebrae, but changes of equal intensity are difficult to obtain even when the highest tolerable doses of Thorotrast® are injected into the common carotid artery.

The reason for these discrepancies is not clear. Perhaps certain challengers (e.g.,

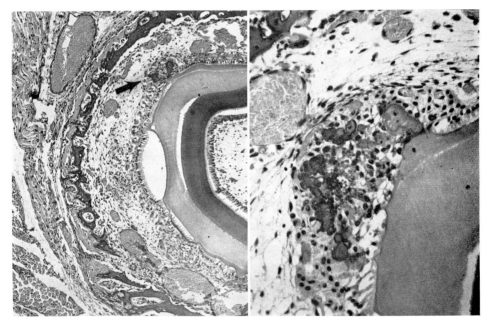

Fig. 19. Dental changes produced by DHT + CrCl₃ intracarotid. Rat (50 g. ♀): DHT (0.5 mg. p.o.) 1st day + CrCl₃ (300 μg. in 1 ml. water, into left common carotid artery) 2d day; killed 60th day. *Left:* General view, root of lower left incisor. The enamel is distinctly deformed. At one place the ameloblasts appear to lose their normal columnar shape and invade the periodontal membrane, while enamel-like, irregular granules are formed within the latter (arrow). Somewhat lower, the ameloblasts shrink away from the enamel. The periodontal membrane is thickened throughout and contains inflammatory infiltrates. *Right:* Higher magnification of region indicated by arrow in picture on left. Here, the deformation and irregular proliferation of ameloblasts, as well as the abnormal enamel-like granules, are more clearly visible. (PAS, left ×85, right ×300.)

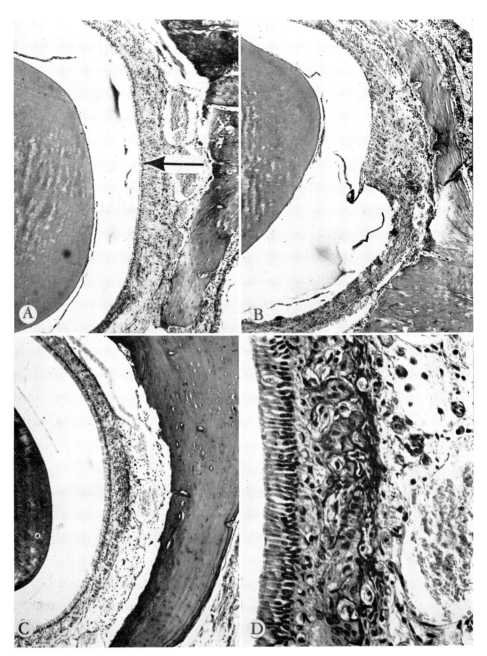

Fig. 20. Dental changes produced by DHT + CrCl₃ intracarotid. Two rats (260 g. ♀):
DHT (3 mg. p.o.) 1st day + CrCl₃ (2 mg. in 2 ml. water, into left common carotid artery)
2d day; killed 15th day. *A:* Right incisor. Normal ameloblast layer (arrow). *B:* Left incisor.
Ameloblasts virtually disappeared and large ulcer developed in periodontal membrane. *C:* Left
incisor of second, similarly treated rat. Here, ameloblast layer is still preserved, but underlying
stroma is infiltrated with PAS-positive material, especially near center of field. *D:* Higher
magnification, central portion of "C." Here, infiltration with PAS-positive material in stroma
underneath ameloblast layer is even more evident. (PAS, A, B, C ×95, D ×325.)

66

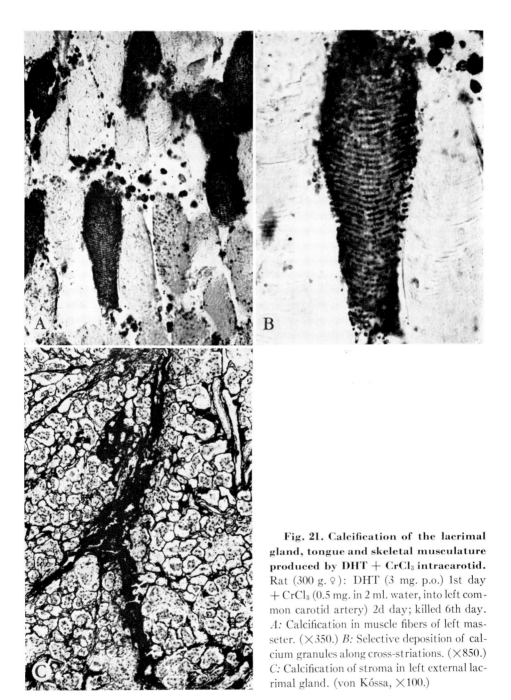

Fig. 21. Calcification of the lacrimal gland, tongue and skeletal musculature produced by DHT + CrCl₃ intracarotid. Rat (300 g. ♀): DHT (3 mg. p.o.) 1st day + CrCl₃ (0.5 mg. in 2 ml. water, into left common carotid artery) 2d day; killed 6th day. *A:* Calcification in muscle fibers of left masseter. (×350.) *B:* Selective deposition of calcium granules along cross-striations. (×850.) *C:* Calcification of stroma in left external lacrimal gland. (von Kóssa, ×100.)

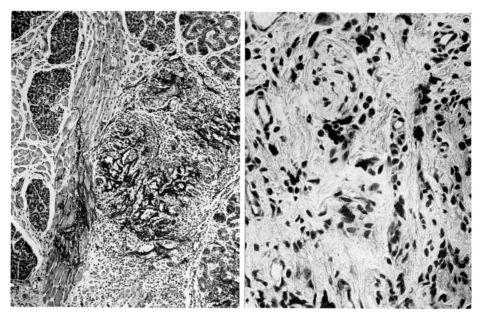

Fig. 22. Calcification of the tongue produced by DHT + CrCl₃ intracarotid. Rat (270 g. ♀): DHT (3 mg. p.o.) 1st day + CrCl₃ (1.5 mg. in 0.5 ml. water, into left common carotid artery) 2d day; killed 10th day. Calcification was limited to left side of head and neck. *Left:* Tongue, left side. Calcium deposition between muscle fibers and in stroma of lingual salivary glands. Intense inflammatory infiltration and sclerosis around calcium deposits. In this field, the infiltrating cells were predominantly eosinophilic. *Right:* Another region from same tongue. More advanced sclerosis and great predominance of large, "fuzzy" mast cells. (von Kóssa, left ×80, right ×325.)

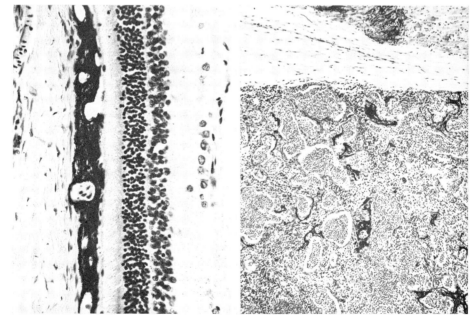

Fig. 23. Ocular changes produced by DHT + CrCl₃ intracarotid. Rat (270 g. ♀): DHT (3 mg. p.o.) 1st day + CrCl₃ (1 mg. in 2 ml. water, into left common carotid artery) 2d day; killed 7th day. *Left:* Heavy calcification of connective-tissue fibers (but not of vessels) just underneath the retina. *Right:* Purulent inflammation with slight calcification of left Harder's gland. Pus is seen both in parenchyma and in the ducts. (von Kóssa, left ×310, right ×90.)

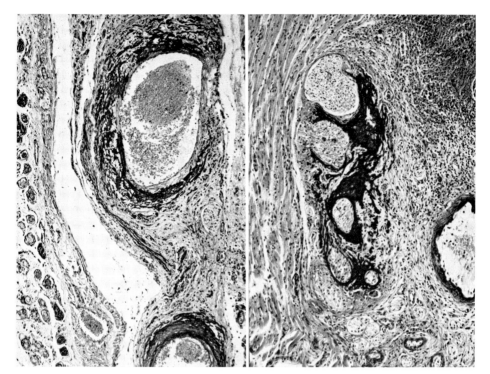

Fig. 24. Evolution of calciphylactic changes produced by DHT + CrCl₃ intracarotid. Rat (60 g. ♀): DHT (0.5 mg. p.o.) 1st day + CrCl₃ (500 μg. in 1 ml. water, into left common carotid artery) 2d day; killed 60th day. *Left:* Heavy calcification with preosseous tissue formation in walls of two subcutaneous arteries in left cheek. The calcified tissue (dark areas) is strongly PAS-positive. *Right:* In adjacent region, large nerve bundle likewise surrounded by calcified, PAS-positive, preosseous tissue in the perineural sheaths. (PAS, ×100.)

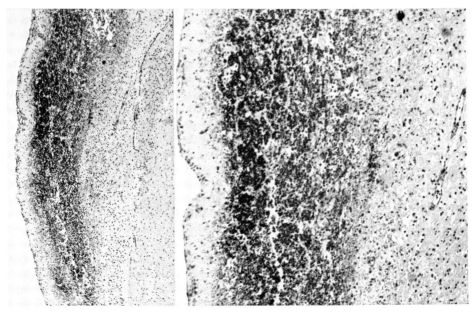

Fig. 25. Calcification and necrosis in the brain produced by DHT + CrCl₃ intra-carotid. Rat (270 g. ♀): DHT (3 mg. p.o.) 1st day + CrCl₃ (1.5 mg. in 2 ml. water, into left common carotid artery) 2d day; died 11th day. Large necrotic focus underneath brain surface with calcification of cell debris. (von Kóssa, left ×24, right ×110.)

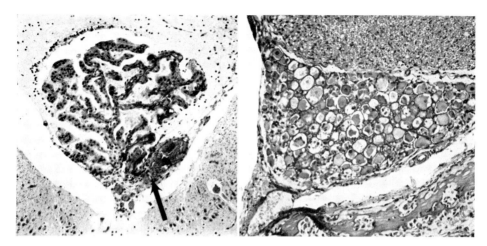

Fig. 26. Unilateral changes in the choroid plexus and Gasserian ganglion produced by DHT + CrCl₃ intracarotid. Rat (50 g. ♀): DHT (0.5 mg. p.o.) 1st day + CrCl₃ (300 µg. in 1 ml. water, slowly injected into left common carotid artery) 2d day; killed 60th day. The animal had a left-sided atrophy with intense calcification of the entire face, thyroid, parathyroid and tongue. *Left:* Calcification, sclerosis and hyalinization only on left side (here right) of the choroid plexus, although contralateral capillaries are connected by many anastomoses. Some of the vascular loops are completely obliterated by calcified masses (arrow). *Right:* Almost all nerve cells in left Gasserian ganglion show signs of degeneration or necrosis, although the nerve itself (top) appears to be normal. (von Kóssa, ×120.)

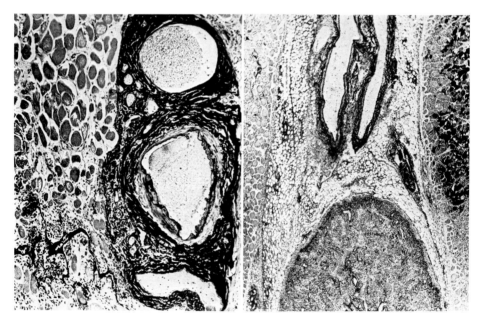

Fig. 27. Calcinosis of hind limb produced by DHT + CrCl₃ intra-iliac. Rat (230 g. ♀): DHT (2.5 mg. p.o.) 1st day + CrCl₃ (4 mg. in 2 ml. water, into right common iliac artery near its origin) 2d day; killed 7th day. *Left:* Intense calcification of connective tissue surrounding the large muscular artery and nerve. Some calcification also in intima and media of artery, but not within nerve itself. Mild calcification with inflammation and edema in stroma of surrounding muscle. *Right:* Popliteal lymph node, adjacent vessels, adipose tissue and muscles likewise exhibit calcinosis. (von Kóssa, left ×85, right ×25.)

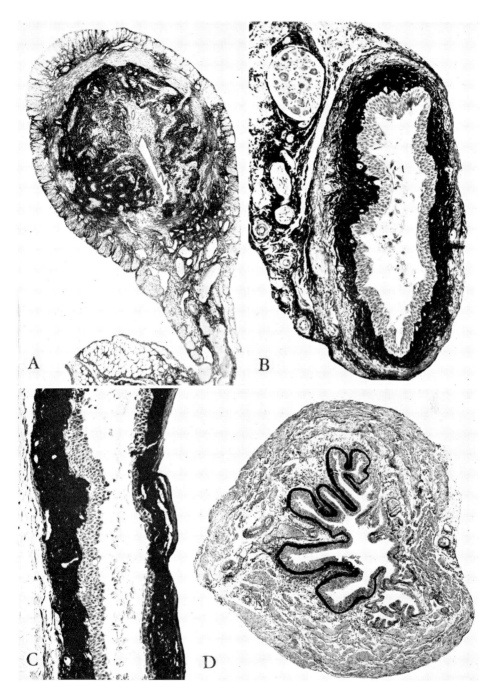

Fig. 28. Calcification of uterus, ureter and urinary bladder produced by DHT +
CrCl₃ intra-iliac. Rat (200 g. ♀): DHT (1 mg. p.o.) 1st day + CrCl₃ (3.1 mg. in 2 ml. water,
into right common iliac artery near its origin) 2d day; killed 6th day. *A:* Calcification of right
myometrium and mesometrium. *B:* Calcinosis of right ureter and surrounding connective
tissue without trace of calcium deposition in epithelium; small ganglion and nerves in adjacent
connective tissue likewise spared. *C:* Longitudinal section through lower portion of same ureter.
D: Calcification of submucosa of urinary bladder, on right side only (in picture left); left uterine
horn and left ureter showed no calcinosis. (von Kóssa, A, D ×29, B, C ×100.)

CrCl₃) when given intravenously produce fatal systemic calciphylaxis in organs
that are particularly sensitive to them (e.g., the lung) at dose levels that are below
the threshold of responsiveness of less sensitive targets (e.g., the face). Conversely,
other challengers (e.g., Thorotrast®) may be comparatively ineffective when injected directly into the carotid artery simply because they are so toxic by this
route that only doses below the calciphylactic-challenge threshold are tolerated.

In the DHT-sensitized rat a calcified **granuloma pouch** can be produced by
the injection of Fe-Dex or CrCl₃ into a pneumodermal pouch. Except along the
cutaneous vessels the tissue thus separated from the skin by air is much less sensitive to local challenge than the intact subcutis (Fig. 30). Presumably, the local
trauma and perhaps also circulatory disturbances in the detached skin interfere
with optimum calciphylactic reactivity. Yet, as we shall see later, such an air

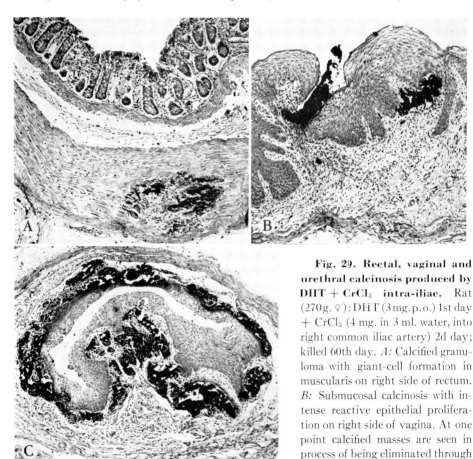

**Fig. 29. Rectal, vaginal and
urethral calcinosis produced by
DHT + CrCl₃ intra-iliac.** Rat
(270g. ♀): DHT (3 mg. p. o.) 1st day
+ CrCl₃ (4 mg. in 3 ml. water, into
right common iliac artery) 2d day;
killed 60th day. *A:* Calcified granuloma with giant-cell formation in
muscularis on right side of rectum.
B: Submucosal calcinosis with intense reactive epithelial proliferation on right side of vagina. At one
point calcified masses are seen in
process of being eliminated through
breach in epithelium. *C:* Almost
complete (in this case not unilateral!) ring of connective-tissue calcinosis with giant-cell formation underneath the urethral epithelium. (von Kóssa, ×90.)

pouch is almost normally sensitive to the direct calcifying action of $KMnO_4$, which does not depend upon calciphylactic sensitization.[944]

Peritoneum and pleura.—Almost all agents that produce topical calciphylaxis in the skin exert a similar local action upon the peritoneum or pleura (e.g., $FeCl_3$, albumen, $CrCl_2$). In fact, as previously stated, intraperitoneal injections of certain challengers (e.g., albumen, Fe-Dex) produce not only peritoneal but also pleural calcification. This is apparently due to the fact that the challenger is removed toward the thoracic duct and the thoracic lymph nodes through the lymphatics traversing the diaphragm.[849] However, many challengers—especially metallic salts—produce only topical calciphylaxis upon intraperitoneal injection, perhaps because they tend to form massive precipitates that cannot be readily absorbed through the lymphatics.

Fig. 30. Calcified granuloma pouch produced by DHT + CrCl₃ topically. Rat (100 g. ♀): DHT (1 mg. p.o.) 1st day + 25 ml. air (s.c. on back) followed by $CrCl_3$ (100 µg. in 5 ml. water injected into air sac); 2d day; killed 4th day. Granuloma pouch was fixed *in situ* by injection of alcohol-formol into its lumen; then entire rat was sectioned through mid-sagittal plane to expose inner surface of pouch. Calcification predominates near base of pouch and ascends along regularly spaced cutaneous vessels (one of these marked by arrow). Vertebrae (near lower margin of picture) and base of pouch black (von Kóssa).

Interestingly, intraperitoneal injections of very diffusible challengers (e.g., albumen, Fe-Dex) produce not only local and pleural lesions but also diffuse calcium impregnation of the pancreatic stroma. At the same time, certain subcutaneous regions (around the xiphoid and the flanks) calcify at points where the abdominal wall is thin and, hence, readily permits outward diffusion. Conversely, most of the metallic salts tested (e.g., $AlCl_3$, $CrCl_2$, $CuCl_2$)—even when they cause intense calcification on the peritoneal surface and around the pancreas—do not penetrate either into the pancreatic stroma or into the subcutaneous tissue in this manner.[829a] Since many challengers produce systemic calcinosis in distant organs when administered intraperitoneally, most of our relevant observations will be discussed in the chapter "Systemic Calciphylaxis."

Kidney.—Renal tissue is notoriously susceptible to the "dystrophic," or topogenic, calcification that occurs without previous sensitization by hypercalcemia-producing agents. However, in the DHT-sensitized rat local trauma to the kidney —or even the mere compression of the renal papilla induced by ligature of the ureter—suffices to induce particularly pronounced local calcification.[820, 852]

Infiltration of renal tissue with the commonly used challengers (e.g., $CrCl_3$, $FeCl_3$) can likewise produce nephrocalcinosis. But the distribution of the calcium deposits is somewhat unpredictable because it depends upon how the injected solution happens to break through the rigid parenchyma.

Liver.—Hepatic tissue is comparatively resistant to topical challenge by physical trauma. For example, ligature of the hepatic duct causes no calcification in the liver after sufficient sensitization by DHT to predispose the kidney to the induction of nephrocalcinosis by ureter ligature.[800] Yet, rough digital massage of the liver during the critical period after sensitization with DHT causes calcification, but only in the hepatic stroma, not in the parenchyma.[852]

Pronounced calcification of the portal vein and its intrahepatic branches is produced by i.p. injection of $CrCl_3$ or $FeCl_2$ in the DHT-sensitized rat (Figs. 31–33). This calcification is followed by intense proliferation of the subintimal connective tissue, which eventually may lead to complete obliteration of the vascular spaces. Simultaneously, there is also much calcification and sclerosis of the stroma in the portal spaces. The central veins are much less affected. The extrahepatic part of the hepatic artery may likewise undergo moderate calcification. This is perhaps a result of direct contact, by diffusion, with the $CrCl_3$ injected into the vein or with traces of the challenger that may have come in contact with the artery by spilling at the time of the intervention.

Lung.—Pulmonary calciphylaxis induced by topical challenge is of special interest in relation to the possible connections which may exist between this condition and the various forms of clinical pulmonary fibrosis (e.g., anthracosis, silicosis) that are known to result from topical irritation. In the rat selective pulmonary calciphylactic responses with initial calcinosis followed by fibrosis may be obtained if after sensitization (e.g., by DHT) a topical challenger (e.g., $FeCl_3$, $CrCl_3$) is introduced into the trachea by injection or inhalation. Especially pronounced lesions of this type are produced in the DHT-sensitized animal by the intratracheal injection of $KMnO_4$, which, in addition to being a challenger, is also a direct calcifier (Fig. 34).[865b]

Skeletal musculature.—Striated muscles, like renal tissue, are particularly predisposed to calcification in response to various forms of damage. However, without previous sensitization ***trauma*** (e.g., crushing or an incision) causes no calcinosis of the abdominal musculature in the rat, while after DHT-pretreatment the muscles around laparotomy wounds can become heavily calcified.[820]

Challengers (e.g., ***albumen, Fe-Dex***) introduced into the peritoneum usually produce topical calcium deposits in the musculature of the diaphragm and the abdominal wall.[849]

A singular type of muscle calcification not wholly dependent upon calciphylactic sensitization is induced by the topical injection of ***histamine liberators,*** such as PMX and 48/80. Wherever these compounds come into contact with the muscles, the latter undergo selective calcification in which the surrounding stroma rarely participates. The resulting fibrous, "asbestos-like" patches of calcification have already been discussed (p. 58).

We have also seen that topical calciphylaxis can readily be obtained in muscles by the ***intra-arterial injection of challengers.*** For example, the injection of

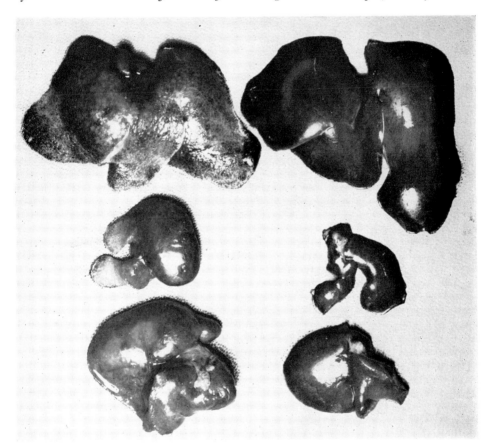

Fig. 31. Hepatic calcification and regeneration produced by DHT + FeCl₂ intraportal. Rat (180 g. ♀): DHT (2 mg. p.o.) 1st day + FeCl₂ (1 mg. in 2 ml. water, intraportal) 2d day; killed 60th day. *Left:* The principal hepatic lobes are shown after dissection. There is massive calcification and sclerosis with atrophy of some lobes and compensatory hypertrophy of others. *Right:* Corresponding lobes of an untreated control for comparison.

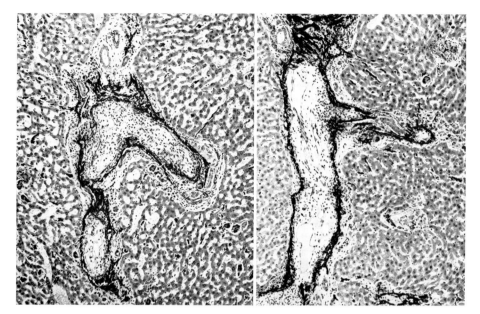

Fig. 32. **Calcification and partial occlusion of portal vein branches produced by DHT + CrCl₃ intraportal.** Rat (280 g. ♀): DHT (2.5 mg. p.o.) 1st day + CrCl₃ (2 mg. in 2 ml. water, into portal vein) 2d day; killed 60th day. Calcification of portal vein branches with intense proliferation of subintimal connective tissue, resulting in virtually complete occlusion of lumen. (von Kóssa, ×90.)

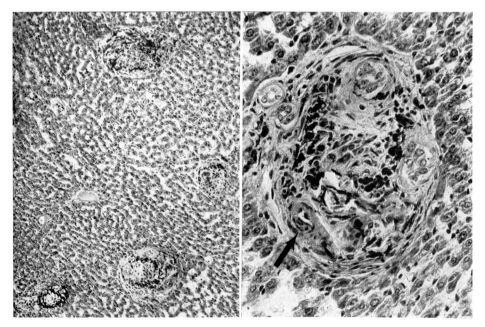

Fig. 33. **Hepatic lesions produced by DHT + FeCl₂ intraportal.** Rat (200 g. ♀): DHT (2 mg. p.o.) 1st day + FeCl₂ (1 mg. in 2 ml. water, slowly injected into portal vein) 2d day; killed 60th day. *Left:* Several calcium-containing granulomas in portal spaces. Hepatic veins and sinusoids are unaffected; hepatic parenchyma is atrophic in this region but showed intense regeneration in other portions of liver. (von Kóssa, ×85.) *Right:* Higher magnification of one of the granulomas shown in preceding picture. Intense fibrosis around bile ducts and adjacent vessels, with granular calcium deposition. Lumen of portal vein is completely obliterated but corresponding branch of hepatic artery (arrow) is intact. (von Kóssa, ×300.)

1–2 mg. of $CrCl_3$ into the left *common carotid* artery of a sensitized rat causes calcification and preosseous tissue formation in the arteries, nerve sheaths, and striated muscles supplied by this vessel, particularly in the masseters but also in other muscles of the face, orbit, and neck (Fig. 24). The resulting picture is especially striking in the tongue, which becomes laden with calcium on the left side. The affected white tissue is sharply delimited from the contralateral normal tissue by a straight line (Fig. 35). Curiously, here—in contradistinction to the "asbestos-like" calcification produced by histamine liberators—the muscle fibers themselves merely undergo atrophy without calcification; heavy calcium deposits are seen only in the stroma and in the arteries. The surface epithelium and the small intra-lingual salivary glands are quite refractory.[837a] Similar atrophy and fibrosis accompanied by massive calcification and preosseous tissue formation is sometimes produced in the muscles of the hind limb by the injection of $CrCl_3$ into the *common iliac* artery (Fig. 36).

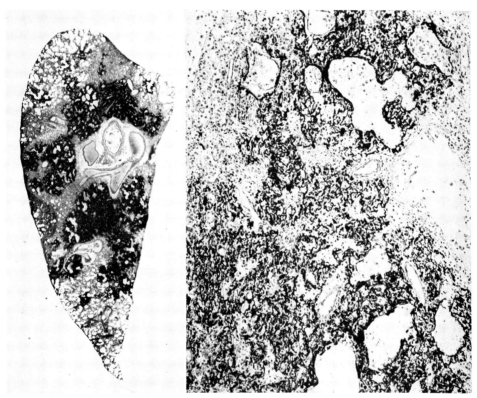

Fig. 34. Pulmonary calcification produced by DHT + KMnO₄ intratracheal. Rat (100 g. ♀): DHT (1 mg. p.o.) 1st day + $KMnO_4$ (5 mg. in 0.5 ml. water, direct intratracheal injection) 2d day; killed 6th day. *Left:* Section through entire pulmonary lobe. Intense calcification with inflammatory reaction through most of parenchyma, though hilar region is respected. *Right:* Higher magnification of same lung. Intraseptal localization of calcium and heavy inflammatory infiltration. (von Kóssa, left ×6.5, right ×110.)

Carotid body.—The stroma of the carotid body undergoes intensive calcification following the injection of $CrCl_3$ or certain iron preparations into its surroundings or into the common artery. This response is obtained only following sensitization (e.g., with DHT). Topical treatment of nonsensitized rats with a direct calcifier (e.g., $KMnO_4$) causes extensive calcification of the entire region without any selective predisposition of the carotid body itself.[837a]

Eye.—$CrCl_3$, $FeCl_3$, Thorotrast®, or 5HT injected under the conjunctiva produces local calcification of the eyelids and sometimes also of Harder's gland and the ocular muscles. However, among the agents tested up to this time only 5HT produced calcification of the ciliary body after sensitization with DHT.

Salivary and external lacrimal glands.—The *submaxillary glands* of the sensitized rat are particularly susceptible to the induction of topical calciphylaxis by various challengers (Fe-Dex, albumen, Thorotrast®) injected **subcutaneously** in the neck region. Of all the agents tested, 5HT was the most effective in this respect. Subcutaneous injection of 1 mg. of 5HT in the mid-thoracic region causes no local

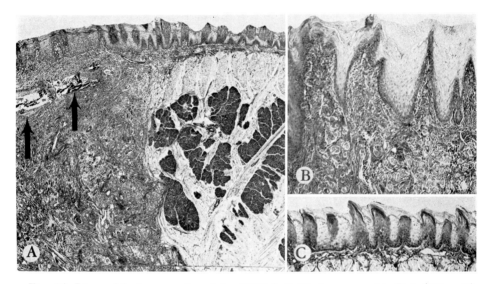

Fig. 35. Lingual lesions produced by DHT + CrCl₃ intracarotid. Rat (250 g. ♀): DHT (3 mg. p.o.) 1st day + CrCl₃ (1 mg. in 2 ml. water, into left common carotid) 2d day; killed 60th day. *A:* Transverse section through dorsum linguae shows strict linear delimitation of normal epithelium, muscles (light) and glands (dark) on right side from corresponding damaged tissues on left side. On side of injection epithelium is greatly thickened and irregular. Some calcified blocks (left arrow) are completely enclosed in a squamous epithelial cyst, while others (right arrow) lie free in stroma. Lingual musculature and glands are almost completely replaced by granuloma containing many giant cells. (von Kóssa, ×26.) *B:* Section of epithelium covering left margin of tongue exhibits intense hyperkeratosis with proliferating epithelial pegs invading deep into the underlying tissue. (von Kóssa, ×90.) *C:* Corresponding normal epithelium from right margin of tongue. (von Kóssa, ×90.)

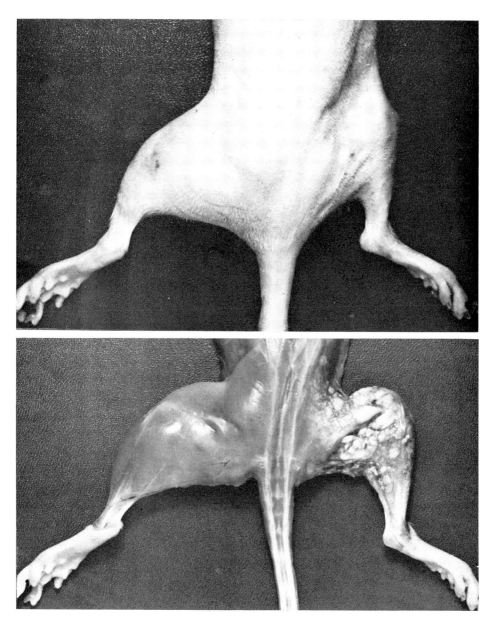

Fig. 36. **Intense calcinosis and atrophy in the right hind limb musculature produced by DHT + CrCl₃ intra-iliac.** Rat (80 g. ♀): DHT (1 mg. p.o.) 1st day + CrCl₃
(1 mg. in 2 ml. water, into right common iliac artery) 2d day; killed 60th day. *Top:* Severe
muscular atrophy with contracture of right hind limb. The scars are consequences of massive
calcification with the subsequent rejection of skin during first few weeks following challenge.
Bottom: The voluminous, calcified masses are seen within the atrophic, contracted muscles
after removal of the skin. Note great difference between this calciphylactic response and the
simple muscular atrophy without calcification produced by intra-iliac injection of KMnO₄
(cf. Fig. 243).

cutaneous or connective-tissue calcification at the injection site, yet it induces massive calcium precipitation in the submaxillary glands, several centimeters away from this point. It might have been thought that the effect is due exclusively to the absorbed 5HT that reaches the salivary glands through the blood stream. However, this is not the case since the same amount of 5HT injected subcutaneously in the suprapubic or lumbar region is ineffective. Apparently, 5HT diffuses readily through connective tissue and causes calcification in the specially sensitive submaxillary gland mainly, if not entirely, owing to its topical action.

The *parotid and major sublingual glands*, on the other hand, are quite resistant to this type of calciphylaxis, although the *external lacrimal glands* of the rat (which are further removed from the pectoral site of 5HT injection) are as markedly calcified as the submaxillary glands. This selective effect is especially noteworthy because both in the submaxillary and in the lacrimal glands calcification occurs mainly in the stroma. Yet the essentially similar connective tissue of the derma

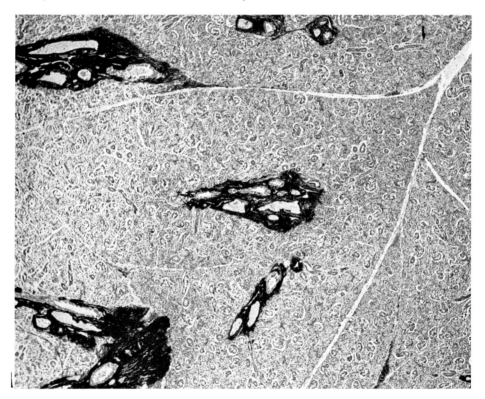

Fig. 37. Selective calcinosis of the periductal connective tissue in the submaxillary gland produced by DHT + FeCl₂ intracarotid. Rat (280 g. ♀): DHT (3 mg. p.o.) 1st day + FeCl₂ (1.12 mg. in 2 ml. water, slowly injected into left common carotid artery) 2d day; killed 6th day. Calcinosis is restricted to the connective tissue immediately surrounding the excretory ducts. (von Kóssa, ×39.)

and subcutis are refractory. Apparently, calcification within the sensitive glandular structures depends upon some interaction between parenchymal and stromal elements.

Extraordinarily intense calcification usually followed by preosseous tissue formation in the salivary and lacrimal glands also occurs when suitably sensitized rats are given intracarotid injections of challengers (e.g., $CrCl_3$, $FeCl_2$). Depending upon the kind and dose of the challenger used, the calcinosis may affect all glandular tissues, only the stroma, or even only the connective tissue around the ducts; the latter is particularly sensitive to this type of challenge (Fig. 37).

Teeth.—The continuously growing incisors of the rat are sensitive indicators of variations in calcium metabolism. Even without the use of any challenger, single massive doses of vitamin D_2 produced pronounced changes in the teeth, accompanied by calcinosis of the pulp chamber and periodontal membrane in dogs.

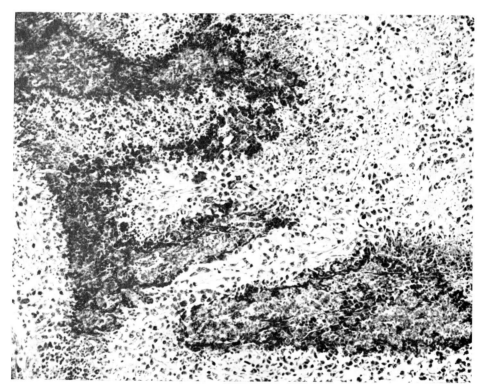

Fig. 38. Calcification and necrosis in a Walker tumor transplant produced by DHT + Fe-Dex intratumoral. Rat (100 g. ♀): Walker tumor (implant into thigh) 1st day + DHT (1 mg. p.o.) 16th day + Fe-Dex (1 ml. = 100 µg. Fe, direct intratumoral infiltration, twice) 18th day; killed 22d day. Tumor showed partial liquefaction with extensive calcium deposition. Calcium is visible not only in stroma but in the neoplastic cells themselves, especially along the borderline between necrotic and still viable tumor tissue. (Celestin blue, ×135.)

At the same time the animals exhibited the usual signs of nonspecific calcinosis in the lung and kidney.[82] These changes persist even long after discontinuation of vitamin-D overdosage.[83] However, much more severe and localized lesions can be induced—unilaterally and in the absence of severe systemic changes—if moderate treatment with DHT is combined with the injection of $CrCl_3$ into one carotid artery (Figs. 19, 20).

Neoplasms.—Extensive calcification, inflammation, and necrosis can be obtained in transplantable tumors—such as the Murphy rat lymphosarcoma or the Walker tumor—if after sensitization with DHT certain challengers (e.g., Fe-OS, 5HT, or Fe-Dex) are injected directly into the tumor tissue. After this treatment not only stroma elements but often even the malignant cells themselves contain calcium precipitates. Comparable experiments in which the neoplasms were implanted in the thigh and the challengers injected into the common iliac artery suggested that this method of local treatment is even more effective in destroying malignant growths[829a] (Fig. 38). However, this work has not yet progressed sufficiently far to permit final evaluation.

Other tissues.—Many other organs are likewise subject to topical calciphylactic challenge in one form or another, at least as far as their stroma is concerned. For example, direct trauma (crushing with a hemostat) can cause topical calcification in the *aorta* of the DHT-sensitized rat.[820]

Similar local calcification can be obtained by topical chemical challenge (e.g., with $FeCl_3$) in the *blood vessels, heart, adrenals, thyroids, parathyroids,* etc.[829a]

III

Systemic Calciphylaxis

A. THE CALCIPHYLACTIC SYNDROMES

GENERALITIES

In principle the great variety of systemic calciphylactic syndromes that can be obtained by the introduction of challengers into the general circulation could be classified either according to the resulting changes (e.g., cardiovascular, renal, hepatic lesions) or to the agents (e.g., DHT, parathyroid hormone, $FeCl_3$, $CrCl_2$, albumen) used to elicit them. However, neither procedure is wholly satisfactory because the categories necessarily overlap.

For example, treatment with DHT + Fe-OS induces particularly pronounced calcification of the left auricular appendage of the heart, but this change is usually accompanied by more or less intense calcium deposition in the subepicardial layers of both ventricles, the renal cortex, the biliary passages, and the duodenum; hence, the syndrome cannot properly be classified under any one of the affected organs. On the other hand, this response is not characteristic of any one treatment either: almost identical changes are produced by parathyroid hormone + Fe-OS. Therefore, it would be equally misleading to classify the experimental disease according to its etiology.

We shall refer to the calciphylactic syndromes either by their *most characteristic lesions* (e.g., "calciphylactic scleroderma with arthritis") or by the combination of *agents most suited to elicit them* (e.g., the "DHT + Thorotrast®" type). Yet, we must keep in mind that the "most characteristic lesion" is not necessarily the only one typical of the syndrome and that "the treatment most suited to elicit it" may merely be the one that under our experimental conditions in the rat happens to have given us the most consistent results up to now. With these limitations our dual system is quite in keeping with general usage in medicine, since most diseases are classified both according to their outstanding characteristics and their most common causative agent (e.g., allergic dermatitis is both a skin disease and an allergy).

The specificity of the various organ lesions differs considerably. Of course, the most nonspecific types are the topical calciphylactic reactions, which have already been described and do not concern us here. In these sensitization by virtually any calciphylactic sensitizer (e.g., DHT, vitamin D, parathyroid hormone, NaAST) followed by the topical application to the target of almost any calciphylactic challenger (e.g., albumen, yolk, metallic compounds) produces essentially the same lesion. Here organ specificity is assured only by the direct application of the challenger to the selected tissue.

In the systemic calciphylactic syndromes the action of the sensitizer is also largely nonspecific. It cannot significantly alter the quality of the response; only the intensity of the resulting change depends on specific characteristics of the sensitizers (e.g., their speed of action, which affects the critical period for challenge, and their stressor effect, which tends to inhibit calciphylactic responses). Here, *it is the nature of the challenger that endows each syndrome with its particular specific characteristics*, presumably because various challengers have different distribution patterns within the body and perhaps also because they induce different chemical responses in their target organs. Whenever a systemic challenger fails to produce any specific organ changes but merely aggravates the kind of calcinosis that can be produced by large doses of sensitizers (e.g., gastric, cardiovascular, and renal calcification by DHT), the resulting change will be called a syndrome of *"nonspecific calcinosis."*

Since the sensitizer is least important in determining specificity and since most of our work was performed with DHT, we shall first review those systemic calciphylactic syndromes that can be produced by this agent in combination with diverse challengers. Then we shall turn our attention to experiments with less commonly employed sensitizers.

DHT was always administered in 0.5 ml. of corn oil, so that only the dose, route, and time of treatment need be indicated, but in the case of the challengers (usually given in 0.2–2.0 ml. of water) the manner of administration will also be mentioned. The severity of the organ lesions has been assessed on the basis of our "arbitrary four-grade scale" (p. 31), which distinguishes: 0 = no lesion, 1 = just visible, 2 = moderate, and 3 = maximal, lesions; "maximal" being defined as the most severe degree of calciphylactic change that has been noted under any conditions in the target under consideration. The means given are based on a very large number of observations, but since our gradings are at best semiquantitative, the standard errors will not be listed. However, the statistical significance of the data has been discussed in the original publications which we shall quote.

In view of the very large number of challengers tested, only the most interesting syndromes can be described in detail. Yet, even data concerning challengers which produce no calciphylactic response or merely aggravate the nonspecific calcinosis normally produced by DHT alone are of importance—especially in connection with the clarification of those particular characteristics that are necessary to produce specific changes in one or the other organ. Since this background material has not been published elsewhere, we shall describe it here, but in order to save space this will be done in a highly condensed manner and printed in small type, using the previously listed (p. 13 ff.) abbreviations. The type of experimental animal and the method of treatment will be indicated in the style used for the labeling of figures, as explained on page 17 ff.

The chronology of challenge relative to the time of sensitization ("+" or "−" days) to determine the "critical period" will be listed as outlined on page 22. The condensed manner of describing the results can be illustrated by the following example:

"***Results:*** Calcinosis (in order of decreasing intensity) was found in: stomach, heart (tigro-vascular) > kidney (cortical) > thymus [traces in diaphragm, intestines]. Mortality: 50%."

This expression indicates that the most intense calcinosis was noted in the stomach and heart and in these organs the degree of the lesion was essentially the same. In the heart, the distribution of the calcium within the myocardial muscle fibers was of the type that gives a "tigroid" pattern upon macroscopic inspection, and the blood vessels were also affected. Less marked calcinosis was seen in the kidney, and here the cortical portion was predominantly affected. Thymic calcification was still less pronounced, while only traces of calcium were visible in the diaphragm and in the intestinal tract outside the stomach. Fifty per cent of the animals died prior to the date of autopsy stated under "***Method.***"

Ancillary findings that do not warrant a detailed description of the method used are listed under "***Remarks***" after the description of the data obtained with the most comparable experimental procedure. For example, minor observations concerning the response of animals of different age groups, the "critical period" of challenge, or the evolution and healing of the lesions will be briefly noted under this heading.

Effective doses of certain challengers are very poorly tolerated by the intravenous route if the whole required amount is given in one injection. However, many of these agents (particularly inorganic chromium and iron salts) are well tolerated if a small intravenous dose is followed a few hours later by one or more larger doses of the same compound. Whenever repeated doses of challengers were given i.v., this was done to take advantage of such tachyphylactic desensitization.

CALCIPHYLACTIC SYNDROMES PRODUCED AFTER SENSITIZATION BY DHT

DHT + Ag₂SO₄ i.v.

Nonspecific Calcinosis

Method: Rat (100 g. ♀): DHT (1 mg. p.o.) 1st day + Ag_2SO_4 (500 μg. in 0.1 ml. water, i.v. ×2) 2d day.

Results: Nonspecific calcinosis. Mortality: 0.

DHT + Albumen i.v.

Auriculo-Cutaneous Calciphylaxis

Method 1: Rat (100 g. ♀): DHT (1 mg. p.o.) 1st day + albumen (50%, 5 ml. i.v.)
2d day; killed 6th day.

Results: Intense calcification was noted in the *coronary* arteries and often in the
auricular appendages and the *subepicardial* layer of the ventricular musculature.
Except for occasional mild calcification in the coronary arteries, these regions
never showed calcification in controls treated with DHT alone. The mortality was
about 25%[826, 849] (Fig. 39).

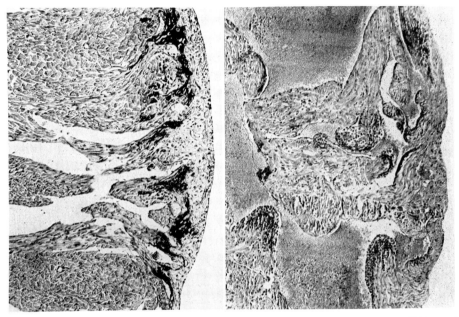

Fig. 39. Cardiac calcification produced by DHT + albumen i.v. Rat (100 g. ♀):
DHT (1 mg. p.o.) 1st day + albumen (50%, 5 ml. i.v.) 2d day; killed 6th day. *Left:* Subepicardial calcium deposition in wall of left ventricle. *Right:* Calcification and leukocytic infiltration,
especially in subendocardial layers of left auricular appendage. (von Kóssa, ×90.)

Calcinosis (in order of decreasing intensity) was found in: kidney (cortical),
stomach, bronchi [traces in heart (tigro-vascular), aorta, skin, salivary glands,
kidney (cortico-medullary), thymic lymph nodes, Brunner's glands] (Figs. 40, 41).

Remarks: Essentially similar, but less pronounced lesions were obtained when
the same amount of albumen was injected on the 1st, +3d or +4th day, i.v. In
addition, *pancreatic* calcification occurred quite frequently following albumen injection on the +3d day.[841]

Method 2: Rat (100 g. ♀): DHT (1 mg. p.o.) 1st day + albumen (50%, 5 ml. iv.)
2d and 3d day; killed 10th to 30th day.

Results: Three to four days after the second albumen injection almost the entire *skin* surface became calcified and it gradually exfoliated in the form of hard plaques. There was also pronounced aggravation of the "nonspecific calcinosis," normally produced by DHT alone (e.g., in the heart, kidney, stomach, and dia-phragm as well as in the left *auricular appendage* and the *subepicardial* layers of the myocardium). On the cardiac surface, calcium was deposited preferentially in the vicinity of the coronary veins. Occasionally, minor calcium depositions were also seen in the *pancreas, thymus,* and *adrenal* medulla. The mortality was about 25%[827] (Fig. 42; Plate II, *E*).

DHT + Albumen i.p.

Pancreatico-Cutaneous Calciphylaxis

Method 1: Rat (100 g. ♀): DHT (1 mg. p.o.) 1st day + albumen (50%, 5 ml. i.p.) 2d day; killed 6th day.

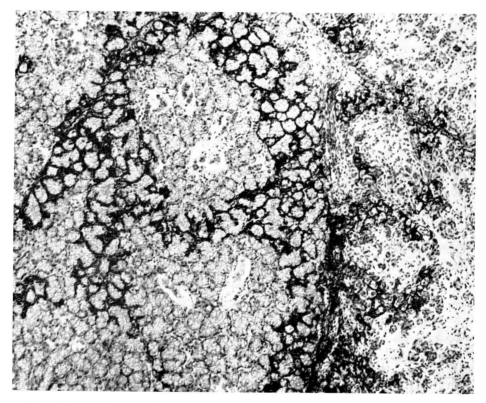

Fig. 40. Calcification of salivary glands produced by DHT + albumen i.v. Rat (100 g. ♀): DHT (1 mg. p.o.) 1st day + albumen (50%, 5 ml. i.v.) 2d day; killed 6th day. Calcium is deposited particularly in the stroma of both salivary glands, but some lobules (*left*) do not undergo necrosis, while others (*right*) disintegrate completely. Salivary gland ducts contain cellular debris. (von Kóssa, ×135.)

Results: About 48 hours after i.p. injection of albumen *three circumscribed cutaneous plaques* appeared: one just above the cartilaginous tip of the xiphoid bone, the other two in the costovertebral angles. The lesions were first painful to touch and adherent to the underlying muscle layers, but by the fourth day it became possible to move them more or less freely over the subcutaneous tissue without causing pain. Histologically, the plaques consisted of heavy calcium deposits in the various muscular, fascial, and dermal layers through the entire thickness of the abdominal wall, between peritoneum and epidermis. The skin is especially sensitive to calciphylactic challenge, and we assume that it responded at the three points just mentioned because here the abdominal musculature is thin and hence readily permits outward diffusion of albumen (Fig. 43; Plate II, *F, G*).

The *pancreatic stroma* underwent virtually complete calcification, which imparted a dense, chalky appearance to the organ. Here, calcium deposition could be demonstrated with particular clarity after staining the fixed specimen with $AgNO_3$.

Histologically, the calcification was strictly limited to the pancreatic stroma and consisted of extremely fine, von Kóssa-positive granules, surrounded by inflammatory changes (particularly marked infiltration with eosinophils and pseudoeosino-

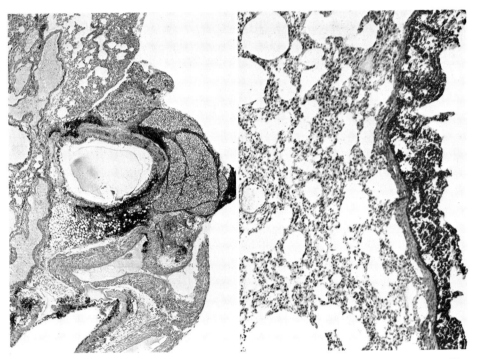

Fig. 41. Pulmonary calcification produced by DHT + albumen i.v. or i.p. Two rats (100 g. ♀): DHT (1 mg. p.o.) 1st day + albumen (50%, *left:* 0.5 ml. i.v., *right:* 5 ml. i.p.); killed 6th day. Albumen i.v. produced calcification around the major bronchi in the hilar region, while i.p. it caused calcium deposition predominantly on the surface of the pleura. (von Kóssa, left ×29, right ×100.)

phils) and intense sclerosis. There was no trace of stainable calcium in the parenchyma, nor in the ducts and islets of Langerhans (Figs. 44, 45; Plate III, *A*, *B*)
except occasionally in the capillaries of the islets (Fig. 46).

Heavy calcification was regularly found in the *gastric mucosa* (especially its
middle layer), *duodenum* (especially around *Brunner's glands*), retroperitoneal *fat*,
and *diaphragm*. The *kidneys* exhibited only traces of cortico-medullary calcinosis,

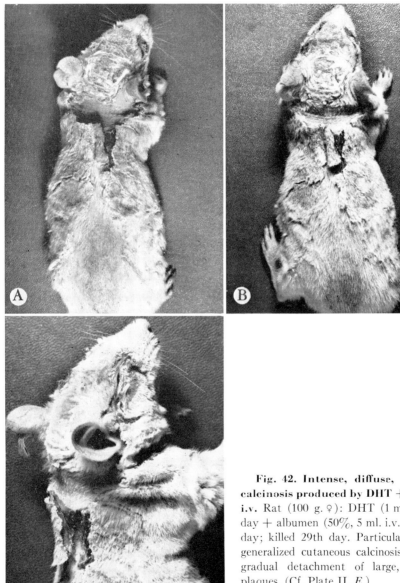

Fig. 42. Intense, diffuse, cutaneous
calcinosis produced by DHT + albumen
i.v. Rat (100 g. ♀): DHT (1 mg. p.o.) 1st
day + albumen (50%, 5 ml. i.v.) 2d and 3d
day; killed 29th day. Particularly intense,
generalized cutaneous calcinosis leading to
gradual detachment of large, hard skin
plaques. (Cf. Plate II, *E*.)

("C" After Selye,[327] courtesy Allergie u.
Asthma.)

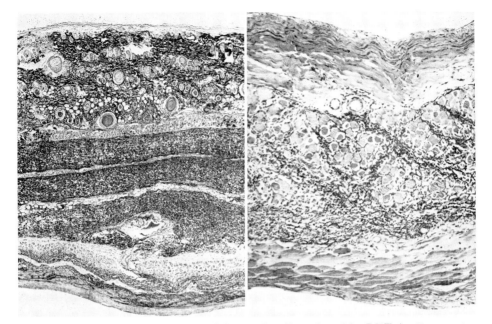

Fig. 43. Calcification of the entire abdominal wall produced by DHT + albumen i.p.
Two rats (100 g. ♀): DHT (1 mg. p.o.) 1st day + albumen (50%, 5 ml. i.p.) 2d day. *Left:*
killed 6th day. Entire thickness of abdominal wall, from peritoneum to epidermis, is incrusted
with calcium. *Right:* killed 11th day. Most of the calcium appears to have been reabsorbed,
so that the affected region now consists mainly of connective tissue and regenerating muscle
fibers. (von Kóssa, left ×26, right ×90.)

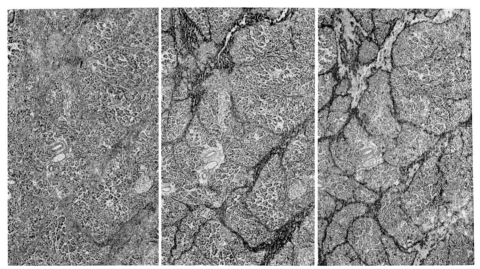

Fig. 44. Pancreatic calcification produced by DHT + albumen i.p. Rat (100 g. ♀):
DHT (1 mg. p.o.) 1st day + albumen (50%, 5 ml. i.p.) 2d day; killed 6th day. Three consecutive
sections through same pancreas. *Left:* PAS stain reveals intense proliferation of connective tissue
accompanied only by slight deposition of PAS-positive material. *Middle:* von Kóssa technique
shows calcification limited to stroma. *Right:* Celestin blue technique is definitely superior to
von Kóssa stain in demonstrating mild degrees of calcification, but massively calcified regions
take up the dye only along their margin. (×29.)

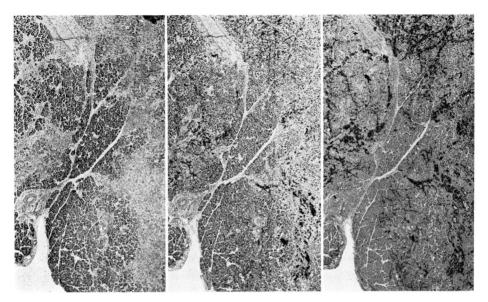

Fig. 45. Intense fibrosis with little calcification of the pancreas produced by DHT +
albumen i.p. Rat (100 g. ♀): DHT (1 mg. p.o.) 1st day + albumen (50%, 5 ml. i.p.) 2d day;
killed 15th day. Three adjacent sections after staining with PAS (*left*), von Kóssa (*middle*)
and celestin blue (*right*). A large portion of the pancreatic parenchyma is substituted by connective tissue, but at this time only very slight calcium deposits can be demonstrated, even with
the particularly sensitive celestin blue technique. (×24.)

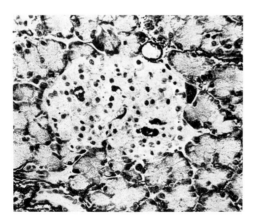

Fig. 46. Calcification of vessels in the Langerhans' islets produced by DHT +
albumen i.p. Rat (100 g. ♀): DHT (1 mg. p.o.) 1st day + albumen (50%, 5 ml. i.p.) 3d day;
killed 6th day. Majority of capillaries in this Langerhans' islet are heavily calcified, although
in this region surrounding pancreatic tissue is free of calcium. (von Kóssa, ×450.)

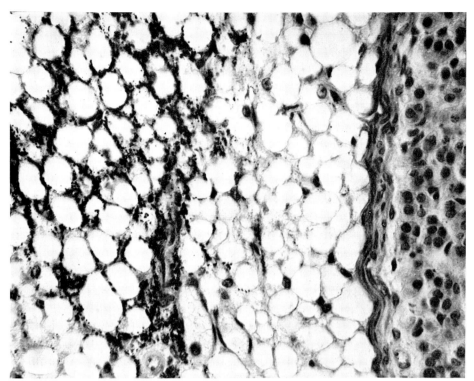

Fig. 47. **Calcification of periadrenal fat produced by DHT + albumen i.p.** Rat (100 g. ♀): DHT (1 mg. p.o.) 1st day + albumen (50%, 4 ml. i.p.) 2d day; killed 6th day. Fine granular calcium deposition between fat cells around adrenal cortex. (von Kóssa, ×470.)

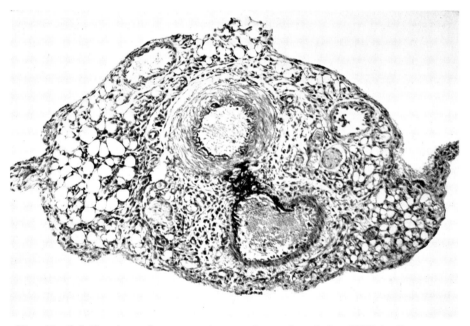

Fig. 48. **Calcification of mesenteric vessels produced by DHT + albumen i.p.** Rat (100 g. ♀): DHT (1 mg. p.o.) 1st day + albumen (50%, 5 ml. i.p.) 2d day; killed 6th day. Mesenteric fat and artery are virtually free of calcium, while vein (especially in the wall adjacent to the artery) as well as connective tissue between vein and artery are heavily calcified. (von Kóssa, ×135.)

while the omentum, liver, spleen, and adrenal remained unaffected (Fig. 47). In the *mesentery* the adipose tissue was spared, but calcinosis occurred in the vessels especially along the border between arteries and veins (Fig. 48). There was moderate to heavy calcification in the atretic follicles and involuting corpora lutea of the *ovary*, but normal, well-developed follicles and corpora lutea remained unaffected. In the *oviduct* calcium deposition was most evident just underneath the epithelium (Figs. 49, 50).

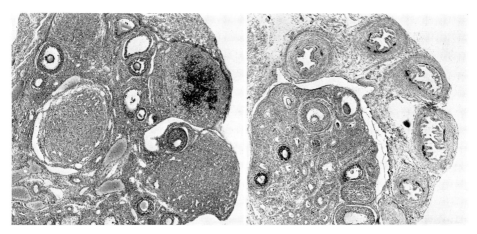

Fig. 49. Calcification in the ovary produced by DHT + albumen i.p. Rat (100 g. ♀): DHT (1 mg. p.o.) 1st day + albumen (50%, 5 ml. i.p.) 2d day; killed 6th day. *Left:* Intense calcification in an involuting corpus luteum, while the two fully developed corpora lutea as well as the follicles in this field are unaffected. *Right:* Calcification in several involuting Graafian follicles and submucosa of oviduct. (von Kóssa, ×29.)

Heavy deposits of calcium were seen throughout the thickness of the *thoracic wall* especially around the sternum and on the pleural and pericardial surfaces. The thymus and pulmonary parenchyma showed little if any calcification but the *pleural surface* (Fig. 41) and the *perithymic lymph nodes* were heavily calcified. Calcium deposition in the *coronary arteries* was not definitely in excess of the trace amounts produced by this dose of DHT in controls.

Finally, there was always pronounced *osteitis fibrosa* with predominantly osteolytic changes.[826, 849]

Calcinosis (in order of decreasing intensity) was found in: stomach, pancreas, diaphragm, skin (3 plaques), peritoneum > abdominal wall, thymic lymph nodes [traces in kidney (cortical), pleura, retroperitoneal fat, mesenteric vessels, ovary, oviduct, heart (tigro-vascular and subpericardial), Brunner's glands].[841]

Remarks: Rat (100 g. ♀) sensitized with DHT (1 mg. p.o.) 1st day and challenged with albumen (50%, 5 ml. i.p.) responded with marked pancreatic calcification on +2d and +3d day, but not on 1st day or −3d day.

Method 2: As Method 1, but animals killed on 10th–25th day.

The characteristic three *skin* plaques and the internal lesions developed as usual. The *pancreas* became extremely hard and brittle. Histologically, the calcium was found to have been partly resorbed and partly aggregated into large amorphous or preosseous tissue blocks which were surrounded by giant-cell containing circumscribed granulomatous capsules (Fig. 51). The remaining calcium was still located within the cirrhotic stroma. The parenchyma, including the islets of Langerhans, was largely destroyed.

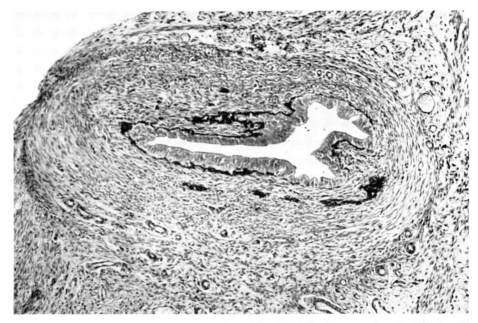

Fig. 50. Calcification in oviduct produced by DHT + albumen i.p. Rat (100 g. ♀): DHT (1 mg. p.o.) 1st day + albumen (50%, 5 ml. i.p.) 2d day; killed 6th day. Calcification is particularly prominent along basement membrane of oviduct and in muscular layer, while epithelium is unaffected. (von Kóssa, ×135.)

In all other sites of calcinosis the resorption of the precipitates and their substitution by sclerotic, frequently hyalinized and somewhat PAS-positive connective tissue was equally evident. In the *retroperitoneal fat* this process led to the formation of a singular honeycomb-like structure consisting of residual calcium deposits that outlined the position previously occupied by fat cells but was now replaced by granuloma (Fig. 52).

In the *striated musculature,* for example that of the diaphragm (Fig. 53) or the intercostal spaces (Fig. 54), the granulomatous tissue replacing the calcified areas was much more uniform in appearance. However, in most locations (especially in the pancreas and subcutaneous tissue) the outstanding feature was the fragmenta-

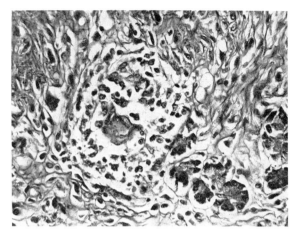

Fig. 51. Pancreatic fibrosis and giant-cell formation produced by DHT + albumen i.p. Rat (100 g. ♀): DHT (1 mg. p.o.) 1st day + albumen (50%, 5 ml. i.p.) 2d day; killed 15th day. Intense fibrosis with a large polynuclear giant cell and many epithelioid histiocytes in the middle. Only a few acini remain in this region of the pancreas. (PAS, ×450.)

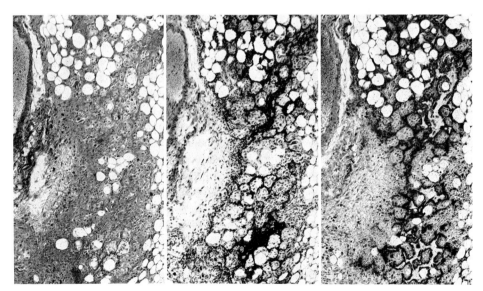

Fig. 52. Sclerosis and calcification of the retroperitoneal fat produced by DHT + albumen i.p. Rat (100 g. ♀): DHT (1 mg. p.o.) 1st day + albumen (50%, 5 ml. i.p.) 2d day; killed 15th day. Three adjacent sections after staining with PAS (*left*), von Kóssa (*middle*), and celestin blue (*right*). As calcium deposit around signet-ring-shaped fat cells vanishes, connective tissue proliferates and invades space originally occupied by fat globule within adipose cell. (×80.)

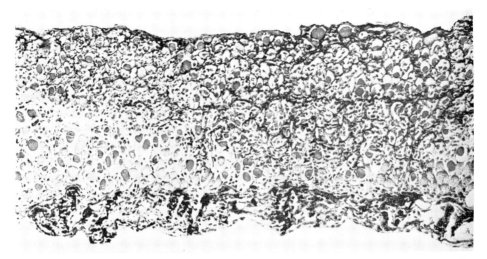

Fig. 53. Calcification of the diaphragm produced by DHT + albumen i.p. Rat (100 g. ♀): DHT (1 mg. p.o.) 1st day + albumen (50%, 5 ml. i.p.) 2d day; killed 11th day. Much of the calcium deposited in diaphragm during first few days has disappeared already and is replaced by connective tissue that surrounds degenerating and regenerating muscle cells. (von Kóssa, ×135.)

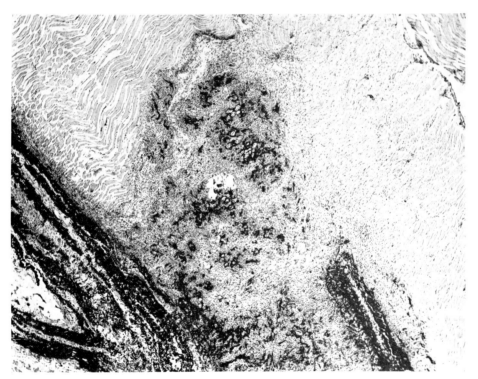

Fig. 54. Calcification and sclerosis of intercostal muscles produced by DHT + albumen i.p. Rat (100 g. ♀): DHT (1 mg. p.o.) 1st day + albumen (50%, 5 ml. i.p.) 2d day; killed 15th day. Most of the calcium has vanished and is replaced by fibrous tissue. Only surroundings of costal periosteum (lower left corner) are still heavily calcified. (von Kóssa, ×39.)

tion of the calcified connective-tissue strands into smaller units, the residual calcified blocks being gradually transformed into preosseous tissue and surrounded by polynuclear giant cells, epithelioid cells, and dense connective tissue. The giant cells were of the Langhans type and often contained calcified and strongly PAS-positive inclusions, somewhat reminiscent of those seen in sarcoidosis.

As these soft-tissue changes progressed, the *osteitis fibrosa* gradually changed its character and gave way to reactive osteogenesis throughout the skeleton.[827]

Method 3: Rat (200 g. ♀): DHT (2 mg. p.o.) 1st day + albumen (50%, 10 ml. i.p.) 2d day; killed 6th day.

Results: Calcinosis (in order of decreasing intensity) was found in: stomach, retroperitoneal fat, mesentery > pancreas, diaphragm, kidney (cortical) [traces in Brunner's glands, kidney (cortico-medullary), thymus, heart (tigro-vascular)].[841]

DHT + AlK(SO$_4$)$_2$ i.v.
Nonspecific Calcinosis
Method: Rat (100 g. ♀): DHT (1 mg. p.o.) 1st day + AlK(SO$_4$)$_2$ (10 mg. in 1 ml. water, i.v. ×2) 2d day; killed 6th day.

Results: Calcinosis (in order of decreasing intensity) was found in: stomach, kidney (cortical, cortico-medullary) > heart (tigro-vascular) [traces in liver]. Mortality: 20%.[841]

DHT + AlK(SO$_4$)$_2$ i.p.
Peritoneal Calciphylaxis
Method: Rat (100 g. ♀): DHT (1 mg. p.o.) 1st day + AlK(SO$_4$)$_2$ (20 mg. in 1 ml. water, i.p. ×2) 2d day; killed 6th day.

Results: Calcinosis of peritoneum [traces in heart (tigro-vascular), kidney (cortical)].[827]

DHT + AlNH$_4$(SO$_4$)$_2$ i.v.
Nonspecific Calcinosis
Method: Rat (100 g. ♀): DHT (1 mg. p.o.) 1st day + AlNH$_4$(SO$_4$)$_2$ (10 mg. in 1 ml. water, i.v. ×2) 2d day; killed 6th day.

Results: Calcinosis of kidney, heart, and stomach. Mortality: 40%.[841]

DHT + AlNH$_4$(SO$_4$)$_2$ i.p.
Peritoneal Calciphylaxis
Method: Rat (100 g. ♀): DHT (1 mg. p.o.) 1st day + AlNH$_4$(SO$_4$)$_2$ (20 mg. in 1 ml. water, i.p. ×2) 2d day; killed 6th day.

Results: Calcinosis of peritoneum [traces in stomach, heart (tigro-vascular), kidney (cortical)].[827]

DHT + As-Acetate i.v.

Nonspecific Calcinosis

Method: Rat (100 g. ♀): DHT (1 mg. p.o.) 1st day + As-acetate (30 mg. in 1 ml. water, i.v.) 2d day; killed 6th day.

Results: Nonspecific calcinosis. Mortality: 0.

DHT + BiCl₃ i.v.

Nonspecific Calcinosis

Method: Rat (100 g. ♀): DHT (1 mg. p.o.) 1st day + BiCl₃ (10 mg. in 1 ml. water, i.v.) 2d day; killed 6th day.

Results: Nonspecific calcinosis occasionally with splenic calcification. Mortality: 0.

DHT + CdCl₂ i.v.

Nonspecific Calcinosis

Method: Rat (100 g. ♀): DHT (1 mg. p.o.) 1st day + CdCl₂ (500 μg. in 0.1 ml. water, i.v. ×2) 2d day; killed 6th day.

Results: Nonspecific calcinosis occasionally associated with calcification in the thymus or Brunner's glands. Mortality: 30%.

DHT + CeCl₃ i.v.

RES-Type of Calciphylaxis

Method: Rat (100 g. ♀): DHT (1 mg. p.o.) 1st day + CeCl₃ (10 mg. in 1 ml. water, i.v. ×2) 2d day; killed 6th day.

Results: The most outstanding and constant consequence of challenge with this cerium salt was the deposition of calcium in the periphery of the Malpighian follicles of the spleen (Fig. 55) and in the hepatic RES. Calcinosis (in order of decreasing intensity) was found in: spleen, liver, stomach > kidney (cortical) [traces in heart (tigro-vascular)].

DHT + CeCl₃ i.p.

Peritoneal Calciphylaxis

Method: Rat (100 g. ♀): DHT (1 mg. p.o.) 1st day + CeCl₃ (20 mg. in 1 ml. water, i.v. ×2) 2d day; killed 6th day.

Results: Calcinosis of peritoneum.[841]

DHT + Chondroitin Sulfuric Acid i.v., i.p.

Gastric, Pancreatic and Peritoneal Calcinosis

Method 1: Rat (100 g. ♀): DHT (1 mg. p.o.) 1st day + chondroitin sulfuric acid (100 mg. in 5 ml. water, i.v.) 2d day; killed 6th day.

Results: Calcinosis was found in the stomach, pancreas [traces in heart (tigro-vascular), kidney (cortical)].

Method 2: Rat (100 g. ♀): DHT (1 mg. p.o.) 1st day + chondroitin sulfuric acid (200 mg. in 5 ml. water, i.p.) 2d day; killed 6th day.

Results: Calcinosis (in order of decreasing intensity) was found in: pancreas, pleura, stomach > diaphragm [traces in thymus, retroperitoneal fat, kidney (cortical), heart (tigro-vascular), skin].[841]

Remarks: Since these experiments were performed with a comparatively impure commercial preparation of chondroitin sulfuric acid, we can only conclude from them that this particular extract when given i.v. or i.p. produces predominantly gastric and pancreatic calcinosis. When the material was administered i.p., it also caused local calcinosis in the peritoneal organs and some degree of pleural calcinosis, presumably owing to its lymphatic spread into the thoracic cavity.

Fig. 55. Calcification of spleen produced by DHT + CeCl₃ i.v. Two rats (100 g. ♀): DHT (1 mg. p.o.) 1st day + CeCl₃ (10 mg. in 1 ml. water, i.v.) 2d day; killed 6th day. *Left:* Fresh specimens. *Right:* Same spleens stained with AgNO₃. Selective calcium deposition around, but not within, center of Malpighian follicles.

DHT + CoCl₂ i.v.

Nonspecific Calcinosis

Method: Rat (100 g. ♀): DHT (1 mg. p.o.) 1st day + $CoCl_2$ (0.5 mg. in 0.1 ml. water, i.v.) 2d day; killed 6th day.

Results: Nonspecific calcinosis in rare instances combined with moderate cutaneous and salivary gland calcification. Mortality: 20%.

DHT + CrCl₃ i.v.

Thyroid–Parathyroid–Carotid-Body Calciphylaxis

Method: Rat (100 g. ♀): DHT (1 mg. p.o.) 1st day + $CrCl_3$ (10 mg. in 1 ml. water, i.v.) 2d day; killed 6th–15th day.

Results: The *carotid bodies and parathyroids* became very conspicuous because they assumed a brilliant white color; both these organs also showed histologic evidence of stroma calcinosis. Less pronounced calcification was seen in the thyroids, where it appeared to radiate into the organ from the parathyroids (Figs. 56–59; Plate IV, *C*, *D*, *F*).

The *salivary glands, Brunner's glands, pancreas, renal cortex, diaphragm* (Fig. 63), *pulmonary septa, pleura, tracheal mucosa* (Fig. 60), and *heart* were similarly affected. In all instances calcification was limited to the stroma.[835, 836, 837]

Calcification was also present throughout the vascular system of the entire *choroid plexus*. Sometimes even the most minute capillary branches appeared to be totally saturated with calcium. Yet the covering epithelium and the brain tissue itself remained normal; only occasionally did we see swelling and homogenization of individual ganglion cells throughout the brain substance[837a] (Plate V, *A*).

Under essentially similar conditions both in 100 g. and in 200 g. rats, particularly severe calcium deposition was observed in the *urinary passages*. A sharply demarcated band of calcification began within the renal pelvis at a level corresponding to the middle of the papilla. This change appeared to be the direct consequence of the renal chromium excretion (Fig. 61; Plate IV, *G*).

A singular aftermath of the DHT + $CrCl_3$ i.v. treatment was a superficial, macular, scaly *dermatosis* that tended to appear rather late during the second week, much after the other manifestations. It differed from the usual calciphylactic skin lesions in that calcinosis, even if it affected large areas, occurred only just under the epidermis and the skin did not become particularly thick or painful to touch. Yet, the condition was manifestly related to the psoriasiform lesions (e.g., those produced by DHT + Fe-Dex i.p.) in that here also inspection from the subcutis revealed a reticular pattern of calcification which followed the course of the blood vessels.

Discussion: This simultaneous predominant calcification seen in the carotid bodies and parathyroids brings to mind certain earlier experiments which sug-

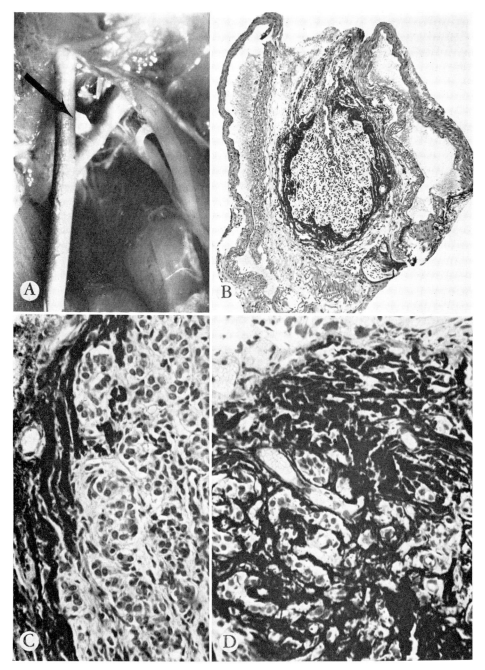

Fig. 56. Calcification of the carotid body produced by DHT + CrCl₃ i.v. Two rats (100 g. ♀): DHT (1 mg. p.o.) 1st day + CrCl₃ (10 mg. in 1 ml. water, i.v.) 2d day; killed 6th day. *A:* Macroscopic aspect of calcified left carotid body (arrow). *B:* General view of carotid body with capsular type of calcification. Cross sections of two main carotid branches visible to right and left, while principal artery of carotid body itself is cut longitudinally as it enters the organ from above. (von Kóssa, ×29.) *C:* High magnification of margin of same carotid body. Essentially normal epithelial cells and heavily calcified capsule. (von Kóssa, ×350.) *D:* High magnification of carotid body with intense stroma calcification and beginning disintegration of epithelioid cells in another rat. (von Kóssa, ×350.) (Cf. Plate IV, *G.*)

(After Selye and Dieudonné,[837] courtesy Biochim. et Biol. sper.)

gested a functional relationship between these organs. It has been said that in dogs removal of the carotid bodies elicits a considerable hypercalcemia, eventually conducive to disease and even death. The syndrome was ascribed to hyperfunction of the parathyroids because the hypercalcemia vanished after parathyroidectomy, while extirpation of the carotid bodies allegedly caused marked parathyroid hypertrophy.[210, 747, 748]

In any event, the concurrent and usually parallel development of calciphylactic lesions in the parathyroids and the carotid bodies suggests the existence of some similarity in the chemical characteristics of these organs.[837]

Critical period: No sharply delimited critical period could be found in rats (100 g. or 200 g. ♀) sensitized by DHT (1 mg. per 100 g. body weight, p.o.) on 1st day and challenged with $CrCl_3$ (10 mg. per 100 g. body weight, i.v.) at different times between 8 days before and 10 days after DHT treatment (Figs. 62, 63, 64). In rats (200 g. ♀) sensitized with DHT (2 mg. p.o.), an even larger dose of $CrCl_3$

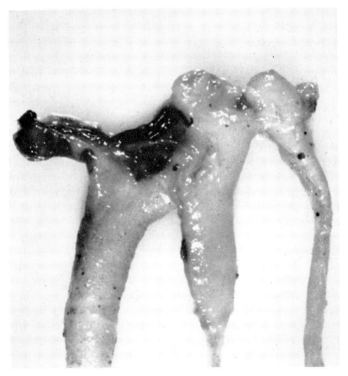

Fig. 57. Calcification of the carotid body produced by DHT + $CrCl_3$ i.v. Rat (290 g. ♀): DHT (3 mg. p.o.) 1st day + $CrCl_3$ (30 mg. in 1 ml. water, i.v.) 2d day; killed 6th day. $AgNO_3$-stained specimen. Calcified (here black) carotid body in bifurcation of carotid artery (left), superior cervical sympathetic ganglion (middle) and vagus nerve (right).

(20 mg. in 1 ml. water, i.v.) produced intense calcinosis in the thyroid, parathyroid, carotid body, lung (Fig. 65), heart, and Brunner's glands (Fig. 66) when given any time between −8th and +2d day; minor calcifications were also seen after injection any time between the +3d and +8th day. Here, there was no sign of a dissociation between the lesions in the various target organs upon challenge at different times. Although the intensity of the calcinosis varied, its proportional severity was roughly the same in all affected tissues. It is noteworthy that treatment with the challenger as much as 8 days prior to sensitization was still maximally effective.

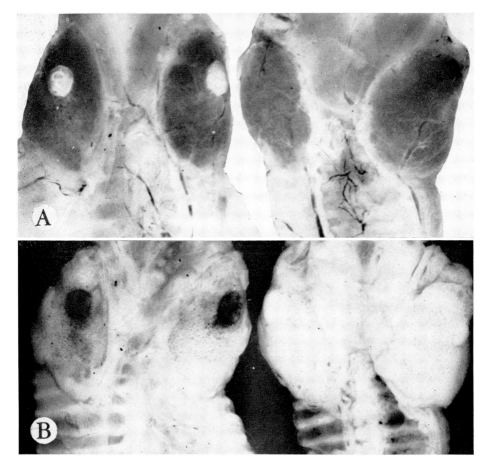

Fig. 58. Selective calcification of the parathyroids produced by DHT + CrCl₃ i.v.
Two rats (105 g. ♀): DHT (1 mg. p.o.) 1st day + (left) CrCl₃ (10 mg. in 1 ml. water, i.v.) 2d day; killed 6th day. The calcified parathyroids (left) are white in the fresh (*A*), black in the AgNO₃-stained (*B*), specimens and hardly distinguishable in the control rat (right).

[After Selye and Dieudonné,[835] courtesy Birkhäuser Verlag Basel (Experientia).]

DHT + CrCl₂ i.v.

Thyroid-Parathyroid-Carotid-Body Calciphylaxis

Method: Rat (100 g. ♀): DHT (1 mg. p.o.) 1st day + CrCl₂ (2.5–5.0 mg. in 0.35 ml. water, i.v.) 2d day; killed 6th day.

Results: The syndrome was essentially the same as that induced by DHT + CrCl₃, but CrCl₂ was less well tolerated though more effective as a calciphylactic challenger[835, 836] (Figs. 67–70; Plate IV, *A, B*).

DHT + Other Chromium Salts i.v.

Thyroid-Parathyroid-Carotid-Body Calciphylaxis

Several other chromium salts, such as $Cr(NO_3)_3$ (15 mg.) and $Cr(SO_4)_3$ (10 mg.), were shown to produce essentially the same calciphylactic syndrome in the DHT-sensitized rat as was obtained with CrCl₃ and CrCl₂. It would be unnecessary, therefore, to describe these observations in detail. It is noteworthy, however, that other chromium compounds, particularly CrO_3 (1.5 mg.), $K_2Cr_2O_7$ (2.5 mg.) and K_2CrO_4 (5 mg.), were poorly tolerated and ineffective in producing thyroid-

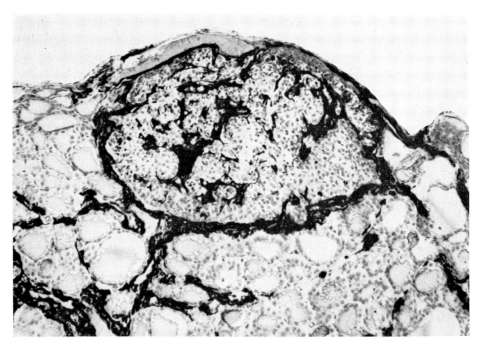

Fig. 59. Selective calcification of the parathyroids produced by DHT + CrCl₃ i.v. Rat (100 g. ♀): DHT (1 mg. p.o.) 1st day + CrCl₃ (10 mg. in 1 ml. water, i.v.) 2d day; killed 6th day. Intense calcification of parathyroid stroma tends to spread into stroma of surrounding thyroid tissue; parenchymal cells are unaffected. (von Kóssa, ×135.)

[After Selye and Dieudonné,[835] courtesy Birkhäuser Verlag Basel (Experientia).]

parathyroid-carotid-body calcification under otherwise comparable circumstances, even at just sub-lethal or lethal dose levels. These compounds merely aggravated the nonspecific calcinosis induced by DHT alone.[260a] Apparently, here as in so many other calciphylactic reactions, not only the mere presence of the challenging metal (in this case chromium) is of importance, but also the form in which it is introduced into the body.

DHT + CuCl$_2$ i.v.

Nonspecific Calcinosis

Method: Rat (100 g. ♀): DHT (1 mg. p.o.) 1st day + CuCl$_2$ (1 mg. in 0.1 ml. water, i.v. ×4) 2d day; killed 6th day.

Results: Nonspecific calcinosis (in order of decreasing intensity) was found in: stomach, heart (tigro-vascular), kidney (cortical), and thymus. Although the calcinosis was nonspecific in its distribution, it was more pronounced than could be expected from DHT alone. Mortality: 0.

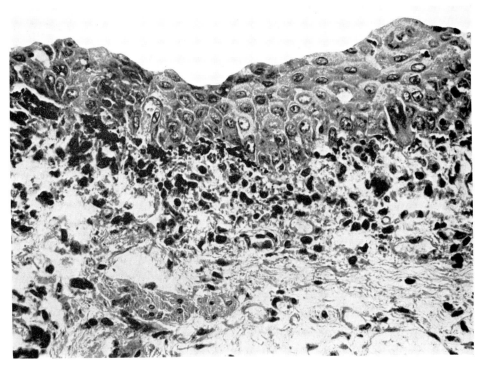

Fig. 60. Squamous metaplasia of tracheal epithelium, with submucosal calcification, produced by DHT + CrCl$_3$ i.v. Rat (100 g. ♀): DHT (1 mg. p.o.) 1st day + CrCl$_3$ e10 mg. in 1 ml. water, i.v.) 2d day; died 5th day. Granular calcium deposit. Numerous fine (osinophilic granules in submucosa with squamous metaplasia of adjacent tracheal epithelium. (von Kóssa, ×450.)

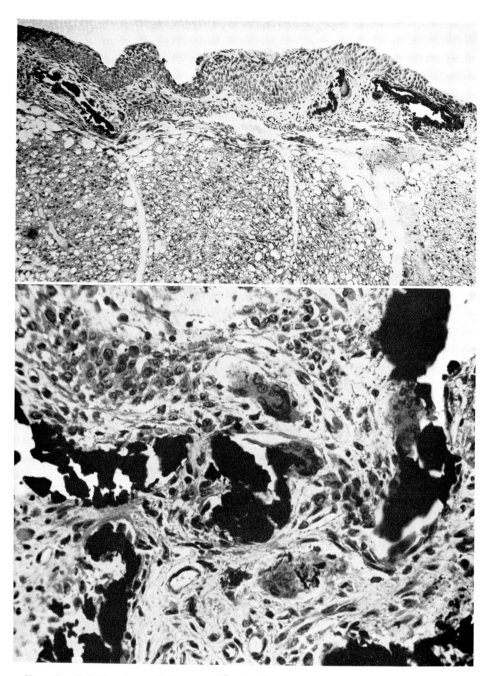

Fig. 61. Calcification of the renal pelvis produced by DHT + CrCl₃ i.v. Rat (100 g. ♀): DHT (1 mg. p.o.) 1st day + CrCl₃ (8 mg. in 1 ml. water, i.v.) 2d day; killed 6th day. *Top:* Several nodular or platelike, calcified deposits underneath transitional epithelium of renal pelvis. *Bottom:* Under higher magnification, calcium-ingesting, polynuclear giant cells are visible within the calcified subepithelial foci. (von Kóssa, top ×135, bottom ×470.)

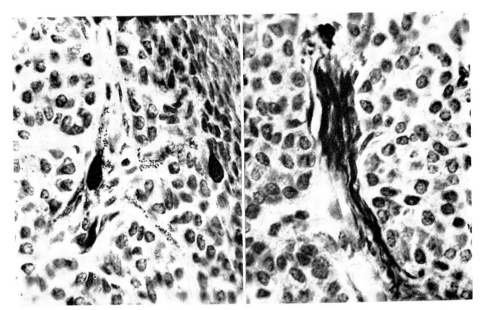

Fig. 62. Incrustation of the parathyroid stroma produced by DHT + CrCl₃ i.v.
Rat (100 g. ♀): CrCl₃ (increasing doses of 10–20 mg. in 2 ml. water, i.v.) 1st–11th day + DHT (1 mg. p.o.) 8th day; killed 12th day. After heavy, prolonged CrCl₃-overdosage, DHT failed to produce usual, macroscopically visible parathyroid calcification. Even histologically, only traces of very faintly von Kóssa-positive granules (*left*) or fibers (*right*) were detectable at one point in one of the parathyroids. The three ovoid, dark cells in left picture are blue hematoxylin-stained mastocytes. (von Kóssa, ×700.)

Fig. 63. Calcification of the diaphragm produced by DHT + CrCl₃ i.v. Rat (100 g. ♀): CrCl₃ (10 mg. in 1 ml. water, i.v.) 1st and 10th day + DHT (1.5 mg. p.o.) 20th day; died 24th day. Here, though challenge long preceded sensitization, calcification of diaphragm is very obvious on AgNO₃-stained preparation, showing predominantly perivascular arborizing arrangement of calcinosis (especially in the centrum tendinosum); in the periphery, muscle calcification largely overlays the calcified vessels. (Arrows point to costal attachment of diaphragm.)

**Fig. 64. Pattern of calcium deposition within a duodenal loop produced by DHT +
CrCl₃ i.v.** Rat (200 g. ♀): DHT (2 mg. p.o.) 1st day + CrCl₃ (20 mg. in 1 ml. water, i.v.)
1st day; killed 12th day. Darkly stained calcium deposits in and around the common bile
duct (which runs through the pancreas, parallel to the duodenum), the main pancreatic duct
(which joins the bile duct near the ampulla of Vater and is marked by arrow), the gastric mucosa
(exposed through oblique section near pylorus) and throughout the duodenum. Heavily calcified
region of Brunner's glands forms stiff ring, whose diameter greatly exceeds that of the pylorus.
In the duodenum, the calcium penetrates close to the serosa, while in the stomach, only the
mucosa is calcified. (AgNO₃-stained specimen under loupe magnification.)

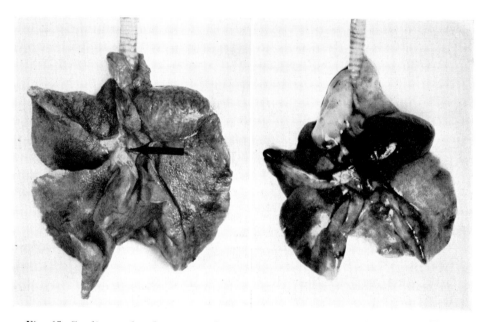

Fig. 65. Cardiac and pulmonary calcinosis produced by DHT + CrCl₃ i.v. Two rats
(200 g. ♀): DHT (2 mg. p.o.) 1st day + (*left*) CrCl₃ (20 mg. in 2 ml. water, i.v.) 2d day; died
12th day. Pronounced diffuse calcification of cardiac surface and of atrophic thymus (in front
of trachea). Lung failed to collapse; its surface is corrugated, while the major bronchi (arrow)
are white as a result of calcification. Untreated control is shown (*right*) for comparison.

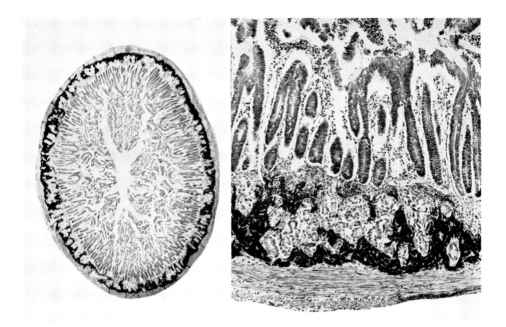

Fig. 66. Calcinosis of Brunner's glands produced by DHT + CrCl₃ i.v. Rat (200 g. ♀): DHT (2 mg. p.o.) 1st day + CrCl₃ (20 mg. in 1 ml. water, i.v.) 3d day; killed 12th day. *Left:* Cross section through entire duodenum shows selective calcification of Brunner's gland stroma. (von Kóssa, ×13.5.) *Right:* Higher magnification of a portion of preceding picture. Calcinosis is strictly limited to stroma of the Brunner's gland layer. (von Kóssa, ×105.)

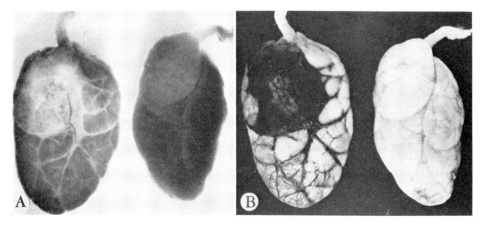

Fig. 67. Calcification of the salivary glands produced by DHT + CrCl₂ i.v. Two rats (100 g. ♀): DHT (1 mg. p.o.) 1st day + (left) CrCl₂ (2.5 mg. in 0.25 ml. water, i.v. ×2) 2d day; killed 6th day. *A:* Fresh. *B:* AgNO₃-stained, specimens. Intense calcification affecting particularly stroma of submaxillary and virtually entire tissue of major sublingual gland.

109

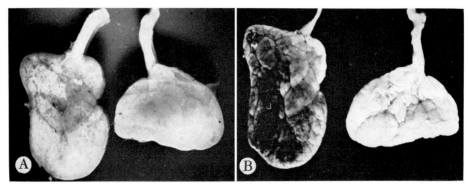

Fig. 68. Calcification of the lacrimal glands produced by DHT + CrCl₂ i.v. Two rats (100 g. ♀): DHT (1 mg. p.o.) 1st day + (left) CrCl₂ (2.5 mg. in 0.25 ml. water, i.v. ×2) 2d day; killed 6th day. *A:* Fresh. *B:* AgNO₃-stained specimens. The particularly hard, calcified gland appears to be much enlarged. Though barely visible here in the fresh specimen, the calcium deposits were obvious at autopsy and are clearly distinguishable here after staining with AgNO₃.

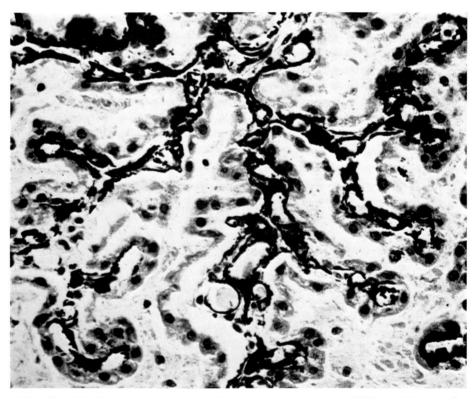

Fig. 69. Calcification of the choroid plexus produced by DHT + CrCl₂ i.v. Rat (100 g. ♀): DHT (1 mg. p.o.) 1st day + CrCl₂ (3.5 mg. in 0.35 ml. water, i.v.) 2d day; killed 6th day. Extensive calcification of blood vessels in choroid plexus of third ventricle. The epithelial cells themselves have not undergone calcification and appear to be free of any noticeable damage from the intense calcium deposition in the adjacent vessels. (von Kóssa, ×490.) (Cf. Plate V, *A*.)

(After Selye and Dieudonné,[836] courtesy Zhur. Nevropath. i. Psikhiat.)

110

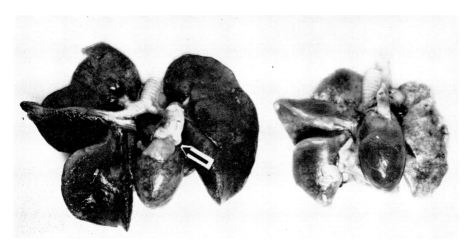

**Fig. 70. Calcification of the heart, thymus, trachea and lung produced by DHT +
CrCl₂ i.v.** Two rats (100 g. ♀): DHT (1 mg. p.o.) 1st day + (left) CrCl₂ (2.5 mg. in 0.25 ml.
water, i.v. ×2) 2d day; killed 6th day. *Left:* Combined treatment resulted in intense calcification
of the heart surface, especially the auricular appendage (below arrow), thymus (above arrow),
trachea and lungs (which failed to collapse). *Right:* No significant organ lesion in the control
animal.

Remarks: Essentially similar results were obtained with DHT (2 mg.) and
CuCl₂ (1 mg., i.v. ×4) in 200 g. rats, but here hepatic necroses developed occasionally and the mortality was 75%.

DHT + CuCl i.v.
Nonspecific Calcinosis
Method: Rat (100 g. ♀): DHT (1 mg. p.o.) 1st day + CuCl (4 mg. in 0.8 ml. water,
i.v.) 2d day; killed 6th day.

Results: Nonspecific calcinosis. Mortality: 20%.

DHT + Din i.v.
Nonspecific Calcinosis
Method: Rat (100 g. ♀): DHT (1 mg. p.o.) 1st day + Din (1 mg. in 0.2 ml. water,
i.v.) 2d day; killed 6th day.

Results: Nonspecific calcinosis.
Remarks: Upon i.p. injection Din produced typical peritoneal calciphylaxis.

DHT + Fe (Ferric) Albuminate i.p.
Peritoneal Calciphylaxis
Method: Rat (100 g. ♀): DHT (1 mg. p.o.) 1st day + ferric albuminate (100 mg.
in 4 ml. water, i.p.) 2d day; killed 6th day.

Results: Typical peritoneal calciphylaxis. Calcinosis (in order of decreasing intensity) was found in: stomach, peritoneal surface, diaphragm > thymic lymph nodes > thymus, spleen, Brunner's glands, and kidney (cortex and cortico-medullary junction) [traces in pancreas, duodenum, heart (tigro-vascular)].

Remarks: Under similar circumstances, up to 20 mg. of ferric albuminate i.v. merely aggravated the usual gastric and cardiac (tigro-vascular) lesions characteristic of DHT alone.[841]

DHT + FeCl₂ i.v.

Thyroid-Parathyroid-Carotid-Body Calciphylaxis

Method 1: Rat (100 g. ♀): DHT (1 mg. p.o.) 1st day + FeCl₂ (to avoid the toxicity of a single large dose, four injections of 1 mg., 2 mg., 3 mg., and again 3 mg. are given, each in 1 ml. water, i.v.) throughout 2d day; killed 6th day.

Results: This syndrome was virtually indistinguishable from that produced by DHT + CrCl₃ i.v. or DHT + CrCl₂ i.v. (Plate IV, *E*). Its most prominent characteristic was calcification in the stroma of the *thyroid, parathyroid,* and *carotid body*. In addition, intense calcinosis occurred also in the *pulmonary septa, pleura, heart, tracheal mucosa, diaphragm,* and to a lesser extent in the *salivary glands, Brunner's glands, pancreas, adrenals,* and *renal cortex*.

The cardiac calcinosis resembled that produced by chromium salts also in that there was a virtually complete, very superficial pericardial calcific covering, which gave the impression of being due to contact with the heavily calcified visceral pleura; in addition there were tigroid streaks of myocardial calcification and calcinosis of the coronary vessels.

Calcium deposition in the stroma of the *urinary passages*—similar to that seen after challenge with chromium salts—was also observed here, but in addition there tended to be such calcification of the *biliary passages* as characterizes the DHT + Fe-OS i.v. syndrome. However, unlike after treatment with Fe-OS, here the choledochus was not dilated. The intensity of the associated *osteitis fibrosa* ran approximately parallel to that of the soft-tissue calcification.

A particularly distinctive feature of the DHT + FeCl₂ i.v. syndrome was calcinosis of the *proventriculus*. The mucosa of the ventriculus is extremely sensitive to the action of calcifiers (DHT, parathyroid hormone) even apart from any calciphylactic response, and the intensity of this gastric calcification is greatly augmented by most of the systemic challengers. However, the mucosa of the proventriculus hardly ever showed any signs of calcinosis when challengers other than FeCl₂ were used (Fig. 71).

Remarks: In rats killed 60 days or more after challenge, plasmocytic infiltrations were common in the affected regions. For example, in the lung, sleeves of plasmocyte accumulations developed around the blood vessels (Fig. 72). However, this type of response occurs in the various calciphylactic syndromes and is by no means specific for treatment with DHT + FeCl₂ i.v.

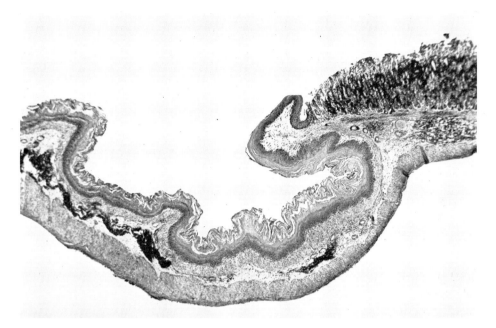

Fig. 71. Calcification in the proventriculus and ventriculus produced by DHT +
FeCl₂ i.v. Rat (100 g. ♀): DHT (1 mg. p.o.) 1st day + FeCl₂ (3 mg. in 1 ml. water, i.v. ×3)
2d day; killed 7th day. Calcification in mucosa of ventriculus (right); pronounced calcium deposition in submucosa of proventriculus, with intense mucosal hyperkeratosis (left and center). (von Kóssa, ×39.)

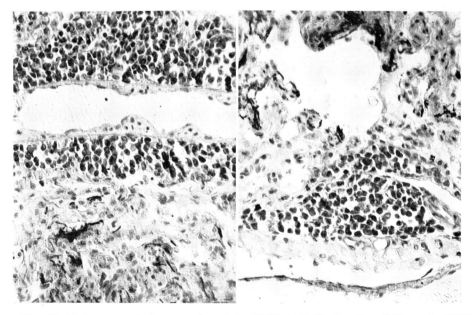

Fig. 72. Pulmonary lesions produced by DHT + FeCl₂ i.v. Rat (100 g. ♀): DHT
(1 mg. p.o.) 1st day + FeCl₂ (1, 2, 3 and 3 mg. always in 1 ml. water, i.v.) throughout 2d day;
killed 60th day. Periarterial heavy plasma-cell infiltrations and calcified collagen fibers in surrounding pulmonary tissue. (von Kóssa + plasma-cell stain, ×320.)

Method 2: Rat (200 g. ♀): DHT (2 mg. p.o.) 1st day + FeCl₂ (2, 4, 6, and 4 mg. in 0.2, 0.4, 0.6, and 0.4 ml. water, respectively, i.v.) throughout 3d day; killed 11th day.

Results: The organ changes in these larger rats were essentially the same as in the 100 g. animals. A particularly striking lesion was a singular form of mesenteric arteriosclerosis, characterized by high-peaked endothelial crests, covered with polynuclear giant cells of endothelial origin (Fig. 73).

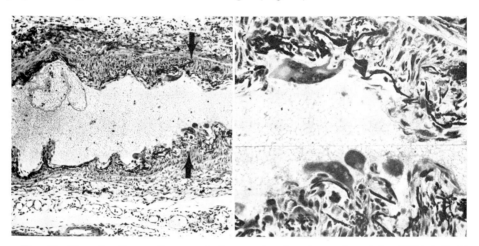

Fig. 73. Singular form of mesenteric arteriosclerosis produced by DHT + FeCl₂ i.v. Rat (200 g. ♀): DHT (2 mg. p.o.) 1st day + FeCl₂ (2, 4, 6 and 4 mg. in 0.2, 0.4, 0.6 and 0.4 ml. water, respectively, i.v.) throughout 3d day; killed 11th day. *Left:* Longitudinal section through mesenteric artery shows singular high-peaked endothelial crests (near left margin), calcified and frequently fragmented fibers in intima, and polynuclear endothelial giant cells protruding into lumen (arrows). (von Kóssa, ×90.) *Right:* Higher magnification of areas marked by arrows in preceding picture. (von Kóssa, ×320.)

DHT + FeCl₃ i.v.

Nonspecific Calcinosis

Method: Rat (100 g. ♀): DHT (1 mg. p.o.) 1st day + FeCl₃ (4 mg. in 0.4 ml. water, i.v. ×4) 2d day; killed 7th day.

Results: Unlike FeCl₂ and other ferrous salts, FeCl₃ produced no evidence of thyroid, parathyroid, or carotid body calcification; it merely accentuated the non-specific calcinosis normally produced by DHT alone. The only detectable change that might have been due to challenge by FeCl₃ was an unusual degree of gastric calcification and some evidence of calcinosis in the region of Brunner's glands.

Discussion: Incidentally, FeCl₃—again unlike the ferrous salts—did not appear to produce any evidence of tachyphylaxis; accordingly the total daily amount of the compound was given in the form of four equal doses, since subsequent increases in dosage were badly tolerated.

Similar experiments, performed with a total dose of 20 mg. of FeCl₃ given during the 2d day under otherwise equal circumstances, still produced only nonspecific calcinosis with particularly pronounced calcification in the gastric mucosa and Brunner's glands. Mortality (among the animals that survived the injection period itself) was zero.

DHT + Fe-Dex i.v.
Pancreatic and Psoriasiform Calciphylaxis

Method 1: Rat (100 g. ♀): DHT (1 mg. p.o.) 1st day + Fe-Dex (1 ml. = 50 mg. Fe, i.v.) 2d day; killed 10th day.

Results: Preponderantly *pancreatic* calcification with subsequent sclerosis (Figs. 74, 75; Plate VI, *B*). Yet, considerable calcinosis occurred also in the stroma of the *duodenum* (particularly Brunner's glands) and the *gastric mucosa*. The *skin* usually showed evidence of calciphylactic psoriasis (cf. p. 45).

Intense iron deposition could be demonstrated histologically not only in the affected sites but also in the RES of the liver and spleen, where it did not induce calcification. Mortality: 50%.[827]

Method 2: Rat (100 g. ♀): DHT (1 mg. p.o.) 1st day + Fe-Dex (1 ml. = 50 mg. Fe, i.v.) 1st day; killed 6th day.

Results: Calcinosis (in order of decreasing intensity) was found in: stomach > Brunner's glands (very rarely, uterus). Mortality: 0.[841]

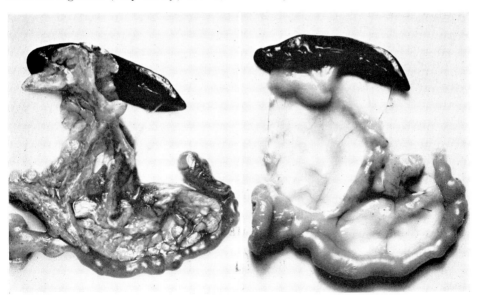

Fig. 74. Pancreatic calcification produced by DHT + Fe-Dex i.v. Two rats (100 g. ♀): DHT (1 mg. p.o.) 1st day + (left) Fe-Dex (1 ml. = 50 mg. Fe, i.v.) 4th day; killed 8th day. *Left:* Intense calcification, contraction and sclerosis of entire pancreas, throughout region between duodenum and spleen. *Right:* Loose, normal structure of pancreas in control animal.

Method 3: Rat (100 g. ♀): DHT (1 mg. p.o.) 1st day + Fe-Dex (1 ml. = 50 mg. Fe, i.v.) 3d day; killed 6th day.

Results: Calcinosis (in order of decreasing intensity) was found in: pancreas, stomach > skin (calciphylactic psoriasis), Brunner's glands > heart (tigro-vascular), duodenum, thymus [traces in liver, omentum, kidney (cortex and cortico-medullary junction), intestine, peritoneum]. Mortality: 70%.

Method 4: Rat (200 g. ♀): DHT (2 mg. p.o.) 1st day + Fe-Dex (1 ml. = 75 mg. Fe, i.v.) 2d or 3d day; killed 6th day.

Results: Calcinosis (in order of decreasing intensity) was found in: pancreas, stomach, Brunner's glands, peritoneal fat > uterus, skin (calciphylactic psoriasis), mesentery > intestine, kidney (cortico-medullary) [traces in thymus, omentum, aorta, duodenum, intestine, renal cortex, heart (tigro-vascular)].[841]

Remarks: In rats (100 g. ♀) sensitized with DHT (1 mg. p.o.) 1st day, challenge by Fe-Dex (1 ml. = 50 mg. Fe, i.v.) produced little pancreatic calcification on 1st day but maximal effects on +2d, +3d, and +4th day. Essentially similar

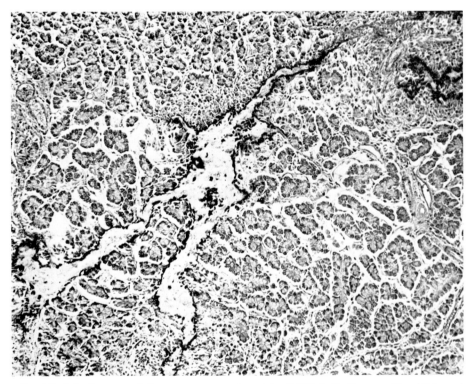

Fig. 75. Calcification of the pancreas produced by DHT + Fe-Dex i.v. Rat (100 g. ♀): DHT (1 mg. p.o.) 1st day + Fe-Dex (1 ml. = 50 mg. Fe, i.v.) 3d day; killed 12th day. Heavily calcified pancreatic stroma areas are necrotic and surrounded by celestin-blue-positive material. (×135.) (Cf. Plate VI, *B*.)

results were obtained in 200 g. rats sensitized by DHT (2 mg. p.o.) and challenged by Fe-Dex (1 ml. = 50–75 mg. i.v.).

DHT + Fe-Dex i.p.

A. Pancreatic and Psoriasiform Calciphylaxis

Method 1: Rat (100 g. ♀): DHT (1 mg. p.o.) 1st day + Fe-Dex (1 ml. = 50 mg. Fe, i.p.) 2d or 3d day; killed 15th day.

Results: Almost immediately after the Fe-Dex injection there appeared irregular, brown (iron-containing) patches on the *skin*, which disappeared almost completely after 24 hours. However, in the course of the next two weeks a nodular, scaly dermatosis developed which remotely resembled psoriasis. Upon gentle removal of the scales fine bleeding points appeared ("Auspitz' sign" of psoriasis). Histologically, dustlike calcium precipitates could be demonstrated in the dermal collagen, but massive calcification did not occur. The dermal capillaries were frequently dilated and occasionally we found microabscesses in the epithelium. It is this lesion that, for want of a better term, we meanwhile designate as "calciphylactic psoriasis."

Among the internal organs, calcification was almost completely limited to the *pancreas* and *duodenum* (Plate V, *B, C, D, E, F*), where it induced intense sclerosis. *Uterine* calcification was virtually never noted.[827]

Calcinosis (in order of decreasing intensity) was found in: pancreas, stomach, Brunner's glands > kidney (cortico-medullary) > heart (tigro-vascular), duodenum [traces in peritoneum, retroperitoneal fat, mesentery, skin (calciphylactic psoriasis), renal cortex, pleura, uterus].[841]

Method 2: Rat (100 g. ♀): DHT (1 mg. p.o.) 1st day + Fe-Dex (1 ml. = 50 mg. Fe, i.p.) 1st day; killed 6th day.

Results: Calcinosis (in order of decreasing intensity) was found in: stomach, skin (calciphylactic psoriasis) [traces in intestine, peritoneum, renal cortex].[841]

Method 3: Rat (100 g. ♀): DHT (1 mg. p.o.) 2d day + Fe-Dex (1 ml. = 50 mg. Fe, i.p.) 1st day; killed 6th day.

Results: Calcinosis was found in: stomach, skin [traces in intestine, peritoneum, renal cortex].[841]

Method 4: Rat (200 g. ♀): DHT (2 mg. p.o.) 1st day + Fe-Dex (1 ml. = 50 mg. Fe, i.p.) 2d or 3d day; killed 8th day.

Results: Intense calcification of *pancreas* and *peritoneal fat*, but not of uterus.[851]

Method 5: Rat (200 g. ♀): DHT (2 mg. p.o.) 1st day + Fe-Dex (1.5 ml. = 75 mg. Fe, i.p.) 2d day; killed 6th day.

Results: Calcinosis (in order of decreasing intensity) was found in: pancreas, stomach, retroperitoneal fat > Brunner's glands > skin (calciphylactic psoriasis), mesentery [traces in kidney (cortico-medullary), thymus, intestine, abdominal wall, uterus, peritoneum, duodenum, liver].

Critical period: Rats (200 g. ♀) sensitized with DHT (1 mg. p.o.) 1st day and challenged with Fe-Dex (2 ml. = 100 mg. Fe, i.p.) responded with maximal pancreatic calcification when challenged on +2d day, somewhat less on 1st or +3d day, while challenge on −4th, −5th and +4th day was virtually ineffective in this respect. Uterine calcification, on the other hand, was most effectively produced by challenge on 1st or −2d day. Calciphylactic psoriasis was observed irrespective of the time of Fe-Dex administration within the period of observation. Essentially similar results were obtained on rats (200 g. ♀) sensitized with DHT (2 mg.) and challenged by Fe-Dex (1 ml. = 50 mg. Fe). Here Fe-Dex produced severe pancreatic calcinosis when given on +2d, +3d, or +4th day, minor pancreatic lesions on 1st day, and no lesions on +8th or −2d to −8th day. On the other hand, maximal uterine calcification occurred upon treatment with Fe-Dex on −2d or −3d day. Cutaneous calcinosis was maximal following injection on 1st or −2d day, but traces of it were noted in rats receiving Fe-Dex any time between the −8th and +8th day.

Healing: In rats killed 60 days after the induction of pancreatic and psoriasiform calciphylaxis there were signs of healing by sclerosis and hyalinization of the stroma. In the pancreas the originally diffuse calcification of the stroma was transformed into homogeneous or preosseous calcified spicules surrounded by granulomatous capsules, or it disappeared completely. However, the pancreatic parenchyma tended to become increasingly more damaged, and if the lesion was severe, finally, most of the acinar tissue as well as Langerhans' islets were replaced by sclerotic scar tissue (Fig. 76).

The process of healing was essentially the same in the skin. Here, in addition to the homogeneous calcified nodules and preosseous tissue, we often found morphea-guttata-like, circumscribed, sclerotic patches in which there was no trace of either calcification or osteogenesis (Fig. 77).

B. Uterine and Psoriasiform Calciphylaxis

Method 6: Rat (200 g. ♀): DHT (1.5 mg. p.o.) 2d day + Fe-Dex (2 ml. = 100 mg. Fe, i.p.) 1st day; killed 15th day.

Results: Immediately after the Fe-Dex injection the brown *cutaneous* patches were even more pronounced here than in 100 g. rats, but they likewise disappeared, gradually being replaced by scaly calciphylactic psoriasis. *Pancreatic* and *duodenal* (Brunner's glands) calcification was noted only occasionally but—unlike in the 100 g. rats—the *uterus* also underwent calcification. This calcinosis became so intense that the uterus could be broken between the fingers like a piece of chalk. Usually the uterine horns assumed a "bamboo-stick" appearance, owing to the formation of fairly thick, calcified rings regularly spaced along their course.[827]

Of course, numerous challengers produce generalized peritoneal calcification when given i.p., and in this case the surface of the uterus is also involved. However, when challenged by Fe-Dex i.p. at the proper critical time for uterine calciphylaxis, there is comparatively little generalized peritoneal calcification, and it is not the superficial subserosal layer, but the endometrium that shows the most pronounced calcinosis. The difference between the two types is particularly evident when challenges by Fe-Dex i.p. and by Fe-OS i.p. are compared. Fe-OS i.p.—as most challengers given i.p., but quite unlike Fe-Dex—produces calcium deposition merely on the serosal surface with secondary inflammatory changes (Fig. 83).

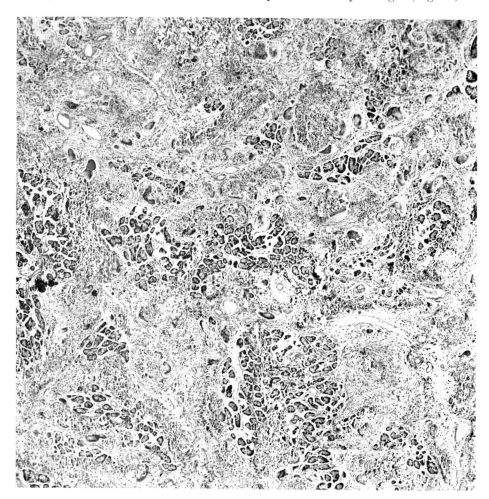

Fig. 76. Severe pancreatic sclerosis produced by DHT + Fe-Dex i.p. Rat (200 g. ♀): DHT (1.5 mg. p.o.) 1st day + Fe-Dex (1 ml. = 50 mg. Fe, i.p.) 2d day; killed 60th day. Advanced sclerosis with hyalinization and giant-cell formation in pancreatic stroma. Almost complete disappearance of excretory parenchyma and Langerhans' islets. (PAS, ×49.)

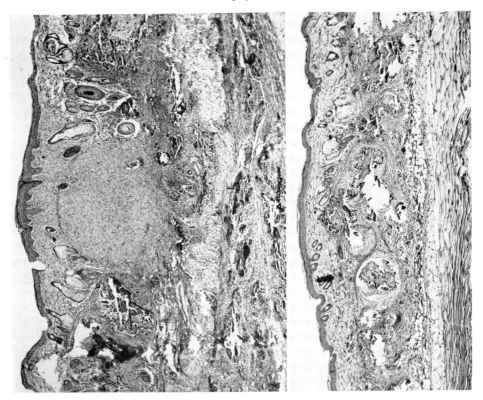

Fig. 77. Cutaneous lesions produced by DHT + Fe-Dex i.p. Rat (200 g. ♀): DHT (1.5 mg. p.o.) 1st day + Fe-Dex (1 ml. = 50 mg. Fe, i.p.) 2d day; killed 60th day. *Left:* Dorsal skin region with morphea-guttata-like, circumscribed, sclerotic patch in center, surrounded by calcified and preosseous nodules. *Right:* Adjacent region with numerous calcified preosseous nodules surrounded by thick sclerotic capsules. (PAS, ×32.)

Method 7: Rat (200 g. ♀): DHT (2 mg. p.o.) 2d, 3d, or 4th day + Fe-Dex (1 ml. = 50–100 mg. Fe, i.p.) 1st day; killed 8th–15th day.

Results: Intense calcification of *uterus*, but not of the pancreas or peritoneal fat. *Calciphylactic psoriasis* developed as an aftermath late during the second week (Figs. 78, 79, 80). Calcinosis (in order of decreasing intensity) was found in: uterus, aorta, stomach, abdominal wall, skin (calciphylactic psoriasis) [traces in peritoneum, Brunner's glands, omentum, heart (tigro-vascular, auricle), pancreas][841] (Figs. 81, 82, 83; Plates V, *E, F;* VI, *A*).

Discussion: If Fe-Dex is given one to two days after DHT (Method 4), only pancreas and peritoneal fat are affected. If Fe-Dex is given one day prior to DHT, there is some calcification in uterus, pancreas, and peritoneal fat. If Fe-Dex is given two or three days prior to DHT (Method 7), calcification is limited to the

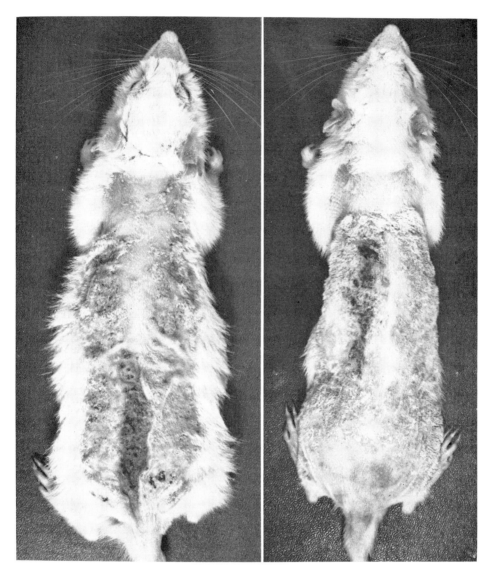

Fig. 78. Calciphylactic psoriasis produced by DHT + Fe-Dex i.p. Rat (200 g. ♀): Fe-Dex (1 ml. = 50 mg. Fe, i.p.) 1st day + DHT (2 mg. p.o.) 4th day; photographed 15th day. *Left:* Extensive nodular calcium infiltration with marked scaling of skin. Scale removal (by gentle scratching along midline over lumbar and sacral regions) caused diffuse surface bleeding corresponding to Auspitz' sign in psoriasis. *Right:* Auspitz' sign in other similarly treated rat with less advanced lesions. (Cf. Fig. 13.)

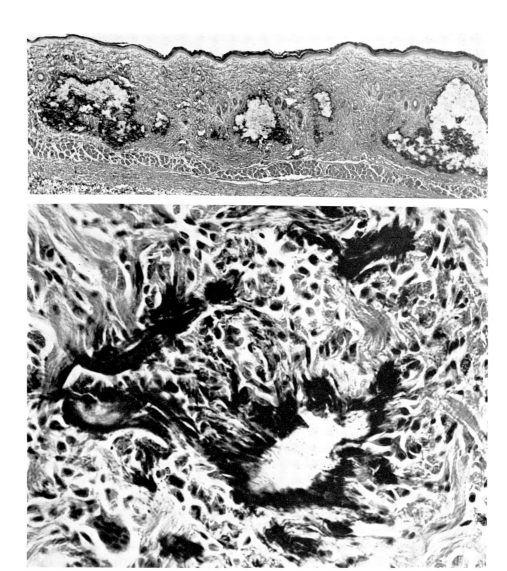

Fig. 79. Calciphylactic psoriasis produced by DHT + Fe-Dex i.p. Rat (200 g. ♀): Fe-Dex (1 ml. = 50 mg. Fe, i.p.) 1st day + DHT (2 mg. p.o.) 2d day; killed 12th day. The skin was scale-covered, somewhat hyperemic and hard, but free of extensive calcified plaque formation. Even gentle removal of scales resulted in surface bleeding. *Top:* Three large, and numerous small, calcified nodules without tendency to coalesce. *Bottom:* High magnification of small calcified nodule within derma region in previous picture. Central white area is necrotic but the surrounding swollen collagen fibers are intensely stained and infiltrated by inflammatory cells, many of which are eosinophilic. (Celestin blue, top ×40, bottom ×480.)

uterus. The importance of the critical period for the selective localization of the lesions was further substantiated on rats (200 g. ♀) sensitized with DHT (2 mg. p.o.) 1st day and challenged with Fe-Dex (1 ml. = 50 mg. Fe, i.v.). This treatment produced maximal pancreatic calcification on +2d and +3d day, a trace response on +4th day and occasionally even on 1st day, but no pancreatic calcification could be produced in this manner on 1st, −2d or −3d day. Uterine calcification, on the other hand, was most pronounced upon challenge on 1st, −2d, and −3d day. Essentially similar results were obtained in rats (200 g. ♀) sensitized with DHT (1 mg. p.o.) and challenged by Fe-Dex (1.5 ml. = 75 mg. Fe, i.v.) on the same day.

On the other hand—as previously stated—younger (100 g.) rats do not tend to develop uterine calcification under any of these conditions.[851]

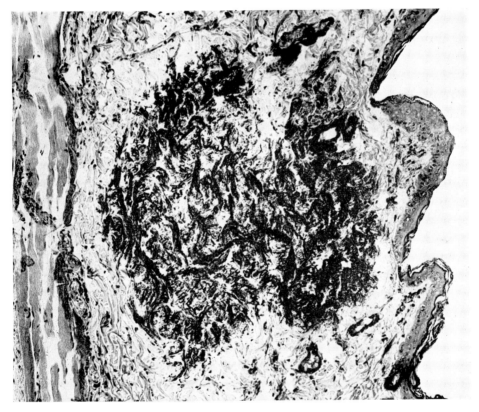

Fig. 80. Calciphylactic psoriasis produced by DHT + Fe-Dex i.p. Rat (200 g. ♀): DHT (2 mg. p.o.) 1st day + Fe-Dex (1 ml. = 50 mg. Fe, i.p.) 2d day; killed 6th day. Skin covered with scales. In derma disseminated roundish nodules containing calcified collagen fibers. (von Kóssa, ×95.)

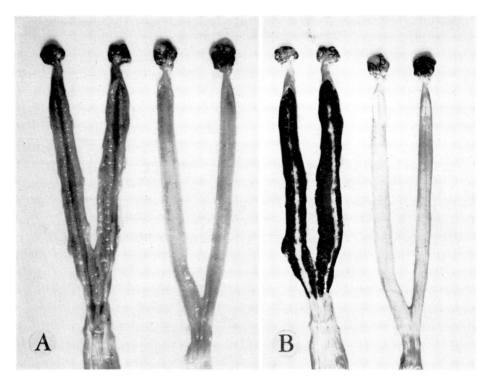

Fig. 81. Calcification of the uterus produced by DHT + Fe-Dex i.p. Two rats (200 g. ♀): DHT (2 mg. p.o.) 2d day + (left) Fe-Dex (2 ml. = 100 mg. Fe, i.p.) 1st day; killed 7th day. *A:* Fresh. *B:* AgNO₃-stained, specimens. Uterine horns (split open) show calcium in submucosa combined treatment, uterus is heavily calcified, except along insertion line of mesometrium. *Right:* No calcification is produced by DHT alone.

Fig. 82. Calcification of the genital fat and uterus produced by DHT + Fe-Dex i.p. Two rats (200 g. ♀): DHT (2 mg. p.o.) 2d day + Fe-Dex (1 ml. = 50 mg. Fe, i.p.) 1st day; killed 9th day. *Left:* Intense calcification of the uterus in the form of rings, which give it a "gooseneck" appearance. *Right:* In second animal only sexual fat in mesometrium is calcified although it received the same treatment (AgNO₃-stain). Such individual variations occur only in rats challenged soon before or after sensitization, that is, during the transition from the "critical period" for uterine to that of pancreatic and peritoneal fat calcification. (Cf. Plate VI, *A.*)

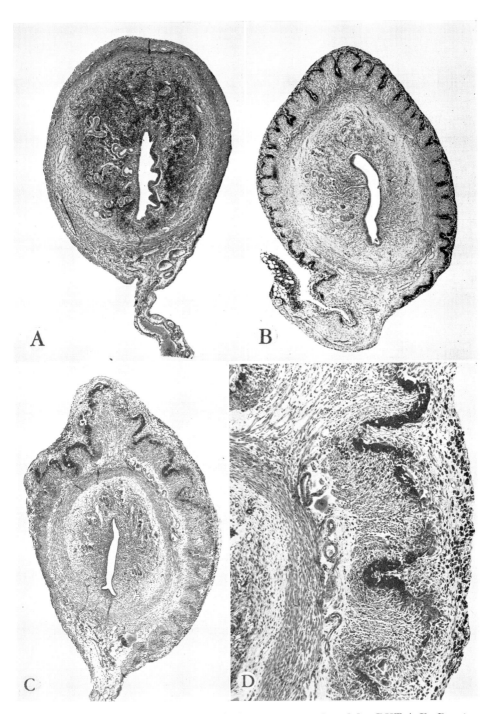

Fig. 83. **Comparison of uterine calcification as produced by DHT + Fe-Dex i.p. and by DHT + Fe-OS i.p.** Four rats (190 g. ♀): DHT (2 mg. p.o.) 2d day + (A) Fe-Dex (1 ml. = 50 mg. Fe, i.p.) 1st day or + (B, C, D) Fe-Os (3 ml. = 60 mg. Fe, i.p.) 1st day; killed 7th day. *A:* Combined treatment with Fe-Dex produced intense calcification of endometrium. (von Kóssa, ×35.) *B, C* and *D:* An even larger dose of Fe-OS invariably caused only thin line of calcification with giant-cell formation underneath peritoneal surface, as part of its topical action when given i.p. (von Kóssa, B, C ×28, D ×80.)

DHT + Fe-Dex i.v. + Insulin s.c.

The "Butterfly and Sleeves" Syndrome

Method: Rat (100 g. ♀): DHT (1 mg. p.o) 1st day + Fe-Dex (1 ml. = 1 mg. Fe, i.v.) 1st day + insulin (10 I.U. in 0.25 ml. water, s.c.) 1st day; killed 7th day. Sugar cubes are made abundantly available to raise insulin resistance.

Results: No obvious changes are visible during the first days after this treatment, but beginning on third or fourth day there appears a singularly shaped cutaneous calcinosis in the face reminiscent of the "butterfly" pattern of lupus erythematosus. On both cheeks there are large wing-shaped patches connected by a thin isthmus across the nose. At the same time the skin above the wrists and ankles undergoes calcification and forms hard circular "sleeves" while the paws themselves remain unaffected. Somewhat less regularly calcified and eventually necrotizing lingual lesions are also noted (Fig. 83*a*).

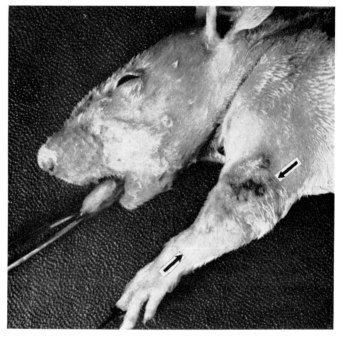

Fig. 83a. "Butterfly and sleeves" syndrome with lingual lesions produced by DHT + Fe-Dex i.v. + insulin s.c. Rat (100 g. ♀): DHT (1 mg. p.o.) 1st day + Fe-Dex (1 ml. = 1 mg. Fe, i.v.) 1st day + insulin (10 I.U. in 0.25 ml. water, s.c.) 1st day; killed 7th day. Butterfly-shaped calcified lesions in the face with a large patch on the cheek which is connected with a similar patch on the other side by a narrow bridge across the nose. There is also a calcified lesion on the side of the tongue, and the forelimb from elbow to wrist (between arrows) is enveloped in a calcified skin-sleeve.

DHT + Fe-Dex i.v. + PMX s.c.

Calciphylactic Dermatomyositis

Method 1: Rat (100 g.♀): DHT (1 mg. p.o.) 1st day + Fe-Dex (1 ml. = 1 mg. Fe, i.v.) 2d day + PMX (2 mg. in 0.2 ml. water, s.c.) 2d day; killed 6th day.

Results: All animals became seriously ill immediately after Fe-Dex + PMX treatment and there was a 40% mortality during the course of observation. Clinically, the most striking features were a pronounced, painful, symmetrical erythema and a nonpitting cutaneous edema of the neck, face (particularly the periorbital region), ears, and frontal extremities. Judging by the few animals that died during the first days of the experiment, the hyperemia and edema also affected the muscles in the same regions as well as the brain.

Beginning on the 3d day and progressing to the end of the experiment, there developed a patchy stomatitis while the affected skin regions became indurated and scaly, although the erythroderma tended to disappear. Finally, severe muscular weakness set in.

At autopsy, the most striking change was a calcific infiltration of the skin, subcutaneous tissue, fasciae, and muscles; this was particularly prominent around the face, ears, neck, and frontal extremities. In the affected regions the muscles assumed a grayish, light color and a peculiar doughy consistency. At the same time, there developed a moderate degree of cortical nephrocalcinosis and occasionally inflammation with calcification in the myocardium.

The most evident histologic changes in the *skin* were patchy liquefaction necrosis of the epidermal junction, mucoid degeneration of connective tissue and subcutaneous fat, with diffuse clusters of fine calcium granules. Occasionally the surface epithelium became detached in the form of scales. The blood vessels were engorged, especially in the nuchal region, but perivascular infiltration was rare.

In the *musculature*, degenerative and inflammatory changes varied greatly in intensity, but usually the lesions were severest in the regions covered by the most markedly affected skin. The cross-striation tended to disappear, the sarcoplasm became swollen, homogeneous, and often fragmented; in certain patches it disappeared completely, while the nuclei exhibited intense proliferation. Here the interstitial tissue also contained numerous minute clusters of calcium granules (Figs. 84, 85; Plate VII, *D*).

Essentially similar changes were sometimes observed around the *joints* in association with panniculitis and mild periarticular calcification, especially in the elbow-, knee-, and shoulder-joints. In some places, fat and muscle were completely replaced by inflamed fibrous tissue.

The *myocardium* was less constantly affected but, where present, the lesions histologically resembled those seen in skeletal muscles; they exhibited a particular tendency to localize near the apex of the heart. Sometimes the cardiac valves were massively calcified, but this was more common when treatment with Fe-Dex + PMX was given on the third day after DHT-sensitization, which appears to be the peak of the critical period for this type of response (Fig. 86).

The *mediastinum* was always heavily calcified and the calcinosis occasionally extended into the esophagus (Fig. 87). However, here calcification was usually limited to the connective tissue around that portion of the esophagus which is in direct contact with the mediastinum. It appears to be a secondary consequence of calcification in the pulmonary hilus and the adjacent fasciae. This change differs distinctly from the primarily esophageal submucosa calcification that characterizes, for example, the DHT + Thorotrast® i.v. or DHT + Fe-Din i.v. syndromes.

The *bones* exhibited a uniformly moderate degree of porosis.

An entirely unexpected change occurred in the *mastocytes* of all affected regions. In the rat the skin normally contains very many compact, small mastocytes,

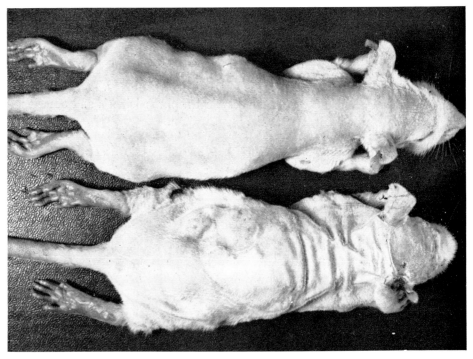

Fig. 84. **Calciphylactic dermatomyositis produced by DHT + Fe-Dex i.v. + PMX s.c.** Two rats (100 g. ♀): DHT (1 mg. p.o.) 1st day + Fe-Dex (1 ml. = 1 mg. Fe, i.v.) 2d day + (bottom) PMX (2 mg. in 0.2 ml. water, s.c. in left flank region) 2d day; killed 6th day. *Top:* Combined treatment with DHT + small dose of Fe-Dex produced no obvious macroscopically visible change. *Bottom:* Additional administration of PMX elicited particularly severe calciphylactic dermatomyositis, characterized by thick infiltration of skin and by swelling of musculature, especially in head and neck regions.

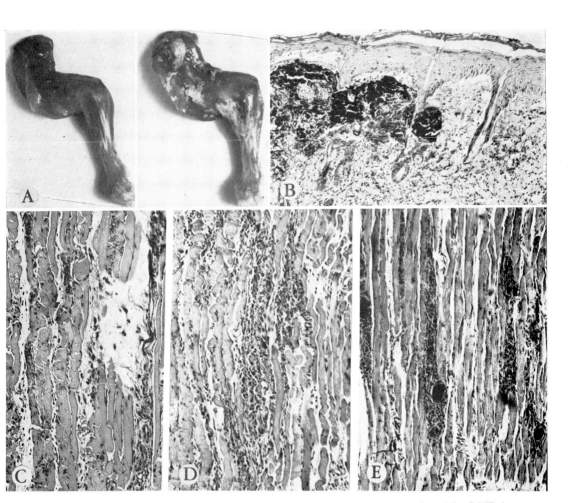

**Fig. 85. General appearance of the musculocutaneous lesions produced by DHT +
Fe-Dex i.v. + PMX s.c.** Two rats: DHT + Fe-Dex + (all but A left) PMX. *A:* Only animal
on right shows lesions in and around muscles of left front paw. *B:* Histologic appearance of
severely affected skin after DHT + PMX + Fe-Dex. Scaling with inflammation and calcification of derma. Liquefaction necrosis along epithelial attachment and (left upper corner) within
epithelium itself. (von Kóssa, ×120.) *C:* Edema, hyalinization and fragmentation of muscle
fibers in acute stage. (von Kóssa, ×120.) *D* and *E:* Nuclear proliferation and inflammation in
more advanced stage. Dark spots correspond to calcium deposits. (von Kóssa, ×120.) (Cf.
Plate VII, *A, B.*)

(After Selye *et al.*,[843] courtesy Canad. M.A.J.)

which are so intensely filled with granules that the nucleus is hardly visible. In the affected regions, such normal mastocytes could never be found—not even in the snout and the base of the ears, which usually contain the greatest mastocyte accumulations. Instead, small clusters of minute calcified granules were seen distributed in approximately the same arrangement and location that is characteristic of mastocytes. On sections simultaneously stained with the von Kóssa technique (for calcium) and with cresyl violet, toluidine blue, or methylene blue (for mastocytes), these clusters almost invariably contained both regular small granules that stained metachromatically with mastocyte dyes and irregularly shaped larger granules tingible with von Kossa's stain. In many instances the nucleus and the swollen, vacuolated cytoplasm of the mastocytes could be clearly distinguished in the midst of these clusters[843] (Fig. 88).

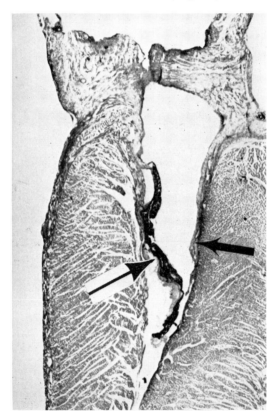

Fig. 86. Calcification of cardiac valve produced by DHT + Fe-Dex i.v. + PMX s.c. Rat (100 g. ♀): DHT (1 mg. p.o.) 1st day + Fe-Dex (1 ml. = 1 mg. Fe, i.v.) 3d day + PMX (300 μg. in 0.2 ml. water, s.c. in flank region) 3d day; died 5th day. Solid calcification of one tricuspid valve leaflet (thin arrow), while the other (thick arrow) remains free of calcium. (von Kóssa, ×22.)

Method 2: Qualitatively similar but much more intense lesions are produced if treatment with Fe-Dex + PMX is given on the 3d day after sensitization with DHT. In this case, under otherwise similar circumstances, both the sensitizing dose of DHT and the challenging dose of PMX can be decreased to 500 μg. without diminishing the severity of the resulting organ changes.[837a]

Discussion: Under comparable conditions neither DHT nor Fe-Dex, nor combined treatment with DHT + Fe-Dex produces this syndrome. PMX alone induces the usual anaphylactoid inflammation of the skin, particularly in the acral regions. This is accompanied by mastocyte degranulation, but lasts only for a few

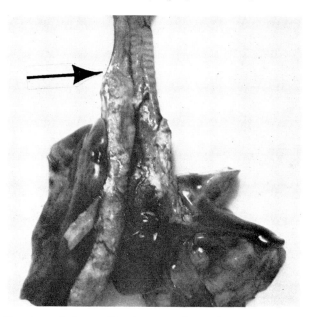

Fig. 87. Calcification of the mediastinum and esophagus produced by DHT + Fe-Dex i.v. + PMX s.c. Rat (100 g. ♀): DHT (1 mg. p.o.) 1st day + Fe-Dex (1 ml. = 1 mg. Fe, i.v.) 3d day + PMX (500 μg. in 0.2 ml. water., s.c. in flank region) 3d day; killed 6th day. Diffuse calcium deposition in mediastinum and mediastinal portion of esophagus; esophageal wall above this level (arrow) remains free of calcium.

hours and never induces calcification or even lasting inflammation. DHT + PMX is slightly effective in itself (without Fe-Dex) in inducing a longer lasting erythroderma with moderate mastocyte-granule calcification, especially when 2 mg. of PMX are given s.c. two days after 1 mg. of DHT p.o. Apparently, Fe-Dex greatly sensitizes for this response, but is not indispensable. As we shall see (cf. "Speculations"), iron enhances calcification under various conditions, and presumably here the discharged mastocyte granules act as vital mordants and capture calcium, especially in the presence of iron. The resulting calcified granules then incrustate

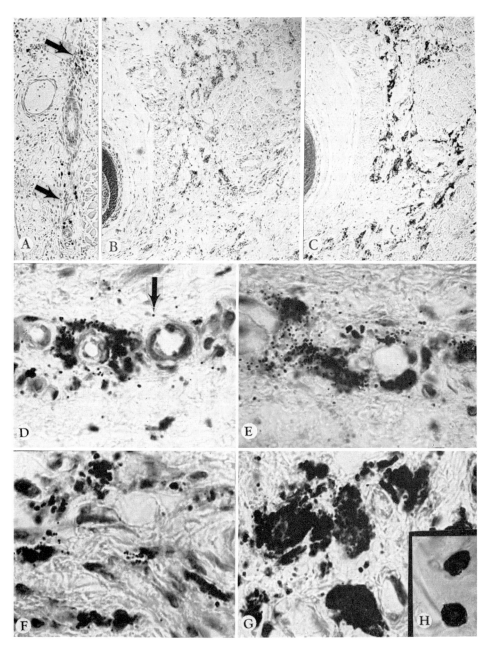

Fig. 88. Mast cell "explosion" and calcification produced by DHT + Fe-Dex i.v. + PMX s.c. *A:* Compact mast cells (on slide purple, here black) in normal subcutaneous tissue. Main accumulations marked by arrows. No trace of calcification. (von Kóssa + methylene blue, ×120.) *B:* Distribution of "exploded" mast cells in subcutaneous tissue near bristle hair of lip after treatment with DHT + Fe-Dex + PMX. The granules (on slide purple, here gray) have been discharged into surroundings. (Methylene blue, ×120.) *C:* Adjacent section stained both for mast cell granules (methylene blue) and for calcium (von Kóssa). Each cluster corresponds to mixture of uncalcified (here gray) and calcified (black both on slide and here) mast cell granules. (×120.) *D, E, F* and *G:* Successive stages in calcification of discharged mast cell granules. Uncalcified granules are purple, small and regular (one marked by arrow in "D"), while upon calcification they become larger and coalesce into black clumps. *H:* Two normal mast cells for comparison. (von Kóssa + methylene blue, ×1000.)

(After Selye *et al.*,[843] courtesy Canad. M.A.J.)

connective-tissue fibers and cause more or less evanescent calcinosis followed by intense inflammation and sclerosis.[843]

During the late stages in the **evolution** of the calciphylactic dermatomyositis syndrome, the skin changes become increasingly more reminiscent of those produced by direct cutaneous challenge or intravenous injection of albumen in the sensitized rat: calcification progresses to the surface, the affected skin exfoliates and a new dermal covering develops underneath. At first the new skin is sensitive to touch, its surface epithelium is thin, and it contains few hair follicles and sebaceous glands. However, unless exfoliation affects the deepest layers, the new skin gradually resumes an approximately normal appearance. When even the deep layers are affected, healing occurs without neoformation of cutaneous appendages; the surface epithelium can be either atrophic or hypertrophic. In such instances, the resemblance of the experimental lesions to clinical scleroderma may become very striking (Fig. 89; Plate VII, *C*).

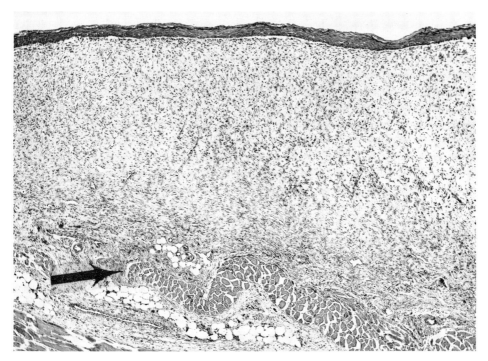

Fig. 89. **Typical calciphylactic scleroderma produced by DHT + Fe-Dex i.v. + PMX s.c.** Rat (100 g. ♀): DHT (1 mg. p.o.) 1st day + Fe-Dex (1 ml. = 1 mg. Fe, i.v.) 4th day + PMX (2 mg. in 0.2 ml. water, s.c. in flank region) 4th day; killed 60th day. From flattened epithelium to cutaneous muscle (arrow), entire cutis consists of dense connective tissue without cutaneous appendages or fat. Calcification no longer detectable. (von Kóssa, ×42.)

DHT + Fe-Din i.v.
Calciphylactic Scleroderma with Esophageal
Calcinosis and Arthritis

Method 1: Rat (100 g. ♀): DHT (1 mg. p.o.) 1st day + Fe-Din (1 ml. = 20 mg. Fe, i.v.) 2d day; killed 6th day.

Results: This syndrome was almost indistinguishable from that obtained by DHT + Thorotrast® i.v. The *cutaneous* lesions had a very characteristic distribution in that they localized primarily around the snout, the eyes, and the roots of

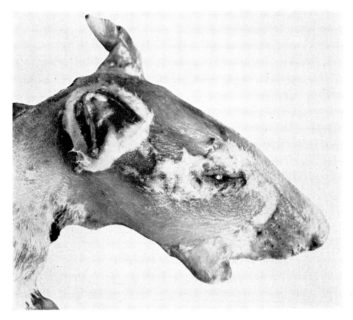

Fig. 90. Cutaneous calcinosis of the face produced by DHT + Fe-Din i.v. Rat (100 g. ♀): DHT (1 mg. p.o.) 1st day + Fe-Din (1 ml. = 20 mg. Fe, i.v.) 2d day; died 5th day. After shaving head and cutting off right external ear at root, white calcium deposits become clearly visible in skin of snout, lips, eyelids and their surroundings, as well as at root of external ear.

the ears (Fig. 90). Histologically the calcium deposition was seen to occur mainly along the connective-tissue fibers, although some mastocyte degranulation with consequent calcification of the discharged particles was usually also evident, especially during the early phases. There were some diffuse macular calcifications elsewhere on the skin surface, but these were comparatively mild. As the skin lesions healed, sclerosis gradually replaced calcinosis, so that scleroderma-like pictures resulted. Occasionally, ring-shaped cutaneous lesions of this type developed around the wrists with consequent edema of the forepaws comparable to the clinical picture of "annular scleroderma" (Fig. 91). On sections stained with the Prussian-blue technique, ferrification was seen to precede calcification in virtually every location.

Essentially similar changes with ferrification followed by calcinosis and sclerosis were observed in the *esophageal mucosa, palate, stomach, Brunner's glands, renal cortex, mediastinum, and heart* (tigro-vascular). The perioral lesions frequently progressed to the buccal mucosa and, in conjunction with the esophageal calcinosis, produced great difficulties in food ingestion and swallowing. Hence, the animals had to be given some soft food (e.g., rice boiled in milk) to keep them alive. Even so, mortality was approximately 60%.

Calcareous arthritis was another very characteristic feature of this syndrome. Calcinosis occurred in the bursae—especially those of the knee and hip joints—as well as in the surrounding connective tissue and muscles. These changes led to inflammation with cellular pyknosis and the accumulation of nuclear debris which resembled the "hematoxylin bodies" of lupus erythematosus. In the affected skeletal parts there was intense periosteal new-bone formation.

In all these respects the DHT + Fe-Din i.v. syndrome resembled that pro-

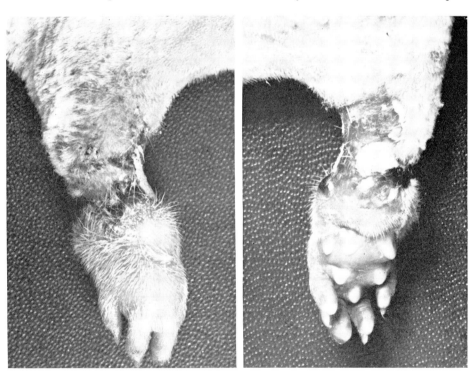

Fig. 91. Calciphylactic "annular scleroderma" produced by DHT + Fe-Din i.v. Rat (200 g. ♀): DHT (2 mg. p.o.) 1st day + Fe-Din (1 ml. = 20 mg. Fe, i.v.) 2d day; photographed 34th day. As in annular scleroderma of man, constrictive skin lesion surrounding forelimb (proximad from carpal region) induces pronounced edema in paw.

duced by DHT + Thorotrast® i.v.; but in addition, we occasionally saw *pancreatic* calcification and *ocular* changes in the former, while such alterations were hardly ever observed in the latter. The ocular lesions consisted of keratitis and iridocyclitis accompanied by calcification of the palpebrae around Meibom's glands. Harder's gland was sometimes infiltrated with lymphatic tissue.

Calcinosis also occurred in the *adrenals*, particularly in the stroma of the medulla. The "medullary cortical cells" (lipid-containing cortical-type cells diffusely distributed through the medulla) tended to proliferate and many of them assumed the aspect of ganglion cells in that the nucleus became vesicular and large, while strongly basophilic Nissl-body-like inclusions appeared in the cytoplasm. The true ganglion cells of the medulla underwent degeneration with nuclear pyknosis and the formation of vacuoles which often contained iron or calcium inclusions.

Finally, in some animals ferrification with subsequent calcification was observed in *lymph nodes* and in the *choroid plexus*.

In the course of their **evolution** and **healing**, the lesions produced by this technique (and minor modifications of it) underwent preosseous transformation or suppuration with subsequent encapsulation, often forming subcutaneous or deep-seated abscesses. Only the calcified plaques near the surface, especially in the lips and tongue, healed by the gradual extrusion of the calcified masses. This process sometimes resulted in severe distortion of the face with extensive scarring (Fig. 92).

After two or three months a surprisingly large number of these animals developed multiple bronchiectases associated with heavy sclerosis of the calcified bronchi. It is questionable whether there is any causal relationship between the initial, diffuse, pulmonary calcinosis and the subsequent appearance of suppurating bronchiectases, since occasionally the latter also occur in untreated controls. The possibility must be considered, however, that chronic pulmonary fibrosis induced by calciphylactic means can predispose the rat for the formation of bronchiectasis.

The esophageal calcification persisted for several months, but gradually tended to develop into circumscribed, encapsulated aggregates of calcified masses which often led to intense fibrosis and ulcer formation (Fig. 93).

Method 2: Rat (200 g. ♀): DHT (2 mg. p.o.) 1st day + Fe-Din (1 ml. = 20 mg. Fe, i.v.) 2d day; killed 6th day.

Results: Calcinosis (in order of decreasing intensity) was found in: face, esophagus, Brunner's glands > joints, skin > heart (tigro-vascular), stomach, pancreas. Mortality: 50%.

Remarks: The manifestations of this syndrome were essentially the same in 100 g. and 200 g. rats, except that the joint lesions tended to become increasingly more prominent with advancing **age**.

The **healing** of the lesions progressed as usual: the calcified connective-tissue plaques near the surface of the skin were eliminated through exfoliation (Fig. 94;

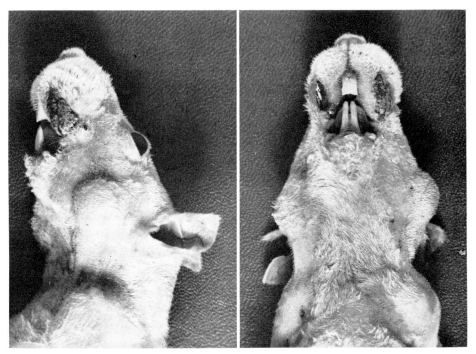

Fig. 92. Evolution of facial lesions produced by DHT + Fe-Din i.v. Rat (100 g. ♀):
DHT (1 mg. p.o.) 1st day + Fe-Din (0.5 ml. = 10 mg. Fe, i.v.) 2d day; photographed 60th
day. The extensive facial calcinosis that developed during first few days after challenge is now
in process of healing by scar formation in lower lip and by extrusion of calcified masses on both
sides of upper lip. Symmetrical bilateral swellings in masseter region correspond to abscesses
formed around necrotic calcified material.

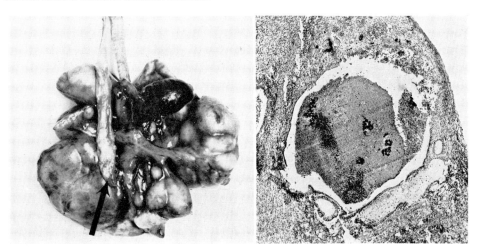

Fig. 93. Evolution of pulmonary lesions produced by DHT + Fe-Din i.v. Rat (100 g. ♀):
DHT (1 mg. p.o.) 1st day + Fe-Din (0.5 ml. = 10 mg. Fe, i.v.) 2d day; killed 63d day.
Left: From dorsal aspect of mediastinum, calcification in large bronchi, as well as fibrocalcareous
masses in mediastinal portion of esophagus (arrow), are still visible. Lung is almost completely
transformed into multiple suppurating bronchiectatic cavities attached to bronchi in grapelike
fashion. Here, extensive pulmonary calcinosis may have acted as predisposing element in formation of bronchiectases; however, sometimes these do occur spontaneously in the rat. *Right:*
Large bronchiectatic focus filled with pus. Calcium precipitates (black) both in pus and in
surrounding pulmonary tissue. (von Kóssa, ×26.)

Plate VI, *E*), while deep-seated plaques tended to be fragmented and transformed into preosseous tissue foci surrounded by Langhans' giant cells and connective tissue.

DHT + Fe-OS i.v.

A. Auriculo-Biliary Calciphylaxis

Method 1: Rat (100 g. ♀): DHT (1 mg. p.o.) 1st day + Fe-OS (1 ml. = 20 mg. Fe, i.v.) 1st or 2d day; killed 5th–10th day.

Results: The most striking macroscopically detectable change was the whiteness of the left *auricular appendage*. Frequently there were also tigroid streaks of white, calcified muscle bundles beneath the epicardium of the *ventricles*, especially around the coronary veins and occasionally the *coronary arteries* could be distinguished as white lines. The affected parts contained histochemically demonstrable iron and calcium deposits (Plate VIII, *A*).

In addition, there was *nephrocalcinosis*, strictly limited to the stroma of the cortex and some glomerular loops. The medullary rays were never affected (Fig. 95; Plate IX, *B*, *D*). There was also calcification in the *pulmonary septa* and

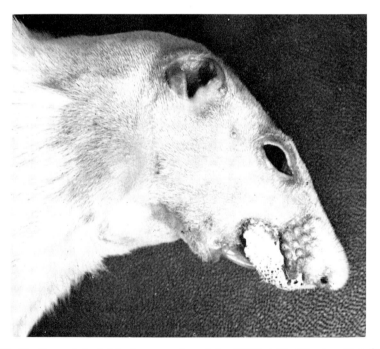

Fig. 94. Healing of facial lesions produced by DHT + Fe-Din i.v. Rat (100 g. ♀): DHT (1 mg. p.o.) 1st day + Fe-Din (0.35 ml. = 7 mg. Fe, i.v.) 2d day; photographed 60th day. During the first two weeks after challenge, animal had widespread calcinosis of lips and ears. Here two months later, ears have undergone spontaneous amputation and large portions of the calcified right lip are about to be detached and rejected.

gastric mucosa. Calcification and sclerosis of the *hepatic veins* and the stroma around the extrahepatic *bile ducts* were frequently combined with complete functional obstruction of the ampulla of Vater and subsequent retention icterus (Plate VIII, *E*). The stroma of *Brunner's glands* also became calcified and occasionally the *duodenum* underwent complete necrosis, presumably as a consequence of vascular thrombosis, since histologic examination showed thrombi in many duodenal arteries. The mortality was 20%.[401, 826]

Critical period: In rats (100 g. ♀) sensitized with DHT (1 mg. p.o.) 1st day challenge by Fe-OS (1 ml. = 20 mg. Fe, i.v.) produced the auricular type of cardiac calcification most effectively on the 1st, somewhat less on the +2d, and least effectively on the +3d, day; on the +4th day it was minimal. In these young rats, bile duct and duodenal calcinosis was usually absent.

Method 2: Rat (200 g. ♀): DHT (1–2 mg. p.o.) 1st day + Fe-OS (1–2 ml. = 20–40 mg. Fe, i.v.) 1st or 2d day; killed 4th–10th day.

Results: Here, the organ changes were essentially the same as in the 100 g. rats treated according to Method 1, but the lesions in the *biliary tract and duo-*

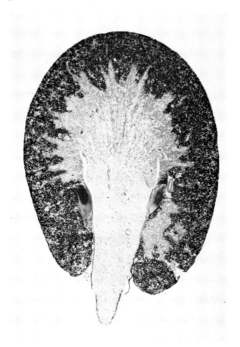

Fig. 95. Selective calcification of the renal cortex stroma produced by DHT + Fe-OS i.v. Rat (100 g. ♀): Fe-OS (1 ml. = 20 mg. Fe, i.v.) 1st and 2d day + DHT (1.5 mg. p.o.) 2d day; killed 6th day. Calcium deposition is sharply limited to stroma of renal cortex and some glomerular loops. Medullary rays remain unaffected. (Celestin blue, ×8.) (Cf. Plate IX, *B, D*.)
[After Grasso and Selye,[401] courtesy Oliver & Boyd Ltd. (J. Path. and Bact.).]

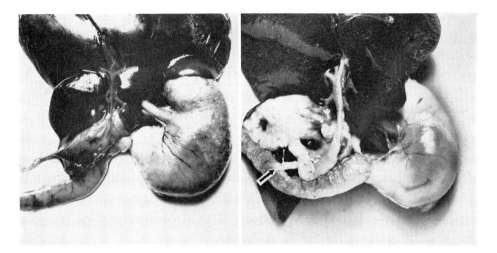

Fig. 96. Calcific cholangitis produced by DHT + Fe-OS i.v. Two rats (220 g. ♀): DHT (1 mg. p.o.) 1st day + (right) Fe-OS (1.5 ml. = 30 mg. Fe, i.v.) 1st day; killed 4th day. *Left:* No evident change in control animal. *Right:* Combined treatment caused dilatation, inflammation and calcareous infiltration of all extrahepatic bile duct branches, white calcified linear streaks in liver and irregularly shaped spots in duodenal wall. Pancreas calcified only in immediate vicinity of bile duct. Particularly pronounced calcification at terminal portion of bile duct, where principal pancreatic duct enters it above papilla of Vater (arrow).

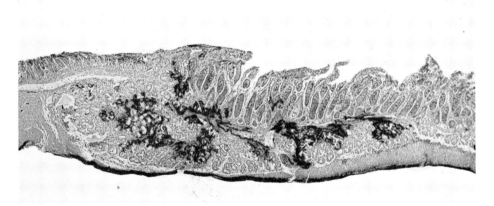

Fig. 97. Calcification of Brunner's glands produced by DHT + Fe-OS i.v. Rat (200 g. ♀): DHT (2 mg. p.o.) 1st day + Fe-OS (1 ml. = 20 mg. Fe, i.v.) 1st day; killed 6th day. Longitudinal section through pylorus. Selective calcium deposition in stroma of Brunner's glands, though stroma of duodenal mucosa (right) also shows minor patches of calcium deposition. (Celestin blue, ×39.)

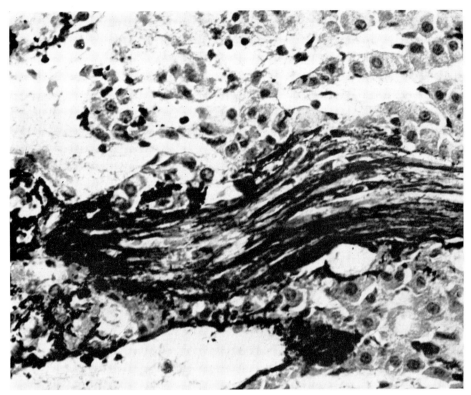

Fig. 98. Calcification of adrenal nerve produced by DHT + Fe-OS i.v. Rat (200 g. ♀):
DHT (1 mg. p.o.) 1st and 2d day + Fe-OS (1.5 ml. = 7 mg. Fe, i.v.) 1st day; killed 7th
day. Intense calcium incrustation between fibers of nerve coursing through adrenal medulla.
(von Kóssa, ×550.)

denum were more severe and constant[827] (Fig. 96; Plate VIII, *C, D*). Calcinosis
in the stroma of *Brunner's glands* (Fig. 97) was always very pronounced. Frequently there was calcification in the *adrenals*, especially along the endothelial covering of the sinusoids and often extending into the adrenal medullary
nerves (Fig. 98).

Remarks: While most of the organ changes just described are manifestations of
calciphylaxis, the *dilatation of the bile ducts*—associated with obstruction of the
papilla of Vater and frequently conducive to hemorrhagic *pancreatitis*—appears to
be largely independent of sensitization (Figs. 99, 100); these changes are the result
of simple intoxication with this particular iron preparation. On the other hand, the
subsequent calcification of the biliary tract and hepatic vessels is dependent upon
sensitization with DHT and may therefore be regarded as calciphylactic.[865d]

B. Occlusive Coronary Lesions

Method: Rat (100 g. ♀): DHT (1 mg. p.o.) 1st day + Fe-OS (1 ml. = 20 mg. Fe,
i.v.) 10th day; killed 14th day.

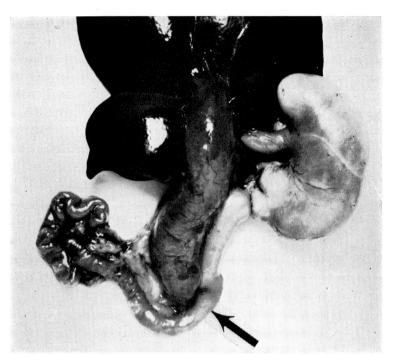

Fig. 99. Biliary tract lesions produced by Fe-OS i.v. Rat (200 g. ♀): Fe-OS (1 ml. = 20 mg. Fe, i.v.) 1st, 3d and 5th day; killed 12th day. Extraordinarily pronounced dilatation of bile duct with pigmentation of stenosed ampulla of Vater (arrow).

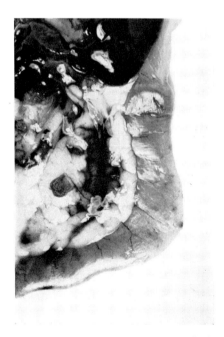

Fig. 100. Hemorrhagic pancreatitis with dilatation of the bile duct produced by Fe-OS i.v. Rat (220 g. ♀): Fe-OS (1.5 ml. = 30 mg. Fe., i.v. ×2) 1st day; died 2d day. Marked dilatation of bile duct with hemorrhagic pancreatitis along its course from liver (top) to papilla of Vater (lower left corner).

Results: Fe-OS administered 10 days after DHT treatment produced an altogether different syndrome. In this case there was no auricular calcification, while the *myocardial necroses* were much more extensive and more irregularly distributed throughout the myocardium. Even over extensive regions of necrosis the muscle layer just underneath the endocardium usually remained intact. This fact is particularly significant since the myocardial necroses produced in the rat by various hormones, electrolytes, or dietary measures—although infarct-like in many other respects—differ from the true infarcts induced by coronary ligature precisely in that only the latter tend to affect the subendocardial muscle layers selectively[823] (Fig. 101).

In similarly treated animals, there was also calcification in all the branches of the *coronary* arterial system and the calcium deposits formed plaques surrounded by proliferating fibrous tissue. In these foci there was an increase in the number of endothelial and subintimal cells, many of which contained fine, Prussian-blue-positive granules, some being actually transformed into iron-laden, large macrophages. As the lesions developed, these phagocytes increased in number and became aggregated in clusters within the subendothelial connective tissue. Such changes were rather reminiscent of those seen in man when Mönckeberg's medial calcifying sclerosis occurs together with atherosclerosis in the same vessel, except that here iron was phagocytosed instead of lipid. In many arteries there developed an intense subintimal edema, which led to considerable reduction of the vascular lumen. Sometimes the lumina became completely occluded and this resulted in infarction of the affected myocardium. The mortality in such experiments varied between 30 and 90%.

Discussion: It is assumed that during the critical period (1st, 2d day) of calciphylaxis Fe-OS acted as a vital mordant and prepared the tissues for calcification. However, when given after the critical period (10th day) the iron no longer acted as a mordant; hence no auricular calcification resulted, but a different "atheroma-like" occlusive cardiopathy.[401]

DHT + Fe-OS i.p.
Peritoneal Calciphylaxis

Method 1: Rat (100 g. ♀): DHT (1 mg. p.o.) 1st day + Fe-OS (1 ml. = 20 mg. Fe, i.p.) 1st day; killed 6th day.

Results: When given i.p., Fe-OS produced a typical peritoneal calciphylaxis, such as is obtained with most other challengers if they are administered by this route to the DHT-sensitized rat. In addition the DHT-induced nonspecific calcinosis was somewhat accentuated.

Calcinosis (in order of decreasing intensity) was found in: diaphragm, omentum and abdominal wall [with traces in the kidney (cortico-medullary), heart (tigro-vascular), aorta, stomach, Brunner's glands, and thymic lymph nodes].

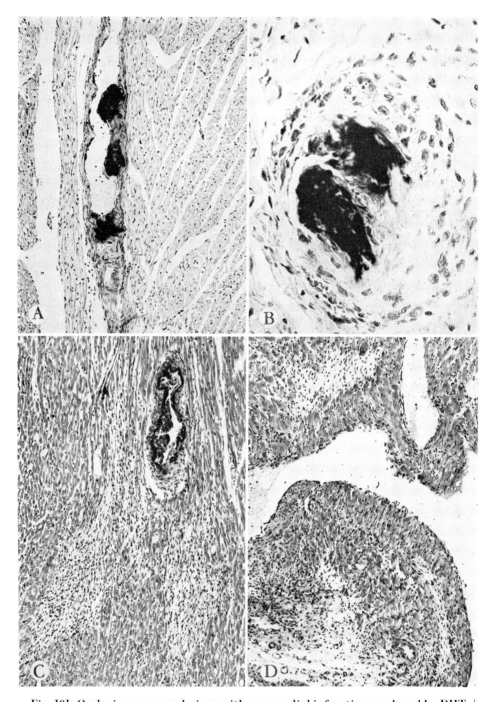

**Fig. 101. Occlusive coronary lesions with myocardial infarction produced by DHT +
Fe-OS i.v.** Rat (100 g. ♀): DHT (1.5 mg. p.o.) 1st day + Fe-OS (1 ml. = 20 mg. Fe, i.v.)
10th day; killed 12th day. *A:* Heavy iron deposition in proliferating subintimal plaques encroach-
ing deep into lumen. (Pearl stain, ×100.) *B:* Virtually complete obliteration of coronary artery
by similar iron-containing plaque. (Pearl stain, ×360.) *C:* Myocardial infarct in vicinity of
artery with lumen narrowed by subintimal plaque, calcification occurring only in media. (von
Kóssa, ×100.) *D:* Around two small myocardial infarcts, subintimal muscle layer is characteristically preserved. (von Kóssa, ×100.)

[After Grasso and Selye,[401] courtesy Oliver & Boyd Ltd. (J. Path. and Bact.).]

Critical period: Essentially similar but still more severe lesions are obtained if under the same circumstances Fe-OS is injected i.p. on 2d day. Treatment with Fe-OS on 4th day is somewhat less effective.[841]

Method 2: Rat (200 g. ♀): DHT (2 mg. p.o.) 1st day + Fe-OS (1 ml. = 20 mg. Fe, i.p.) 2d day; killed 10th day.

Results: The lesions were essentially the same in these older rats as those obtained with Method 1 in younger animals.[827]

DHT + FeSO₄ i.v.
Thyroid-Parathyroid-Carotid-Body Calciphylaxis

Method: Rat (200 g. ♀): DHT (2 mg. p.o.) 1st day + FeSO₄ (2, 4, and 6 mg. i.v. in 0.2, 0.4, and 0.6 ml. water, respectively) 2d day; killed 5th day.

Results: The sulfate produced essentially the same response as the chloride (cf. p. 112), so that we need not discuss these experiments in detail here. It suffices to point out that the intestinal lesions were often very obvious and exhibited the lacelike pattern of calcification that reflects the arborizing course of the intestinal vessels (Fig. 102; Plate X, *B*).

DHT + Fe-Sol i.v.
Atypical Calciphylactic Scleroderma

Method: Rat (100 g. ♀): DHT (1 mg. p.o.) 1st day + Fe-Sol (11 mg. in 0.3 ml. water, i.v.) 2d day; killed 6th day.

Results: Calcinosis (in order of decreasing intensity) was found in: stomach > renal cortex, Brunner's glands [traces in skin, esophagus, face, heart].[841]

DHT + Ga₂(SO₄)₃ i.v.
No Change

Method: Rat (100 g. ♀): DHT (1 mg. p.o.) 1st day + Ga₂(SO₄)₃ (30 mg. in 3 ml. water, i.v.) 2d day; killed 6th day.

Results: No aggravation of the usual, mild nonspecific calcinosis produced by this dose of DHT. Mortality: 50%.

DHT + Gelatin s.c.
No Change

Method: Rat (100 g. ♀): DHT (1 mg. p.o.) 1st day + gelatin (1 mg. in 0.2 ml. water, s.c.) 2d day; killed 6th day.

Results: Nonspecific calcinosis not aggravated by this small dose of gelatin.

DHT + Glucocorticoids s.c.
Thymic Calciphylaxis

Method: Rat (100 g. ♀): DHT (1 mg. p.o.) 1st day + triamcinolone (2 mg. in 0.5 ml. water, s.c.) 2d day; killed 6th day.

Results: Intensive selective calcification of the thymus was readily detectable at autopsy by the hardness and whiteness of the organ (Fig. 103; Plate X, *A*). Histologic examination showed that most of the calcium was located within the cortex in degenerating thymocytes, but some calcified granules were also found in phagocytes or free in the form of large intercellular clumps, presumably aggregates of disintegrating calcified thymocytes. Smaller amounts of calcium were present in the medulla of the thymus, but here, almost exclusively within the vessel walls (Figs. 104, 105).

Discussion: This thymic calcification was highly *selective:* neither the usual sites of predilection for DHT-induced calcification (heart, vessels, stomach, kidney) nor even other lymphatic organs (spleen, lymph nodes, Peyer's plaques) showed any comparable aggravation of calcification under these conditions.

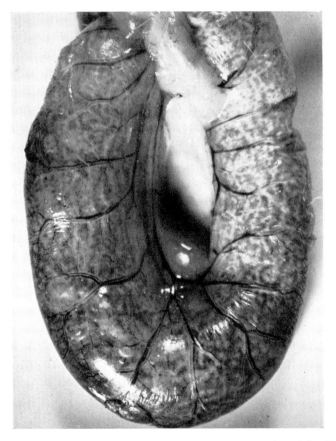

Fig. 102. Arborizing pattern of intestinal calcification produced by DHT + FeSO₄ i.v. Rat (200 g. ♀): DHT (2 mg. p.o.) 1st day + FeSO₄ (3 injections in aqueous solution of 2 mg. in 0.2 ml., 4 mg. in 0.4 ml., and 6 mg. in 0.6 ml., i.v.) 2d day; killed 5th day. Lacelike pattern of calcification follows blood-vessel arborization in this small-intestinal segment. (Cf. Plate X, *B*.)

The effect also appeared to be highly *specific* since it could be obtained only with glucocorticoids. Desoxycorticosterone, estradiol, progesterone, testosterone, methyltestosterone, ethylnortestosterone, and STH failed to cause similar thymic calcification under comparable conditions, but 9α-fluorocortisol acetate (F-COL) was approximately as active as triamcinolone. It is possible, however, that other thymolytic steroids (e.g., estrogens, androgens) would likewise be effective in this respect when given at higher dose levels or in the form of more readily absorbable esters. Besides, the critical period of administration may be different for the various thymolytic steroids; for triamcinolone it is the day of and the day after DHT treatment, but for other hormones the optimum time of administration has not yet been determined.[863]

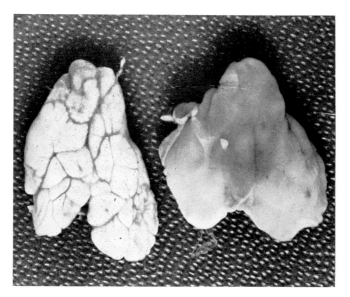

Fig. 103. Thymic calcification produced by DHT + F-COL s.c. Two rats (100 g. ♀): DHT (1 mg. p.o.) 1st day + (left) F-COL (2 mg. microcrystal suspension in 0.2 ml. water, s.c.) 2d day; killed 6th day. Intense calcification of thymus (*left*) compared with normal thymus of control rat treated with DHT alone.

DHT + Glucocorticoids s.c. + NaH₂PO₄ p.o.

Cardiac and Skeletal-Muscle Lesions

The changes produced in the DHT-sensitized animal by simultaneous treatment with corticoids and NaH_2PO_4 have been described in detail elsewhere,[821, 823] so that here it will suffice to characterize them briefly.

Concurrent treatment with 2α-methyl-9α-chlorocortisol (Me-Cl-COL) greatly aggravates the cardiac lesions normally produced by DHT + NaH_2PO_4 in the rat,[820a] mouse, rabbit, dog, and hamster.[821a] In the rabbit simultaneously treated

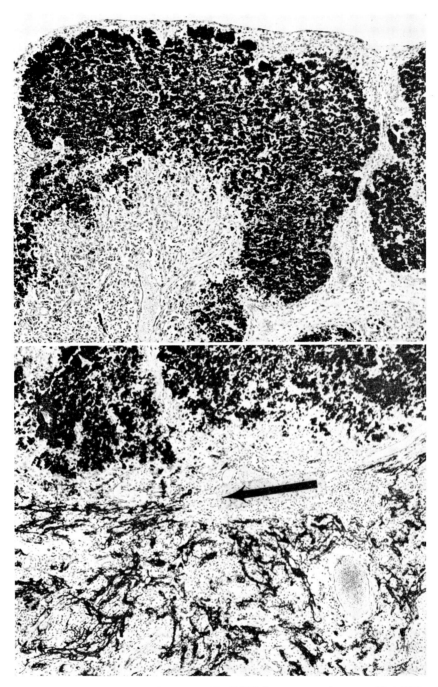

Fig 104. Thymic calcification produced by DHT + triamcinolone s.c. Rat (100 g. ♀):
DHT (1 mg. p.o.) 1st day + triamcinolone (2 mg. in 0.5 ml. water, s.c.) 1st day; killed 6th day.
Top: Cortex. Intense calcium deposition in and around thymocytes. *Bottom:* Cortico-medullary
junction (arrow). Granular calcium deposition in necrotic, disintegrating thymocytes of cortex
(above arrow); calcification in medulla almost exclusively vascular. (von Kóssa, ×120.)

(After Selye and Padmanabhan,[863] courtesy J. Endocrinol.)

with DHT + Me-Cl-COL, only minor motor disturbances develop (decreasing muscular tone, "head drop" due to weakness of cervical muscles), but these progress to complete paralysis and 75% mortality when NaH_2PO_4 is administered simultaneously with DHT + Me-Cl-COL. In such rabbits there also occurs intense cardiac necrosis and calcification, but histologic study of the skeletal musculature reveals only occasional small necrotic foci. Both KCl and $MgCl_2$ inhibit the severe paralytic condition normally induced by combined treatment with DHT + Me-Cl-COL s.c. + NaH_2PO_4 p.o.[831a]

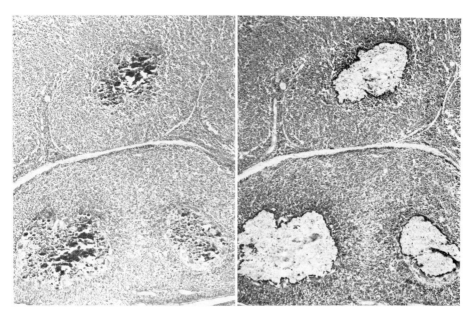

Fig. 105. **Nodular calcification of the thymus long after treatment with DHT +** **triamcinolone s.c.** Rat (100 g. ♀): DHT (1 mg. p.o.) 1st day + triamcinolone (2 mg. in 0.2 ml. water, s.c.) 2d day; killed 61st day. Two adjacent sections stained with PAS (*left*) and celestin blue (*right*). Long after treatment well-circumscribed nodules of calcification developed in centers of thymic lobules. (×75.)

DHT + 5HT s.c., i.p.

Calcinosis of the Salivary Glands (Excluding the Parotid)

Method 1: Rat (100 g. ♀): DHT (1 mg. p.o.) 1st day + 5HT (3 mg. in 0.5 ml. water, s.c. ×2) 2d or 3d day (the treatment is most effective if 5HT is administered in the immediate vicinity of the submaxillary glands); killed 7th day.

Results: A goiter-like swelling of the *submaxillary gland* region was detectable on the day after 5HT administration. At autopsy these glands were hard and white, owing to calcification. Calcium deposition was most intense at the caudal pole of the submaxillary glands but usually affected them in their entirety. The *major sublingual* and *external lacrimal glands* showed similar lesions (Figs. 106, 107; Plate X, *C*). The minor sublingual glands, the parotid glands, and the pancreas were never affected.

Histologically, the calcium was seen to be deposited predominantly in the stroma, but occasionally also in glandular acini; it was accompanied by inflammation, sclerosis, and especially pronounced infiltration by eosinophils and pseudoeosinophils. There was also pronounced calcification in the *renal infarcts* that are usually

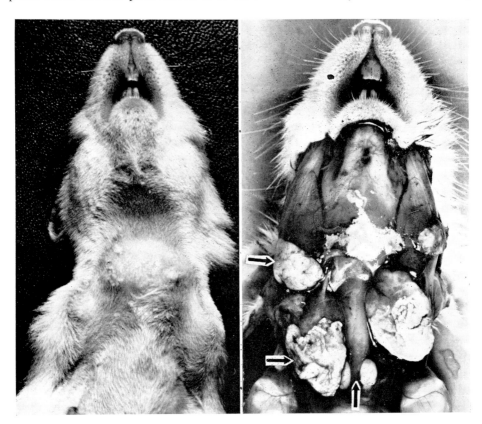

Fig. 106. Calcification of salivary and lacrimal glands produced by DHT + 5HT. s.c. Rat (100 g. ♀): DHT (1 mg. p.o.) 1st day + 5HT (3 mg. in 0.5 ml. water, s.c. ×2) 3d day; killed 7th day. *Left:* The calcified submaxillary glands form a prominent goiter-like nodule whose whitish color is visible through the skin of the neck. *Right:* After removal of the skin, white calcium deposits are visible in the lacrimal (top arrow), submaxillary and major sublingual glands (middle arrow) as well as in paratracheal hibernating glands (bottom arrow). Submaxillary and major sublingual glands form a single, almond-shaped unit on each side under chin in vivo and have been turned around here to show that the dorsal aspect near the duct (between lacrimal gland and trachea) is much less affected than the rest. Large irregular calcified plaque between mandible and trachea is in connective tissue contiguous with calcified portion of submaxillary-major-sublingual units when these are in normal position.

produced by 5HT. Less regularly, calcinosis was observed in the *heart*, *gastric mucosa*, and, occasionally, in the *adipose tissue* and *skin* around the submaxillary glands[839] (Fig. 108).

Less constantly, *ocular* changes developed in the rats so treated. The cornea became cloudy owing to the deposition of calcium and the development of a reactive inflammation with phlyctena formation. Sometimes there was inflammation of the ciliary zonule, with or without demonstrable calcium precipitation (Fig. 109). In exceptional cases we observed calcification in the retina, the acinar epithelium of Harder's gland, and the surrounding striated ocular musculature. However, in short-term experiments the ocular changes were rarely pronounced and quite inconstant.

Method 2: Rat (100 g. ♀): DHT (1 mg. p.o.) 1st day + 5HT (3 mg. in 0.2 ml. water, i.p.) 2d or 3d day; killed 6th day.

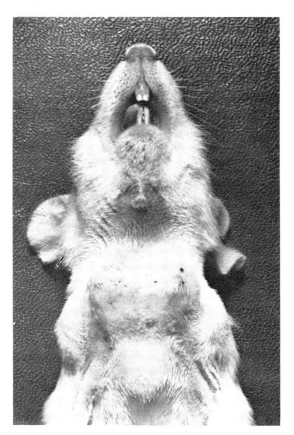

Fig. 107. Calcification of salivary glands produced by DHT + 5HT s.c. Rat (100 g. ♀): DHT (1 mg. p.o.) 1st day + 5HT (3 mg. in 0.5 ml. water, s.c. × 2) 2d day; killed 7th day. Goiter-like enlargement of calcified salivary glands with massive calcinosis of contiguous skin.

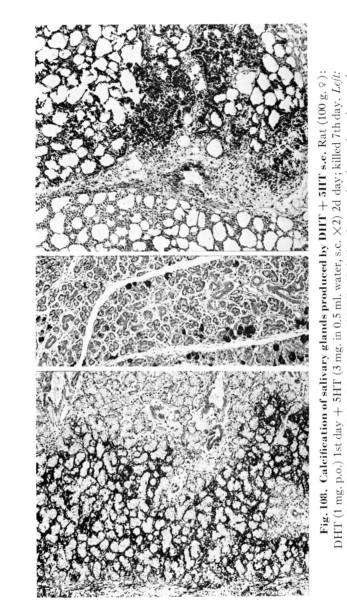

Fig. 108. Calcification of salivary glands produced by DHT + 5HT s.c. Rat (100 g. ♀): DHT (1 mg. p.o.) 1st day + 5HT (3 mg. in 0.5 ml. water, s.c. ×2) 2d day; killed 7th day. *Left:* Extensive calcification limited to stroma. *Middle:* Calcification predominant in acinar epithelium. *Right:* Calcification in adjacent fat. Marked inflammatory infiltration without calcification in adipose tissue near left margin of picture. (von Kossa, ×70.)

Results: The *salivary glands* were less markedly affected after i.p. treatment with 5HT than after s.c. injection in the throat region, but more markedly than when 5HT was given s.c. at a great distance from the glands, on the back. The calcifying *renal* infarcts, however, were as pronounced after i.p. as after s.c. injection of the drug.[841]

Critical period: Rat (100 g. ♀) sensitized with DHT (1 mg. p.o.) 1st day and challenged with 5HT (1 mg. in 0.2 ml. water, s.c. ×2) responded even to this comparatively small dose of 5HT with maximal salivary gland calcification when the drug was given on +3d day. Only a trace response was seen in a few of the animals treated with 5HT on 1st, −2d, and −4th day.

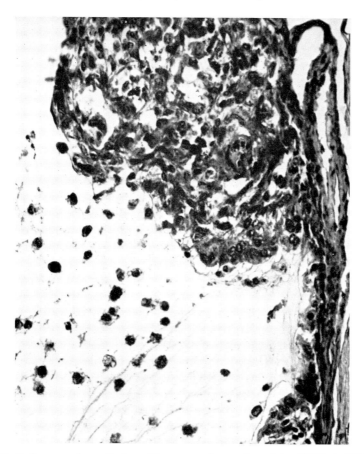

Fig. 109. **Inflammation of the ciliary zonule produced by DHT + 5HT s.c.** Rat (100 g. ♀): DHT (1 mg. p.o.) 1st day + 5HT (3 mg. in 0.5 ml. water, s.c. ×2) 2d day; killed 7th day. Marked cellular infiltration with some calcification of ciliary zonule; intense exudation of large mononuclear and polynuclear cells between fibers of zonule into posterior chamber of eye. (von Kóssa, ×420.)

Healing: The healing of the 5HT-induced lesions was very slow irrespective of the method used to produce them. In the salivary glands, lacrimal glands, and adipose tissue, the diffusely calcified stroma tended to become fragmented, often with definite signs of preosseous tissue formation. The individual blocks thus formed were surrounded by polynuclear giant cells and much fibrous tissue. The calcified renal infarcts showed no sign of preosseous tissue formation; they exhibited considerable connective-tissue proliferation around the affected tubules, which retained much of their calcium even after 60 days (Fig. 110).

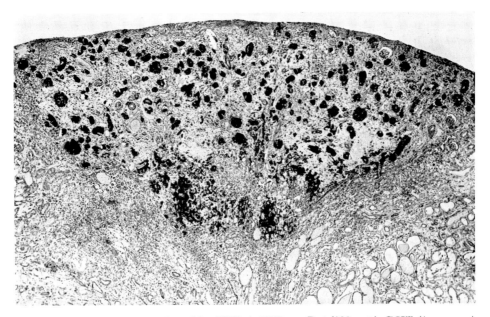

Fig. 110. **Renal lesion produced by DHT + 5HT s.c.** Rat (100 g. ♀): DHT (1 mg. p.o.) 1st day + 5HT (5 mg. in 1 ml. water, s.c. ×2) 2d day; killed 60th day. Infarct-like, wedge-shaped area with many calcified tubules and reactive fibrosis. (von Kóssa, ×39.)

DHT + 5HT s.c.
Calciphylactic Muscular Dystrophy

Method 1: Rat (200 g. ♀): DHT (2 mg. p.o.) 1st day + 5HT (5 mg. in 0.2 ml. water, s.c.) 3d, 4th, or 5th day; killed 10th day.

Results: Profound shock followed immediately upon administration of 5HT, and many rats died within the subsequent 24 hours. The survivors exhibited a lasting *paralysis* especially of the hind limbs. The animals that died during the first day after 5HT treatment showed only indistinct reddish patches in the *musculature.* However, the rats killed at the termination of the experiment invariably exhibited very obvious grayish-yellow and somewhat prominent (edematous) foci throughout the musculature, particularly in the gluteal muscles and the extensors of both fore and hind limbs (Fig. 111).

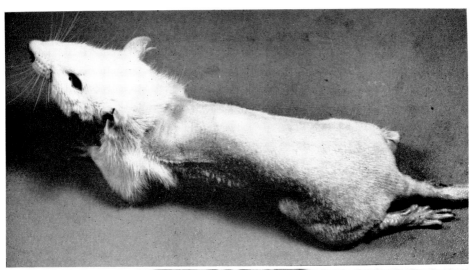

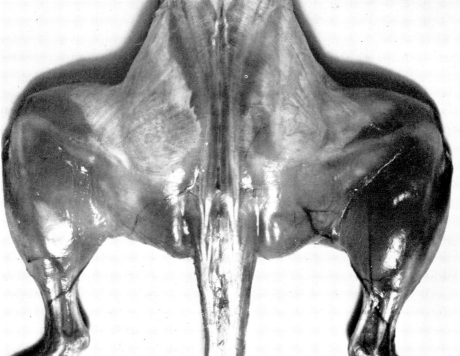

Fig. 111. **Calciphylactic muscular dystrophy produced by DHT + 5HT s.c.** Rat (200 g. ♀): DHT (2 mg. p.o.) 1st day + 5HT (5 mg. in 0.5 ml. water, s.c.) 3d day; killed 15th day. *Top:* Animal dragging particularly affected, paralyzed hind limbs. Motility of fore limbs also handicapped. *Bottom:* Large, light patches of dystrophic musculature in gluteus maximus and proximal part of quadriceps. (Cf. Plate X, *E*.)

(After Selye *et al.*,[838] courtesy Proc. Soc. Exper. Biol. and Med.)

Histologically, the affected regions were characterized by swelling, acidophilic waxy coagulation, and disintegration of the muscle fibers with histiocytic infiltration and giant-cell formation. Edema was prominent only in the animals that died early. Proliferation of sarcolemma nuclei led to the formation of long chains of cells forming rodlike or tubular structures (Fig. 112). Calcification of the connective tissue or of the adjacent skin (especially characteristic of other calciphylactic responses) was not seen. Only few of the necrotic muscle fibers underwent calcification, but this is quite typical of muscle tissue damaged in various ways (e.g., by trauma or anoxemia). In some animals structurally similar lesions also occurred in the *heart* and *tongue*. Mildly calcified small arteries and arterioles were seen in virtually all the affected muscles.

This calciphylactic muscular dystrophy developed quite independently of the area chosen for the s.c. administration of 5HT; in general we noted no predilection for the localization of lesions just underneath the injection site. However, when

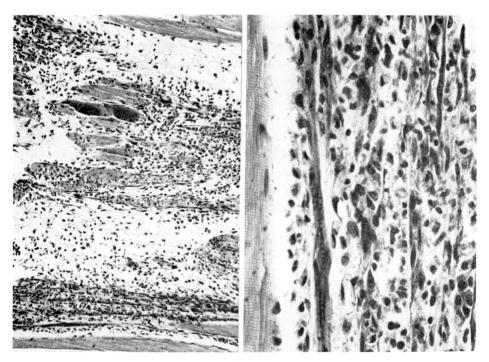

Fig. 112. Muscular dystrophy produced by DHT + 5HT s.c. Rat (200 g. ♀): DHT (2 mg. p.o.) 1st day + 5HT (5 mg. in 0.5 ml. water, s.c.) 3d day; killed 15th day. *Left:* Large focus in gluteal musculature, with coagulation necrosis, edema and predominantly histiocytic infiltration. (von Kóssa, ×100.) *Right:* Lower portion of previous picture under higher magnification. One normal striated muscle fiber (near left margin); parallel to it, several rod-shaped or tubular regenerating myocytes with rows of sarcolemmal nuclei. No calcification detectable in this field. (von Kóssa, ×350.)

(After Selye et al.,[838] courtesy Proc. Soc. Exper. Biol. and Med.)

5HT was injected between the shoulder blades in the vicinity of the *hibernating gland*, the epithelioid cells of this organ became surrounded by dustlike calcium granules and the adjacent striated musculature was more intensely affected in this region than elsewhere in the body. Furthermore, here as in other muscular foci, the connective-tissue fibers between the muscles were also impregnated with calcium (Fig. 113; Plate X, *C, D*). The hibernating glands appeared to be especially sensitive to the topical effect of 5HT, and the resulting local calcification tended to spread into the adjacent musculature (Fig. 113).

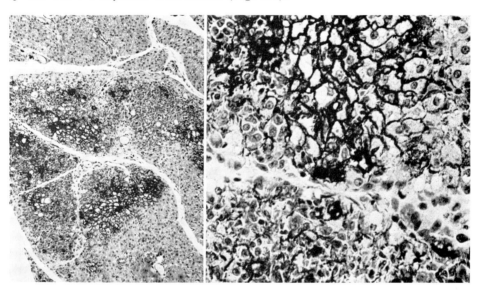

Fig. 113. Calcification and sclerosis of the hibernating gland produced by DHT + 5HT s.c. Rat (100 g. ♀): DHT (1 mg. p.o.) 1st day + 5HT (5 mg. in 0.5 ml. water, s.c. ×2) 3d day; died 7th day. Epithelioid hibernating-gland cells are first surrounded by dustlike calcium deposits and secondarily replaced by connective-tissue cells. (von Kóssa, left ×100, right ×330.) (Cf. Plate X, *F*.)

In these experiments, in which a single dose of 5HT was given s.c. on the back, the *salivary glands* were only mildly affected except when the 5HT was injected into their immediate vicinity or between the shoulder blades, whence it sank into the salivary gland region owing to gravity. In this case, the adjacent muscular connective tissue also exhibited calcinosis.

The calcified *renal* infarcts characteristic of 5HT overdosage developed with approximately the same intensity and frequency as in the previously mentioned experiments, which were primarily designed to produce salivary gland calciphylaxis.

Discussion: Quite unexpectedly, the muscular changes produced by 5HT under these circumstances, though dependent upon sensitization with a calcifying agent (DHT), did not exhibit any significant amount of calcification (except in the vicinity of heavily calcified non-muscular tissues). This fact suggests that the true nature of similar calciphylactic reactions—should they occur in man—may easily escape the pathologist's attention owing to the paucity or absence of calcium granules in the affected foci. Yet, the structural resemblance of calciphylactic muscular dystrophy to the progressive muscular dystrophy of man does not necessarily imply any fundamental relationship between them, since the histologic changes in both types of derangements are essentially nonspecific expressions of muscular injury.

The calciphylactic muscular dystrophy thus induced is quite *organ-specific.* Minor lesions similar to those seen in the skeletal musculature occur also in the heart, but tissues other than striated muscles remain virtually unaffected. In particular, the skin, which is always prominently involved in calciphylactic dermatomyositis, remains quite normal here, even just over heavily affected muscle regions. Salivary gland calcification—so characteristic of treatment with DHT and 5HT if the latter compound is injected in the salivary-gland region or i.p.—was also only mild or absent in these animals in which 5HT was injected under the dorsal skin.

The *mechanism* of this type of muscular dystrophy remains to be elucidated. However, DHT pretreatment produces at least mild degrees of arterial calcification in the subsequently affected muscles, and immediately after 5HT injection there is severe cyanotic pallor of the skin (particularly that covering the extremities); hence, the possibility of an anoxemic muscular damage should be considered. It is conceivable that mild degrees of arterial calcification predispose the vessels to the vasoconstrictor effect of subsequently administered 5HT.

Contrary to most forms of calciphylaxis, the *critical period* for the production of this muscular dystrophy is not sharp, as shown by experiments in which a standard dose of 5HT (5 mg. s.c.) was given at various times before and after DHT sensitization. Apart from transient and comparatively mild motor disturbances immediately following 5HT treatment, no muscle damage was noted when the compound was administered prior to DHT. Varying degrees of morbid changes were induced in the skeletal muscles by treatment with 5HT at any time between the day of, and the 10th day after, treatment with DHT, but sensitivity was at its maximum between the 3d and 5th day after DHT.[838]

Owing to the absence of a sharply delimited critical period, it was possible to produce a more chronic form of calciphylactic muscular dystrophy by *continuous treatment* with small doses of DHT and 5HT. In this event the *lingual* and *ocular* lesions were much more constant than in the acute form (Figs. 114, 115, 116).

The *healing* of the muscular lesions progressed quite rapidly. The necrotic muscle fibers were absorbed, there was rapid regeneration of muscle tissue with intense proliferation of sarcolemmal nuclei and compensatory hypertrophy of the remaining healthy muscles. On the other hand, the ocular changes tended to become worse as time progressed and in many animals unilateral or bilateral cataracts developed. The opacity can affect the whole lens uniformly (Fig. 117), but especially in the initial stages, maximal clouding was seen along the Y-shaped junction line of the lens fibers (Fig. 118). In advanced cases there was usually a very pronounced hyperemia of the iris and disintegration of the subcapsular layer of the lens with intense proliferation of histiocytes, especially on the posterior surface (Fig. 119), and sometimes even panophthalmia (Plate XIII, *D*).

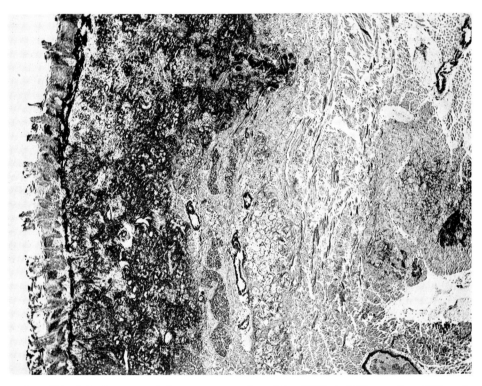

Fig. 114. Calcification of the tongue produced by DHT + 5HT s.c. Rat (200 g. ♀): DHT [(100 μg., p.o./day) 1st–6th day, (500 μg, p.o./day) 7th–10th day] + 5HT (5 mg. in 0.5 ml. water, s.c.) 1st day; died 10th day. Calcification of tongue (near surface) and its vessels. (von Kóssa, ×38.) Minor degrees of this change can also be obtained by heavy overdosage with indirect calcifiers (e.g., DHT, parathyroid hormone) alone, without use of challengers.

DHT + 5HT s.c. + IPR i.p.

Calcinosis of the Salivary Glands (Including the Parotid)

Method 1: Rat (100 g. ♀): IPR (20 mg. in 0.2 ml. water, i.p. ×2/day) beginning on 1st day + DHT (2 mg. p.o.) 16th day + 5HT (5 mg. in 0.5 ml. water, s.c. in throat region) 17th day; killed 21st day.

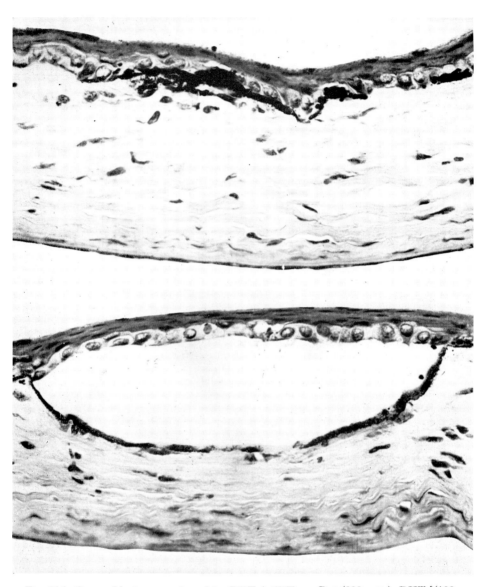

Fig. 115. Corneal lesions produced by DHT + 5HT s.c. Rat (200 g. ♀): DHT [(100 µg., p.o./day) 1st–6th day, (500 µg., p.o./day) 7th–10th day] + 5HT (5 mg. in 0.5 ml. water, s.c.) 1st day; died 11th day. *Top:* Calcium deposition along Bowman's membrane, underneath corneal epithelium. *Bottom:* Detachment of corneal epithelium over calcified area. (von Kóssa, ×470.)

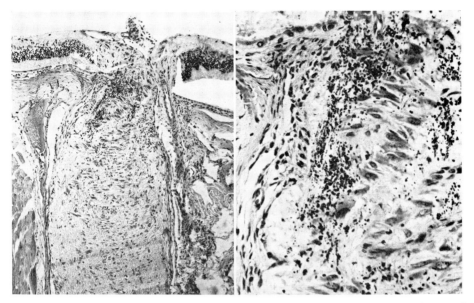

Fig. 116. Calcification of the optic nerve produced by DHT + 5HT s.c. Rat (200 g. ♀):
DHT (100 μg. in 0.5 ml. corn oil, p.o./day) + 5HT (5 mg. in 0.5 ml. water, s.c./day); killed
9th day. *Left:* Heavy granular calcium precipitation near papilla of optic nerve. (von Kóssa,
×85.) *Right:* Higher magnification of preceding picture showing calcium precipitation in optic
nerve near its emergence from retina. (von Kóssa, ×300.)

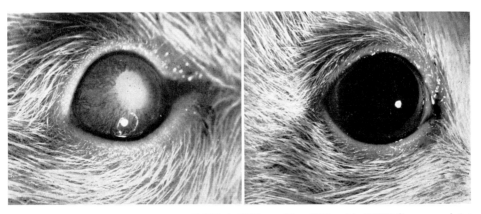

Fig. 117. Cataract produced by DHT + 5HT s.c. Rat (100 g. ♀): DHT (1 mg. p.o.) 1st
day + 5HT (4 mg. in 0.2 ml. water, s.c.) 2d day; photographed under anesthesia 60th day.
Cataract with intense hyperemia of iris (*left*) compared with control eye (*right*).

161

Fig. 118. Opacity of lens produced by DHT + 5HT s.c. Rat (240 g. ♀): DHT (2 mg. p.o.) 1st day + 5HT (7.5 mg. in 1.5 ml. water, s.c. ×2) 2d day; photographed 60th day. Typical **Y**-shaped opacity of lens, seen through pupil of intensely hyperemic iris. (White spots merely due to reflected light.)

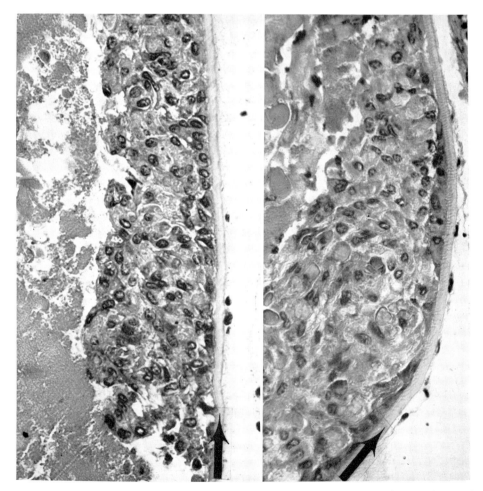

Fig. 119. Retrolental changes produced by DHT + 5HT s.c. Rat (100 g. ♀): DHT (1 mg. p.o.) 1st day + 5HT (5 mg. in 0.5 ml. water, s.c.) 2d day; killed 60th day. Granular disintegration of lens; intense proliferation of histiocytes just inside (here left of) capsule which is marked by arrows. Phagocytosis of lenticular debris particularly obvious on right picture. No sign of calcinosis. (von Kóssa, ×480.)

Results: In animals thus pretreated with IPR, the *salivary glands* underwent enormous hypertrophy and hyperplasia. This was in agreement with earlier observations.[834, 866] However, if the animals were then sensitized by DHT and subsequently challenged by 5HT, the enlarged salivary glands underwent precipitous calcification and in this case (unlike in animals not pretreated with IPR) even the parotid glands became calcified. Interestingly, here the calcification was often selectively localized in the nuclei, especially around the nuclear membranes (Fig. 120). The *lacrimal glands* likewise showed calcinosis, but to a lesser degree than the salivary glands.

The *skeletal musculature* was also severely affected under these conditions and developed changes that structurally resembled those produced by DHT + 5HT in the absence of IPR pretreatment. However, the clinical manifestations were different in that here during the first hours after 5HT administration, the pre-

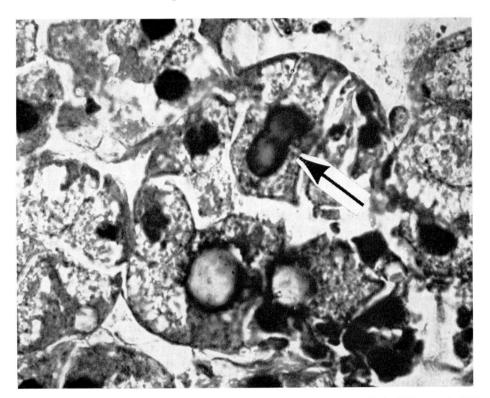

Fig. 120. Calcification of the salivary gland produced by DHT + 5HT s.c. + IPR i.p. Rat (100 g. ♀): IPR (20 mg. in 0.2 ml. water, i.p. ×2) 1st–20th day + DHT (2 mg. p.o.) 16th day + 5HT (5 mg. in 0.5 ml. water, s.c. in throat region once) 17th day; killed 21st day. Calcification almost selectively localized in nuclei, especially around nuclear membranes. Some nuclei apparently in amitotic division, as judged by central constriction (arrow). (Celestin blue, ×1100.)

ponderantly damaged muscles of the hind limbs became extremely rigid, as if they had undergone rigor mortis, and about 30 per cent of the rats died during the subsequent 24 hours. In the surviving animals, the characteristic feature of the muscular lesions was a comparatively intense calcification of the muscle fibers themselves, which was rarely observed in animals treated with DHT and 5HT only. Essentially similar changes were seen in the *myocardium,* and the *kidneys* contained calcified infarcts.

In older rats (200 g. ♀) given the same treatment the muscular lesions were even more severe (Fig. 121) and mortality was 90 per cent, although the dosage was not adjusted to the higher body weight.

Method 2: Rat (90 g. ♀): IPR (10 mg. in 0.5 ml. water, i.p. ×2/day) 1st–15th day + DHT (1.5 mg. p.o.) 15th day + 5HT (5 mg. in 0.2 ml. water, s.c. ×2) 16th day; killed 19th day.

Results: Here the changes were very similar to those obtained by Method 1. Calcification of the *parotid* glands occurred only after IPR pretreatment but

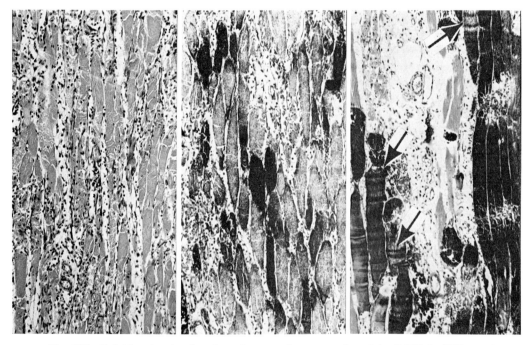

Fig. 121. Calcification in the gluteal musculature produced by DHT + 5HT s.c. + IPR i.p. Rat (200 g. ♀): IPR (20 mg. in 0.2 ml. water, i.p. ×2/day) 1st–20th day + DHT (2 mg. p.o.) 16th day + 5HT (5 mg. in 0.5 ml. water, s.c.) 17th day; killed 21st day. Varying intensity of calcification in three different regions. *Left:* Muscle necroses and inflammation, but no calcification. *Middle:* Moderate calcification. *Right:* Intense calcium deposition with characteristic transverse rings apparently related to cross-striation (arrows). (von Kóssa, ×85.)

curiously, even then, the major sublingual glands (which are contiguous to the heavily calcified submaxillary glands) were usually spared. Pretreatment with IPR alone induced pronounced hypertrophy of all salivary glands, but it did not prepare them for calcification under the influence of subsequent DHT treatment (Fig. 122).

The *lacrimal glands* underwent particularly severe calcinosis after combined treatment with DHT + IPR + 5HT and were transformed into hard, brittle, calcareous discs.

The *ocular* changes were of moderate intensity and hence particularly suitable for the study of incipient changes, such as the deposition of minute calcified granules underneath the epithelium along the surface of Bowman's membrane (Fig. 123).

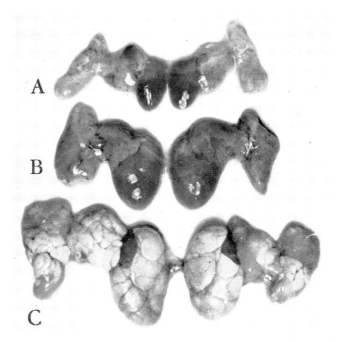

Fig. 122. Calcification of salivary glands produced by DHT + 5HT s.c. + IPR i.p. All three rats (90 g. ♀) received: DHT (1.5 mg. p.o.) 15th day + (A and C) 5HT (5 mg. in 0.2 ml. water, s.c. ×2) 16th day + (B and C) IPR (10 mg. in 0.5 ml. water, i.p. ×2/day) 1st–15th day; killed 19th day. *A:* DHT + 5HT caused very slight, only histologically visible, calcification limited to submaxillary glands. *B:* DHT + IPR induced some hypertrophy of submaxillary and parotid glands but no calcification. *C:* DHT + 5HT + IPR produced intense calcification and enlargement of submaxillaries (central portion) and even in parotids (peripheral wing-shaped glands) which never undergo calcification as result of DHT + 5HT administration without pretreatment with IPR. Here only sublingual glands are dark because uncalcified.

(After Selye and Gentile.[841])

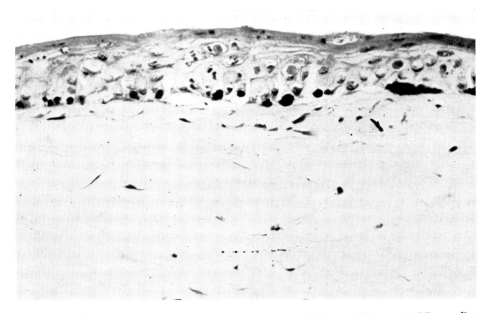

Fig. 123. Calcification of the cornea produced by DHT + 5HT s.c. + IPR i.p. Rat (90 g. ♀): IPR (10 mg. in 0.5 ml. water, i.p. ×2/day) 1st–18th day + DHT (1.5 mg. p.o.) 15th day + 5HT (5 mg. in 0.2 ml. water, s.c. ×2) 16th day; killed 19th day. Minute, granular calcium deposits along Bowman's membrane of corneal epithelium. (von Kóssa, ×550.)

DHT + Hematoporphyrin i.v.
No Change

Method: Rat (100 g. ♀): DHT (1 mg. p.o.) 1st day + hematoporphyrin (20 mg. in 2 ml. water, i.v. ×2) 2d day; killed 6th day.

Results: Even the very large dose of hematoporphyrin used in these experiments produced no aggravation of the usual, extremely mild nonspecific calcinosis elicited by this dose of DHT. Mortality: 0.

DHT + HgCl₂ i.v.
Renal Cortical Calcinosis

Method: Rat (100 g. ♀): DHT (1 mg. p.o.) 1st day + HgCl₂ (500 μg. in 0.1 ml. water, i.v. ×2) 2d day; killed 6th day.

Results: Intense calcification of the renal cortex virtually unaccompanied by calcium deposition in other organs except occasionally in the aorta. Mortality: 80%.

Remarks: As is well known, sublimate intoxication produces cortical nephrocalcinosis even without DHT pretreatment; hence, this lesion is not calciphylactic, although it appears to be slightly aggravated by DHT sensitization.

DHT + InCl₃ i.v.

Pancreatic and RES-Type of Calciphylaxis

Method: Rat (100 g. ♀): DHT (1 mg. p.o.) 1st day + InCl₃ (10 mg. in 1 ml. water, i.v.) 2d day.

Results: Calcinosis in the pancreas, liver (here accompanied by multiple necroses), and spleen as well as a moderate degree of nonspecific calcinosis. Mortality: 100%.

DHT + IPR i.p.

Auriculo-Apical and Renal Calcinosis

Method: Rat (100 g. ♀): DHT (1 mg. p.o.) 1st day + IPR (20 mg. in 0.2 ml. water, i.p. ×3) 2d day; killed 8th day.

Results: Here the distribution of calcium precipitates in the *myocardium* was very distinctive. It superficially resembled the lesions produced by DHT + Fe-OS in that the left auricular appendage was always predominantly affected. But here there was also marked calcification of the cardiac muscle near the apex and along the branches of the coronary arteries (Fig. 124). In addition, a predominantly cor-

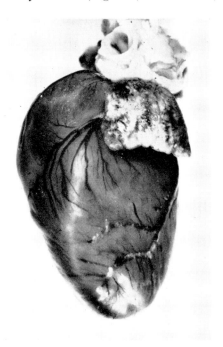

Fig. 124. Peculiar pattern of cardiac calcification produced by DHT + IPR i.p. Rat (100 g. ♀): DHT (1 mg. p.o.) 1st day + IPR (20 mg. in 0.2 ml. water, i.p. ×3) 2d day; killed 8th day. Calcification virtually limited to left auricular appendage, coronary arteries and tip of heart. Descending branch of left coronary artery shines through myocardial musculature.

tical *nephrocalcinosis* developed, but other organs affected by DHT + Fe-OS— particularly the biliary ducts—remained normal.

Critical period: In rats (100 g. ♀) sensitized with DHT (1 mg. p.o.) 1st day and challenged with IPR (20 mg. in 0.2 ml. water, i.p. ×2 on one day only), maximal cardiac lesions were obtained by giving IPR on +2d and +3d day, less on 1st day, and none on −2d and −3d day. Manifestly, IPR must be given after DHT sensitization in order to obtain this response.

DHT + KMnO₄ i.v.

Nonspecific Calcinosis

Method: Rat (100 g. ♀): DHT (1 mg. p.o.) 1st day + KMnO₄ (1 mg. in 1 ml. water, i.v. ×4) 2d day; killed 6th day.

Results: Nonspecific calcinosis with occasional calcification in Brunner's glands, thymus, and lung. Sometimes calcifying hepatic necroses.

DHT + KMnO₄ i.p.

Peritoneo–Pleural Calciphylaxis

Method: Rat (100 g. ♀): DHT (1 mg. p.o.) 1st day + KMnO₄ (10 mg. in 1 ml. water, i.p.) 2d day; killed 6th day.

Results: Calcinosis (in order of decreasing intensity) was found in: peritoneum, pleura, kidney (cortical) > pancreas, heart (pericardium) [traces in stomach, liver, omentum, diaphragm, retroperitoneal fat]. Mortality: 50%.

DHT + LaCl₃ i.v.

Nonspecific Calcinosis

Method: Rat (100 g. ♀): DHT (1 mg. p.o.) 1st day + LaCl₃ (20 mg. in 1 ml. water, i.v.) 2d day; killed 6th day.

Results: Nonspecific calcinosis. Mortality: 60%.

DHT + LaCl₃ i.p.

Peritoneal Calciphylaxis

Method: Rat (100 g. ♀): DHT (1 mg. p.o.) 1st day + LaCl₃ (40 mg. in 2 ml. water, i.p.) 2d day; killed 6th day.

Results: Calcinosis of peritoneum. Mortality: 20%.[827, 841]

DHT + MgH₄(PO₄)₂ p.o.

Papillary Nephrocalcinosis

Method: Rat (100 g. ♀): MgH₄(PO₄)₂ (1 mM in 2 ml. water, p.o. ×2/day) 1st–15th day; killed 15th day.

Results: The only noteworthy change produced under these conditions was a selective calcification of the renal papilla without any significant calcium precipitation elsewhere in the kidney (Fig. 125). Histologically, the calcium was found just underneath the surface of the tip of the papilla, where it formed massive plaques which gradually detached themselves and became renal calculi.

This lesion may have some interesting clinical implications. According to current concepts, spontaneous urinary calculi in man are also formed by initial calcification of the renal papilla with subsequent detachment of the affected parts, which then act as "seeds" for the further growth of the concrements.

It will be recalled that a similar selective renal papillary calcinosis had been obtained in DHT-sensitized rats by merely subjecting the papilla to pressure through the production of a hydronephrosis by ureter ligature.[820]

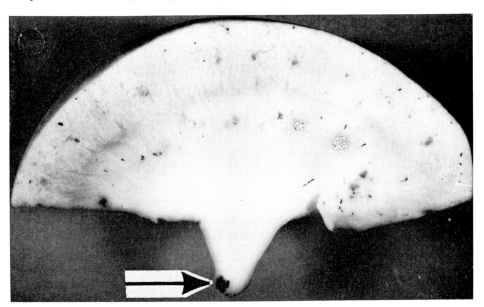

Fig. 125. Papillary nephrocalcinosis produced by DHT + magnesium phosphate p.o. Rat (100 g. ♀): $MgH_4(PO_4)_2$ (1 mM in 2 ml. water, p.o. ×2) + DHT (50 μg. p.o.); died 14th day. $AgNO_3$-stained specimen through central portion of kidney. Clearly circumscribed, calcified (black) plaque, near tip of papilla (arrow).

[After Selye,[826] courtesy Williams & Wilkins (J. Urol.).]

DHT + $NaClO_4$ p.o. or s.c.

Cardiac and Muscular Lesions

Early observations have shown that, following DHT-pretreatment, $NaClO_4$ p.o. (or s.c. by the granuloma-pouch technique) can produce severe cardiac lesions with calcification as well as a special form of myositis.[822] As regards their histologic structure, the resulting changes in the skeletal musculature resemble those produced by DHT + 5HT s.c. (p. 154 ff.) or by Me-Cl-COL s.c. + $NaClO_4$ p.o.[823] They simulate the latter even as regards the associated functional disturbance which manifests itself in a positive "flick-test" (intense extensor cramps elicited by a mild flick with the finger against the sacral region). It is not clear why a corticoid hormone such as Me-Cl-COL, like DHT, acts as a sensitizer for this singular effect of $NaClO_4$, but the strikingly similar conditioning action of the two compounds suggests some relationship between the steroid hormone and the steroid vitamin-D derivative.

DHT + NaH_2PO_4 p.o.
Suppurating Myocarditis

Normally overdosage with DHT produces only calcification in the coronary vessels and the myocardium of the rat. However, if rats receive DHT concurrently with dietary supplements of NaH_2PO_4, the character of the cardiac lesions changes and an acute suppurative myocarditis results. At first it was thought that perhaps this change is merely due to an aggravation of the DHT effect rather than to a qualitative alteration of the response to DHT. However, unless NaH_2PO_4 is administered at the same time, even fatal doses of DHT (or vitamin D_3) produce only calcinosis without inflammation.[820a] This form of myocarditis can be prevented by simultaneous treatment with KCl or $MgCl_2$.[820b, 865a]

DHT + Na_2SnO_3 i.v.
Nonspecific Calcinosis

Method: Rat (100 g. ♀): DHT (1 mg. p.o.) 1st day + Na_2SnO_3 (10 mg. in 1 ml. water, i.v. ×2) 2d day; killed 6th day.

Results: Nonspecific calcinosis with particularly pronounced calcium deposition in the *kidney, Brunner's glands,* and the *lung.* Pulmonary calcification affected exclusively the septa, leaving the vessels and bronchioles unaffected (Fig. 126). Mortality: 50%.

DHT + Pb-acetate i.v.
RES-Type of Calciphylaxis

Method: Rat (100 g. ♀): DHT (1 mg. p.o.) 1st day + Pb-acetate (5 mg. in 0.5 ml. water, i.v. ×3) 2d day; killed 6th day.

Results: Here the calcification was most intense in the organs that are richest in RES cells, particularly the *spleen* (Fig. 127) and *liver.* There was also pronounced calcinosis of the *adrenals,* especially in the stroma of the medulla and along the surface of the cortical sinusoids. Some calcinosis (in order of decreasing intensity) was also found in: stomach, Brunner's glands, thymus, kidney (cortical) [traces in heart (tigro-vascular), duodenum, intestine, aorta, diaphragm].

Remarks: An essentially similar picture was obtained in 100 g. ♀ rats with 2.5 mg., and in 200 g. ♀ rats with 5 mg., of $PbCl_2$ in 0.5 ml. water, i.v., under otherwise similar circumstances; but mortality was almost 100% because the chloride is far less well tolerated than the acetate.

Treatment with Pb-acetate (5 mg. in 1 ml. water, i.v. ×2) on 3d day after similar DHT sensitization produced, in addition to the lesions just described, massive calcification of the renal papilla, which became as hard as a stone and was clearly demarcated from the adjacent soft tissue of the renal medulla (Fig. 127a). This change was usually fatal within a few days because of the uremia that resulted from the impossibility of excreting urine through the calcified papilla. Experiments are now under way to determine whether minor degrees of the same lesion could lead to urinary calculus formation because detachment of the calcified papilla might furnish the solid nucleus necessary for the growth of a concrement.

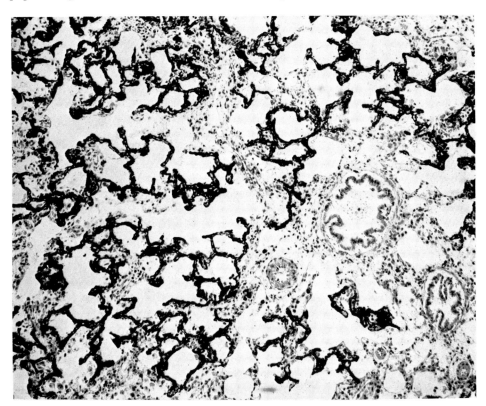

Fig. 126. Pulmonary calcification produced by DHT + Na₂SnO₃ i.v. Rat (100 g. ♀): DHT (1 mg. p.o.) 1st day + Na₂SnO₃ (10 mg. in 1 ml. water, i.v. ×2) 2d day; killed 6th day. Calcium deposition in stroma of pulmonary septa throughout lung, but not in vessels and bronchioles. (von Kóssa, ×135.)

DHT + PMX s.c.

Calciphylactic Dermatomyositis

Method 1: Rat (120 g. ♀): DHT (1 mg. p.o.) 1st day + PMX (1 mg. in 0.2 ml. water, s.c. in each of the two posterior and one of the anterior paws) 2d day; killed 6th day.

Fig. 127. Splenic calcification produced by DHT + Pb-acetate i.v. Two rats (100 g. ♀): DHT (1 mg. p.o.) 1st day + (top) Pb-acetate (5 mg. in 0.5 ml. water, i.v. ×3) 2d day; killed 6th day. *Top:* Combined treatment resulted in massive calcification with hardening of spleen (rigid in curved position, as shown by its shadow). *Bottom:* Spleen of control animal unaffected.

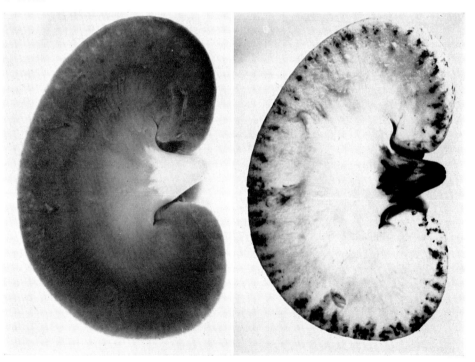

Fig. 127a. Papillary and cortical calcinosis produced by DHT + Pb-acetate. Rat (100 g. ♀): DHT (1 mg. p.o.) 1st day + Pb-acetate (5mg. in 1 ml. water, i.v. ×2) 3d day; died 5th day. *Left:* On cross section through fresh specimen papilla is seen as a selectively calcified stone-like, hard structure. Cortical calcinosis is hardly visible. *Right:* On AgNO₃-stained specimen calcification of papilla is even more evident and here cortical calcinosis is also clearly visible.

Results: Here PMX was administered intrapedally because preliminary experiments had shown that this mode of administration is more effective than s.c. injection elsewhere. The changes observed under these conditions were qualitatively similar to those obtained by DHT + Fe-Dex + PMX (cf. p. 127), but much less pronounced.

Following PMX injection there was marked hyperemia of the *skin* with the usual anaphylactoid reaction characteristic of treatment with this mastocyte discharger. During the subsequent few days calcification appeared in the snout region as well as within the skin of the head and shoulders. The intensity of the lesions decreased in the cephalo-caudal direction.

Histologically the changes were virtually indistinguishable from those produced by DHT + Fe-Dex + PMX; they consisted primarily of the discharge, with subsequent calcification, of mastocyte granules (Fig. 128). This acute change was gradually followed by inflammation and sclerosis. Occasionally there were minor lesions of this type in the nuchal *musculature*, but these were never pronounced.

With somewhat larger doses of PMX, calcification was also noted in *Peyer's*

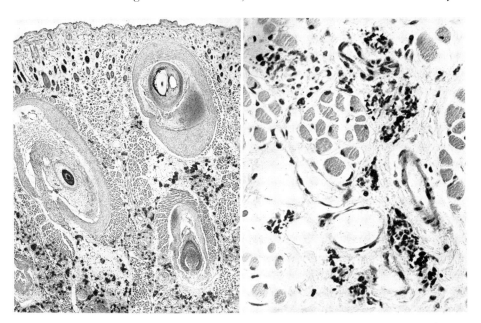

Fig. 128. Granular cutaneous calcification in the snout produced by DHT + PMX intrapedal. Rat (120 g. ♀): DHT (1 mg. p.o.) 1st day + PMX (1 mg. in 0.2 ml. water, s.c. in two posterior and one anterior paws) 2d day; killed 6th day. *Left:* Section through skin of snout showing three bristle roots (conspicuous by their size in comparison with roots of ordinary hair near upper margin) and numerous minute granular calcium accumulations in discharged mastocyte granules of surrounding muscle cell stroma. (von Kóssa, ×25.) *Right:* Higher magnification of region from previous picture. Dark calcified granules form clumps in correspondence with disintegrated mast cells which have become unrecognizable. (von Kóssa, ×360.)

patches, whose peripheral sinuses became clearly outlined by white calcium deposits, so that they could be seen readily with the naked eye (Fig. 129).

Calcinosis of the *salivary glands* was observed especially in rats which received repeated courses of treatment with DHT + PMX. The calcinosis was most pronounced in the submaxillary gland, where it affected predominantly the parenchyma itself and often led to necrosis. Conversely, in the adjacent major sublingual gland there was only slight stroma calcification (Fig. 130). By the use of our celestin blue technique modified for alkaline phosphatase it could be shown that this enzyme was most plentiful in those regions of the salivary glands that underwent calcification (Fig. 131).

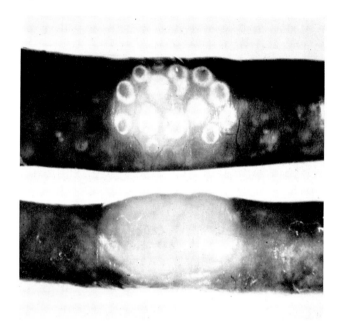

Fig. 129. Calcification of Peyer's patches produced by DHT + PMX s.c. Two rats (110 g. ♀): DHT (1 mg. p.o.) 1st day + (top) PMX (2 mg. in 0.25 ml. water, s.c.) 2d and 3d day; killed 6th day. *Top:* Macroscopic appearance of calcified, white, ringlike peripheral sinuses of lymphatic follicles composing patch. *Bottom:* Unaffected Peyer's patch in control rat.

DHT + PVP i.v.

Nonspecific Calcinosis

Method: Rat (100 g. ♀): DHT (1 mg. p.o.) 1st day + PVP (25%, 2 ml. i.v.) 2d day; killed 6th day.

Results: Traces of calcinosis were found in stomach, heart (tigro-vascular), and kidney (cortical).

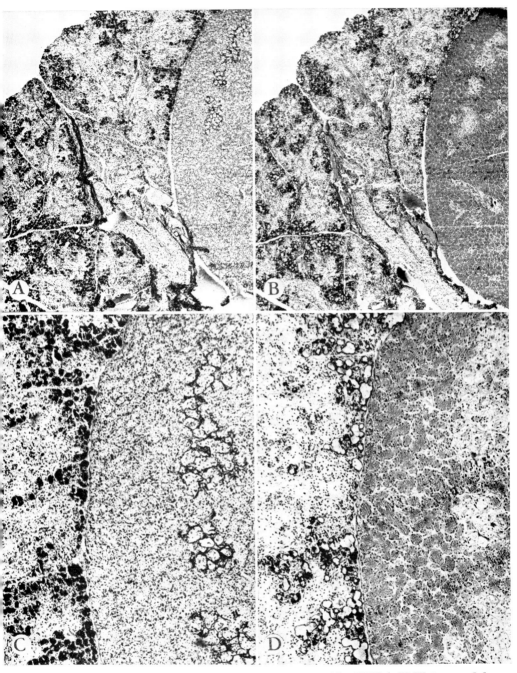

Fig. 130. Calcification of the salivary glands produced by DHT + PMX intrapedal.
Rat (100 g. ♀): DHT (1 mg. p.o.) 1st + 15th day + PMX (2 mg. in 0.2 ml. water, s.c.) in left
hind paw on 2d day, in right hind paw 16th day; killed 31st day. Four sections through border
line of serous, submaxillary (left side on each picture) and mucous major sublingual glands.
Calcification most pronounced in submaxillary gland, where it occurs only in parenchyma. Calcified parenchymal cells are largely necrotic. Adjacent major sublingual gland shows only slight
stroma calcification, parenchyma is essentially normal (A and C von Kóssa, B and D celestin
blue for calcium, A and B ×30, C and D ×85.)

DHT + PVP i.p.

Nonspecific Calcinosis

Method: Rat (100 g. ♀): DHT (1 mg. p.o.) 1st day + PVP (25%, 1.5 ml. i.p.) 2d day; killed 6th day.

Results: Traces of calcinosis were found in stomach, heart (tigro-vascular), and kidney (cortical), none in peritoneum. Mortality: 90%.[841]

DHT + Reserpine i.v.

Nonspecific Calcinosis

Method: Rat (100 g. ♀): DHT (1 mg. p.o.) 1st day + reserpine (750 µg. in 0.2 ml. water, i.v.) 2d day; killed 6th day.

Results: Nonspecific calcinosis with occasional calcification in the thymus and salivary glands.

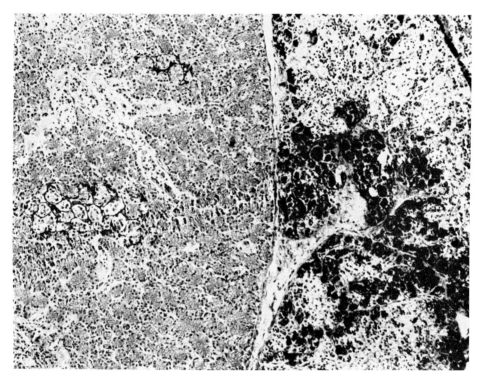

Fig. 131. Calcification of the salivary glands produced by DHT + PMX s.c. Rat (100 g. ♀): DHT (1 mg. p.o.) 1st, 16th, 31st and 47th day + PMX (2 mg. in 0.2 ml. water, s.c.) 2d, 17th, 32d and 48th day; killed 50th day. Positive alkaline phosphatase reaction in stroma of major sublingual gland (left) and in parenchyma of submaxillary gland (latter with extensive destruction of epithelial cells). (Celestin blue for alkaline phosphatase, ×135.)

DHT + SnCl$_2$ i.v.

Nonspecific Calcinosis

Method: Rat (100 g. ♀): DHT (1 mg. p.o.) 1st day + SnCl$_2$ (1 mg. in 0.1 ml. water, i.v. ×3) 2d day; killed 6th day.

Results: Nonspecific calcinosis. Mortality: 50%.

Remarks: In 200 g. rats treated with 2 mg. of DHT p.o. and 3 mg. of SnCl$_2$ in 0.3 ml. water, i.v. ×2, mortality was 100%; but the animals died so soon after injection that no morphologic lesions were observable. Under the same circumstances even 2 mg. of SnCl$_2$ produced a 60% mortality and the survivors showed only nonspecific calcinosis.

DHT + TiCl$_3$ i.v.

Nonspecific Calcinosis

Method: Rat (100 g. ♀): DHT (1 mg. p.o.) 1st day + TiCl$_3$ (1.5 mg. in 0.15 ml. water, i.v.) 2d day; killed 6th day.

Results: Nonspecific calcinosis. Mortality: 30%.

DHT + TiCl$_4$ i.v.

Nonspecific Calcinosis

Method: Rat (100 g. ♀): DHT (1 mg. p.o.) 1st day + TiCl$_4$ (0.5 mg. in 0.1 ml. water, i.v.) 2d day; killed 6th day.

Results: Nonspecific calcinosis. Mortality 20%.

DHT + ThCl$_4$ i.v.

Nonspecific Calcinosis

Method: Rat (100 g. ♀): DHT (1 mg. p.o.) 1st day + ThCl$_4$ (4 mg. in 0.4 ml. water, i.v.) 2d day; killed 6th day.

Results: Nonspecific calcinosis. Mortality: 0.

DHT + Th(NO$_3$)$_4$ i.v.

Nonspecific Calcinosis

Method: Rat (100 g. ♀): DHT (1 mg. p.o.) 1st day + Th(NO$_3$)$_4$ (8 mg. in 0.8 ml. water, i.v.) 2d day; killed 6th day.

Results: Nonspecific calcinosis and occasionally hepatic necroses. Mortality: 80%.

DHT + Thorotrast® i.v.

Calciphylactic Scleroderma with Esophageal Calcinosis and Arthritis

Method 1: Rat (100 g. ♀): DHT (1 mg. p.o.) 1st day + Thorotrast® (0.3–0.6 ml. i.v.) 2d day; killed 6th day.

Results: Two to three days after Thorotrast® injection there appeared multiple calcific deposits with reactive connective-tissue proliferation and inflammatory infiltration (particularly by eosinophils and pseudoeosinophils) in the facial *skin*, the *fauces, tongue, esophagus*, and *mediastinal* connective tissue (Figs. 132–135). The cutaneous lesions resembled calcareous scleroderma (Plate XI, *A*). Calcification of *joints* was rarely prominent in 100 g. rats, especially in such short-term experiments (Fig. 136). The splenic and hepatic RES as well as the large *phagocytes* in the bristle-hair root sinusoids contained many ThO₂ crystals, but, curiously, here ThO₂ did not tend to stimulate calcification. There was always marked *osteitis fibrosa*. Mortality: 30%.[845]

**Fig. 132. Calcification of the tongue, pharynx and esophagus produced by DHT +
Thorotrast® i.v.** Rat (100 g. ♀): DHT (1 mg. p.o.) 1st day + (bottom) Thorotrast® (1 ml.
i.v.) 2d day; killed 6th day. Pronounced calcium deposition at root of tongue on both sides of
glottis as well as along entire length of esophagus except its most cranial portion. *Top:* Fresh.
Bottom: AgNO₃-stained, specimen. (Cf. Plate XI, *C*.)
(After Selye *et al.*,[845] courtesy Brit. M.J.)

Remarks: Pure ThO₂ crystals (20 mg. suspended in 1 ml. water) given i.v. on 2d day under similar circumstances (rat 100 g. ♀, DHT 1 mg. p.o., 1st day) produced. only traces of calcification in the renal cortex, stomach, spleen, liver, thymus, and heart, presumably because, in the absence of the usual suspending agent (dextrin), the coarse crystals become rapidly sequestered in the RES. Mortality was 50%. The same dose i.p. produced only calcium deposition on the peritoneal surface and no mortality.[841]

Method 2: Rat (100 g. ♀): DHT (1 mg. p.o.) 1st day + Thorotrast® (1 ml. i.v.) 2d day; killed 6th day.

Results: This very large dose of Thorotrast® produced 75% mortality, but the lesions in the *skin, fauces, tongue, esophagus, mediastinum,* and *joints* developed more rapidly than in the rats treated according to Method 1 with 0.6 ml. of Thorotrast®. Qualitatively, the picture thus elicited differed from that just described mainly in that calcification was also noted in the *pancreas* (Fig. 137), which is never affected by smaller doses of Thorotrast®. In several animals calcium precipitation occurred in the marginal zone of the *splenic* Malpighian corpuscles (Fig. 138). These observations show how organ selectivity can be influenced by merely changing the dosage of the challenger.

Method 3: Rat (210 g. ♀): DHT (2 mg. p.o.) 1st day + Thorotrast® (1 ml. i.v.) 2d day; killed 10th day.

Results: These large rats tolerated 1 ml. of Thorotrast® well at first, but three to four days after the injection they became manifestly ill. At that time they developed the previously described calcareous scleroderma-like skin changes, especially around the *face.* Deglutition became difficult owing to the associated *eso-*

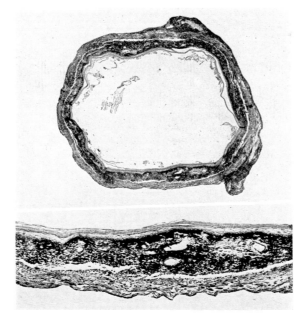

Fig. 133. Calcification of the esophagus produced by DHT + Thorotrast® i.v. Rat (100 g. ♀): DHT (1 mg. p.o.) 1st day + Thorotrast® (1 ml. i.v.) 2d day; killed 6th day. Cross section through esophagus. *Top:* Continuous layer of calcification in wall. (von Kóssa, ×25.) *Bottom:* Higher magnification of section through portion adjacent to that in preceding picture. Calcinosis strictly limited to connective-tissue stroma between epithelium and outer fascial layer. (von Kóssa, ×65.)

(After Selye *et al.*,[845] courtesy Brit. M.J.)

phageal changes; hence, we fed them with rice boiled in milk, instead of the usual hard Purina cubes.

The most striking change in these older rats was the appearance of an uncommonly intense calcification about the large *joints*, particularly in and around the subdeltoid bursa, but also in the adjacent tendons and muscles, which consequently assumed a chalky consistency and white color. When the bursa was opened, a milky or gritty, white material was found in the lumen. In these same regions there was inflammation and sclerosis, presumably as a consequence of the topically irritating calcium deposition. Inflammatory changes were likewise seen in the synovial membranes and fat pads of the articulation, but the joint-cartilage itself was rarely affected (Figs. 139, 140). The periarticular calcification that could be obtained with this technique and its various modifications was sufficiently severe to be readily demonstrable radiographically (Fig. 141).

This form of calciphylaxis may be viewed as an experimental model of a cal-

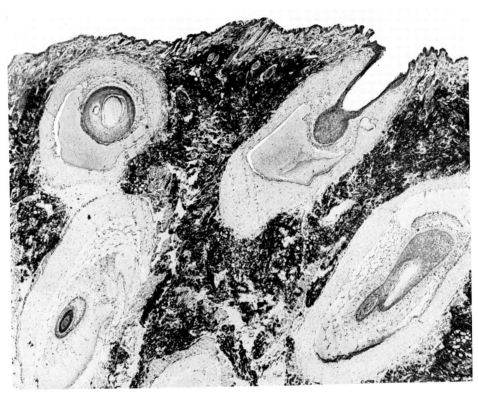

Fig. 134. Cutaneous calcinosis of the face produced by DHT + Thorotrast® i.v. Rat (100 g. ♀): DHT (1 mg. p.o.) 1st day + Thorotrast® (0.6 ml. i.v.) 2d day; died 5th day. In snout, skin between large bristle roots incrusted with diffuse calcium deposits. (von Kóssa, ×39.)

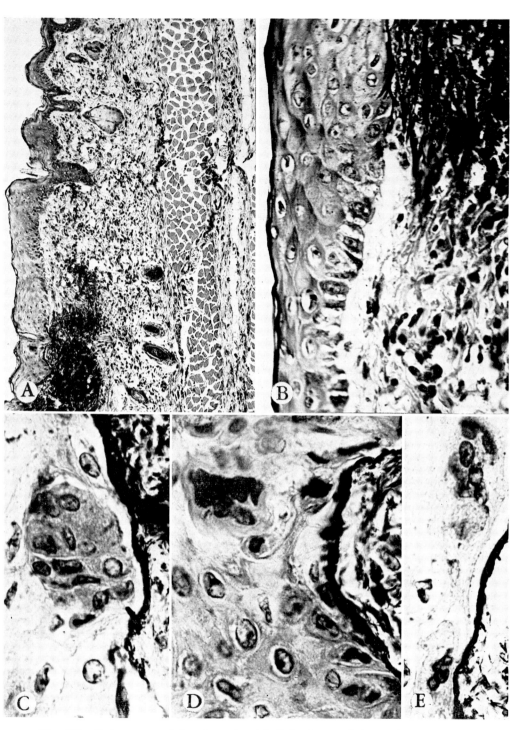

Fig. 135. **Cutaneous calcinosis and epithelial giant-cell formation produced by DHT + Thorotrast® i.v.** Rat (100 g. ♀): DHT (1 mg. p.o.) 1st day + Thorotrast® (0.4 ml. i.v.) 2d day; killed 6th day. Skin from various regions of dorsal neck. *A:* Superficial dermal calcification associated with thickening of epidermis owing to hyperkeratosis and acanthosis, extending beyond demonstrably calcified area. (von Kóssa, ×110.) *B:* Basal layer of epidermis, flattened above calcified region and transformed into very high "peg cells" in adjacent area. (von Kóssa, ×950.) *C, D* and *E:* Three stages in development of syncytia, owing to confluence of epidermal cells above calcified basement membrane. (von Kóssa, ×950.)

careous subdeltoid bursitis, without implying that a calciphylactic mechanism is necessarily responsible for structurally comparable lesions in man.[846]

Calcification with inflammatory changes was also frequently observed in other large joints, particularly those of the elbow, wrist, hip, and knee.

Similar lesions occurred somewhat less regularly around the sciatic *nerves* at the point of their emergence from the pelvis as well as between the greater trochanter of the femur and the tuberosity of the ischium (Fig. 140). Sometimes the tendon insertions on this tuberosity were also calcified.

In the *adrenals*, the cortical and to a lesser extent the medullary sinusoids were often diffusely impregnated with calcium. The scattered "medullary cortical cells" were particularly numerous, and many of them gave the impression of being in the process of transformation into ganglion cells, since they contained dark granules which resembled Nissl bodies.

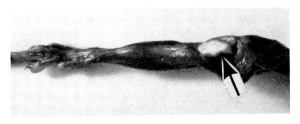

Fig. 136. Calcification of the shoulder musculature produced by DHT + Thoro-trast® i.v. Rat (100 g. ♀): DHT (1 mg. p.o.) 1st day + Thorotrast® (0.3 ml. i.v.) 2d day; killed 7th day. Large white patch of calcium deposition in deltoid muscle (arrow).

In the *kidney*, calcification predominated around the basement membranes of the tubules, but the epithelial cells sometimes also underwent calcification and occasionally there were calcified thrombi in the glomerular capillaries.

Ocular changes were inconstant except for calcification of the palpebrae. Occasionally calcium deposits were also seen in Harder's gland, but only very rarely did we note calcification in the ciliary body.

The *evolution* and *healing* of these calciphylactic lesions has been studied in detail. Just as in other calciphylactic lesions, the originally diffuse, dustlike precipitates of calcium gradually tend to aggregate into circumscribed and often encapsulated foci. This transformation is invariable, irrespective of location, the age of the animal at the time of treatment, or the dosage of DHT and Thorotrast®. In the *tongue* and the *buccal mucosa* the initially diffuse lesions take on the aspect of well-circumscribed, hard and often ulcerating calcareous nodules (Plate XI, *D*). Lesions of lesser severity merely become heavily encapsulated without showing any tendency to exulcerate even after more than two months (Fig. 142). Similar nodular foci also develop in the *fauces, esophagus,* and *soft palate* and around the *glottis* (Figs. 143, 144; Plate XI, *E, F*) and *joints* (Figs. 145, 146; Plate XI, *G*).

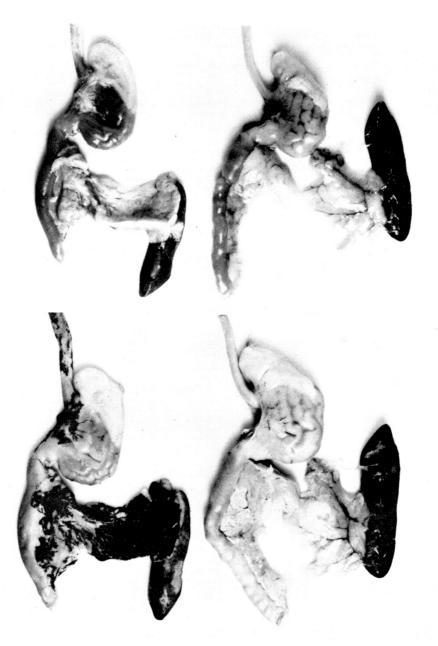

Fig. 137. **Calcification of the pancreas produced by DHT + Thorotrast® i.v.** Two rats (100 g. ♀): DHT (1 mg. p.o.) 1st day + (left) Thorotrast® (1 ml. i.v.) 2d day; killed 6th day. *Top:* Fresh. *Bottom:* AgNO₃-stained, specimens. Combined treatment with large dose of Thorotrast® (left) produced intense calcification with sclerotic shrinkage of pancreas, as well as less pronounced subserosal calcium deposition along esophagus and lesser curvature of stomach. No obvious macroscopic change in control rat (right).

In the *adrenal* cortex myeloid infiltrates tend to appear toward the end of the second month and there is intense proliferation of medullary cortical cells. The medullary ganglion cells are often manifestly deformed and some of them contain calcified granules. Numerous calcific and Thorotrast® deposits are found in the cortex and some of the Thorotrast® crystals are enveloped in slightly amphophilic, but predominantly basophilic material. In addition there are fine, dustlike granules reminiscent of "hematoxylin bodies." Often extraordinarily voluminous foreign-body giant cells envelop the larger accumulations of Thorotrast® and calcium crystals.

In evaluating the role of calciphylaxis in the production of all these lesions it is important to keep in mind that ***without sensitization Thorotrast® produces no calcification,*** even at the highest dose levels tested (Fig. 147).

Indeed, in certain locations, e.g., the phagocytes of the bristle-hair roots and the Kupffer cells of the liver, calcification does not occur, even after sensitization with DHT although here the concentration of Thorotrast® granules is always very high. The splenic phagocytes assume an intermediate position in this respect; there is a dense accumulation of Thorotrast® granules around the Malpighian corpuscles but

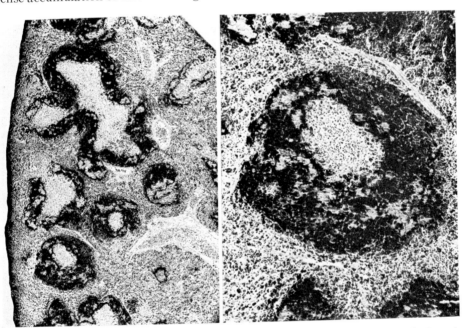

Fig. 138. Splenic calcification produced by DHT + Thorotrast® i.v. Rat (100 g. ♀): DHT (1 mg. p.o.) 1st day + Thorotrast® (1 ml. i.v.) 2d day; died 5th day. Central portions of Malpighian follicles underwent fibrosis and are surrounded by calcified shells. Within these there are numerous necrotic foci which characteristically do not stain with the celestin blue technique used here, yet presumably they contain calcium since they stain with von Kóssa's technique. (Celestin blue, left ×26, right ×75.)

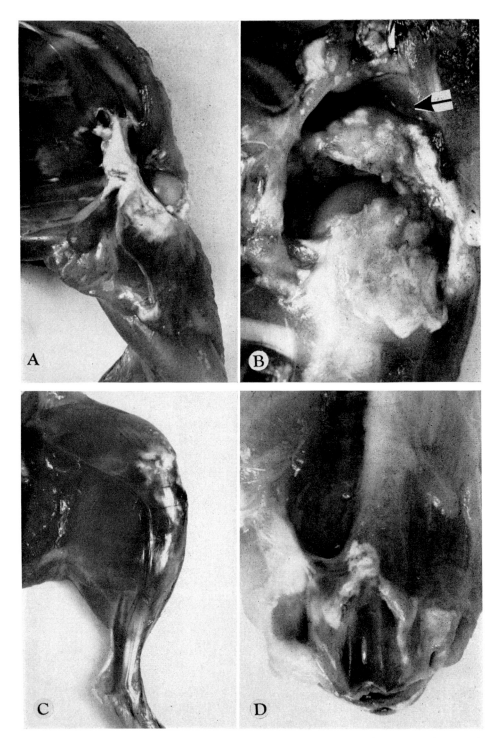

Fig. 139. Articular lesions produced by DHT + Thorotrast® i.v. Rat (210 g. ♀):
DHT (2 mg. p.o.) 1st day + Thorotrast® (1 ml. i.v.) 2d day; killed 10th day. *A:* Ring-shaped
calcium deposition in and around shoulder joint. Exposed head of humerus shows intact cartilage. *B:* Opened shoulder joint exposes subacromial bursa (arrow); white calcium deposits
throughout joint region. *C:* Calcium deposition in muscles and tendons of knee joint. *D:* Capsule
of knee joint calcified along its attachment to femur.

(After Selye *et al.*,[846] courtesy Arthritis and Rheumatism.)

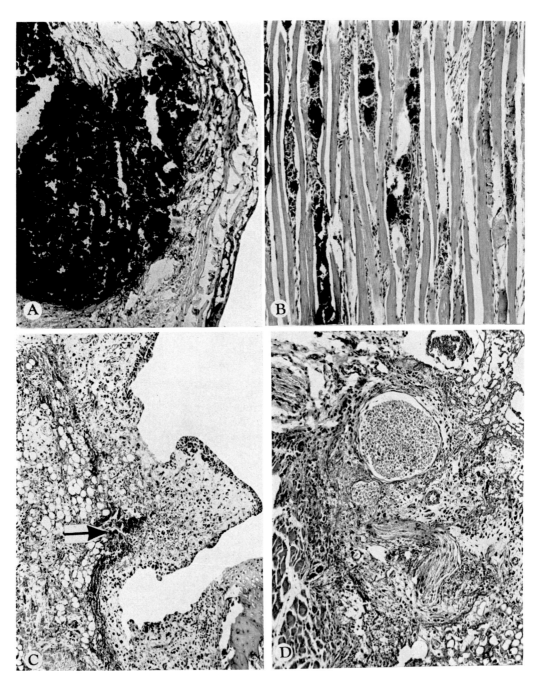

Fig. 140. Articular, muscular and perineural lesions produced by DHT + Thoro-
trast® i.v. Rat (210 g. ♀): DHT (2 mg. p.o.) 1st day + Thorotrast® (1 ml. i.v.) 2d day; killed
10th day. *A:* Calcified connective tissue in wall of subdeltoid bursa. (von Kóssa, ×95.) *B:*
Calcified foci in deltoid muscle. (von Kóssa, ×95.) *C:* Pronounced inflammatory changes in
synovial villi; somewhat basophilic, necrotic band (arrow) presumably calcified (though calcium undetectable on this decalcified section). (PAS, ×95.) *D:* Intense inflammatory infiltration
around branches of brachial plexus in vicinity of calcified shoulder joint. (PAS, ×95.)

(After Selye *et al.*,[846] courtesy Arthritis and Rheumatism.)

186

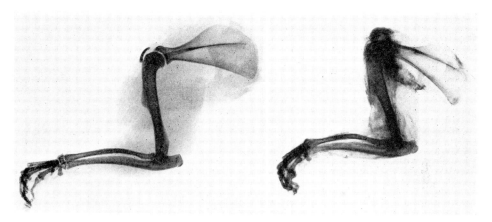

Fig. 141. Soft tissue calcification produced by DHT + Thorotrast® i.v. Two rats (200 g. ♀): DHT (2 mg. p.o.) 1st day + (right) Thorotrast® (1.25 ml. i.v.) 2d day; died 21st day. X-ray pictures of fore limbs after removal of skin. *Left:* Normal control. *Right:* Pronounced calcinosis, especially around shoulder and elbow joints; calcium deposition distinctly visible also in adjacent musculature.

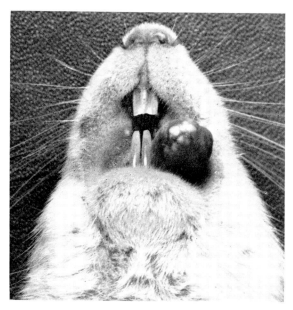

Fig. 142. Lingual calcification produced by DHT + Thorotrast® i.v. Rat (200 g. ♀): DHT (2 mg. p.o.) 1st day + Thorotrast® (1 ml. i.v.) 2d day; killed 70th day. Well-delimited, roundish nodules of calcification at tip of tongue.

187

it rarely elicits local calcinosis. Other challengers, such as egg yolk, regularly produce calcification in the Kupffer cells and the phagocytes of the spleen, but the cells so affected rapidly disintegrate and are soon renewed by new RES cells that contain no calcium. These observations illustrate the *importance of the terrain* for the induction of calcinosis and clearly demonstrate that the capture of calcium is not merely the result of a direct interaction between challenger and blood calcium.

Critical period: In rats (200 g. ♀) treated with DHT (2 mg. p.o.), challenge by Thorotrast® (1 ml. i.v.) produced intense esophageal calcinosis when given on −2d, 1st, +2d, +3d, or +4th day; minor lesions were also observed on −3d, −4th, and +8th day. Calcinosis of the lips was most pronounced upon Thorotrast® administration on +3d and +4th day, but to a lesser extent also after injection at any other time between −2d and +8th day. Calcareous arthritis was extremely pronounced upon injection of Thorotrast® on −2d to +4th day, while

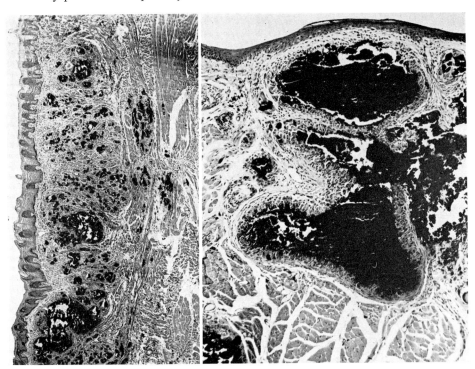

Fig. 143. **Nodular calcification in tongue and cheek produced by DHT + Thorotrast® i.v.** Rat (100 g. ♀): DHT (1 mg. p.o.) 1st day + Thorotrast® (0.3 ml. i.v.) 2d day; killed 60th day. *Left:* Originally diffuse stromal calcification now transformed into numerous well-delimited solid calcium concretions surrounded by dense sclerotic capsules. (von Kóssa, ×4.) *Right:* Two large and several smaller calcified concretions (underneath mucosa of lips), their capsules consisting of granuloma with histiocytes, foreign-body giant cells and external layer of dense connective tissue. (von Kóssa, ×100.)

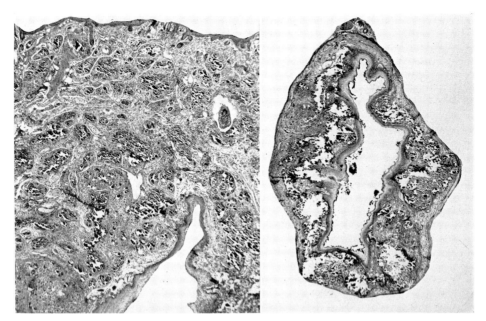

Fig. 144. Evolution of nodular calcification in cheek and esophagus after treatment with DHT + Thorotrast® i.v. Rat (100 g. ♀): DHT (1 mg. p.o.) 1st day + Thorotrast® (0.4 ml. i.v.) 2d day; killed 61st day. *Left:* Section through entire thickness of cheek. Nodules of PAS-positive calcified matrix surrounded by dense sclerotic tissue. *Right:* Transverse section through esophagus. Similar nodules of calcification in thickened esophageal mucosa. Empty spaces are artifacts due to detachment of brittle, calcified material. (PAS, ×27.)

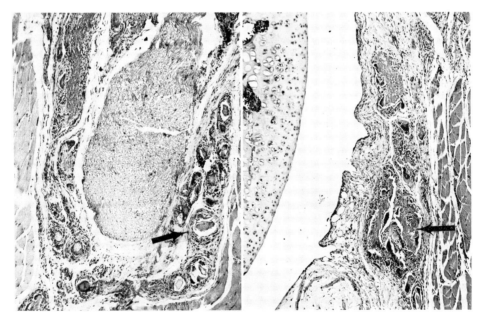

Fig. 145. Healing of perineural and articular lesions produced by DHT + Thorotrast® i.v. Rat (100 g. ♀): DHT (1 mg. p.o.) 1st day + Thorotrast® (0.3 ml. i.v.) 2d day; killed 60th day. *Left:* Large nerve branch in knee region completely surrounded by giant-cell-containing, granulomatous foci (arrow) formed around now aggregated masses of calcified tissue. *Right:* Synovial membrane of humerocapsular joint with many giant-cell-containing, granulomatous foci underneath surface (arrow). (Hematoxylin-phloxine, ×85.)

cutaneous calcinosis was most effectively produced by injection of Thorotrast®
between − 2d and − 4th day (traces were elicited at any time between − 8th and
+4th day).

DHT + Thorotrast® i.p.

Peritoneal Calciphylaxis

Method 1: Rat (100 g. ♀): DHT (1 mg. p.o.) 1st day + Thorotrast® (1 ml. i.p.)
2d day; killed 6th day.

Results: Widespread calcification was found virtually everywhere on the peritoneal surface as well as in the retroperitoneal, mesenteric, and genital fat. The

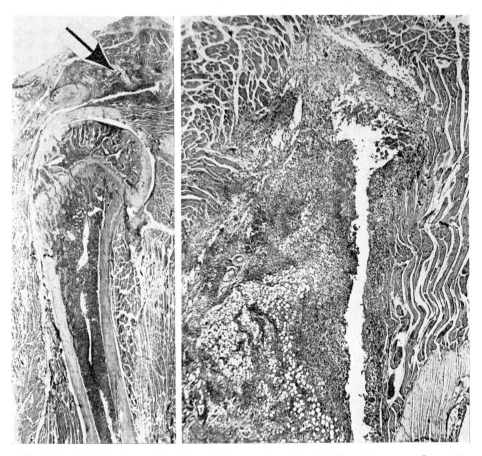

Fig. 146. Calcification of the knee joint produced by DHT + Thorotrast® i.v. Rat
(240 g. ♀): DHT (2 mg. p.o.) 1st day + Thorotrast® (1 ml. i.v.) 2d day; killed 60th day. *Left:*
Calcification and necrosis in capsule of knee joint (arrow). (Hematoxylin-phloxine, ×6.5.)
Right: Higher magnification of region marked by arrow in preceding picture. Disintegration of
synovial membrane with calcium deposition and inflammatory infiltration. (Hematoxylin-
phloxine, ×37.)

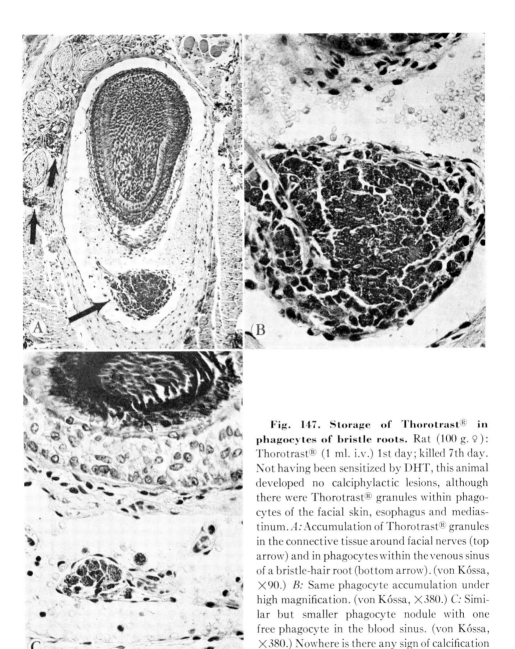

Fig. 147. Storage of Thorotrast® in phagocytes of bristle roots. Rat (100 g. ♀): Thorotrast® (1 ml. i.v.) 1st day; killed 7th day. Not having been sensitized by DHT, this animal developed no calciphylactic lesions, although there were Thorotrast® granules within phagocytes of the facial skin, esophagus and mediastinum. *A:* Accumulation of Thorotrast® granules in the connective tissue around facial nerves (top arrow) and in phagocytes within the venous sinus of a bristle-hair root (bottom arrow). (von Kóssa, ×90.) *B:* Same phagocyte accumulation under high magnification. (von Kóssa, ×380.) *C:* Similar but smaller phagocyte nodule with one free phagocyte in the blood sinus. (von Kóssa, ×380.) Nowhere is there any sign of calcification around the Thorotrast® accumulations.

pancreatic surface was also always calcified but the calcinosis exhibited no tendency to spread into the stroma of the pancreas itself (Fig. 148). In this respect the peritoneal calciphylaxis produced by DHT + Thorotrast® differed sharply from that obtained in DHT-sensitized rats by the i.p. injection of Fe-Dex or albumen; the latter caused calcinosis predominantly in the pancreatic stroma and much less markedly, if at all, on the peritoneal surface and in the omentum.

Method 2: Rat (200 g. ♀): DHT (2 mg. p.o.) 1st day + Thorotrast® (1–2 ml. i.p.) 2d day; killed 6th day.

Results: The changes obtained by this procedure in 200 g. rats were virtually identical with those obtained using Method 1 in 100 g. rats; hence they need not be described here.

DHT + Tl-acetate

Renal (Cortico-Medullary) Calciphylaxis

Method 1: Rat (100 g. ♀): DHT (500 μg. p.o.) 1st day + thallium acetate (2 mg. in 0.2 ml. water, s.c.) 1st day; killed 8th day.[859]

Results: A single dose of thallium acetate (which in itself produces no calcification) caused severe *nephrocalcinosis* strictly limited to the cortico-medullary junc-

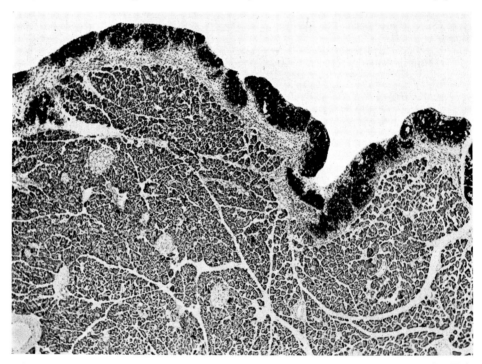

Fig. 148. Peritoneal calcification without pancreatic calcinosis produced by DHT + Thorotrast® i.p. Rat (100 g. ♀): DHT (1 mg. p.o.) 1st day + Thorotrast® (1 ml. i.p.) 2d day; killed 7th day. Intensive calcinosis with reactive inflammation limited to peritoneal surface of pancreas. (von Kóssa, ×39.)

tion-line when an in itself virtually non-nephrotoxic dose of DHT was administered simultaneously. The slight calcification of the *aorta* normally produced by
this dose of DHT was greatly aggravated by the concurrent treatment with thallium acetate.

Discussion: The sensitizing effect of thallium acetate cannot be ascribed to its
stressor actions, since, under comparable circumstances, exposure to stress (restraint) actually prevents DHT-induced nonspecific calcinosis and the calciphylactic responsiveness to cutaneous challenge by trauma[859] (Fig. 149).

Method 2: Rat (100 g. ♀): DHT (50 μg. p.o.) 1st–4th day + thallium acetate
(1 mg. in 0.5 ml. water, s.c.) 1st and 2d day; killed 7th day.

Results: Under these circumstances, the cortico-medullary calcinosis was particularly sharply delimited and of such intensity that usually death ensued from
uremia (Fig. 150).

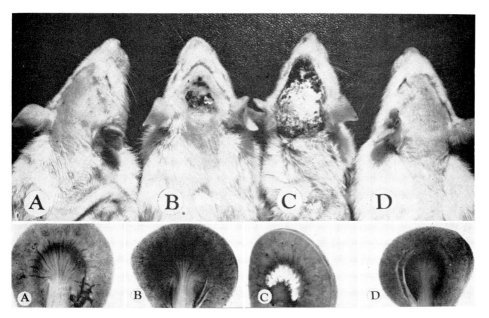

**Fig. 149. Cutaneous calcinosis produced by DHT + thallium acetate s.c. + pluck-
ing of scalp hair, and its prevention by restraint.** Four rats (100 g. ♀), in which hair was
plucked over the calvarium on 2d day; photographed 8th day. *Top row: A:* Pretreatment with
thallium acetate (2 mg. in 0.2 ml. water, s.c.) 1st day caused no sensitization. *B:* DHT (500 μg.
p.o.) 1st day induced mild sensitization conducive to small calciphylactic response in epilated
area. *C:* Pretreatment with same doses of DHT + thallium acetate resulted in pronounced
cutaneous calcinosis. *D:* Restraint (24 hours, immediately following administration of DHT)
prevented the calciphylactic response. *Bottom row:* Cross sections through kidneys of same four
rats. Only combined treatment with DHT + thallium acetate (C) produced massive selective
calcification at cortico-medullary junction line.

(After Selye *et al.*,[859] courtesy Proc. Soc. Exper. Biol. and Med.)

DHT + VOSO₄ i.v.

Nonspecific Calcinosis

Method: Rat (100 g. ♀): DHT (1 mg. p.o.) 1st day + VOSO₄ (0.5 mg. in 0.1 ml. water, i.v.) 2d day; killed 6th day.

Results: Nonspecific calcinosis. Mortality: 0.

DHT + Yolk i.v.

RES-Type of Calciphylaxis

Method: Rat (100 g. ♀): DHT (1 mg. p.o.) 1st day + yolk (50%, 5 ml. i.v.) 2d day; killed 2d–10th day.

Fig. 150. Pure cortico-medullary nephrocalcinosis produced by DHT + thallium acetate s.c. Rat (100 g. ♀): DHT (50 μg. p.o.) 1st to 4th day + thallium acetate (1 mg. in 0.5 ml. water, s.c.) 1st and 2d day; died (presumably of uremia) 7th day. Particularly sharp delimitation of calcification to cortico-medullary junction line. Medullary rays traversing cortico-medullary junction are free of calcium.

(After Selye,[332] courtesy Charles C Thomas Publ., Springfield, Ill.)

Results: Intense calcification of the *spleen* made the organ whitish, hard, and brittle (Plate III, *E, F*). Histologically, calcification was found to occur predominantly in the splenic phagocytes, but the adjacent connective-tissue fibers were frequently also incrustated with calcium, especially in the animals killed on the 3d and 4th day of the experiment, that is 2–3 days after yolk injection. In mild cases there were only isolated islets of calcification, irregularly distributed throughout the splenic tissue (Fig. 151). But in animals whose spleen became evidently white and brittle a generalized, regular pattern of calcinosis developed in that all splenic phagocytes became overloaded with calcium and only the central portions of all the Malpighian corpuscles remained free (Fig. 152).

There was also considerable calcification of the Kupffer cells and of the isolated connective-tissue fibers around the *hepatic* sinusoids (Fig. 153; Plate III, *G*). The hepatic parenchyma, blood vessels, and biliary ducts remained unaffected.

Nephrocalcinosis was limited mainly to the cortico-medullary junction line (Fig. 154). In addition there often developed intravascular PAS-positive aggregates, which eventually occluded the glomerular capillaries (Fig. 155).

Very intense calcinosis was regularly found in the mucosa of the ventricular

Fig. 151. Islets of calcification in spleen produced by DHT + yolk i.v. Rat (100 g. ♀): DHT (1 mg. p.o.) 1st day + yolk (50%, 5 ml. i.v.) 2d day; killed 4th day. Several irregular foci of calcification. (von Kóssa, ×30.)

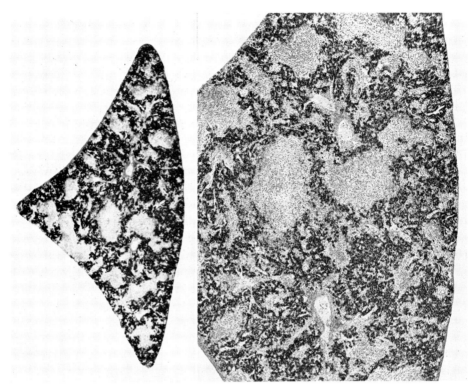

Fig. 152. Calcification of spleen produced by DHT + yolk i.v. Rat (100 g. ♀): DHT (1 mg. p.o.) 1st day + yolk (50%, 5 ml. i.v.) 2d day; killed 4th day. Intense calcification throughout spleen, especially of red pulp. (von Kóssa, left ×15, right ×31.)

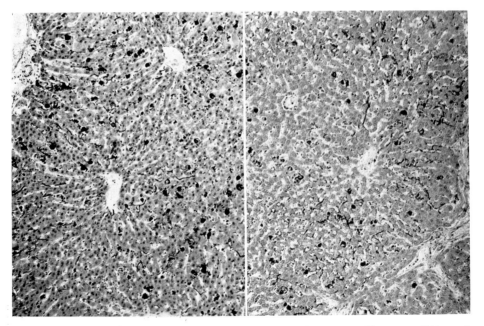

Fig. 153. Calcification of liver produced by DHT + yolk i.v. Two rats (100 g. ♀): DHT (1 mg. p.o.) 1st day + yolk [50%, 5 ml. i.v. (left) and i.p. (right)] 2d day; killed 4th day. Calcium deposition affects Kupffer cells and some connective-tissue fibers along walls of sinusoids. (von Kóssa, ×90.) (Cf. Plate III, *G*.)

(After Selye,[827] courtesy Allergie u. Asthma.)

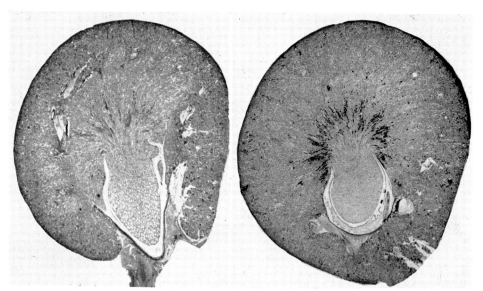

Fig. 154. Nephrocalcinosis produced by DHT + yolk i.v. Two rats (100 g. ♀): DHT
(1 mg. p.o.) 1st day + (right) yolk (50%, 5 ml. i.v.) 2d day; killed 4th day. *Left:* No detectable
renal calcification in control animal. *Right:* Combined treatment with yolk resulted in marked
cortico-medullary nephrocalcinosis. (von Kóssa, ×7.5.)

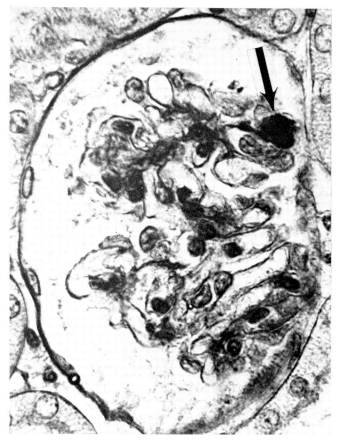

Fig. 155. Glomerular hyalinization produced by DHT + yolk i.v. Rat (100 g. ♀):
DHT (1 mg. p.o.) 1st day + yolk (50%, 5 ml. i.v.) 2d day; killed 4th day. Occlusion of glomerular loop (arrow) by hyaline thrombus. (PAS, ×1100.)

part of the *stomach*, but never in the proventriculus. As a result of this calcinosis and the associated edema, the wall of the ventriculus became extremely thick, but its whitish color was masked by intense hyperemia (Fig. 156). Histologically, calcification proved to be localized predominantly along the middle portion of the mucosa, while the edema was in the submucosa (Fig. 157).

The stroma of *Brunner's glands* likewise underwent heavy calcinosis, but calcification in the *pancreas* occurred only in very exceptional cases. Traces of calcium could be found in the *thymus, heart* (tigro-vascular), *aorta*, and *adrenals*.

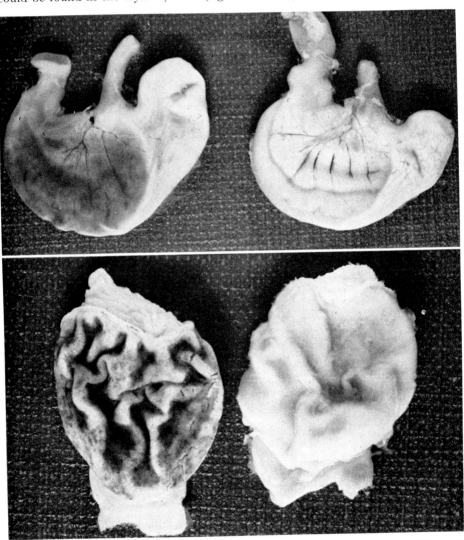

Fig. 156. Calcification of the stomach produced by DHT + yolk i.v. Two rats (100 g. ♀): DHT (1 mg. p.o.) 1st day + (left) yolk (50%, 5 ml. i.v.) 2d day; killed 4th day. *Left:* Heavy calcification of the entire ventriculus (proventriculus is unaffected) in rat treated with DHT + yolk. *Right:* DHT alone elicited no macroscopically visible change at this dose level.

The intense systemic calcinosis was invariably associated with a pronounced *osteitis fibrosa*. Mortality was 25%.[826, 827, 849]

Discussion: The induction of selective calcification within the RES is presumably due to the fact that the lipid-containing particles of yolk are preferentially taken up by the phagocytes of this system and subsequently undergo calcification. The rapid disappearance of this calcinosis might have been due to the gradual disintegration and subsequent removal of the calcium-impregnated phagocytes.

To verify this interpretation the ***evolution*** and ***healing*** of this syndrome was followed. Rats were treated according to the method just described and then divided into groups killed at daily intervals: the first group five hours, the last, nine days, after yolk injection. Yolk particles were seen in RES cells, pulmonary capillaries, and renal collecting tubules as soon as five hours after the injection. However, sections stained with the von Kóssa or celestin blue techniques showed that at this time calcium deposition within these lipid globules was minimal and the yolk particles gave only a very faint PAS reaction. On the other hand, 24–72 hours after the injection the yolk globules were already heavily calcified and their PAS tingibility had increased. During the following few days the calcified RES cells

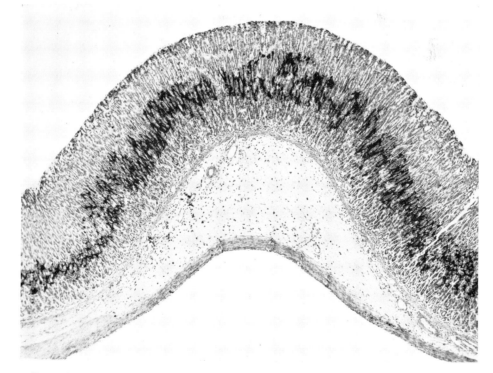

Fig. 157. Calcification of the gastric mucosa produced by DHT + yolk i.v. Rat (100 g. ♀): DHT (1 mg. p.o.) 1st day + yolk (50%, 5 ml. i.v.) 2d day; killed 4th day. Heavy calcification limited to middle layer of gastric mucosa. Submucosa is very edematous. (von Kóssa, ×39.)

disintegrated. By the ninth day after injection they were almost completely re-placed both in the liver and in the spleen by new RES cells of normal appearance. The removal of the calcified lipid granules from the lung and especially from the kidney progressed more slowly (Fig. 158). Indeed, when larger amounts of DHT and/or yolk were given, the renal lesions tended to progress toward sclerosis and sometimes chronic inflammation developed in the renal pelvis and papilla, with atypical downgrowth of the epithelium and a predominantly plasmocytic inflam-matory response (Fig. 159).

If under similar circumstances **yolk alone** is administered (without DHT pre-treatment), the accumulation of exogenous material in the RES and kidney is es-sentially the same. However, in this case the yolk droplets in the Kupffer cells at-tract virtually no calcium or PAS-positive material and they stain only very faintly, if at all, with Sudan III. The granules deposited in the spleen and lung fix somewhat more calcium and show a definite though moderate deposition of PAS-positive and sudanophilic material. On the other hand, in the kidney, calcification at the cortico-medullary junction is almost as intense in rats treated with yolk alone as in those which were sensitized with DHT. Correspondingly, the epithelia of the affected tubules become intensely tingible with both Sudan III and PAS even without pretreatment with a calcifier.

Yolk may consequently be regarded as a material intermediate between a cal-ciphylactic challenger and a direct calcifier, since its ability to cause calcinosis is greatly enhanced by, but not totally dependent upon, sensitization with DHT.

The capacity of yolk to produce calcification either in the sensitized or in the nonsensitized animal appears to run parallel with its ability to cause storage of sudanophilic and PAS-positive materials in various organs. Yolk is rich in lipids and stains intensely with Sudan while in the circulating blood, but it loses these characteristics in the Kupffer cells much more rapidly than in other phagocytes,

---

Fig. 158. Evolution of calciphylactic changes produced by DHT + yolk i.v. Three rats (100 g. ♀): DHT (1 mg. p.o.) 1st day + yolk (50%, 5 ml. i.v.) 2d day. Organs shown 5 hours (left), 24 hours (middle) and 9 days (right) after yolk injection. *Top row:* At 5 hours, Kupffer cells of *liver* are greatly enlarged by yolk ingestion but there are only a few calcified granules in and around them. At 24 hours, Kupffer cells are heavily calcified and numerous fine calcium granules line hepatic sinusoids. After 9 days, only occasional calcium granules remain (right upper corner) and virtually all Kupffer cells are normal. *Second row:* In *spleen* initial appearance of heavily yolk-laden but only slightly calcified phagocytes at 5 hours is also followed by massive calcification after 24 hours and almost complete disappearance of calcified phagocytes (only one left in lower right corner) after 9 days. *Third row:* In *lung*, yolk globules of varying sizes are predominantly located within capillaries. They likewise show intense calci-fication only after 24 hours and are almost completely cleared away by 9th day (one remaining calcified globule in this field is marked by arrow). *Bottom row:* In *renal medulla*, yolk casts are found within tubules at 5 hours but these show only traces of calcification. At 24 hours casts and some connective-tissue fibers of stroma are calcified but this change persists even after 9 days. (von Kóssa, ×420.)

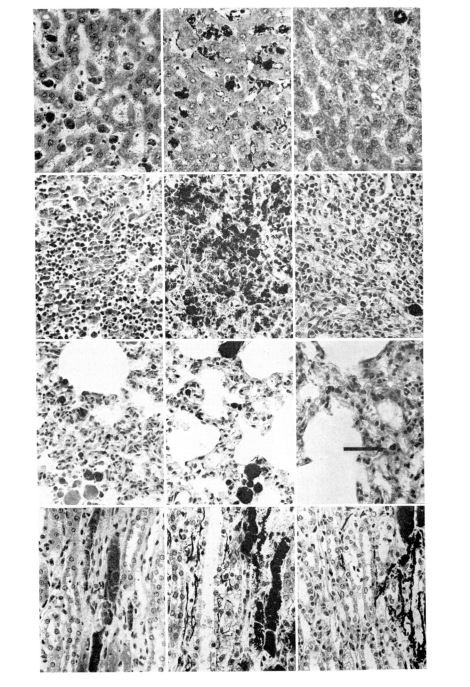

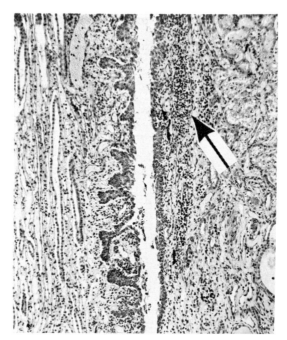

Fig. 159. Atypical epithelial proliferations and chronic inflammation in renal pelvis produced by DHT + yolk i.v. Rat (240 g. ♀): DHT (2 mg. p.o.) 1st day + yolk (50%, 7 ml. i.v.) 2d day; killed 60th day. Atypical down-growths of transitional epithelium into renal papilla (left); chronic inflammation with predominantly plasmocytic infiltration underneath epithelium facing the kidney tissue (arrow). Calcification virtually absent. (von Kóssa, ×120.)

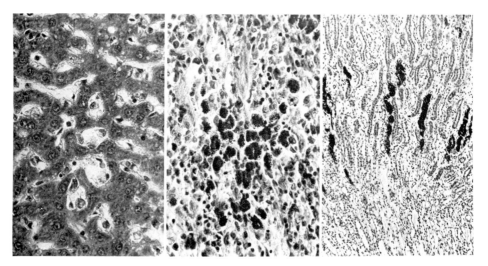

Fig. 160. Calcinosis produced by yolk i.v. alone. Rat (100 g. ♀): yolk (50%, 5 ml. i.v.) 1st day; killed 24 hours later. *Left:* Kupffer cells are greatly enlarged but contain no calcium. (von Kóssa, ×300.) *Middle:* Splenic phagocytes are engorged with calcified granules, but calcinosis is not as pronounced as it would be following DHT sensitization. (von Kóssa, ×300.) *Right:* Heavily calcified, tubular epithelia at the cortico-medullary junction line are in process of becoming detached and forming cylinders. (von Kóssa, ×80.)

while sudanophilia is not lost during its uptake and excretion by the renal tubule. However, there is no strict parallelism between the degree of sudanophilia and the tendency to take up calcium. The Kupffer cells are only slightly more sudanophilic in DHT-pretreated than in control animals treated with the same amount of yolk; yet, they undergo intense calcification in the sensitized, and virtually none in the nonsensitized, rat (Fig. 160).

This form of calciphylactic response has a fairly sharply delimited *critical period*. Essentially similar though less intense lesions were produced if the same amount of yolk was injected i.v. on the +2d or +3d day, but challenge by yolk on the +4th day no longer induced much calcification, although it produced a considerable mortality.[841]

DHT + Yolk i.p.

Omental, Thymic, and RES-Type of Calciphylaxis

Method 1: Rat (100 g. ♀): DHT (1 mg. p.o.) 1st day + yolk (50%, 5 ml. i.p.) 2d day; killed 6th–10th day.

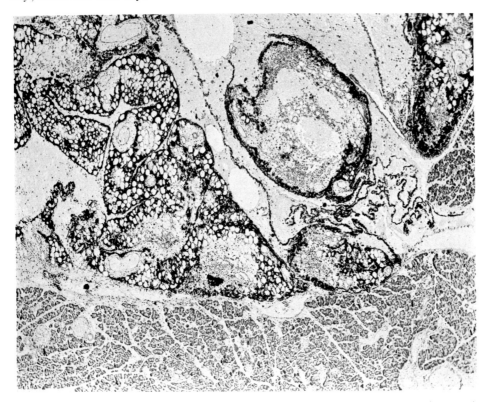

Fig. 161. Calcification of omentum produced by DHT + yolk i.p. Rat (100 g. ♀): DHT (1 mg. p.o.) 1st day + yolk (50%, 5 ml. i.p.) 2d day; killed 5th day. Intense calcification of omentum; adjacent pancreatic parenchyma remains entirely unaffected. (von Kóssa, ×39.) (After Selye,[829] courtesy Allergie u. Asthma.)

Results: Unlike after the intraperitoneal injection of albumen, here there was no calcification of the skin, abdominal wall, or pancreas, although the *omentum* (which is not affected by albumen i.p.) as well as the *peritoneal* and *retroperitoneal fat* showed intense calcification (Fig. 161). The response also differed from the generalized peritoneal calcification that is obtained in DHT-sensitized rats by a great variety of intraperitoneally injected topical challengers (e.g., ThO₂, CeCl₃, LaCl₃, various aluminum salts), which induce a fairly even calcium incrustation of the entire peritoneal surface without any particular predilection for the omentum and fat.

The frequent occurrence of calcification in the *perithymic lymph nodes* (Fig. 162) may be due to yolk brought to them by way of the ascending lymphatics that connect them with the peritoneal cavity; it may also be due to cell debris coming from the thymus.

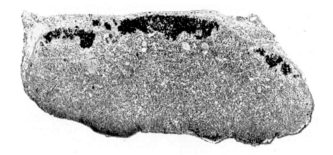

Fig. 162. Calcification of a thymic lymph node produced by DHT + yolk i.p. Rat (100 g. ♀): DHT (1 mg. p.o.) 1st day + yolk (50%, 5 ml. i.p.) 2d day; killed 5th day. Calcification, especially in and around subcapsular sinus. (von Kóssa, ×35.)

Since a large portion of the intraperitoneally injected yolk soon reaches the general circulation, it is not unexpected that the other manifestations of this calciphylactic response are quite similar to those obtained by DHT + yolk i.v. Calcinosis of the *thymus* was even more pronounced when yolk was given i.p. rather than i.v., perhaps because the intraperitoneal treatment represents a greater stress and the acute thymus involution characteristic of the alarm reaction notoriously predisposes the organ for this type of calcinosis (Figs. 163, 164).

In the *liver* and *spleen* yolk i.p. produced comparatively mild lesions, but these were of the same kind as those elicited by yolk i.v. There was transient calcification of the RES cells during the first few days, while later only the stroma fibers retained their calcium (Figs. 165, 166) and eventually the organ regained its normal appearance. Only in the most sensitive animals were there large aggregates of calcified masses, which were difficult to absorb.

Calcinosis at the cortico-medullary junction of the *kidney, stomach,* and *duo-*

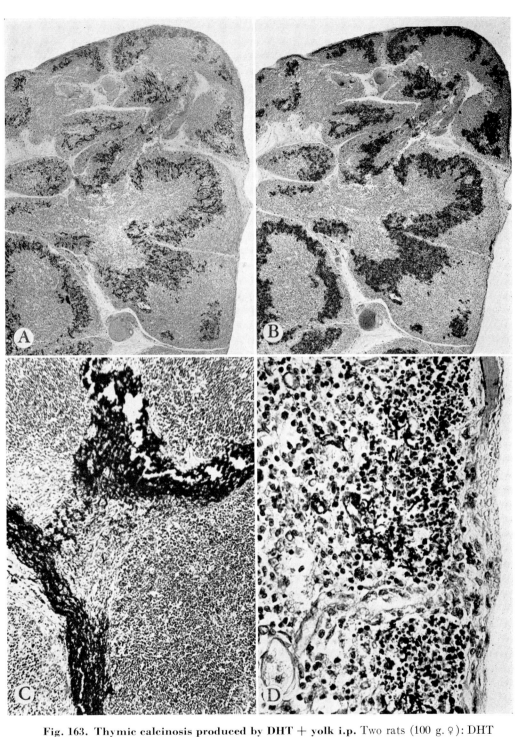

Fig. 163. Thymic calcinosis produced by DHT + yolk i.p. Two rats (100 g. ♀): DHT (1 mg. p.o.) 1st day + yolk (50%, 5 ml. i.p.) 2d day; killed 5th day. *A* and *B:* Calcification is limited to subcortical region of parenchyma (A von Kóssa, B celestin blue, ×30). *C* and *D:* In the other rat, calcium deposition takes place predominantly in stroma (C), although in another region (D), some cortical calcification is also noticeable. (von Kóssa, C ×85, D ×420.)

denum was likewise severe, but the *retroperitoneal fat, mesentery,* and *pancreas* showed only traces of calcification.[826, 827, 849]

Discussion: The dissimilarity in the distribution of the calcium deposits produced by albumen i.p. and yolk i.p. is presumably due, in part, to differences in their direct and lymphatic spreading. Control experiments in similarly DHT-sensitized animals showed that if introduced directly into the subcutaneous tissue, both albumen and yolk induce approximately equal degrees of cutaneous calcinosis; hence, it may be assumed that their basic challenging potency is nearly the same. However, yolk does not diffuse through the abdominal wall as easily as albumen and, therefore, it does not produce the three calcified skin patches over the thinnest portions of the abdominal musculature that are characteristic of egg white. Lack of diffusion into the pancreatic stroma may explain why yolk has no special tendency to produce any calcification of the pancreas comparable to that elicited by albumen and other readily diffusible challengers (e.g., Fe-Dex).

Method 2: Rat (200 g. ♀): DHT (2 mg. p.o.) 1st day + yolk (50%, 10 ml. i.p.) 2d day; killed 6th day.

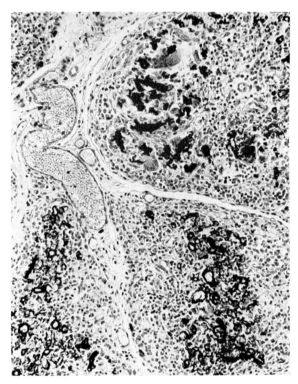

Fig. 164. Thymic calcinosis produced by DHT + yolk i.p. Rat (100 g. ♀): DHT (1 mg. p.o.) 1st day + yolk (50%, 5 ml. i.p.) 2d day; killed 5th day. Calcification, especially in cortical and subcortical layers of thymus. In some lobules (bottom) deposits predominate in capillary walls; in others (top) they tend to be engulfed by multinuclear giant cells. (von Kóssa, ×150.)

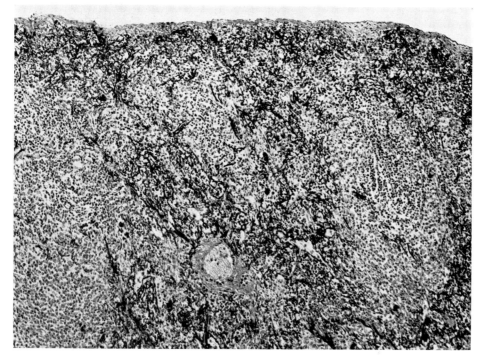

Fig. 165. Splenic calcinosis produced by DHT + yolk i.p. Rat (100 g. ♀): DHT (1 mg. p.o.) 1st day + yolk (50%, 5 ml. i.p.) 2d day; killed 10th day. Calcification predominant in and around stroma fibers. (von Kóssa, ×135.)

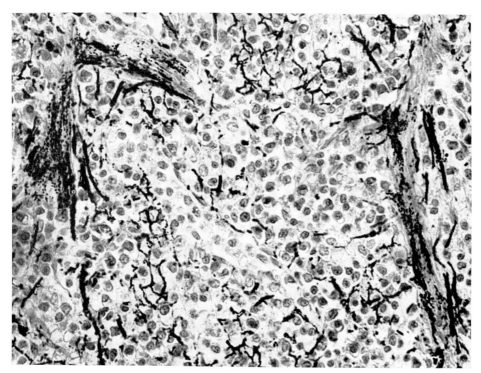

Fig. 166. Splenic calcinosis produced by DHT + yolk i.p. Rat (100 g. ♀): DHT (1 mg. p.o.) 1st day + yolk (50%, 5 ml. i.p.) 2d day; killed 10th day. Calcification limited to stroma. (von Kóssa, ×540.)

Results: In these larger rats the syndrome produced by yolk was not markedly different from that just described as characteristic for smaller animals. However, here *pulmonary* calcinosis was not limited to the calcification of large intravascular lipid particles; it frequently involved the connective tissue of the alveoli in the manner characteristic of most other calciphylactic syndromes (Fig. 167). In addition, we sometimes saw calcification of the *uterus* with predominant participation of the endometrium, a response similar to that produced under certain conditions in large rats treated with DHT + Fe-Dex i.p. (Plate VI, *C*).

DHT + Yolk i.v. + PMX s.c.
Calciphylactic Dermatomyositis

Method: Rat (100 g. ♀): DHT (1 mg. p.o.) 1st day + yolk (25%, 2 ml. i.v.) 2d day + PMX (2 mg. in 0.2 ml. water, s.c. in flank region) 2d day; killed 6th day.

Results: The syndrome produced in this manner was totally unlike that elicited by DHT + yolk i.v. alone and greatly resembled the calciphylactic dermatomyositis normally induced by DHT + Fe-Dex i.v. + PMX s.c. (cf. p. 127). The cutaneous lesions were most obvious in the cephalic region and gradually

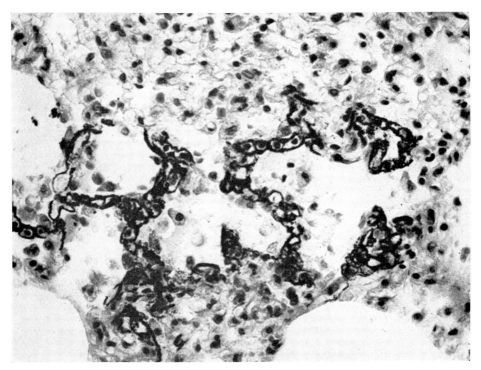

Fig. 167. Pulmonary calcinosis produced by DHT + yolk i.p. Rat (200 g. ♀): DHT (2 mg. p.o.) 1st day + yolk (50%, 10 ml. i.p.) 2d day; killed 6th day. Fine lines of calcium deposition in connective tissue of pulmonary septa surrounding the cells. (von Kóssa, ×560.)

diminished in the cranio-caudal direction. In our first experiments we noted that even the small amounts of yolk which may escape at the time of i.v. injection cause pronounced local reactions. Hence, we subsequently injected the yolk into a femoral vein (rather than into a jugular vein as is usual), but even then the cephalic region responded most severely. Curiously, here the lower lip frequently failed to react (Fig. 168; Plate X, *D*), although it is a site of predisposition for the lesions induced by Thorotrast® i.v. or Fe-Din i.v.

DHT + ZnCl₂ i.v.
Hepato-Splenic Calciphylaxis

Method: Rat (100 g. ♀): DHT (1 mg. p.o.) 1st day + ZnCl₂ (2.5 mg. in 0.25 ml. water, i.v. ×2) 2d day; killed 6th day.

Results: The most striking changes were hemorrhagic necroses in the spleen (with great enlargement, hardening, and dark discoloration of the organ), hemorrhagic pancreatitis, thrombosis of the splenic vein and large yellow patches of calcifying necrosis in the liver (Figs. 169, 170). Occasionally there were also necroses in the wall of the cecum and early stages of mesenteric periarteritis. The multiple

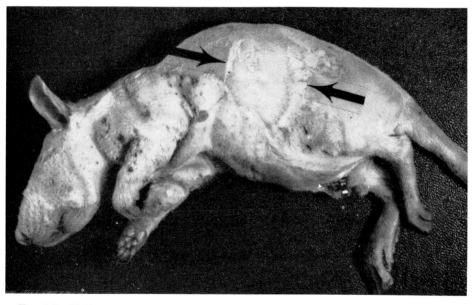

Fig. 168. Fully developed cutaneous lesions produced by DHT + yolk i.v. + PMX s.c. Rat (100 g. ♀): DHT (1 mg. p.o.) 1st day + yolk (25%, 2 ml. i.v.) 2d day + PMX (2 mg. in 0.2 ml. water, s.c. in flank region) 2d day; photographed 6th day. Skin lesions very similar to those of "dermatomyositis" produced by DHT + Fe-Dex i.v. + PMX s.c.; their intensity also decreases gradually in cranio-caudal direction. PMX-injection site unresponsive, owing to "overchallenge," but is surrounded by halo of calcinosis (arrows). "Michel" clip in right inguinal region indicates site of yolk injection into femoral vein. (Cf. Plate X, *D*.)

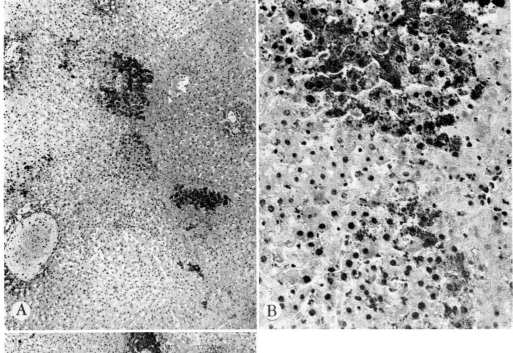

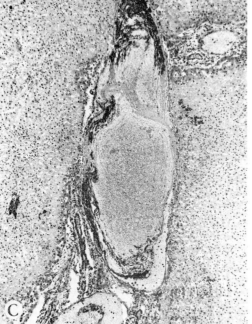

Fig. 169. Hepatic calcification and necrosis produced by DHT + ZnCl₂ i.v. Rat (100 g. ♀): DHT (1 mg. p.o.) 1st day + ZnCl₂ (2.5 mg. in 1 ml. water, i.v., injected very slowly, ×2) 2d day; died 6th day. *A:* Several calcified islets with massive necrosis (left half of picture), respecting only vicinity of hepatic veins. (von Kóssa, ×95.) *B:* Central area of preceding picture. Calcinosis affecting predominantly perinuclear area, though near upper margin cytoplasm likewise contains calcified granules. (von Kóssa, ×330.) *C:* Thrombosis in a large hepatic vein with calcification of fibrin-net near vessel wall; necrosis of surrounding parenchyma. (von Kóssa, ×95.)

abdominal necroses may have resulted from thromboses in the splanchnic vessels; calcification in the affected sites was minimal and could hardly have accounted for the necroses.

Calcinosis (in order of decreasing intensity) was found in: stomach > heart (tigro-vascular), kidney (cortical), and pancreas, but occasionally also in skin, esophagus, and Brunner's glands. Mortality was 80%.

Remarks: Essentially similar results were obtained with the comparable doses of DHT (2 mg.) + $ZnCl_2$ (6 mg.) in 200 g. rats, but here the lesions were less severe and there was no mortality.

DHT + $ZrOCl_2$ i.v.

Nonspecific Calcinosis

Method: Rat (100 g. ♀): DHT (1 mg. p.o.) 1st day + $ZrOCl_2$ (5 mg. in 0.5 ml. water, i.v. ×3) 2d day; killed 6th day.

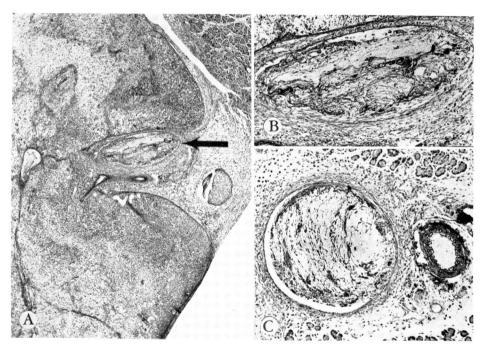

Fig. 170. Vascular lesions produced by DHT + $ZnCl_2$ i.v. Rat (100 g. ♀): DHT (1 mg. p.o.) 1st day + $ZnCl_2$ (3 injections in aqueous solution of 1 mg. in 0.1 ml., 1.5 mg. in 0.15 ml. and 2.5 mg. in 0.25 ml., i.v.) throughout 2d day; killed 6th day. *A:* Complete thrombotic occlusion of splenic vein near hilum (arrow). Most of the spleen is necrotic, except for small area just below vein. (PAS, ×26.) *B:* Higher magnification of splenic vein shown in A. Here, PAS-positive, fibrinoid threads within thrombus are clearly visible. (PAS, ×90.) *C:* Section through adjacent pancreas shows large occlusive thrombus in vein while artery remains normal. Stroma exhibits inflammatory changes. (PAS, ×90.)

Results: Nonspecific calcinosis and occasionally necrosis of the tail. Mortality: 0.

Remarks: In 200 g. rats sensitized with 2 mg. of DHT and challenged with 10 mg. ×2 of $ZrOCl_2$ under similar circumstances, the results were the same but mortality was 40%.

CALCIPHYLACTIC SYNDROMES PRODUCED AFTER SENSITIZATION BY VITAMIN D_3

As previously explained, our standard calciphylactic sensitizer was DHT, and all challengers (local and systemic) were first tested in rats pretreated with this agent. For comparative purposes it then became necessary to verify whether the same responses could also be produced following sensitization with other calcifiers (e.g., vitamin D_3, parathyroid hormone, bilateral nephrectomy). However, it soon became evident not only that all these systemic calcifiers can sensitize for calciphylactic reactions but that the resulting syndromes are essentially the same as those obtained following sensitization with DHT. Hence, it would serve no purpose to describe all our relevant observations in detail. In the following pages we shall merely list the techniques that we found most appropriate for the production of calciphylactic responses with sensitizers other than DHT, briefly indicating what type of response was obtained. Emphasis will be placed only upon a few minor characteristics that differentiate these syndromes to some extent from those produced after DHT sensitization.

Vitamin D_3 i.v. + Fe-Dex i.v. + PMX s.c.

Calciphylactic Dermatomyositis

Method: Rat (100 g. ♀): vitamin D_3 (2.5 mg. in 0.25 ml. water, i.v.) 1st day + PMX (500 μg. in 0.2 ml. water, s.c.) 2d day + Fe-Dex (1 ml. = 1 mg. Fe, i.v.) 2d day; killed 7th day.

Results: Typical calciphylactic dermatomyositis. Mortality: 10%.

Remarks: This and the following experiments of this series were particularly useful in showing that: (1) like DHT, vitamin D_3 can act as a calciphylactic sensitizer, (2) the intravenous administration of the sensitizer (possible in the case of vitamin D_3 hydrosol) is just as effective as oral administration of DHT. The latter fact proved that no circumstance attending the intestinal absorption of the calcifier is indispensable for calciphylactic sensitization.

Vitamin D_3 i.v. + 5HT s.c.

Salivary Gland Calciphylaxis

Method: Rat (100 g. ♀): vitamin D_3 (2.5 mg. in 0.25 ml. water, i.v.) 1st day + 5HT (2 mg. in 0.5 ml. water, s.c. in throat region) 2d day; killed 7th day.

Results: Selective calcinosis of the salivary glands, particularly the submaxillary gland. Mortality: 10%.

Remarks: It will be recalled that after sensitization with DHT calciphylactic muscular dystrophy can be produced most readily in 200 g. rats challenged by larger doses of 5HT on the 3d day, but we have not yet tested the possibility of reproducing such lesions after sensitization with vitamin D_3. It is obvious, however, that a calciphylactic response of the salivary glands (such as is obtainable with smaller doses of 5HT injected in the throat region on the 2d day after DHT) is faithfully reproduced under comparable circumstances if vitamin D_3 is used as a sensitizer.*

CALCIPHYLACTIC SYNDROMES PRODUCED AFTER SENSITIZATION BY PARATHYROID HORMONE

Parathyroid Hormone s.c. + CrCl₃ i.v.
Thyroid-Carotid-Body Calciphylaxis

Method: Rat (190 g. ♀): parathyroid hormone (150 units in 1.5 ml. water, s.c. ✕2) 1st and 2d day + CrCl₃ (20 mg. in 1 ml. water, i.v.) 2d day; killed 6th day.

Results: The syndrome produced in this manner greatly resembled the thyroid-parathyroid-carotid-body calciphylaxis induced by CrCl₃ i.v. after DHT sensitization. However, here the parathyroids themselves did not participate in the syndrome even though the adjacent thyroid stroma was heavily calcified. Inhibition of parathyroid secretion through the phenomenon of "compensatory atrophy" (induced by exogenous parathyroid-hormone overdosage) may have protected the gland against calcinosis. On the other hand, the calcification in the carotid body, heart, adrenal medulla, and choroid plexus was exactly the same in quality and intensity as that elicited after sensitization with DHT (Figs. 171, 172).

Parathyroid Hormone s.c. + Fe-Dex i.v. + PMX s.c.
Calciphylactic Muscular Dystrophy

Method: Rat (200 g. ♀): parathyroid hormone (150 units in 1.5 ml. water, s.c. ✕2) 1st and 2d day + Fe-Dex (1 ml. = 2 mg. Fe, i.v.) 2d day + PMX (4 mg. in 0.2 ml. water, s.c.) 2d day; killed 6th day.

Results: The calciphylactic muscular dystrophy thus produced greatly resembled that obtained by challenge with 5HT after DHT sensitization; it differed from the "calciphylactic dermatomyositis" induced by DHT + Fe-Dex + PMX. Unlike in the latter syndrome, here almost the entire striated musculature of the animal was equally affected. The muscles were macroscopically conspicuous by their white discoloration (Fig. 173); hence we expected to find heavy calcium deposits in them, but histologic examination with von Kóssa's stain showed that this was not the case. Actually the muscle lesions were purely degenerative and inflammatory with virtually no calcinosis. The most pronounced difference between this

---

* During the preparation of the galley proofs, we were able to show that the calciphylactic muscular dystrophy can also be reproduced in rats (200 g. ♀) following sensitization with vitamin D_3 (3 mg. in 0.3 ml. water, i.v.) 1st day by 5HT (5 mg. in 0.5 ml. water, s.c. ✕2) on 3d day.[831b]

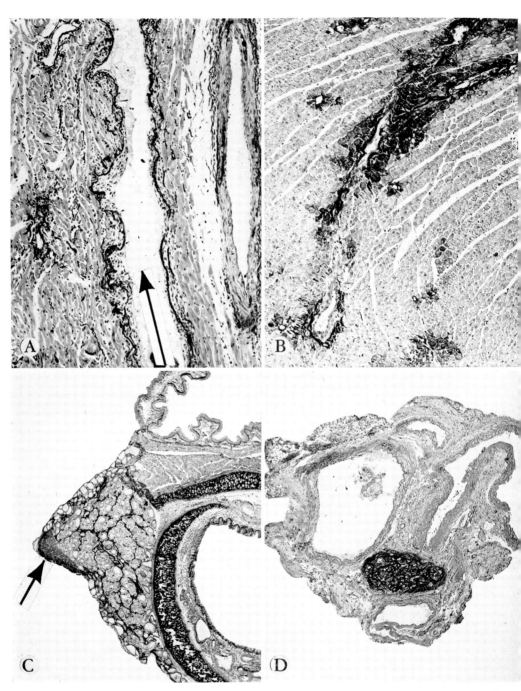

Fig. 171. Cardiac, thyroid and carotid body calcification produced by parathyroid hormone s.c. + CrCl₃ i.v. Rat (190 g. ♀): parathyroid hormone (150 units in 1.5 ml. water, s.c. ×2/day) 1st and 2d day + CrCl₃ (20 mg. in 1 ml. water, i.v.) 2d day; killed 6th day. *A:* Calcification with reactive endothelial proliferation along endocardium of left ventricle (arrow in lumen of ventricle). Adjacent branch of coronary artery is surrounded by edema and exhibits moderate media calcinosis. (von Kóssa, ×100.) *B:* Intense calcification of myocardial fibers in vicinity of coronary arterial branch in right ventricle. (von Kóssa, ×85.) *C:* Intense calcification of thyroid stroma while parathyroid (arrow) remains unaffected. There is also a line of calcinosis underneath tracheal epithelium, but no calcification is visible around esophagus (top). (von Kóssa, ×29.) *D:* Intense and selective calcification of carotid body at bifurcation of common carotid artery. (von Kóssa, ×29.)

syndrome and the corresponding lesions obtained after DHT sensitization was the comparative paucity of cutaneous lesions. Even the skin immediately adjacent to the heavily affected nuchal fasciae and muscles often remained normal; consequently, this lesion must be regarded as primarily a myositis, or muscular dystrophy, although in some animals there was definite evidence of cutaneous participation (Figs. 174, 175). The mortality was 10%.

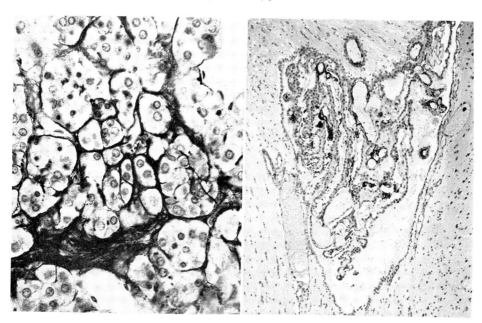

Fig. 172. **Calcification of adrenal medulla and choroid plexus produced by parathyroid hormone s.c. + CrCl₃ i.v.** Rat (190 g. ♀): parathyroid hormone (150 units in 1.5 ml. water, s.c. ×2/day) 1st and 2d day + CrCl₃ (20 mg. in 1 ml. water, i.v.) 2d day; killed 6th day. *Left:* Incrustation of connective-tissue fibers around adrenal-medullary cells. (von Kóssa, ×300.) *Right:* Calcinosis of capillaries within choroid plexus. (von Kóssa, ×85.)

Parathyroid Hormone s.c. + Fe-OS i.v.

Auriculo-Biliary Calciphylaxis

Method 1: Rat (100 g. ♀): parathyroid hormone (100 units in 1 ml. water, s.c.) once 1st day, and ×3 on 2d and 3d day + Fe-OS (1 ml. i.v.) 2d and 3d day; killed 4th day.

Results: This syndrome was almost indistinguishable from that produced by DHT + Fe-OS i.v. as regards calcification in the heart (Fig. 176; Plate VIII, *B*), liver and bile ducts (Fig. 177; Plate VIII, *F*), kidney (Fig. 178), and adrenals (Plate IX, *F*) except that here the Kupffer cells were also heavily calcified. However, even this difference may not be essential, since in the present experimental series the animals were killed earlier than usual. As we have learned in the meantime, the

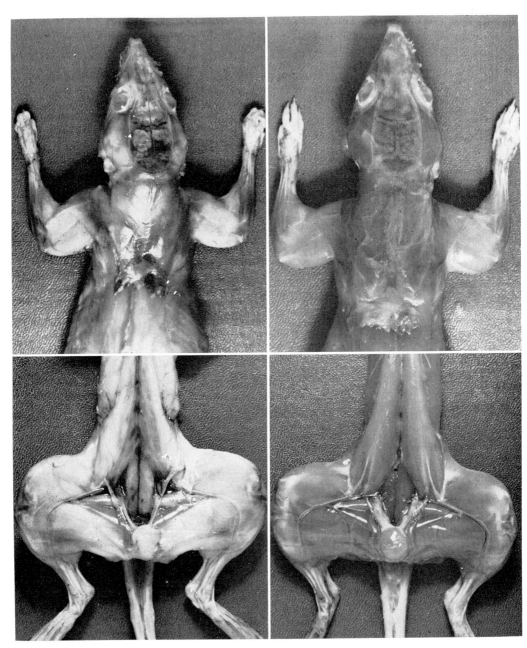

Fig. 173. Muscular dystrophy produced by parathyroid hormone s.c. + Fe-Dex i.v. + PMX s.c. *Left:* Rat (200 g. ♀): parathyroid hormone (150 units in 1.5 ml. water, s.c. ×2) 1st and 2d day + Fe-Dex (1 ml. = 2 mg. Fe, i.v.) 2d day + PMX (4 mg. in 0.2 ml. water, s.c.) 2d day; killed 7th day. Damaged muscles (light) are seen almost everywhere throughout the body. *Right:* Untreated control rat for comparison.

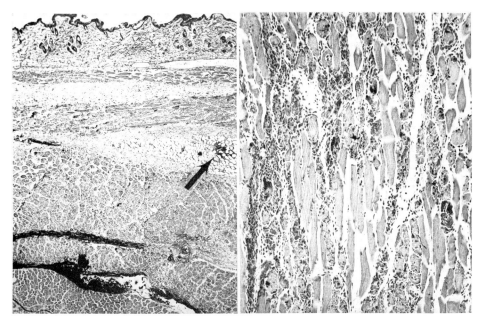

Fig. 174. **Calciphylactic dermatomyositis produced by parathyroid hormone s.c. +
Fe-Dex i.v. + PMX s.c.** Rat (190 g. ♀): parathyroid hormone (150 units in 1.5 ml. water, s.c.
×2/day) 1st and 2d day + Fe-Dex (1 ml. = 2 mg. Fe, i.v.) 2d day + PMX (4 mg. in 0.2 ml.
water, s.c.) 2d day; killed 6th day. *Left:* Diffuse edema and inflammatory infiltration of fasciae
near skin and around partly calcified (arrow) intramuscular fat islet. Intense calcification of
fasciae between deep muscles of neck. (von Kóssa, ×25.) *Right:* Degenerative and inflammatory
changes in muscle near shoulder joint with very little calcification. (von Kóssa, ×85.)

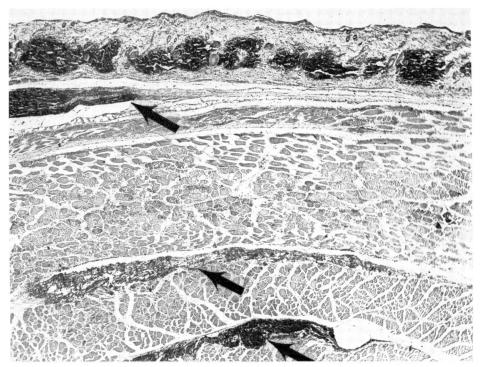

Fig. 175. **Calciphylactic dermatomyositis produced by parathyroid hormone s.c. +
Fe-Dex i.v. + PMX s.c.** Rat (200 g. ♀): parathyroid hormone (150 units in 1.5 ml. water,
s.c. ×2) 1st and 2d day + Fe-Dex (1 ml. = 2 mg. Fe, i.v.) 2d day + PMX (4 mg. in 0.5 ml.
water, s.c.) 2d day; killed 6th day. Intense calcific infiltration of derma and of three fascial
layers (arrows) in underlying nuchal musculature. (von Kóssa, ×39.)

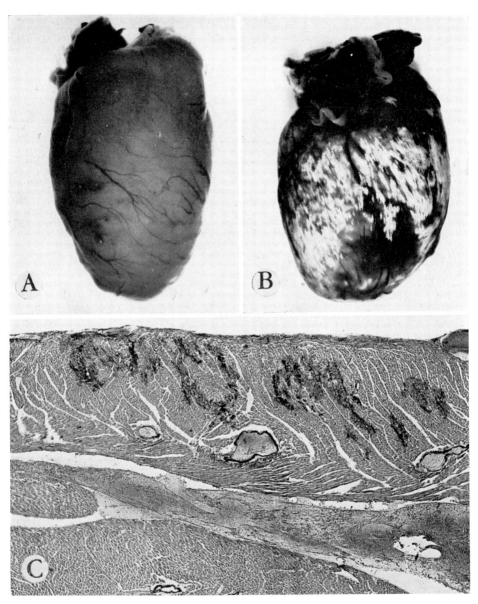

Fig. 176. Cardiac calcification produced by parathyroid hormone s.c. + Fe-OS i.v.
Two rats (100 g. ♀): parathyroid hormone (100 units in 1 ml. water, s.c.) ×1 on 1st day, ×3
on 2d and 3d day + (B and C) Fe-OS (1 ml. = 20 mg. Fe, i.v.) 2d and 3d day; killed 4th day.
A: No trace of macroscopically visible calcification in control rat. *B:* Intense subepicardial calcinosis. *C:* Pronounced calcification in subepicardial foci of musculature and in coronary arteries
of right ventricle. (von Kóssa, ×35.) (Cf. Plate VIII, *B.*)

RES-type of calciphylaxis tends to subside rapidly owing to the speedy disintegration of the calcium-storing phagocytes and their subsequent replacement by normal cells. It is possible, therefore, that during the first few days Kupffer-cell calcification would also be demonstrable after treatment with DHT + Fe-OS.

Method 2: Rat (200 g. ♀): Fe-OS (1.5 ml. = 30 mg. Fe, i.v.) 1st day + parathyroid hormone (150 units in 1.5 ml. water, s.c. ×2) 1st and 2d day; killed 7th day.

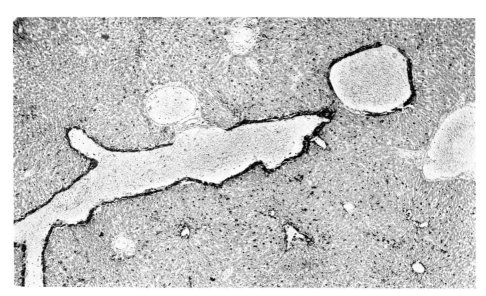

Fig. 177. **Hepatic calcification produced by parathyroid hormone s.c. + Fe-OS i.v.** Rat (100 g. ♀): parathyroid hormone (100 units in 1 ml. water, s.c.) ×1 on 1st day, ×3 on 2d and 3d day + Fe-OS (1 ml. = 20 mg. Fe, i.v.) 2d and 3d day; killed 4th day. Calcification of all hepatic veins, while portal veins and arteries are devoid of calcium. Indeed, large hepatic vein branch in center of field failed to calcify only at one point where it is contiguous with portal space. (von Kóssa, ×40.) (Cf. Plate VIII, *F*.)

Results: Here again, a typical auriculo-biliary type of calciphylaxis was obtained. However, in these larger rats calcification of the biliary ducts was particularly obvious; it was frequently accompanied by periarteritis nodosa (with or without noteworthy arterial calcinosis) in the extrahepatic portion of the hepatic artery (Figs. 179, 180; Plate IX, *A, C, E*). The Kupffer cells contained much iron and smaller amounts of calcium in the animals that died on the 4th day, but by the end of the experiment most of these cells were again normal in appearance. The adrenal medulla underwent heavy calcification and the medullary ganglion cells within the calcified stroma showed signs of vacuolar degeneration (Fig. 181).

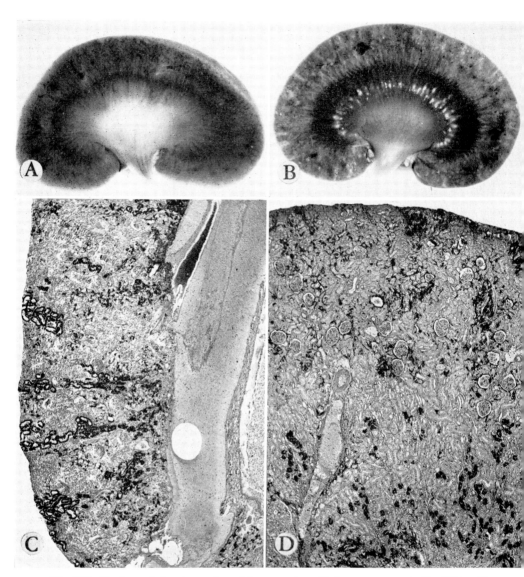

Fig. 178. **Nephrocalcinosis produced by parathyroid hormone s.c. + Fe-OS i.v.** Two rats (100 g. ♀): parathyroid hormone (100 units in 1 ml. water, s.c.) ×1 on 1st day, ×3 on 2d and 3d day + (B, C and D) Fe-OS (1 ml. = 20 mg. i.v.) 2d and 3d day; killed 4th day. *A:* Control kidney shows no macroscopically visible sign of calcification, although histologically traces of cortical nephrocalcinosis were detectable. *B:* Marked nephrocalcinosis throughout cortex and particularly along cortico-medullary junction line. *C* and *D:* Histologically calcium deposits are seen both in tubular epithelia and in stroma around tubules and glomeruli. (von Kóssa, ×34.)

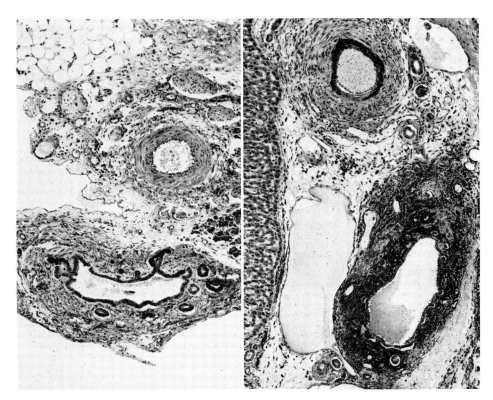

Fig. 179. Calcification of bile ducts and calcifying periarteritis nodosa of hepatic artery produced by parathyroid hormone s.c. + Fe-OS i.v. Two rats (200 g. ♀): Fe-OS (1.5 ml. = 30 mg. Fe, i.v.) 1st day + (right) parathyroid hormone (150 units in 1.5 ml. water, s.c. ×2/day) 1st and 2d day; killed 7th day. *Left:* Fe-OS alone produced only dilatation of bile duct with some inflammatory connective-tissue proliferation and iron deposition. *Right:* Additional treatment with parathyroid hormone resulted in intense calcification of bile duct and periarteritis nodosa with calcium deposition in hyalinized intima. (von Kóssa, ×100.)

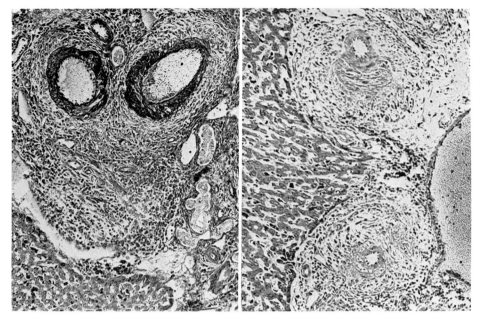

Fig. 180. Periarteritis nodosa of hepatic artery produced by parathyroid hormone s.c. + Fe-OS i.v. Rat (200 g. ♀): parathyroid hormone (200 units in 2 ml. water, s.c. ×2) 1st day + Fe-OS (1 ml. = 20 mg. Fe, i.v. ×2) 1st day; died 4th day. *Left:* Acute periarteritis nodosa with infiltration of media by hyalin material and inflammatory changes throughout thickness of arterial walls. The Kupffer cells contain much iron (fixation in Susa saturated with picric acid; PAS, ×200). *Right:* Adjacent specimen of same liver, fixed in alcohol-formol for perfect preservation of calcium. Here periarteritic changes are again evident, but there is no histochemically demonstrable calcium deposition. The Kupffer cells contain much iron and little calcium. (von Kóssa, ×160.)

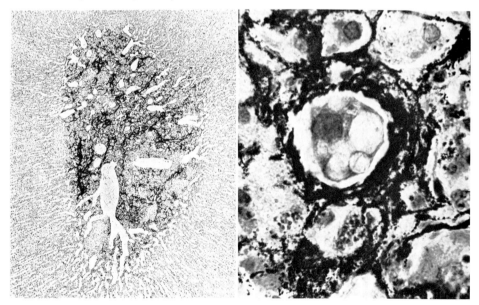

Fig. 181. Calcification of adrenal medulla produced by parathyroid hormone s.c. + Fe-OS i.v. Rat (200 g. ♀): parathyroid hormone (150 units in 1.5 ml. water, s.c. ×2/day) 1st and 2d day + Fe-OS (1.5 ml. = 30 mg. Fe, i.v.) 1st day; killed 7th day. Two sections stained with von Kóssa technique. *Left:* Selective calcification of adrenal medulla, affecting particularly the stroma. (×25.) *Right:* Especially intensive calcification around a nerve cell showing characteristic vacuolar degeneration. (×700.)

Parathyroid Hormone s.c. + 5HT s.c.

Calciphylactic Muscular Dystrophy

Method 1: Rat (200 g. ♀): parathyroid hormone (50 units in 0.5 ml. water, s.c. ×2/ day) 1st–9th day + 5HT (5 mg. in 0.5 ml. water, s.c./day) beginning on 3d day; killed 10th day.

Results: This chronic form of treatment with comparatively small doses of parathyroid hormone was only moderately effective in producing muscular lesions. Clinically no obvious derangement in locomotion could be detected, and histologically only minor myositic foci were observable in the gluteal musculature and occasionally in the myocardium. On the other hand, rather constant changes appeared in the ganglion cells of the adrenal medulla: there were vacuolization, nuclear pyknosis, and the development of both intra- and pericellular edema with fibrin thread formation (Fig. 182).

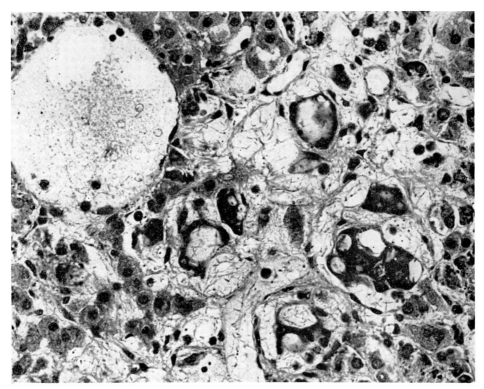

Fig. 182. Changes in ganglion cells of adrenal medulla produced by parathyroid hormone s.c. + 5HT s.c. Rat (200 g. ♀): parathyroid hormone (50 units in 0.5 ml. water, s.c. ×2/day) 1st–9th day + 5HT (5 mg. in 0.5 ml. water, s.c./day) 3d–9th day; killed 10th day. All ganglion cells in adrenal medulla are greatly deformed by vacuoles some of which contain minute calcified granules and fibrin threads. Nuclei of ganglion cells underwent pyknosis. Fibrin threads also in edematous fluid that surrounds ganglia. (von Kóssa, ×480.)

Method 2: Rat (200 g. ♀): parathyroid hormone (300 units in 3 ml. water, s.c. ✕2) 1st day + 5HT (5 mg. in 0.5 ml. water, s.c.) 3d day; killed 6th day.

Results: In this experimental arrangement in which a single injection of 5HT was administered after short-term heavy overdosage with parathyroid hormone the most striking change was a calciphylactic muscular dystrophy quite similar to that produced by DHT + 5HT s.c. After the initial period of shock that followed acute heavy 5HT overdosage, the animals recovered fairly rapidly, but permanent motor disturbances remained owing to the development of severe morphologic changes in the skeletal musculature. Perhaps the most striking feature of this muscular dystrophy was the fact that despite its calciphylactic nature, noteworthy calcium precipitates were histologically not detectable in the affected muscles even during the early stages of the disease (Figs. 183, 184). There was no mortality.

Method 3: Rat (200 g. ♀): parathyroid hormone (150 units in 1.5 ml. water, s.c. ✕2) 1st and 2d day + 5HT (5 mg. in 0.5 ml. water, s.c.) 4th day; killed 8th day.

Results: After this treatment the muscular changes were even more severe than when Method 2 was used. Myocardial lesions were quite common (Fig. 185) and the mortality was 40%.

Method 4: Rat (200 g. ♀): parathyroid hormone (100 units in 1 ml. water, s.c.) on evening of 1st day and ✕3 during 2d day (all four injections being given during 24 hours) + 5HT (5 mg. in 0.5 ml. water, s.c.✕2) 3d or 4th day; killed 6th day.

Results: This proved to be the most reliable method for the production of calciphylactic muscular dystrophy with the smallest effective amount of parathyroid hormone. There was little, if any, of the nonspecific calcinosis that invariably occurs (e.g., in the cardiovascular system and kidney) with heavier parathyroid hormone overdosage, and the muscular changes were always very pronounced and widespread. Mortality was 10%.

Discussion: In order to characterize this muscular dystrophy it is useful to compare it with the histologically somewhat similar changes that are associated with other calciphylactic syndromes. The lesion produced by parathyroid hormone + 5HT resembles the muscular dystrophy induced by DHT + 5HT in that both are unassociated with cutaneous changes and much more readily elicited in 200 g. than in 100 g. rats. Calcification of the muscles themselves is absent or mild in either syndrome. But when DHT is used as a sensitizer the arteries of the striated musculature are usually calcified, while this is not the case in the parathyroid hormone sensitized rat.

The syndrome under discussion differs greatly from calciphylactic dermatomyositis (produced by DHT + Fe-Dex i.v. + PMX s.c.) as well as from calciphylactic scleroderma with esophageal lesions and arthritis (produced by DHT or parathyroid hormone + Thorotrast® i.v. or Fe-Din i.v.). These latter syndromes are invariably associated with severe cutaneous lesions and in some in-

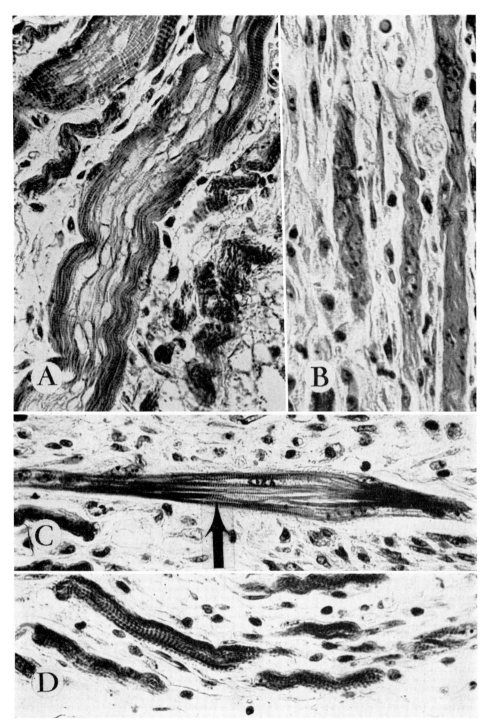

Fig. 183. Calciphylactic muscular dystrophy produced by parathyroid hormone s.c. + 5HT s.c. Rat (200 g. ♀): parathyroid hormone (300 units in 3 ml. water, s.c. ×2) 1st day + 5HT (5 mg. in 0.5 ml. water, s.c.) 3d day; killed 8th day. *A:* Degenerating striated muscle fiber from gluteus maximus. Peripheral fibrils still exhibit cross-striation, but central portions are degenerated and vacuolized so that fiber assumes tubular aspect. *B:* Polynuclear regenerating muscle fibrils without cross-striation. *C:* Spindle-shaped muscle fiber showing beginning cross-striation (arrow). *D:* Numerous young narrow muscle fibers with definite cross-striation. (Phosphotungstic acid fibrin stain, ×550.)

stances with esophageal lesions and arthritis, all of which are totally lacking in the parathyroid hormone + 5HT induced muscular dystrophy.

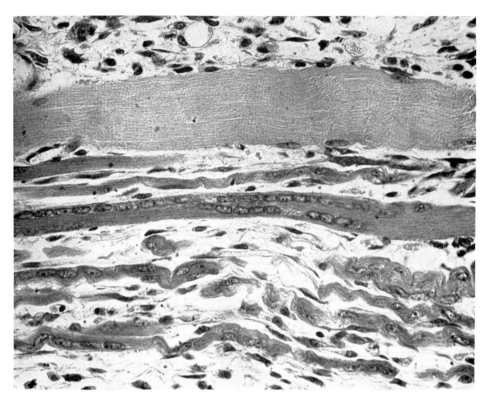

Fig. 184. Calciphylactic muscular dystrophy produced by parathyroid hormone s.c. + 5HT s.c. Rat (200 g. ♀): parathyroid hormone (300 units in 3 ml. water, s.c. ×2) 1st day + 5HT (5 mg. in 0.5 ml. water, s.c.) 3d day; killed 6th day. Large essentially normal muscle fiber near upper margin of picture may serve as control. All other muscle fibers in this field are narrow and show a multitude of centrally located nuclei arranged to form almost uninterrupted rows. No trace of calcium. (von Kóssa, ×460.)

Parathyroid Hormone s.c. + Thorotrast® i.v.

Calciphylactic Scleroderma with Esophageal Calcinosis and Arthritis

Method: Rat (190 g. ♀): parathyroid hormone (150 units in 1.5 ml. water, s.c. ×2) 1st and 2d day + Thorotrast® (1 ml. i.v.) 2d day; killed 6th day.

Results: The lesions thus produced were comparable in every respect to those induced by DHT + Thorotrast® i.v. Especially pronounced calcinosis was noted in the palate, around the glottis, the facial skin, tongue, esophageal mucosa, and the large joints, particularly those of the shoulder, elbow, hip, and knee. In the skin, the heaviest calcium deposits were in the dermal connective tissue, but small calcified inclusions were also seen within the epidermis, whence they were elimi-

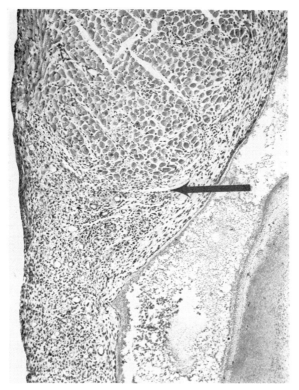

Fig. 185. Cardiac lesion produced by parathyroid hormone s.c. + 5HT s.c. Rat (200 g. ♀): parathyroid hormone (150 units in 1.5 ml. water, s.c.) ×1 on 1st and ×3 on 2d day + 5HT (5 mg. in 0.5 ml. water, s.c.) 4th day; killed 8th day. Below level indicated by arrow fibrous scar tissue replaces entire thickness of right ventricular wall; but calcium is not demonstrable. (von Kóssa, ×100.)

nated through scaling. The calcium deposits around the joints and in the synovial membranes produced local liquefaction necrosis with reactive inflammation, but no noteworthy basophilia; therefore, this type of calcinosis could not be detected on slides not stained especially for calcium (Figs. 186, 187).

CALCIPHYLACTIC SYNDROMES PRODUCED AFTER SENSITIZATION
BY NEPHRECTOMY*

Nephrectomy + CrCl₃ i.v.

Thyroid-Parathyroid-Carotid-Body Calciphylaxis

Method: Rat (200 g. ♀): DOC (5 mg. in 0.2 ml. water, s.c./day) beginning 1st day + bilateral nephrectomy 5th day + CrCl₃ (10 mg. i.v.) 4th or 5th day; died 7th or 8th day.

* In this type of experiment on bilaterally nephrectomized rats we often gave DOC (as the acetate) before and after the operation, since this treatment delays the onset of uremia.[861] However, essentially similar results can be obtained without DOC treatment.

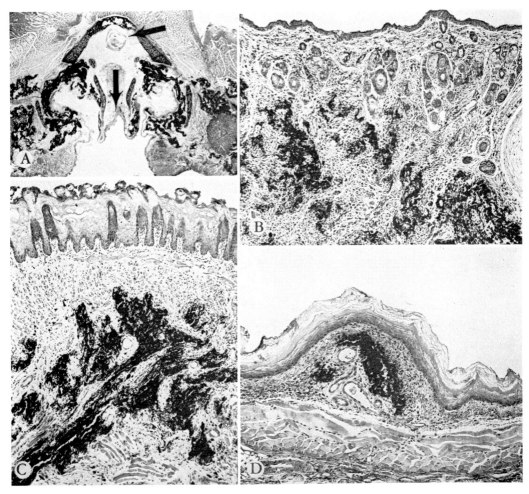

Fig. 186. **Calciphylactic scleroderma with laryngeal, lingual and esophageal lesions produced by parathyroid hormone s.c. + Thorotrast® i.v.** Rat (190 g. ♀): parathyroid hormone (150 units in 1.5 ml. water, s.c. ×2/day) 1st and 2d day + Thorotrast® (1 ml. i.v.) 2d day; killed 6th day. *A:* Cross section through the neck at level of larynx. Diffuse calcium infiltration of fasciae, and of connective tissue near attachment of vocal cords (on both sides of lower arrow). Formation of small, noncalcified abscess below cricoid cartilage (upper arrow). (von Kóssa, ×8.5.) *B:* Diffuse calcinosis around Thorotrast® granules in skin of lips. *C:* Calcification of connective tissue in tongue. *D:* Calcification of esophageal mucosa. (B, C, D: von Kóssa, ×85.)

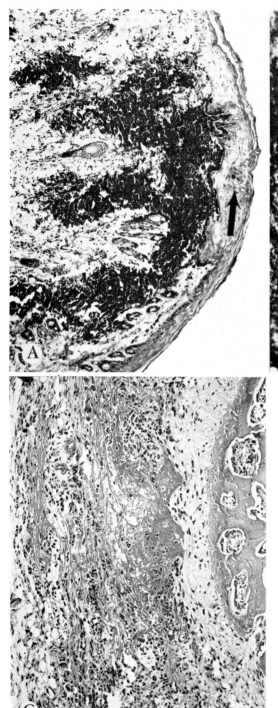

Fig. 187. Cutaneous calcinosis and arthritis produced by parathyroid hormone s.c. + Thorotrast® i.v. Rat (190 g. ♀): parathyroid hormone (150 units in 1.5 ml. water, s.c. ×2/day) 1st and 2d day + Thorotrast® (1 ml. i.v.) 2d day; killed 6th day. *A:* General appearance of affected skin resembles calciphylactic scleroderma produced by DHT + Thorotrast®. At one point (arrow) intraepidermal calcium granules are seen in the process of extrusion. (von Kóssa, ×100.) *B:* Intraepidermal calcium inclusions in another region under high magnification. (von Kóssa, ×350.) *C:* Heavy infiltration of prepatellar region with slightly PAS-positive and partly cellular exudate which contains calcium (as shown by von Kóssa stain), but in amounts not detectable here on slide stained routinely. (Hematoxylin-phloxine, ×100.)

229

Results: The thyroid-parathyroid-carotid-body calcification that developed under these circumstances was essentially the same as that produced by CrCl₃ i.v. following sensitization with DHT. Like the latter, it was accompanied by pulmonary and gastric calcinosis (Fig. 188).

Discussion: These findings show that uremia—presumably by stimulating parathyroid hormone secretion—can sensitize for the action of a typical calciphylactic challenger. Hence, it may be assumed that the phenomenon of *sensitization can be induced by an endogenous metabolite (a hormone) in quantities that the organism is capable of supplying.* This important fact was further sub-

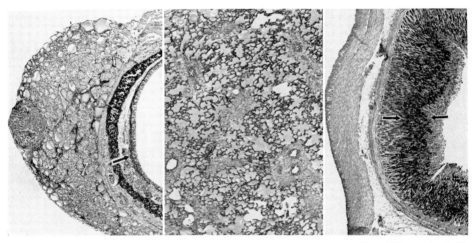

Fig. 188. Organ lesions produced by nephrectomy + CrCl₃ i.v. Rat (190 g. ♀): CrCl₃ (20 mg. in 1 ml. water, i.v.) 1st day + bilateral nephrectomy 5th day; killed 13th day. *Left:* Calcinosis just detectable in stroma of parathyroids, more pronounced in that of thyroid; there is also a narrow line of heavy calcification underneath tracheal epithelium (arrow). *Middle:* Heavy calcinosis of pulmonary septa. Only the regions immediately surrounding bronchi and vessels are not calcified. *Right:* Calcinosis in middle layer of gastric mucosa (between arrows). (von Kóssa, ×24.)

stantiated by the observation that the subcutaneous injection of CrCl₃ can produce topical calcinosis in the nephrectomized rat and that parathyroidectomy prevents the induction of calciphylactic responses by challenge after nephrectomy.

Nephrectomy + Fe-OS i.v.

Auriculo-Biliary Calciphylaxis

Method 1: Rat (200 g. ♀): DOC (5 mg. in 0.2 ml. water, s.c./day) + bilateral nephrectomy 7th day + Fe-OS (1.5 ml. = 30 mg. Fe, i.v.) 7th day; died 9th or 10th day.

Results: Although these animals survived nephrectomy only for a few days, the manifestations of auriculo-biliary calciphylaxis were usually quite obvious. Calcium deposition was particularly prominent in the left auricular appendage, and here it frequently led to thrombus formation. There was also pronounced calcinosis in the duodenum (often with hemorrhages and necrosis) as well as in Brunner's glands. Most of the animals so treated eventually died from uremic lung edema.

Method 2: Rat (200 g. ♀): Fe-OS (1 ml. = 20 mg. Fe, i.v.) 1st, 3d, and 5th day + bilateral nephrectomy 8th day; died 10th or 11th day.

Results: More than 1 ml. of Fe-OS was poorly tolerated when given in a single injection, but three doses of this magnitude could be given with impunity at 48-hour intervals. In this event, the usual auriculo-biliary type of calciphylaxis was very obvious, even in animals receiving no DOC treatment. These large doses of Fe-OS gradually produced a functional blockade of the ampulla of Vater with dilatation of the main bile duct even in controls not subjected to nephrectomy, but in this case there was no calcinosis. Apparently, Fe-OS affected the bile ducts through the production of ferrification within their walls, but these iron deposits attracted calcium only in animals sensitized by some indirect calcifying agent, such as DHT, parathyroid hormone, or nephrectomy.

Critical period: Rats (220 g. ♀) sensitized with bilateral nephrectomy 1st day and challenged by Fe-OS (1.5 ml. = 30 mg. Fe, i.v.) responded with the auriculo-biliary syndrome when challenged on −4th, −2d, 1st or +2d day, but not on +3d day. However, the high mortality and the great stress-sensitivity of these uremic rats made the interpretation of these results difficult.

Nephrectomy + Thorotrast® i.v.
Calciphylactic Scleroderma with Esophageal Calcinosis and Arthritis

Method 1: Rat (200 g. ♀): DOC (5 mg. in 0.2 ml. water, s.c./day) beginning 1st day + bilateral nephrectomy 7th day + Thorotrast® (1.25 ml. i.v.) 7th day; died 9th or 10th day.

Results: The lesions were again the same as those obtained by challenge with Thorotrast® i.v. after sensitization with DHT or parathyroid hormone (Figs. 189–192; Plate XI, *H*). Calcification in the peripheral zone of the Malpighian follicles was especially pronounced in this series, perhaps because the animals did not live long enough for the calcified RES cells to be removed.

Method 2: Rat (200 g. ♀): Thorotrast® (1 ml. i.v.) 1st and 2d day + nephrectomy 5th day; died 7th or 8th day.

Results: The quality and intensity of the lesions was the same as in rats treated according to Method 1; however, to achieve this without DOC treatment we had to give a larger amount of the challenger.

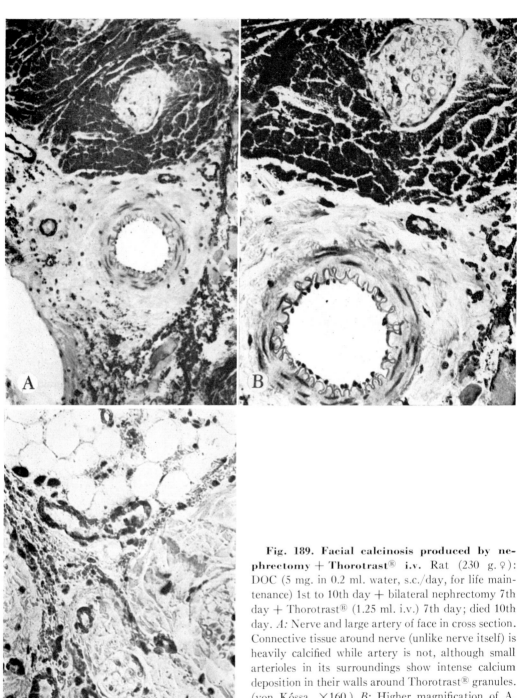

Fig. 189. **Facial calcinosis produced by nephrectomy + Thorotrast® i.v.** Rat (230 g. ♀): DOC (5 mg. in 0.2 ml. water, s.c./day, for life maintenance) 1st to 10th day + bilateral nephrectomy 7th day + Thorotrast® (1.25 ml. i.v.) 7th day; died 10th day. *A:* Nerve and large artery of face in cross section. Connective tissue around nerve (unlike nerve itself) is heavily calcified while artery is not, although small arterioles in its surroundings show intense calcium deposition in their walls around Thorotrast® granules. (von Kóssa, ×160.) *B:* Higher magnification of A. (von Kóssa, ×370.) *C:* Facial connective tissue with calcified (black) and noncalcified (gray) Thorotrast® granules in blood vessels and connective-tissue septa between muscles and fat. (von Kóssa, ×370.) (Cf. Plate XI, *H*.)

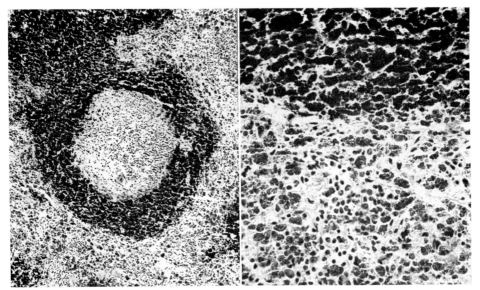

Fig. 190. Splenic calcinosis produced by nephrectomy + Thorotrast® i.v. Rat (230 g. ♀): DOC (5 mg. in 0.2 ml. water, s.c./day) 1st–10th day + bilateral nephrectomy 7th day + Thorotrast® (1.25 ml. i.v.) 7th day; died 10th day. *Left:* Malpighian follicle with typical calcified rim around uncalcified center. (von Kóssa, ×90.) *Right:* Higher magnification of portion of preceding picture. Thorotrast® granules are no longer visible in heavily calcified (black) part, but in surroundings they appear clearly as light gray granules within macrophages. (von Kóssa, ×350.)

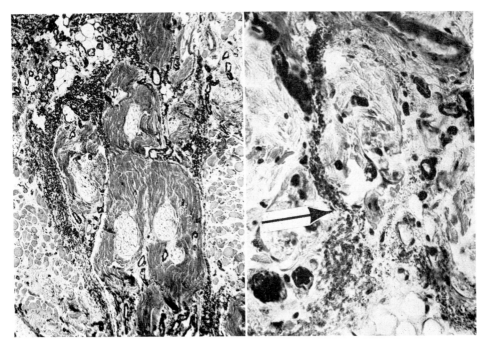

Fig. 191. Facial calcinosis produced by nephrectomy + Thorotrast® i.v. Rat (250 g. ♀): DOC (5 mg. in 0.2 ml. water, s.c./day) 1st–10th day + bilateral nephrectomy 5th day + Thorotrast® (1.25 ml. i.v.) 6th day; killed 10th day. *Left:* Intense calcification of connective-tissue fibers especially in perineurium and fascia of facial muscles, as well as in small arterioles. The nerves themselves are unaffected. (von Kóssa, ×100.) *Right:* Higher magnification of a region from preceding picture. Walls of small arteries and arterioles are calcified and some vessels (lower left corner) are completely occluded by calcified material. Calcified granules are also visible throughout connective tissue (arrow). (von Kóssa, ×350.)

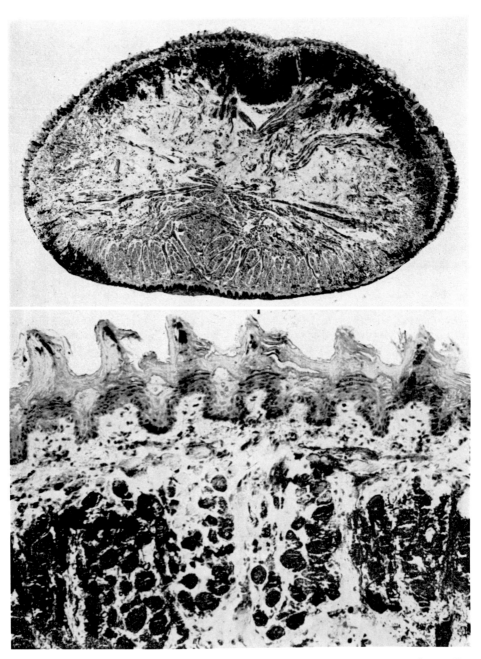

Fig. 192. Lingual calcinosis produced by nephrectomy + Thorotrast® i.v. Rat
(250 g. ♀): DOC (5 mg. in 0.2 ml. water, s.c./day) 1st–9th day + nephrectomy 5th day +
Thorotrast® (1.25 ml. i.v.) 6th day; died 9th day. *Top:* Intense calcification of lingual musculature (especially underneath the surface) and pronounced interstitial edema. (von Kóssa, ×20.)
Bottom: Higher magnification of a field from picture above shows calcium not only on cross
section of lingual musculature but also within epithelium, especially near tips of filiform papillae. (von Kóssa, ×200.)

CALCIPHYLACTIC SYNDROMES PRODUCED AFTER SENSITIZATION BY NaAST

NaAST i.p. (without challenger)
Nonspecific Calcinosis

Method: Rat (200 g. ♀): NaAST (150 mg. in 0.5 ml. water, i.p.) 1st day; killed 30th–50th day.

Results: In agreement with the earlier observations of Lehr, which we reviewed elsewhere,[821, 823] treatment with NaAST alone (without any calciphylactic challenger) produced a severe "occlusive nephropathy," owing to the precipitation of NaAST crystals in the collecting tubules. Like bilateral nephrectomy, NaAST thus induced a tendency for calcification, especially in the cardiovascular system, stomach, intestine, lung, and kidney (Fig. 193). This calcinosis was even more severe than that produced by bilateral nephrectomy, presumably because the renal lesions induced by NaAST developed slowly and hence gave more time for the precipitation of calcium.

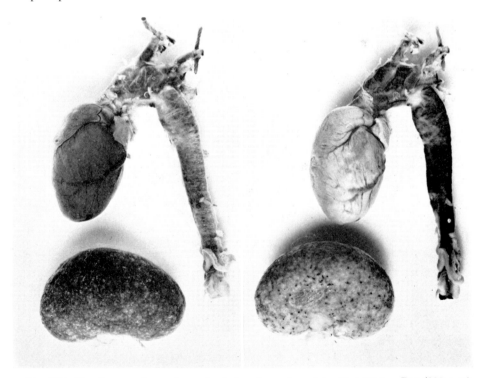

Fig. 193. Cardiovascular and renal calcinosis produced by NaAST i.p. Rat (200 g. ♀): NaAST (150 mg. in 0.5 ml. water, i.p.); killed 42d day. Only mild calcification of myocardium, but aorta with its major branches and kidney are heavily calcified. *Left:* Fresh. *Right:* AgNO₃-stained, specimens.

We repeated these experiments only for comparative purposes, since they did not involve any obvious calciphylactic reaction. It was noteworthy, however, that in short-term experiments in which NaAST produced none of the lesions just enumerated it could still sensitize for the action of a subsequently administered calciphylactic challenger, which then produced calcinosis in the particular target organs for which it has an affinity. On the other hand, NaAST alone—even when administered in fatal doses—caused only a "nonspecific calcinosis" comparable to that produced by heavy overdosage with DHT alone or parathyroid hormone alone; like these other calcifiers it did not affect the specific target organs of various calciphylactic challengers.

NaAST i.p. + Fe-Dex i.v.

Pancreatic Calciphylaxis

Method: Rat (240 g. ♀): NaAST (150 mg. in 0.2 ml. water, i.p.) 1st day + Fe-Dex (1 ml. = 75 mg. Fe, i.v.) 5th day; killed 9th day.

Results: There was intense calcinosis of the pancreatic stroma, quite similar to that produced by Fe-Dex i.v. following sensitization with other calcifiers (Fig. 194). On the other hand, here cutaneous calcinosis was rarely evident, perhaps because the animals did not survive long enough.

NaAST i.p. + Fe-Din i.v.

Calciphylactic Scleroderma with Esophageal Calcinosis

Method: Rat (200 g. ♀): NaAST (150 mg. in 0.2 ml. water, i.p.) 1st day + Fe-Din (1.5 ml. = 30 mg. Fe, i.v.) 3d day; killed 8th day.

Results: Under these conditions Fe-Din produced the usual calcinosis in the face and the esophageal mucosa (Fig. 195). The lesions were quite similar to those elicited by Fe-Din following treatment with other sensitizers.

NaAST i.p. + Fe-OS i.v.

Auriculo-Biliary Calciphylaxis

Method: Rat (200 g. ♀): NaAST (150 mg. in 0.2 ml. water, i.p.) 1st day + Fe-OS (1.5 ml. = 30 mg. Fe, i.v.) 5th day; killed 9th day.

Results: Here, as after DHT, Fe-OS produced a calciphylactic reaction in the left auricular appendage and the biliary tract; in addition, singular lesions developed in the adrenals. There was pronounced hypertrophy of the reticularis and heavy iron deposition in the RES cells of the adrenal cortex. The other cortical layers underwent atrophy and became infiltrated by inflammatory and hemo-poietic cells (Fig. 196).

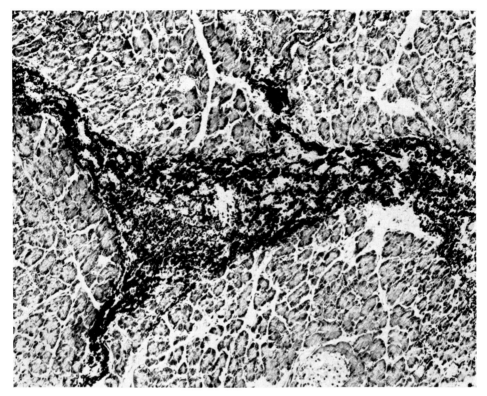

Fig. 194. Pancreatic calcinosis produced by NaAST i.p. + Fe-Dex i.v. Rat (240 g. ♀):
NaAST (150 mg. in 0.2 ml. water, i.p.) 1st day + Fe-Dex (1 ml. = 75 mg. Fe, i.v.) 5th day;
killed 9th day. Intense calcification of pancreatic stroma. (von Kóssa, ×135.)

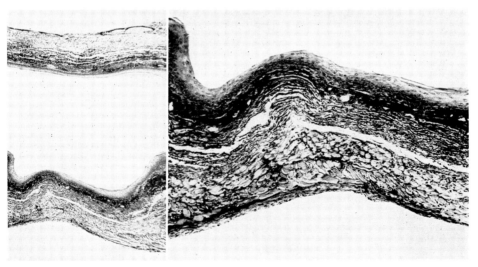

Fig. 195. Esophageal calcinosis produced by NaAST i.p. + Fe-Din i.v. Rat (240 g. ♀):
NaAST (150 mg. in 0.2 ml. water, i.p.) 1st day + Fe-Din (1.25 ml. = 25 mg. Fe, i.v.) 3d day;
killed 8th day. *Left:* Longitudinal section through esophagus showing diffuse calcification around
entire circumference. (von Kóssa, ×25.) *Right:* Higher magnification of lower part of previous
picture. Calcium deposition in connective-tissue fibers of esophageal stroma; muscles and
epithelium free. (von Kóssa, ×90.)

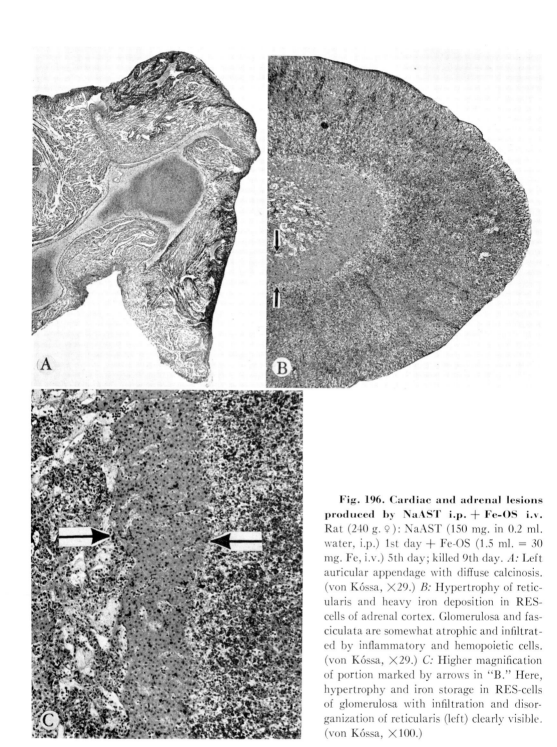

Fig. 196. Cardiac and adrenal lesions produced by NaAST i.p. + Fe-OS i.v. Rat (240 g. ♀): NaAST (150 mg. in 0.2 ml. water, i.p.) 1st day + Fe-OS (1.5 ml. = 30 mg. Fe, i.v.) 5th day; killed 9th day. *A:* Left auricular appendage with diffuse calcinosis. (von Kóssa, ×29.) *B:* Hypertrophy of reticularis and heavy iron deposition in RES-cells of adrenal cortex. Glomerulosa and fasciculata are somewhat atrophic and infiltrated by inflammatory and hemopoietic cells. (von Kóssa, ×29.) *C:* Higher magnification of portion marked by arrows in "B." Here, hypertrophy and iron storage in RES-cells of glomerulosa with infiltration and disorganization of reticularis (left) clearly visible. (von Kóssa, ×100.)

NaAST i.p. + Thorotrast® i.v.

Calciphylactic Scleroderma with Esophageal Calcinosis and Calcareous Arthritis

Method: Rat (200 g. ♀): NaAST (150 mg. in 0.2 ml. water, i.p.) 1st day + Thorotrast® (1.25 ml. i.v.) 3d day; killed 9th day.

Results: The changes were indistinguishable from those produced by Thorotrast® after sensitization with other systemic calcifiers and hence require no further comment (Fig. 197).

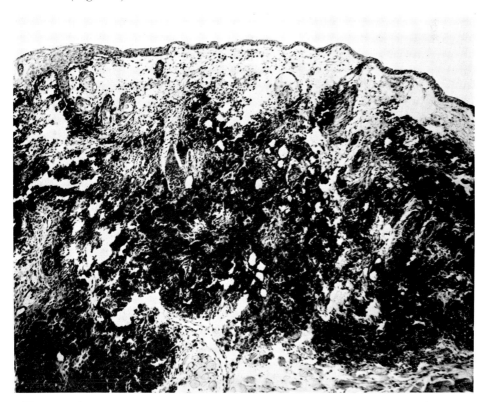

Fig. 197. Calcinosis of facial skin produced by NaAST i.p. + Thorotrast® i.v. Rat (240 g. ♀): NaAST (150 mg. in 0.2 ml. water, i.p.) 1st day + Thorotrast® (1.25 ml. i.v.) 3d day; killed 9th day. Intense calcinosis of skin in upper lip. (von Kóssa, ×90.)

Calciphylactic Syndromes Produced after Sensitization by Esophageal and Gastric Fistulas

Only very few experiments have been done with gastric or esophageal fistulas as sensitizing procedures. The techniques of these operations in the rat have been described elsewhere.[823] In essence, they depend upon the deviation to the outside of the gastric juice (gastric fistula with pylorus ligature) or the salivary secretion (esophageal fistula with ligature of the cardia). The constant loss of these secretions gradually produces a great tendency for calcification in the kidney and the cardiovascular system. This form of calcinosis is obtained without challenge, but it differs in its structural characteristics from the "nonspecific calcinosis" obtained by simple overdosage with DHT or parathyroid hormone.[823]

There appear to be close correlations between these experimental syndromes and the calcinoses that occur occasionally in man as a consequence of alkalosis (e.g., milk-drinkers' syndrome) or chronic vomiting. Furthermore, these surgically induced forms of calcinosis can be prevented by parathyroidectomy;[823] hence their ability to sensitize for calciphylaxis was thought to deserve attention.

Young rats (100 g. ♀) did not survive long enough after these operations to develop calciphylactic syndromes; indeed, they rarely even showed signs of nonspecific calcinosis. After this was established, we continued our work exclusively on older rats (200 g. ♀). In these Fe-OS (1 ml. = 20 mg. Fe, i.v.) on the 2d and 3d day after the intervention produced an auriculo-biliary calciphylactic syndrome which—but for its comparative mildness—resembled that elicited by the same challenger following DHT sensitization.

Work with other challengers has not yet progressed far enough to deserve mention, but even these experiments with Fe-OS suffice to show that at least in principle loss of either gastric juice or saliva can act as a calciphylactic sensitizer.

CALCIPHYLACTIC SYNDROMES PRODUCED AFTER SENSITIZATION BY OTHER MEANS

F-COL s.c. + Na₂HPO₄ p.o. + Fe-OS i.v.

Occlusive Coronary Lesions

Method: Rat (100 g. ♀): F-COL (1 mg. in 0.2 ml. water, s.c.) daily + Na₂HPO₄ (1 mM in 2 ml. water, by gavage ×2) daily + Fe-OS (1 ml. = 20 mg. Fe, i.v.)* 2d and 4th day; killed 5th day.

Results: There developed a cardiopathy characterized by "tigroid" streaks of **myocardial necroses with thromboses** in the capillaries and medium-sized veins of the heart. Apparently, here pretreatment with F-COL and Na₂HPO₄ selectively sensitized the cardiac vessels for the formation of clots.[847] Subsequent experiments showed that sometimes thromboses also develop in the coronary arteries under similar circumstances.

Various Electrolytes + Tl-acetate

Cortico-Medullary Nephrocalcinosis

Method: Rat (100 g. ♀): Ca-acetate, NaH₂PO₄, Na₂HPO₄, NaCl, Na-acetate or Na₃-citrate (2 mM in 2 ml. water, p.o. ×2/day) + Tl-acetate (3 mg. in 0.5 ml. water, s.c.) 4th day; killed 9th day.

---

* Rats thus pretreated with F-COL + Na₂HPO₄ are extremely sensitive to the acute toxic effects of Fe-OS; hence the compound must be injected very slowly under light ether anesthesia.

Results: In the rats receiving either NaH_2PO_4 or Na_2HPO_4 there was pronounced renal hypertrophy with nephrocalcinosis limited to the cortico-medullary junction line. However, the distribution of the calcium deposits was essentially different in these two groups: *NaH_2PO_4* produced only a single, rather clearly delimited white line of calcium deposition along the inner margin of the cortico-medullary junction zone, while *Na_2HPO_4* caused the appearance of two distinct lines, one along the inner, and the other along the outer, margin of the same zone. In addition, the kidneys of the Na_2HPO_4-treated rats exhibited occasional, more or less irregular spots of calcification disseminated throughout the parenchyma, although the papilla and the outer cortex remained almost completely free. Minor degrees of rather irregular calcification, especially along the inner margin of the cortico-medullary junction line, were also seen in a few of the rats treated with *Na-acetate* and *Na_3-citrate*.

In controls treated with Tl-acetate alone and in rats treated with *Ca-acetate* or *NaCl* in addition to Tl-acetate there was not the slightest trace of calcification, although some of the epithelial cells, especially in the proximal convoluted tubules, underwent necrosis under the influence of thallium.[832]

Discussion: Apparently, NaH_2PO_4 and Na_2HPO_4 sensitize the rat for the production of cortico-medullary nephrocalcinosis by Tl-acetate. Equimolecular amounts of other Na-salts (particularly the acetate and citrate, but not the chloride) are only slightly effective in this respect, while Ca-acetate is ineffective as a sensitizer for the production of nephrocalcinosis by Tl-acetate.[832]

B. THE METACALCIPHYLACTIC SYNDROMES

Morbid changes can occur as secondary consequences of calciphylaxis, either in the originally reacting target or in distant organs. The secondary development of inflammation, sclerosis, hyalinization, or ossification at the site of a subcutaneous challenge exemplifies the topical forms, while the induction of osteitis fibrosa by almost any kind of widespread calciphylactic response illustrates the systemic variety of metacalciphylactic lesions. Of course, calciphylactic and metacalciphylactic changes are so closely related that no sharp line can be drawn between them. We shall, nevertheless, review these accompaniments and aftermaths of calciphylaxis conjointly in this section, although some of them—particularly those that merely reflect the evolution and healing of the initial lesions—have already been mentioned in connection with our description of the individual calciphylactic syndromes.

INFLAMMATION, SCLEROSIS, AND HYALINIZATION

Inflammatory changes almost invariably accompany and follow the deposition of calcium in calciphylaxis. It is difficult to decide, however, whether these are integral parts of the calciphylactic response or merely secondary consequences of it. Significantly, heavy overdosage with glucocorticoids (e.g., triamcinolone) can virtually suppress inflammatory changes without interfering with calcium deposition in the cutaneous calciphylactic wheal induced by local challenge. This fact appears to support the view that inflammation is merely a consequence of local irritation by the precipitated calcium salts and not a necessary prerequisite for the calcification of such foci. Yet under certain circumstances both topical calciphylaxis and some of the systemic calciphylactic syndromes (e.g., the "dermatomyositis" produced by DHT + Fe-Dex i.v. + PMX s.c.) can be prevented by glucocorticoid pretreatment.

Secondary *sclerosis,* sometimes conducive to **hyalinization** at the site of a calciphylactic reaction, can occur both in connective tissue and in vessels (e.g., the hepatic artery in the DHT + Fe-OS i.v. syndrome). These lesions are associated with the secondary removal of calcium from the focus and presumably represent a form of healing.

When extensive regions of the skin are cast off after calciphylaxis (e.g., in the "exuviation" elicited by subcutaneous infiltration with Fe-Dex or albumen following DHT sensitization), healing occurs with intense inflammation, proliferation of connective tissue, and the formation of new epidermis underneath the old skin.

ECTOPIC OSTEOGENESIS

Whenever solid plaques of connective-tissue-fiber calcification are induced by a calciphylactic challenger (e.g., in the subcutaneous tissue), the incrustated collagen fibers become intensely PAS-positive and are eventually transformed into homogeneous spicules of "preosseous tissue." These formations greatly resemble cancellous bone in their general aspect and also in the fact that often hemopoietic tissue develops in the crevices between them. However, the formation of true bone with osteocytes, bone canaliculi, and loss of PAS-positive material from the matrix is a very uncommon consequence of calciphylaxis. The cause for its occasional occurrence is not yet known.

OSTEITIS FIBROSA AND OSTEOSCLEROSIS

In rats of different weights sensitized in the usual manner with 1–2 mg/100 g of **DHT** and 24 hours later challenged by the infiltration of virtually the entire subcutaneous tissue with 10 ml. of 50% **albumen** or the same volume of diluted **Fe-Dex** (= 5 mg. Fe/ml), heavy cutaneous and subcutaneous calcinosis develops concurrently with pronounced generalized osteitis fibrosa (Fig. 198). The skeletal changes reach their maximum during the first 4 to 5 days and subsequently give way to secondary osteosclerosis. Apparently, this widespread cutaneous challenge attracts larger amounts of calcium to the subcutaneous and dermal connective tissue than can be derived from the food. The excess mineral must therefore be supplied from the skeletal stores. This is accomplished through a process of osteoclastic bone absorption with fibrosis indistinguishable from that induced by parathyroid hormone overdosage. The initial, acute osteolytic process is then fol-

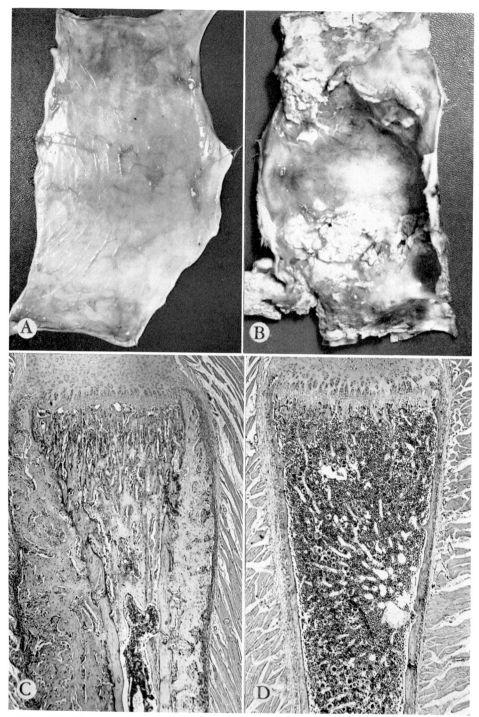

Fig. 198. **Metacalciphylactic lesions produced by DHT + albumen s.c.** Two rats (190 g. ♀): DHT (3.5 mg. p.o.) 1st day + (B and D) albumen (50%, 20 ml. s.c. infiltrated over entire back and belly) 2d day; killed 19th day. *A:* Normal dorsal skin (viewed from subcutis) in rat treated with DHT alone. *B:* Heavily calcified subcutis and cutis of rat challenged by albumen after DHT sensitization. *C:* Extensive osteosclerosis of rib near costochondral junction of rat treated with DHT alone. Trabeculae of spongiosa numerous and very thick, while intense new-bone formation is in progress along periosteum of compacta. (Hematoxylin-phloxine, ×30.) *D:* Comparable region of rib in rat challenged by albumen after DHT sensitization. Essentially normal bone structure. (Hematoxylin-phloxine, ×30.)

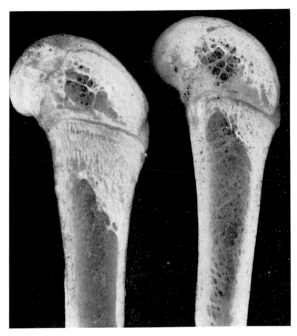

Fig. 199. Osteitis fibrosa produced by DHT + Fe-Dex s.c. Two rats (100 g. ♀): DHT (1 mg. p.o.) 1st day + (right) Fe-Dex (10 ml. = 10 mg. Fe, s.c. infiltration of virtually entire subcutaneous tissue) 2d day; killed 5th day. *Left:* DHT alone produced no macroscopically visible change on this sagittal section through lower end of femur. *Right:* Additional Fe-Dex treatment resulted in intense osteitis fibrosa with absorption of spongiosa underneath junction cartilage and formation of numerous holes on inner surface of shaft.

(After Selye,[828] courtesy Beitr. path. Anat. u. allg. Path.)

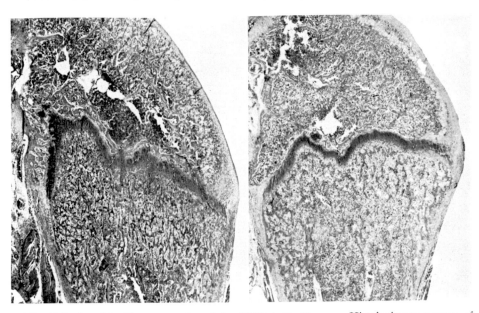

Fig. 200. Osteitis fibrosa produced by DHT + Fe-Dex s.c. Histologic appearance of bones shown in Fig. 199. Absorption, especially of primary bone spicules, is particularly evident. (PAS, ×15.)

(After Selye, [828] courtesy Beitr. path. Anat. u. allg. Path.)

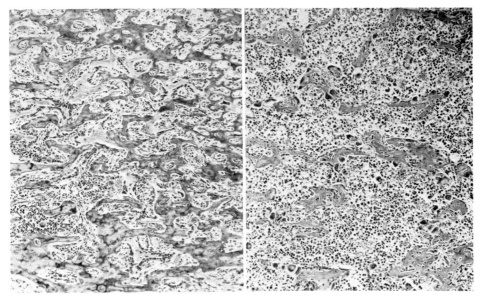

Fig. 201. **Osteitis fibrosa produced by DHT + Fe-Dex s.c.** Higher magnification of subepiphyseal region of bones shown in Figs. 199 and 200. Great predominance of large osteoclasts accompanies disappearance of bone spicules. Marrow cells partly necrotic. (PAS, ×70.)

(After Selye,[828] courtesy Beitr. path. Anat. u. allg. Path.)

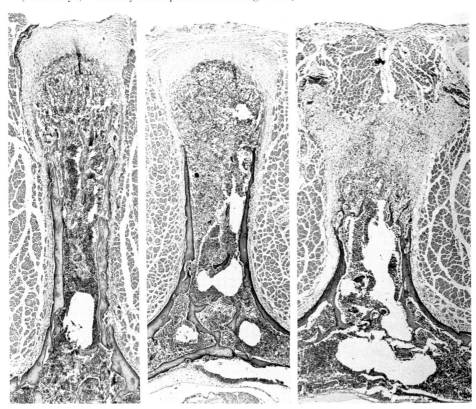

Fig. 202. **Osteitis fibrosa produced by DHT + Fe-Dex s.c. or albumen s.c.** Three rats (100 g. ♀): DHT (1 mg. p.o.) 1st day + (middle) Fe-Dex (10 ml. = 10 mg. Fe, s.c. infiltration) or (right) albumen (50%, 10 ml. s.c. infiltration) 2d day. *Left:* Spinous process of lumbar vertebra essentially normal. *Middle:* Osteitis fibrosa, particularly near tip of spinous process. *Right:* Spinous process almost totally destroyed by osteitis fibrosa. (PAS, ×33.)

(After Selye,[828] courtesy Beitr. path. Anat. u. allg. Path.)

lowed by an often excessive reparative osteogenesis, such as also occurs after a temporary acute hyperparathyroidism[828] (Figs. 199–203). However, calciphylaxis does not elicit these changes through the stimulation of parathyroid hormone secretion, since both the cutaneous calcinosis and the skeletal lesions develop equally well in intact and in ***parathyroidectomized*** animals.[840]

Essentially similar skeletal changes are produced by intravenously administered challengers that elicit widespread calciphylactic syndromes. For example, in the ***DHT***-sensitized rat, ***Thorotrast***® i.v. induces a syndrome characterized by diffuse calcification of the facial skin, the esophagus, and the joints (p. 177 ff.); if this soft-tissue calcification is sufficiently acute and intense, it also results in osteitis fibrosa-like changes.[845] Under similar circumstances ***yolk*** i.v. produces an RES type of calciphylactic syndrome, likewise with particularly severe bone absorption (Fig. 204).

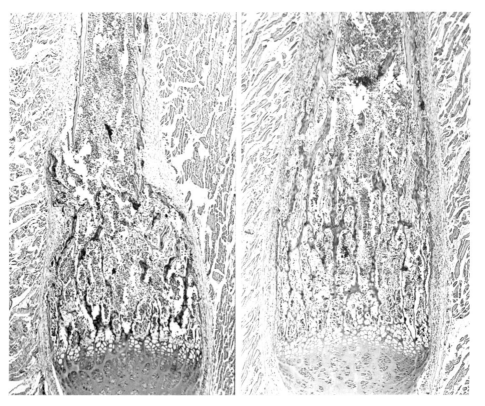

Fig. 203. Osteitis fibrosa produced by DHT + Fe-Dex s.c. Ribs of animals in Figs. 199–202. Only combined treatment (right) resulted in intense osteitis fibrosa with spontaneous fracture, close to costochondral junction. (PAS, ×35.)

(After Selye,[828] courtesy Beitr. path. Anat. u. allg. Path.)

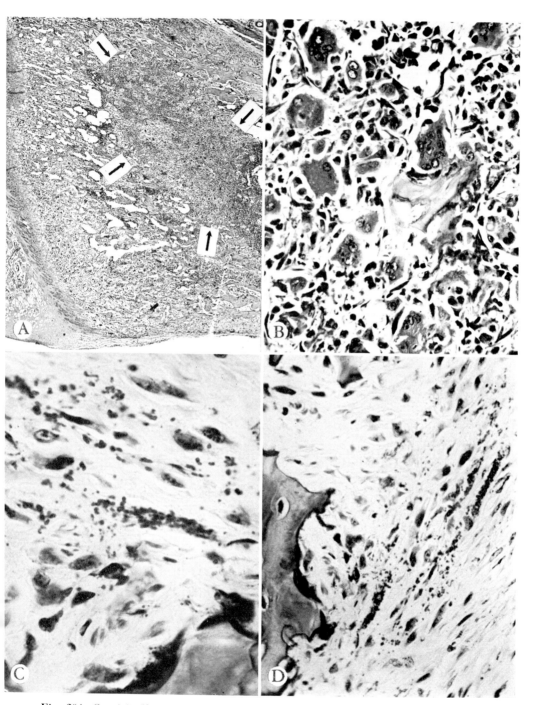

Fig. 204. Osteitis fibrosa produced by DHT + yolk i.v. Rat (100 g. ♀): DHT (1 mg.
p.o.) 1st day + yolk (50%, 5 ml. i.v.) 2d day; killed 4th day. All sections from lower end of
femur. *A:* Extraordinarily intense and acute osteitis fibrosa with replacement of primary bone
trabeculae by osteoclast-containing fibrous tissue, especially in area outlined by arrows. (PAS,
×28.) *B:* Higher magnification of osteoclast-containing area. (PAS, ×340.) *C* and *D:* Primary
bone granule formation in midst of region affected by osteitis fibrosa. (Celestin blue technique
for basophilic bone granules, C ×900, D ×390.)

(After Selye and Nielsen,[861a] courtesy A.M.A. Arch. Path.)

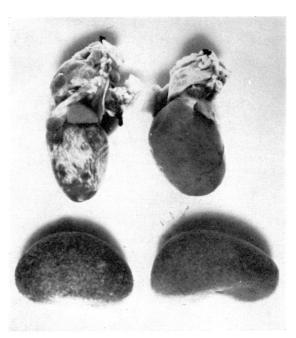

Fig. 205. Prevention by calciphylaxis of lesions produced by DHT + albumen s.c.
Two rats shown in Fig. 198. *Left:* Heavily calcified heart and kidney of rat treated with DHT
alone. *Right:* Essentially normal kidney and heart of rat which was challenged by albumen after
DHT sensitization.

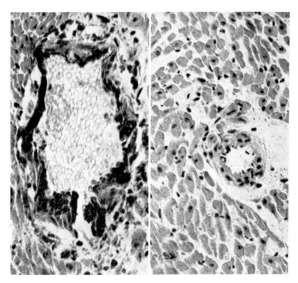

**Fig. 206. Prevention by calciphylaxis of coronary calcinosis produced by DHT +
albumen s.c.** Approximately corresponding branches of coronary arteries in right ventricles of
rats shown in Figs. 199–203. *Left:* DHT alone produced the usual calcium deposition and
dilatation of coronary artery. *Right:* These changes are completely prevented by additional
albumen treatment, presumably owing to shift of calcium into directly challenged skin. (von
Kóssa, ×300.)

(After Selye,[828] courtesy Beitr. path. Anat. u. allg. Path.)

248

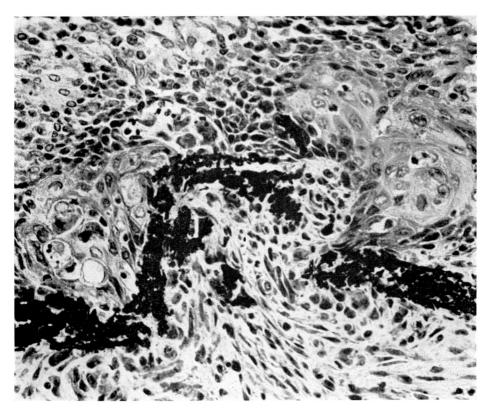

Fig. 207. **Squamous metaplasia of bronchial epithelium produced by DHT + Fe-Dex i.v.** Rat (100 g. ♀): DHT (1 mg. p.o.) 1st day + Fe-Dex (1 ml. = 50 mg. Fe, i.v.) 2d day; killed 16th day. Calcified plaque in wall of large bronchiole near pulmonary hilum surrounded by inflammatory granuloma. Epithelium exhibits two nodules of beginning squamous metaplasia with formation of numerous vacuolated cells and womewhat atypical nuclei. Several mitotic figures. (von Kóssa, ×470.)

OTHER LESIONS

If the attraction of calcium into challenged soft tissues is sufficiently intense to cause decalcification of the bones, it can **protect against the nonspecific calcinosis** usually elicited by DHT overdosage. For example, in rats given very large doses of DHT, calcification develops in the kidney, heart, and vessels. However, this effect can be prevented through the induction of extensive subcutaneous calcification by local challenge with Fe-Dex or albumen[828, 944] (Figs. 205, 206).

Although several of the challengers which we used (Fe-Dex, Thorotrast®) are known to be tumorigenic, we found no evidence of induced **neoplasms** in any of our experiments, perhaps because most of them were of short duration. However, squamous metaplasia of the bronchial epithelium occurred with some frequency in rats (100 g. ♀) treated with DHT (1 mg. p.o.) 1st day + Fe-Dex (1 ml. = 50 mg. Fe) 2d day. The lesions appeared about two weeks after this treatment (Fig. 207).

IV

Factors Influencing Susceptibility to Calciphylaxis

GENERALITIES

Many factors that influence susceptibility to calciphylaxis in general have already been briefly mentioned in the description of the various syndromes. Here, we shall review these and other relevant data synoptically under the following headings:

Site of challenge
Critical period
Diet
Stress
Hormones
Nervous stimuli
Renal lesions
Gastric and esophageal fistulas
Drugs
Resistance induced by previous calciphylactic responses
Age and sex
Species-specific differences in susceptibility

As we shall see, all these factors can exert a decisive influence not only upon the intensity but also upon the quality of calciphylactic responses.

SITE OF CHALLENGE

The *sensitivity of various regions to topical challenge varies:* in general the skin (especially that of the head and belly) is particularly sensitive, while the paws, tail, and many internal organs are comparatively resistant (Figs. 208, 209).

Apart from these regional differences in sensitivity to local challenge, the *distribution of the manifold systemic challengers varies* considerably; hence, they attract calcium to different sites. For example, Thorotrast® tends to cause lesions in the face, esophagus, and joints; $CrCl_3$ in the carotid bodies, thyroids, and parathyroids; Fe-Dex and albumen in the pancreas; thallium salts at the cortico-medullary junction of the kidney; yolk in the RES. The resulting different mosaics of lesions are presumably due to the fact that the challengers are selectively de-

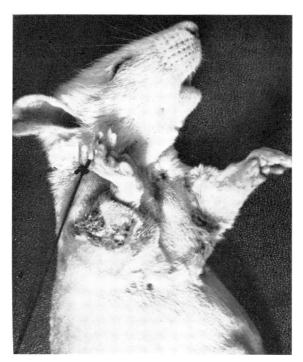

Fig. 208. Cutaneous calcinosis of the limb produced by DHT + Fe-Dex into paw.
Rat (100 g. ♀): DHT (1 mg. p.o.) 1st day + Fe-Dex (0.25 ml. = 1 mg. Fe, into each front paw). Although iron preparation was injected into paw itself, calcification occurred only above wrist because of relative resistance of limbs to induction of calciphylactic responses. (Paw is pulled dorsad by a thread in order to make visible sharp demarcation between normal paw and hard sleeve of cutaneous calcification that begins above wrist.)

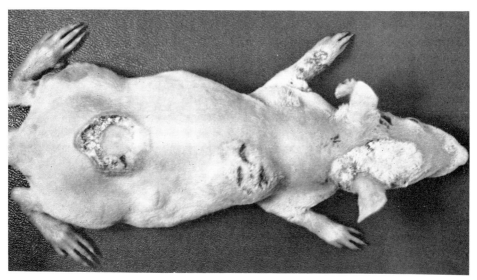

Fig. 209. Responsiveness of various sites to challenge by PMX after treatment with
DHT + Fe-Dex. Rat (100 g. ♀): DHT (1 mg. p.o.) 1st day + Fe-Dex (1 ml. = 1 mg. Fe, i.v.) 2d day + PMX (10 μg. in 0.1 ml. water, at various sites) 2d day; killed 7th day. Topical response to injection of PMX into right ear lobe, left front paw, subcutis over right shoulder blade and derma (intercutaneous injection) in lumbar region. Ear lobe, paw and derma did not respond at site of injection proper though calcinosis developed in surrounding area; subcutaneous injection produced massive topical calciphylactic plaque.

posited at compound-specific sites and cause local changes at those points that predispose for calcium precipitation.

The mere presence of a challenger in the tissue is not necessarily followed by calcification even in the optimally sensitized animal. For example, the phagocytes of the spleen are usually overloaded with ThO_2 crystals after injection of Thorotrast® i.v. and with iron granules after treatment with Fe-Dex i.v.; yet there may be little or no splenic calcification. This is all the more remarkable because much smaller amounts of the same challengers stored in other tissues of the same animal induce severe local calcinosis.

The reason for this difference in topical reactivity has not yet been clarified, but two possibilities deserve special consideration:

1. The excessive deposition of the challenger in one region induces the phenomenon of *"overchallenge,"* which notoriously interferes with calciphylactic reactivity.

2. The calciphylactic responsiveness of different organs is largely dependent upon *tissue-specific, local chemical reactions* which may either enhance or inhibit calcium deposition.

It is probable that both these factors play a part in determining the degree of response to any local challenger deposit.

CRITICAL PERIOD

The time interval that elapses between treatment with the sensitizer and the challenger is of decisive importance in all calciphylactic reactions. This fact has already been mentioned (p. 5) and many pertinent individual data have been listed in connection with our description of the various calciphylactic syndromes (pp. 83 ff.).

Topical calciphylaxis.—In the induction of topical calciphylaxis the importance of respecting the critical period has been demonstrated by our first preliminary experiments. For example, in different groups of rats (100 g. ♀) tested at intervals Fe-Dex (0.2 ml. = 10 µg. Fe, s.c.) was fully efficacious in producing cutaneous calcinosis on the 1st, +2d, and +3d, but not on the +4th, day after sensitization with DHT (1 mg. p.o.).

Essentially similar observations were made in an experiment in which a single group of rats (100 g. ♀) was first sensitized with vitamin D_3 (2 mg. in 0.2 ml. water, i.v.) on the 1st day and then repeatedly challenged with Fe-Dex (10 µg. in 0.2 ml. water, s.c. at various sites). Minimal cutaneous calciphylactic wheals were produced by injection on the 1st day, very marked lesions on the +2d and +3d day, but no response on the +4th day. Apparently here—as in the case of sensitization with DHT—the critical period reaches a maximum between the +2d and +3d day.

Those observations were subsequently extended by systematic experiments in which separate groups of rats were challenged on different days with one or two compounds (each injected at separate subcutaneous sites under the back).[837b] The mean diameters of the calciphylactic wheals (in mm.) were taken as indications of their reactivity; the results are summarized in Table 5.

It will be noted that for certain challengers (e.g., Fe-Dex, albumen) the critical period is quite sharply limited to the first few days following sensitization with DHT, while for others (e.g., $FeCl_3$, $CrCl_3$) there is no strictly limited critical period, since challenge as much as eight days before or after sensitization is effective. It is probable that the ineffectiveness of certain challengers when given before sensitization is due to their absorption or destruction before the action of DHT becomes effective, while compounds which are locally stored for a long time after injection (e.g., $FeCl_3$, $CrCl_3$) remain active even when they are administered long before sensitization. It is more difficult to understand why certain challengers do, while others do not, produce a calciphylactic wheal when given long after sensitization. Additional experiments are now under way to determine the maximum duration of potency of the long-acting challengers when injected more than eight days before or after sensitization.*

Systemic calciphylaxis.—In the preceding chapter we have repeatedly made reference to incidental observations which suggested that the intensity, and sometimes even the quality, of calciphylactic responses is decisively influenced by the time that elapses between sensitization and challenge. This critical period differs considerably for the various calciphylactic syndromes; it depends upon both the sensitizer and the challenger used. Hence, an additional series of experiments was performed to determine the critical period of challenge for some of the most striking systemic calciphylactic syndromes.[838b] The results are summarized in Table 6. Here as in the following tables, the principal targets selected for the characterization of each syndrome are listed with the mean intensity of the change gauged in terms of our arbitrary four-grade scale (0 = no lesion, 1 = just visible, 2 = moderate, and 3 = maximal lesion). The standard errors of these rather subjective readings will be listed in the forthcoming detailed publications, but they are omitted here for simplicity's sake.

The critical period is particularly sharp in the case of treatment with evanescent challengers (e.g., albumen, PMX, 5HT) (Groups 1, 6, 7, 8, 12, 13, 14), while it is of much longer duration following challenge by substances that, once deposited in their respective target areas, remain there unaltered for a long time (e.g., $CrCl_3$ i.v. or Thorotrast® i.v.) (Groups 2, 11).

---

* (*Remark added in proofs.*) In the meantime we have been able to establish that $CrCl_2$, $CrCl_3$, $FeCl_3$, and Fe-OS given s.c. in amounts equivalent to 1 mg. of Cr or Fe, respectively, as long as 20 days prior to sensitization with DHT (2 mg. p.o.) still produced macroscopically demonstrable topical calcified wheals; however, the response was less pronounced than that induced by the same challengers given on the day after DHT sensitization. Up to now we have no evidence that challenge more than eight days after DHT treatment could be effective.

TABLE 5

CRITICAL PERIOD FOR VARIOUS FORMS OF TOPICAL CALCIPHYLAXIS

GROUP	TREATMENT	TARGETS	MEAN DIAMETER OF CALCIPHYLACTIC WHEAL (mm.) upon CHALLENGE on DAY:								
			−8	−4	−3	−2	1	+2	+3	+4	+8
1	**DHT p.o.+Fe-Dex s.c.+albumen s.c.:** Rat (200 g. ♀): DHT (2 mg. p.o.) 1st day+Fe-Dex (0.2 ml.=50 μg. Fe, s.c.)+Albumen (50%, 0.2 ml. s.c.); killed 12th day	Skin {Fe-Dex–site	0	0	0	0	0	16.8	20.3	21.5	0
		{Albumen–site	0	0	0	0	0	25.0	28.0	21.5	0
2	**DHT p.o.+FeCl₃ s.c.+CrCl₃ s.c.:** Rat (200 g. ♀): DHT (2 mg. p.o.) 1st day+FeCl₃ (100 μg. in 0.2 ml. water, s.c.)+CrCl₃ (100 μg. in 0.2 ml. water, s.c.); killed 12th day	Skin {FeCl₃–site	12.3	13.7	11.1	14.1	13.8	12.5	19.1	17.5	5.8
		{CrCl₃–site	7.2	7.2	7.8	7.1	7.6	9.0	11.1	6.8	6.0
3	**DHT p.o.+Fe-Dex s.c.:** Rat (100 g. ♀): DHT (1 mg. p.o.) 1st day+Fe-Dex (1 ml.=50 mg. Fe, s.c.); killed 9th day	Skin Fe-Dex–site	......	......	......	......	20.3	21.7	21.8	7.0	......
4	**DHT p.o.+Fe-OS s.c.:** Rat (100 g. ♀): DHT (1 mg. p.o.) 1st day+Fe-OS (1 ml.=20 mg. Fe, s.c.); killed 9th day	Skin Fe-OS–site	......	......	......	......	5.0	21.0	21.0	0	......

TABLE 6

CRITICAL PERIOD FOR VARIOUS FORMS OF SYSTEMIC CALCIPHYLAXIS

MEAN RESPONSE (SCALE 0–3)* OF TARGETS AND MORTALITY (%) UPON CHALLENGE ON DAY:

Group	Treatment	Targets	-8	-4	-3	-2	1	+2	+3	+4	+5	+8
1	**DHT p.o.+albumen i.p.:** Rat (200 g. ♀): DHT (2 mg. p.o.) 1st day+albumen (50%, 10 ml. i.p.); killed 12th day	Brunner's glands	0	0	0.2	0.2	0	0.6	**2.4**	1.1		0.5
		Pancreas	0	0	0	0	0	0.6	**2.4**	0		0
		Skin (presternal)	0	0	0	0	0	0	**1.2**	0.5		0
		Mortality	0	0	0	0	0	0	30	0		0
2	**DHT p.o.+CrCl₃ i.v.:** Rat (200 g. ♀): DHT (2 mg. p.o.) 1st day+CrCl₃ (20 mg. in 1 ml. water, i.v.); killed 12th day	Heart	2.0	**3.0**	3.0	2.0	3.0	3.0	1.3	0.5		1.0
		Lung	2.7	**3.0**	2.5	2.7	3.0	2.5	2.2	0.5		0.5
		Thyroid	2.7	**3.0**	3.0	2.7	3.0	3.0	0.5	0.5		0.2
		Parathyroid	2.8	**3.0**	3.0	2.7	3.0	3.0	1.2	0.8		1.0
		Glomus	**3.0**	3.0	3.0	3.0	3.0	3.0	1.0	0.7		0.8
		Mortality	0	0	0	0	0	0	0	0		0
3	**DHT p.o.+FeCl₂ i.v.:** Rat (200 g. ♀): DHT (2 mg. p.o.) 1st day+FeCl₂ (2, 4, 6 and 4 mg. in 0.2, 0.4, 0.6 and 0.4 ml. water, respectively); killed 12th day	Thyroid	0.3	0	0	0.4	0.6	**0.7**	0	0		0
		Parathyroid	0.2	0	0	0	0.8	**1.0**	0.3	0.4		0
		Glomus	0.2	0	0	1.2	**2.4**	2.2	1.0	1.0		0
		Bile ducts	0	1.5	1.3	**1.8**	1.0	0.2	0.3	0.4		0
		Mortality	0	50		30	100	50	50	30		0
4	**DHT p.o.+Fe-Dex i.p.:** Rat (200 g. ♀): DHT (2 mg. p.o.) 1st day+Fe-Dex (1 ml.=50 mg. Fe, i.p.); killed 12th day	Uterus	0.2	0	0.8	1.7	1.6	**2.0**	1.8	0		0
		Pancreas	0	0	0	0	2.0	0.5	0.3	**2.2**		0
		Skin	0.3	0.3	0.5	**2.0**	1.2	1.3	0	0.2		0
		Adipose tissue								1.7		0
		Mortality	0	0	0	0	0	0	0	0		0
5	**DHT p.o.+Fe-Dex i.v.:** Rat (200 g. ♀): DHT (2 mg. p.o.) 1st day+Fe-Dex (1 ml.=50 mg. Fe, i.v.); killed 12th day	Uterus	0	1.2	1.2	**2.0**	0.3	0.8	0	0		0
		Pancreas	0	0	0	0	0.3	2.3	2.2	**2.2**		0.2
		Skin	0	2.3	0.7	2.7	1.8	**2.5**	1.7	0		0
		Adipose tissue	0	0	0	0.2	0.5	1.3	**2.7**	0.5		0
		Mortality	0	0	0	0	0	0	30	0		0
6	**DHT p.o.+Fe-Dex i.v.+PMX s.c.:** Rat (100 g. ♀): DHT (500 μg. p.o.) 1st day+Fe-Dex (1 ml.=1 mg. Fe, i.v.)+PMX (2 mg. in 0.2 ml. water, s.c.); killed 10th day	Calciphylactic dermatomyositis					0.4	**2.2**	1.1	0.8	0.5	
		Mortality					0	0	0	0	0	

* Boldface numerals indicate peak responses.

TABLE 6—Continued

Group	Treatment	Targets	\-8	\-4	\-3	\-2	1	+2	+3	+4	+5	+8
7	Rat (100 g, ♀): DHT (1 mg, p.o.) 1st day+Fe-Dex (1 ml.=1 mg. Fe, i.v.)+PMX (500 μg. in 0.2 ml. water, s.c.); killed 10th day	Calciphylactic dermatomyositis					0.3	**1.9**	1.0	0.5	0.2	
		Mortality					0	0	80	0	0	
8	Rat (100 g, ♀): DHT (1 mg, p.o.) 1st day+Fe-Dex (1 ml.=1 mg. Fe, i.v.)+PMX (2 mg. in 0.2 ml. water, s.c.); killed 10th day	Calciphylactic dermatomyositis					0	1.6	0.4	2.3	1.0	
		Mortality					0	30	100	6.0	0	
9	**DHT p.o.+Fe-OS i.v.:** Rat (200 g, ♀): DHT (2 mg, p.o.) 1st day+Fe-OS (1.5 ml.=30 mg. Fe, i.v.); killed 5th day	Auricle		**2.8**		2.0	3.0	1.6		0		
		Bile ducts		1.6		2.0	3.0	0.4		0		
		Mortality		0		0	0	0		0		
10	**DHT p.o.+IPR i.p.:** Rat (200 g, ♀): DHT (2 mg, p.o.) 1st day+IPR (25 mg. in 0.2 ml. water, i.p. ×2); killed 12th day	Heart	0.7	0.8	1.7	2.0	2.6	2.8	2.5	2.0		1.5
		Auricle	0	0.2	0	1.7	2.4	2.5	0.2	0.8		0
		Kidney	0	0.3	0	0.8	**1.8**	1.0	0.7	1.0		0.2
		Mortality	0	0	0	0	30	0	0	0		0
11	**DHT p.o.+Thorotrast® i.v.:** Rat (200 g, ♀): DHT (2 mg, p.o.) 1st day+Thorotrast® (100%, 1 ml.i.v.); killed 12th day	Esophagus	0	0.7	1.3	2.5	2.8	3.0	3.0	2.2		1.7
		Lips	0	0	0	0.3	0.5	1.0	2.0	2.2		0.7
		Joints	0	0	0.5	2.3	2.3	2.8	3.0	2.2		0
		Skin	0.5	**3.0**	2.2	2.5	1.5	0.8	1.0	1.0		0
		Mortality	0	0	0	0	0	0	0	0		0
12	**Parathyroid hormone s.c.+5HT s.c.:** Rat (200 g, ♀): parathyroid hormone (300 I.U. in 3 ml. water, s.c.) 1st day+5HT (5 mg. in 0.5 ml. water, s.c.); killed 9th day	Muscles					0	0	1.5	1.0	0	
		Mortality					0	0	0	0	0	
13	Rat (200 g, ♀): parathyroid hormone (300 I.U. in 3 ml. water, s.c. ×2) 1st day+5HT (5 mg. in0.5 ml. water, s.c.×2); killed 8th day	Muscles					0.5	0.7	0	**1.0**	0.2	
		Mortality					0	0	0	0	0	
14	Rat (200 g, ♀): parathyroid hormone (100 I.U. in 1 ml. water, s.c.) ×1 on 1st day, ×3 on 2d day+5HT (5 mg. in 0.5 ml. water, s.c.×2); killed 8th day	Muscles					0.4	0	1.2	**2.0**	0.4	
		Mortality					0	0	0	0	0	

Mean Response (Scale 0–3)* of Targets and Mortality (%) upon Challenge on Day:

* Boldface numerals indicate peak responses.

As we have said in connection with topical calciphylaxis, it is not unexpected that a challenger can no longer act after it is locally destroyed or removed from the target area; it is more difficult to explain why certain challengers (e.g., Fe-Dex, FeCl$_2$) which demonstrably do remain in a normally receptive region gradually lose their potency, while others (e.g., CrCl$_3$) remain active. We also cannot explain why the critical period for the obtention of responses in different regions of the same animal is not the same (e.g., in uterus and pancreas after Fe-Dex i.v. or i.p., in skin and lips after Thorotrast® i.v.). Evidently, challengers do not produce calciphylactic responses merely by directly precipitating blood calcium; if this were the case, an active challenger would precipitate calcium wherever it was deposited in the body, irrespective of critical period or target site. As we have seen, this is not so: Fe-Dex i.v. causes pancreatic, but not splenic, calcification, although more iron is deposited in the spleen than in the pancreas; 5HT i.p. produces salivary gland calcification, but no calcinosis in the peritoneum. These and many similar observations show that the reactive site, or "soil," is of decisive importance in all calciphylactic reactions. It is probable therefore that even "direct challengers" do not act as such, but through chemical responses induced directly in their immediate environment. Presumably, these changes, which favor calcification, are themselves evanescent and their duration does not depend merely upon the continued presence of the exogenous challenger.

Role of the sensitizer.—Some kind of adaptation to the sensitizer also plays an important part in determining the critical period. For example, chronic pretreatment with DHT can protect against the subsequent induction of a calciphylactic response by an otherwise effective dose of DHT followed by challenge (e.g., epilation, FeCl$_3$ s.c. or albumen s.c.). While, under these conditions, calcinosis of the skin is prevented by the DHT pretreatment, nonspecific calcinosis (in heart, aorta, kidneys, and stomach) is actually aggravated.[704] Observations of this kind strongly suggest that *the critical period exists only as regards calciphylactic reactivity, and not for DHT-induced nonspecific calcinosis in general.* In other words, there is no indication here of any acquired resistance to DHT as such, but only to one of its pharmacologic effects—the sensitization for calciphylaxis.

The question arises whether this adaptation to DHT might not be due to the breakdown of those evanescent local responses that appear to be the immediate prerequisites for effective challenge (e.g., liberation of some endogenous calcium precipitants under the influence of a sensitizer). If this is so, DHT may gradually lose its sensitizing effect merely because upon repeated application its calcium-precipitating target material is eventually exhausted.

DIET

As might be expected, the dietary intakes of *calcium* and *phosphate* are particularly important conditioning factors for the development of calciphylaxis. For example, the oral administration of NaH_2PO_4 or calcium acetate greatly augments the ability of vitamin D_2 to sensitize for the induction of cutaneous calcinosis by topical challenge with $FeCl_3$ or plucking of the hair. The same electrolytes also augment the ability of vitamin-D_2 overdosage to produce calcium deposition in the cardiovascular system and the kidney[830] (Fig. 210). Similar observations have been made regarding various calcium salts and phosphates in rats exposed to cutaneous challenge after sensitization with DHT.[491]

Essentially different types of nephrocalcinosis are produced in the DHT-sensitized rat by a dietary excess of calcium or phosphate: calcium acetate produces an almost exclusively cortical (Fig. 211), Na_2HPO_4 a cortico-medullary, or generalized, nephrocalcinosis (Fig. 212).

Occasionally, we see calcinosis of the tongue in rats sensitized by DHT and given NaH_2PO_4 by stomach tube (Fig. 213); here, either the phosphate as such or even the mere topical trauma incident to daily gavage might act as a local challenger. It is highly debatable, however, whether such dietary aggravation of the effects of DHT by calcium salts or phosphates is in any way comparable to calciphylactic challenge, when these salts merely aggravate "nonspecific calcinosis"

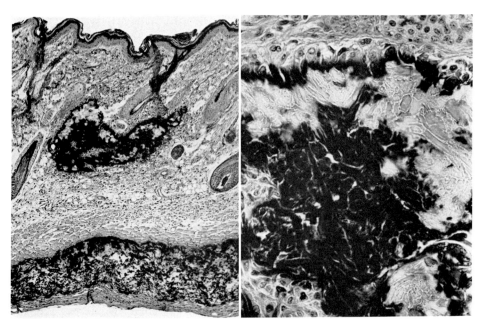

Fig. 210. **Cutaneous calcinosis produced by vitamin D_2 + NaH_2PO_4 p.o.** *Left:* Small calcified plaque in derma and larger one in subcutis below cutaneous muscle. With celestin blue the outer margin of calcified region and incipient calcification on collagen fibers stain selectively. (Celestin blue, ×65.) *Right:* Higher magnification of portion of previous slide. Here, selective calcification of apparently recently calcified regions is even more evident. (Celestin blue, ×350.)

[After Selye *et al.*,[830] courtesy Williams & Wilkins (J. Invest. Dermat.).]

without producing any compound-specific syndromes. Indeed, until more is known about the mechanism of calciphylactic reactions, our classification of electrolyte-induced changes in sensitivity to the production of nonspecific calcinosis by calcifiers is largely arbitrary. We mentioned calcium and phosphate as dietary factors influencing calcifiability as a whole, while some magnesium and thallium salts were listed as challengers. This was done merely because the latter produce highly specific types of nephrocalcinosis that cannot be duplicated even by the highest tolerable doses of vitamin-D compounds or parathyroid hormone, while the effects of calcium salts and phosphates are much more nonspecific. Yet, we have seen that NaH_2PO_4 can qualitatively change the DHT effect (induction of suppurating myocarditis), in addition to the purely quantitative aggravation of nonspecific calcinosis.

The cutaneous calcinosis induced by topical challenge (e.g., plucking of the scalp hair) in the DHT-sensitized rat can be significantly aggravated by the oral administration of $NaClO_4$. On the other hand, equimolecular amounts of NaCl and Na_2SO_4 are ineffective.[491] Oral administration of $MgCl_2$ and to a lesser extent of KCl diminishes the incidence and severity of such skin lesions.[492] This observation

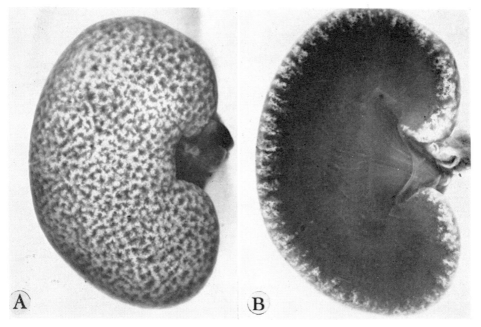

Fig. 211. Pure cortical nephrocalcinosis produced by DHT + calcium acetate p.o.
Rat (100 g. ♀): DHT (35 μg., p.o. ×2/day) 1st–9th day + Ca-acetate (1.5 mM in 2 ml. water, p.o ×2/day) for 9 days; killed 10th day. *A:* Calcified cortical tubules are clearly visible on renal surface. *B:* Section through kidney with selectively cortical localization of calcium deposition.

(After Selye,[823] courtesy Charles C Thomas Publ., Springfield, Ill.)

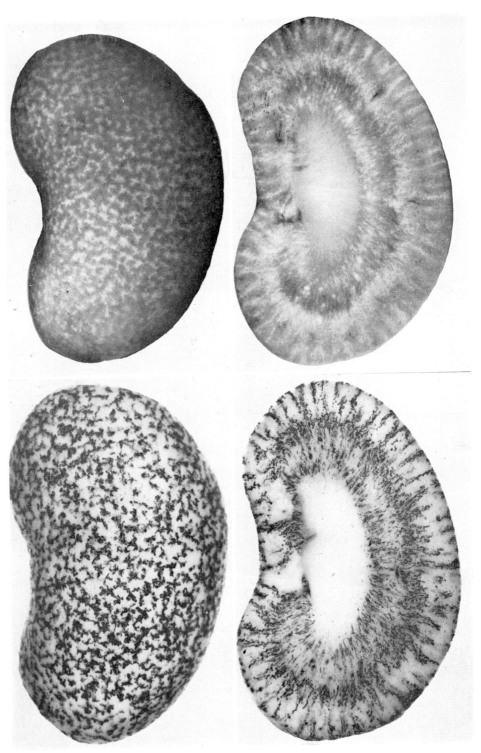

Fig. 212. Generalized nephrocalcinosis produced by DHT + Na₂HPO₄ p.o. Rat (100 g. ♀): DHT (25 μg. p.o. ×2/day) 1st–12th day + Na₂HPO₄ (2 mM in 2 ml. water, p.o. ×2/day) 1st-12th day; died 12th day. Surface and cut surface of kidney. Calcified foci are white in fresh (*top*) and black in AgNO₃-stained (*bottom*) specimens.

[After Selye,[826] courtesy Williams & Wilkins (J. Urol.).]

is reminiscent of the similar but much more pronounced inhibition exerted by these electrolytes against the cardiopathy produced by DHT + phosphates.[821, 823]

In the section on "Methodology" we have already mentioned that DHT is more effective as a calciphylactic sensitizer if it is administered orally in *oil* than if it is given in the form of an aqueous suspension. The influence of fats upon this potency has been studied especially in relation to the production and prevention by various electrolytes and stressors of the DHT- or vitamin-D-induced calcifying cardiopathies[821, 823] and need not be discussed here.

The influence of dietary factors upon the development of the typical systemic calciphylactic syndromes has not yet been explored, but it undoubtedly represents a fruitful field for future study.

STRESS

Among all the factors that can influence calciphylaxis under near-physiologic conditions perhaps the most important one is stress. Both local and systemic stress factors must be taken into account in evaluating the production, aggravation, or inhibition of any calciphylactic reaction. The role of local stress is considered separately later (in connection with the closely related phenomenon of "overchal-

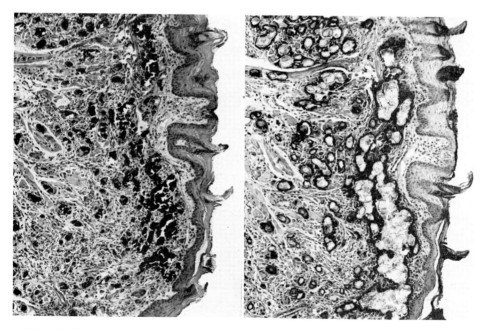

Fig. 213. Lingual calcinosis produced by DHT + NaH₂PO₄ p.o. *Left:* Minute histologic details not visible in calcified areas because of solid black staining and fragmentation of silver-impregnated regions. (von Kóssa, ×85.) *Right:* Margins of calcified areas selectively stained; structural details clearly visible even in necrotic central areas. (Celestin blue, ×85.)
[After Selye *et al.*,[839] courtesy Williams & Wilkins (J. Invest. Dermat.).]

lenge"); here, we shall discuss only systemic stress. The techniques used for the production of systemic stress by restraint, quadriplegia, muscular exercise, cold, heat, etc., have been described in detail elsewhere.[823]

Topical calciphylaxis.—Several observations suggest that systemic stress applied at the proper time can inhibit various and perhaps even all forms of calciphylaxis.[826] In this connection, extensive observations have been performed with regard to topical calciphylaxis elicited by epilation in DHT-sensitized rats. Here, complete or at least significant inhibition could be obtained by exposure immediately after sensitization with DHT to the stress of restraint or quadriplegia (induced by severance of motor nerves); on the other hand, transection of the spinal cord, forced muscular exercise, and exposure to cold or heat exerted little or no protective effect.[491] The topical calciphylaxis thus induced by plucking of the hair after sensitization with DHT can most readily be prevented by forced restraint for 17 hours prior to epilation.[491, 492, 494, 859] Indeed, under these circumstances, even the "nonspecific" renal and cardiovascular calcification normally induced by DHT overdosage itself is inhibited by stress.[493, 859] The time factor is very important here, since under different conditions of timing and sensitization stress can also aggravate these same lesions.[491, 493]

The results of a few typical experiments illustrating the inhibition of topical calciphylaxis by the stress of restraint[837c] are summarized in Table 7.

It is evident that all six topical challengers tested in these three groups of rats were effectively inhibited by restraint only during a critical period, which virtually coincides with the day of sensitization or the day of challenge. The topical action of $CrCl_3$, Fe-Dex, $FeCl_3$, and yolk was also inhibited by exposure to stress on the day preceding DHT administration, the $-2d$ day. On the other hand, the calciphylactic wheal normally produced by Thorotrast® was but slightly affected, and only on the $+2d$ day. This exceptional resistance to Thorotrast® may be due, at least in part, to the fact that, at the dose level given, it produced the greatest response in the controls.

There is also some indication that sensitivity to calciphylaxis can be increased by restraint if the animals are exposed to this stressor long before challenge. For example, exposure to stress on the -6th day almost invariably resulted in calciphylactic wheals larger than those of the controls; this increase was most evident in the rats challenged by $CrCl_3$ or yolk. Apparently, the effect of stress upon calciphylaxis is a dual one; it can either decrease or increase sensitivity depending upon the time of exposure. A similar dual response has been noted with regard to the influence of stressors upon diverse cardiovascular lesions.[823]

The inhibition of cutaneous calcinosis by stress appears to be closely related to the calciphylactic type of response; structurally quite similar calcified cutaneous wheals induced by the topical application of a direct challenger, such as $KMnO_4$, could not be prevented under similar circumstances by the stress of immobiliza-

TABLE 7

Effect of Stress upon Various Forms of Topical Calciphylaxis

Group	Treatment	Targets	Controls	Day of Restraint					
				−6	−4	−2	1	+2	+3
1	**DHT p.o.+CrCl₃ s.c.+Fe-Dex s.c.:** Rat (100 g, ♀): DHT (1 mg. p.o.) 1st day+CrCl₃ (25 μg. in 0.2 ml. water, s.c.) 2d day+Fe-Dex (20 μg. in 0.2 ml. water, s.c.) 2d day+restraint (24 hrs.); killed 7th day	Skin{CrCl₃-site / Fe-Dex-site	14.3 / 24.8	22.0 / 30.2	12.6 / 24.0	8.7 / 5.1	9.5 / 4.1	2.7 / 1.3	14.8 / 25.2
2	**DHT p.o.+FeCl₃ s.c.+yolk s.c.:** Rat (100 g, ♀): DHT (1 mg. p.o.) 1st day+FeCl₃ (25 μg. in 0.2 ml. water, s.c.) 2d day+yolk (10%, 0.2 ml. s.c.) 2d day+restraint (24 hrs.); killed 7th day	Skin{FeCl₃-site / Yolk-site	6.3 / 14.3	9.9 / 26.6	10.2 / 19.8	5.4 / 6.9	3.9 / 3.5	2.9 / 2.2	7.5 / 13.7
3	**DHT p.o.+Thorotrast® s.c.+albumen s.c.:** Rat (100 g, ♀): DHT (1 mg. p.o.) 1st day+Thorotrast® (100%, 0.2 ml. s.c.) 2d day+albumen (10%, 0.2 ml. s.c.) 2d day+restraint (24 hrs.); killed 7th day	Skin{Thorotrast®-site / Albumen-site	23.2 / 13.2	28.5 / 13.6	28.4 / 12.4	25.1 / 13.4	23.8 / 0	19.3 / 0	22.7 / 4.6

tion.[865] This observation again emphasizes the essential difference in the mechanism of directly induced, and calciphylactic, calcinosis.

Systemic calciphylaxis.—Having established that topical calciphylaxis can be prevented by stress, we may ask whether the same is also true of the systemic calciphylactic reactions. A complete analysis of this problem, though not technically difficult, would necessitate a great variety of tests. The topical calciphylactic wheal is rather stereotyped; it does not exhibit a great variety of structural differences no matter what sensitizers or challengers are used to elicit it. Hence, having established that such wheals produced by several agents can be inhibited by various stressors, we may say that the generalization "stress inhibits topical calciphylaxis" appears to be justified as long as we are prepared to find an occasional exception to this rule. In fact, as we have said, some stressors proved to be comparatively or even totally inactive in this respect under our experimental conditions. However, it may be reasonably assumed that these exceptional near-failures or failures depend upon incidental technical details (e.g., intensity or timing of stress) or upon interfering specific actions of the particular sensitizers, challengers, or stressors employed.

The problem proved to be infinitely more complex when we turned to the inhibition by stress of systemic calciphylactic syndromes. Most of these are fundamentally distinct in their manifestations; they affect different target organs and have different latency periods. Hence, it seemed that before we could formulate any generalization, virtually every calciphylactic syndrome would have to be tested for the possibility of being inhibited by various stressors. An extraordinarily large number of experiments would have been required to perform such an analysis; hence, we decided to simplify our task by using only one stressor—restraint—and testing its effect upon the evolution of a selected group of fundamentally distinct calciphylactic syndromes. Still, it was to be expected that syndromes with different critical periods and different speeds of evolution would be affected by stress at different times. Therefore, in analyzing each syndrome, the effect of stress still had to be determined on many groups of animals restrained at varying time intervals after sensitization and challenge.

Yet, as we shall see, under optimal conditions all the calciphylactic syndromes tested up to now could be inhibited by restraint irrespective of their specific organ lesions although the period of maximal responsiveness to stress varied.[837b]

For the sake of simplicity we shall attempt to summarize our most important relevant data in tabular form (Table 8). Since the manifestations of the various syndromes have already been described in detail, it will suffice to designate them by the combination of agents used for their production and to list the principal targets. Inhibitions to less than half the control value are emphasized by bold numerals.

Perusal of Table 8 clearly indicates that all these calciphylactic syndromes can

TABLE 8

Effect of Stress upon Various Forms of Systemic Calciphylaxis

Group	Treatment	Targets	Control	Day of Restraint* −4	−2	1	+2	+3	+4 day	Remarks
1	**DHT p.o.+albumen i.p.:** Rat (100 g. ♀): DHT (1 mg. p.o.) 1st day+albumen (50%, 5 ml. i.p.) 2d day+restraint (24 hrs.); killed 6th day	Pancreas	1.7	1.2	1.0	0	0.2	1.7		Fig. 214. Even the more intense pancreatic and cutaneous calcinosis produced by larger amounts of albumen can be prevented by as little as 17 hrs. restraint on 1st day (Fig. 215)
2	**DHT p.o.+CrCl₃ i.v.:** Rat (100 g. ♀): DHT (1 mg. p.o.) 1st day+CrCl₃ (6 mg. in 2 ml. water, i.v.) 2d day+restraint (24 hrs.); killed 6th day	Thyroid / Parathyroid / Carotid body	2.1 / 2.4 / 2.1	0.4 / 0.3 / 0.6	0.3 / 0.5 / 0.3	0 / 0.3 / 0.3	0.6 / 2.9 / 1.9	1.1 / 1.4 / 1.3		Fig. 216; Plate IV, B
3	**DHT p.o.+Fe-Dex i.v.+PMX s.c.:** Rat (100 g. ♀): DHT (1 mg. p.o.) 1st day+Fe-Dex (1 ml.=1 mg. Fe, i.v.) 2d day+PMX (500 µg. in 0.2 ml. water, s.c.) 2d day+restraint (24 hrs.); killed 7th day	Calciphylactic dermatomyositis	2.3	1.2	0	0.6	0.5	1.6		Fig. 217
4	**DHT p.o.+Fe-Din i.v.:** Rat (100 g. ♀): DHT (1 mg. p.o.) 1st day+Fe-Din (0.5 ml.=10 mg. Fe, i.v.) 2d day+restraint (24 hrs.); killed 7th day	Face / Esophagus	2.0 / 1.6	2.3 / 2.1	2.4 / 0.8	2.0 / 0.3	0.5 / 0.5	1.6 / 1.4		Apparently, calcinosis of the esophagus is more easily inhibited than the facial lesions (Fig. 218)
5	**DHT p.o.+5HT s.c.:** Rat (100 g. ♀): DHT (1 mg. p.o.) 1st day+5HT (2 mg. in 0.5 ml. water, s.c. in throat region) 2d day+restraint (24 hrs.); killed 6th day	Submaxillary gland	2.0	1.9	1.0	0.3	1.1	2.2		Prevention of submaxillary gland calcinosis similar to that obtained in the corresponding vitamin-D₃ syndrome, which is illustrated in Figs. 223, 224
6	**DHT p.o.+5HT s.c.:** Rat (200 g. ♀): DHT (1 mg. p.o.) 1st day+5HT (5 mg. in 0.5 ml. water, s.c.) 3d day+restraint (24 hrs.); killed 7th day	Muscles / Submaxillary gland	2.2 / 0.4	2.0 / 0.5	1.2 / 1.2	0.8 / 0	0.4 / 0	2.3 / 0.3	2.7 / 0.4	

* The day on which the sensitizer (DHT or vitamin D₃) was administered is considered day 1. The preceding days are indicated as "—"; the following days as "+"; accordingly, there is no day −1 or +1 (day 1 being considered "—" during its first and "+" during its second twelve hours). In this manner our days +2, +3, etc., correspond to what is generally designated as the 2d, 3d, etc., day of an experiment and the corresponding + and − days are equidistant from day 1.

TABLE 8—Continued

Group	Treatment	Targets	Control	Day of Restraint*					Remarks
				-4	-2	1	+2	+3	
7	**DHT p.o.+Thorotrast® i.v.:** Rat (100 g. ♀): DHT (1 mg. p.o.) 1st day+Thorotrast® (0.3 ml. i.v.) 2d day+restraint (24 hrs.); killed 6th day	Face Esophagus	1.6 1.3	1.8 1.1	0.9 0	1.5 0	**0.1** **0.1**	1.2 0.7	Even more intense lesions produced by doubling dose of Thorotrast® are prevented by repeated (1st and 3d day) restraint during 17 hrs. Stress does not prevent deposition of Thorotrast® granules in target; it merely diminishes their ability to attract calcium (Figs. 219–221; Plate VI, F)
8	**Vitamin D₃ i.v.+Fe-Dex i.v.+PMX s.c.:** Rat (100 g. ♀): vitamin D₃ (2.5 mg. in 0.25 ml. water, i.v.) 1st day+PMX (500 µg. in 0.2 ml. water, s.c.) 2d day+Fe-Dex (1 ml.=1 mg. Fe, i.v.) 2d day+restraint (24 hrs.); killed 7th day	Calciphylactic dermatomyositis	1.8	……	……	**0.3**	1.7	**0**	Fig. 222
9	**Vitamin D₃ i.v.+5HT s.c.:** Rat (100 g. ♀): vitamin D₃ (2.5 mg. in 0.25 ml. water, i.v.) 1st day+5HT (2 mg. in 0.5 ml. water, s.c. in throat region) 2d day+restraint (24 hrs.); killed 6th day	Submaxillary gland	2.6	……	……	1.3	**0.5**	1.1	Figs. 223, 224

* The day on which the sensitizer (DHT or vitamin D₃) was administered is considered day 1. The preceding days are indicated as "—," the following days as "+"; accordingly, there is no day —1 or +1 (day 1 being considered "—" during its first and "+" during its second twelve hours).

In this manner our days +2, +3, etc., correspond to what is generally designated as the 2d, 3d, etc., day of an experiment and the corresponding + and − days are equidistant from day 1.

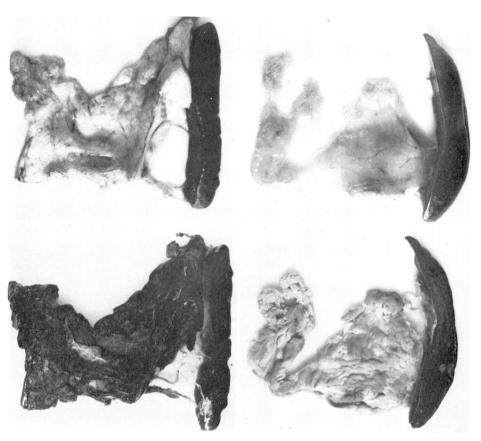

Fig. 214. Prevention by restraint of pancreatic calcinosis produced by DHT + **albumen i.p.** Two rats (100 g. ♀): DHT (1 mg. p.o.) 1st day + albumen (50%, 5 ml. i.p.) 2d day + (right) restraint (24 hours) 1st day; killed 6th day. Intense calcification of entire pancreas (left) inhibited by restraint. *Top*: Fresh. *Bottom*: AgNO₃-stained specimens.

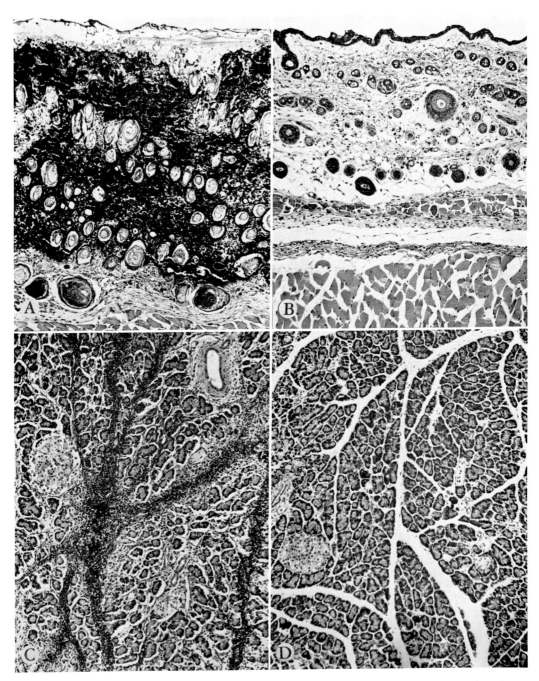

Fig. 215. **Prevention by restraint of cutaneous and pancreatic calcinosis produced by DHT + albumen i.p.** Two rats (100 g. ♀): DHT (1 mg. p.o.) 1st day + albumen (50%, 10 ml. i.p.) 2d day + (right) restraint (17 hours) 1st day; killed 7th day. *A:* Extensive calcinosis of skin in flank region where albumen i.p. causes local lesions by direct diffusion. *B:* Calciphylaxis prevented by restraint. *C:* Extensive calcification and sclerosis of pancreatic stroma. *D:* Prevention of this lesion by restraint. (von Kóssa, ×95.)

be inhibited by restraint. This prophylactic action is manifest only if the stressor is applied during a given limited period (usually the −2d, 1st, or +2d day), although in the case of the DHT + CrCl₃ i.v. syndrome even restraint as early as the −4th day results in a pronounced inhibition.

The responsiveness of various targets to the inhibitory action of restraint differs. For example, in both the DHT + Fe-Din i.v. and the DHT + Thorotrast® i.v. syndromes the facial lesions are less readily prevented by restraint than the esophageal calcinosis.

The inhibitory action of restraint is not due merely to an impairment in the intestinal absorption of the calcifier, since even the syndromes elicited following sensitization by vitamin D₃ i.v. were suppressed by this stressor.

The possibility still remains that restraint acts specifically. The work would have to be repeated with several other stressors to verify this point, but at least we have obtained overwhelming evidence in support of the thesis that restraint does not protect any one target organ selectively, but calciphylactic responsiveness as a whole.

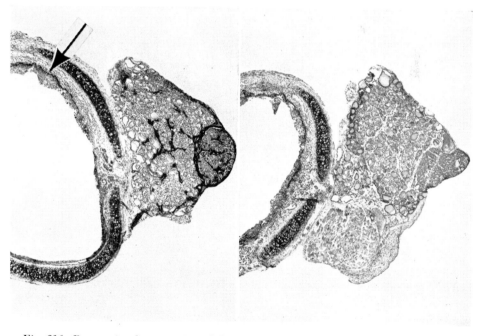

Fig. 216. Prevention by restraint of thyroid and parathyroid calcinosis produced by DHT + CrCl₃ i.v. Two rats (100 g. ♀): DHT (1 mg. p.o.) 1st day + CrCl₃ (8 mg. in 1 ml. water, i.v.) 2d day + (right) restraint (24 hours) 1st day; killed 6th day. *Left:* Intense calcinosis of thyroid and parathyroid stroma, with bandlike calcium deposit in tracheal submucosa (arrow). *Right:* Restraint completely prevented thyro-parathyroid calcification, but not calcinosis of the tracheal submucosa. (von Kóssa, ×29.)

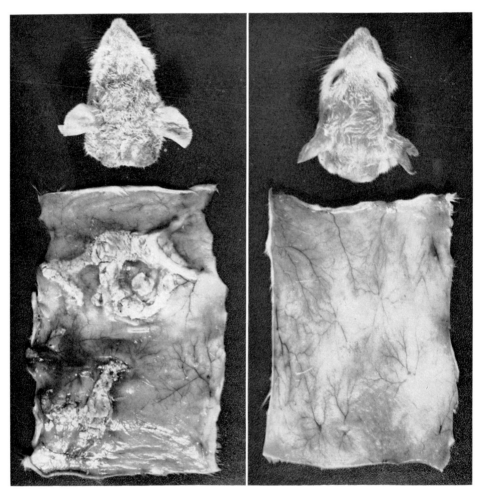

Fig. 217. Prevention by restraint of dermatomyositis produced by DHT + Fe-Dex i.v. + PMX s.c. Two rats (100 g. ♀): DHT (1 mg. p.o.) 2d day + Fe-Dex (1 ml. = 1 mg. Fe, i.v.) 3d day + PMX (500 μg. in 0.2 ml. water, s.c.) 3d day + (right) restraint (24 hours) 1st day; killed 7th day. *Left:* Pronounced inflammation and calcification over head, neck and dorsal skin (the latter viewed from subcutis). *Right:* Morbid changes prevented by restraint.

Fig. 218. **Prevention by restraint of lesions produced by DHT + Fe-Din i.v.** Two rats (100 g. ♀): DHT (1 mg. p.o.) 1st day + Fe-Din (0.5 ml. = 10 mg. Fe, i.v.) 2d day + (bottom) restraint (24 hours) 1st day; killed 7th day. *Top:* Intense calcification of snout, forepaws and esophagus (arrow). *Bottom:* Lesions prevented by restraint.

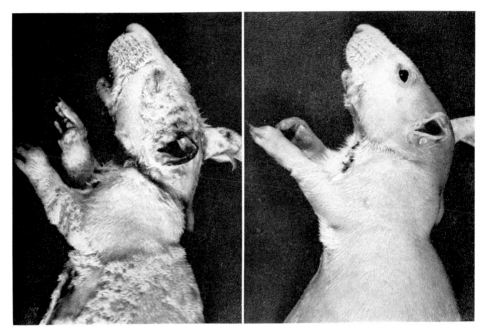

Fig. 219. **Prevention by restraint of cutaneous calcinosis produced by DHT +
Thorotrast® i.v.** Two rats (120 g. ♀): DHT (1 mg. p.o.) 2d day + Thorotrast® (0.6 ml. i.v.)
3d day + (right) restraint (17 hours) 1st and 3d day; killed 7th day. *Left:* Pronounced calcification of skin, especially around mouth, eyes, ears and front paws induced by DHT + Thorotrast®. *Right:* Lesions prevented by restraint. (Cf. Plate VI, *F*.)

(After Selye *et al.*,[845] courtesy Brit. M. J.)

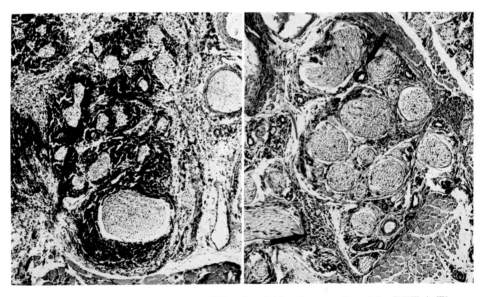

Fig. 220. **Prevention by restraint of facial calcification produced by DHT + Thorotrast® i.v.** Two rats (100 g. ♀): DHT (1 mg. p.o.) 1st day + Thorotrast® (0.3 ml. i.v.) 2d
day + (right) restraint (24 hours) 2d day; killed 6th day. *Left:* Calcification in connective tissue
sheath of facial nerve bundle. *Right:* Lesion almost completely prevented by restraint. Only
small perineural arteries are calcified (upper arrow), although Thorotrast® granules are also
visible in connective tissue (lower arrow). (von Kóssa, ×85.)

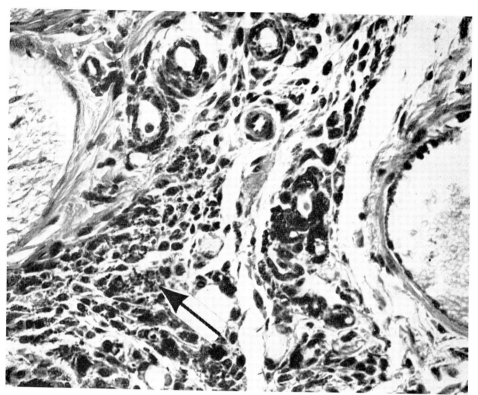

Fig. 221. **Prevention by restraint of facial calcification produced by DHT + Thoro-trast® i.v.** Rat (100 g. ♀): DHT (1 mg. p.o.) 1st day + Thorotrast® (0.3 ml. i.v.) 2d day + restraint (24 hours) 2d day; killed 6th day. Calcification normally produced by Thorotrast® after DHT sensitization almost completely prevented, although numerous Thorotrast® granules are visible in connective tissue (arrow). Only Thorotrast® granules within vascular walls are blackened by calcium stain. (von Kóssa, ×460.)

Finally, it should be kept in mind that stress can also aggravate or indeed elicit a systemic calciphylactic response. As we have said in our description of the calciphylactic syndromes, a selective and intense calcinosis of the thymus is obtained if rats are exposed to restraint three days prior to sensitization by a single oral dose of DHT, perhaps because endogenous challengers are liberated from the disintegrating thymic tissue. At the same time the DHT-induced, cardiovascular and renal calcification tends to be diminished perhaps owing to the deviation of calcium (or of endogenous calcification-promoting substances) to the thymus[863] (Figs. 103, 104, 105; Plate X, *A*). Another calciphylactic syndrome that is readily prevented or aggravated by stress (depending upon timing) is the myocarditis elicited by DHT + NaH_2PO_4 p.o.[821, 823]

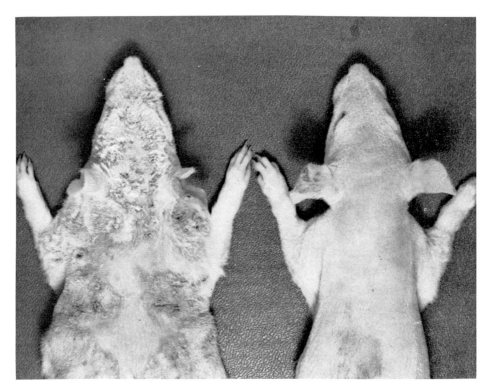

Fig. 222. Prevention by restraint of musculocutaneous lesions produced by vitamin D_3 i.v. + Fe-Dex i.v. + PMX s.c. Two rats (100 g. ♀): vitamin D_3 (2.5 mg. in 0.25 ml. water, i.v. in femoral vein) 1st day + Fe-Dex (1 ml. = 1 mg. Fe, i.v.) 2d day + PMX (500 µg. in 0.2 ml. water, s.c.) 2d day + (right) restraint (24 hours) 2d day; killed 7th day. *Left:* Severe calciphylactic dermatomyositis. *Right:* Lesions completely prevented.

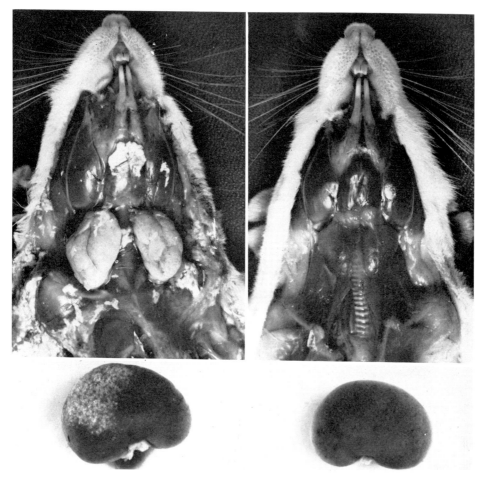

Fig. 223. **Prevention by restraint of salivary gland and renal calcification produced by vitamin D₃ i.v. + 5HT s.c.** Two rats (100 g. ♀): vitamin D₃ (2.5 mg. in 0.25 ml. water, i.v.) 1st day + 5HT (2 mg. in 0.2 ml. water, s.c. in throat region) 2d day + (right) restraint (24 hours) 1st day; killed 7th day. *Left:* Calcification of submaxillary glands, surrounding connective tissue and skin, as well as focal nephrocalcinosis. *Right:* Lesions completely prevented.

Hormones

The endocrine glands undoubtedly exert an important influence upon calciphylactic reactivity. Work along these lines has merely begun, but it is already evident that the pituitary-adrenal system—which we have learned to recognize as a potent regulator of connective-tissue reactions in general—also modifies sensitivity to calciphylaxis. There is reason to believe that other hormones likewise affect this form of tissue response.

Hypophysectomy was performed through the parapharyngeal approach and adrenalectomy through two costovertebral incisions. The techniques of the surgical operations as well as the procedures employed for the preparation of various hormone solutions have been described elsewhere.[823]

Hypophysectomy represents one of the most effective means for the prevention of *topical calciphylaxis* (e.g., that induced by $FeCl_3$, albumen, or plucking of the hair). Here, the operation itself acts as a stressor and corticoids must be given to increase the resistance against the evocative sensitizer and challenger. However, as previously stated, triamcinolone (administered at a dose just sufficient for life maintenance) exerts no inhibitory effect on topical calciphylaxis, and partial hypophysectomy performed as a control operation likewise proved to be ineffective. Hence, the inhibition by hypophysectomy could not be ascribed either to the corticoid treatment or to the stressor effect of the surgical intervention. Finally, the inhibition is most complete if hypophysectomy is performed long before the

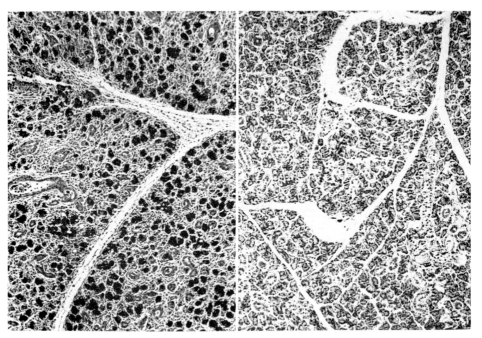

Fig. 224. Prevention by restraint of salivary gland calcification produced by vitamin D_3 i.v. + 5HT s.c. Two rats (100 g. ♀): vitamin D_3 (2.5 mg. in 0.25 ml. water, i.v.) 1st day + 5HT (2 mg. in 0.2 ml. water, s.c. in throat region) 2d day + (right) restraint (24 hours) 2d day; killed 7th day. *Left:* Intense calcification of glandular epithelium with reactive stroma fibrosis. *Right:* Lesion completely prevented by restraint. Here (as in Fig. 223) the protective action of stress cannot be merely due to impaired intestinal absorption of the sensitizer, since vitamin D_3 was administered intravenously. (von Kóssa, ×90.)

calciphylactic treatment rather than if the gland is removed just prior to sensitization; this fact is especially significant because stress prevents topical calciphylaxis best if applied just before challenge[857] (Fig. 225).

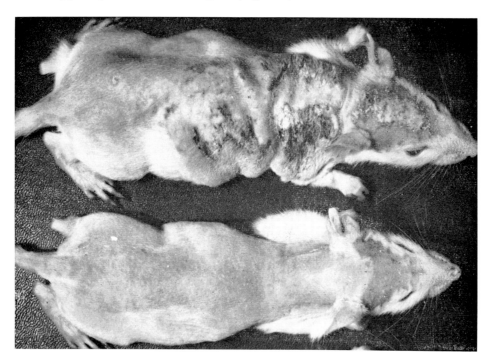

Fig. 225. **Prevention of topical calciphylaxis by hypophysectomy.** *Top:* Intense cutaneous calcinosis at site of plucking (calvarium) and albumen injection (black) in DHT-sensitized, intact rat. *Bottom:* Lesion completely prevented by hypophysectomy.

[After Selye and Jean,[857] courtesy Charles C Thomas Publ. Springfield, Ill. (Endocrinology).]

Only a few observations have been made concerning the effect of hypophysectomy upon *systemic calciphylaxis*, but we do know that the calciphylactic dermatomyositis produced by DHT + Fe-Dex i.v. + PMX s.c. is totally prevented by previous hypophysectomy (Fig. 226).*

The *nonspecific calcinosis induced by DHT alone* is not prevented by hypophysectomy, but its manifestations are altered. In a hypophysectomized animal DHT does not produce the usual "nonspecific calcinosis" but only an almost selective calcification of the renal papilla (Fig. 227).

Little is known about the possible action of exogenous **hypophyseal hormones**

* (*Remark added in proofs.*) Since this manuscript went to the publisher we have shown that the DHT + CrCl₃ i.v. and the DHT + Thorotrast® i.v. syndromes are also prevented by hypophysectomy.

upon calciphylaxis. The topical calcinosis normally induced in the DHT-sensitized rat by plucking of the scalp hair remained uninfluenced by heavy doses of *STH, LTH or vasopressin.*[491] However, the calciphylactic dermatomyositis normally elicited by DHT + Fe-Dex i.v. + PMX s.c. is inhibited by *ACTH*, though far less markedly than by hypophysectomy or by large doses of glucocorticoids.[829a]

In rats sensitized with DHT daily subcutaneous injections of *LAP*, a lyophilized anterior-pituitary preparation, induced calcification and sclerosis of the preputial glands (Fig. 228). This result may be related to the previously described[814] intense preputial-gland-stimulating effect of LAP.

The effect of **adrenalectomy** upon the development of calciphylactic syndromes can be explored only in animals maintained on glucocorticoids; without such substitution therapy rats do not withstand the necessary pretreatment with a sensitizer. However, DHT-sensitized, adrenalectomized rats given maintenance doses of triamcinolone respond normally to *topical challenge* by epilation or the subcutaneous injection of FeCl$_3$.[829a] The inhibition of topical calciphylaxis by the stress of restraint likewise remains uninfluenced by adrenalectomy;[491, 494] evidently this particular effect of stress is not mediated through the adrenals.

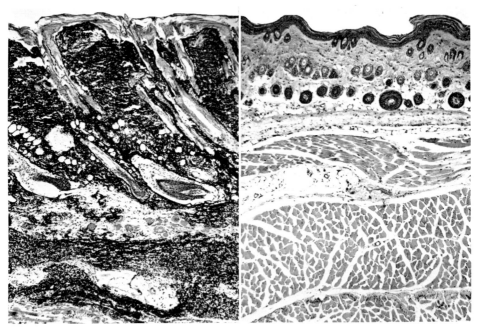

Fig. 226. **Prevention by hypophysectomy of calciphylactic dermatomyositis produced by DHT + Fe-Dex i.v. + PMX s.c.** Two rats (100 g. ♀): DHT (1 mg. p.o.) 1st day + Fe-Dex (1 ml. = 1 mg. Fe, i.v.) 2d day + PMX (2 mg. in 0.2 ml. water, s.c.) 2d day + (right) hypophysectomy 5 days before sensitization; killed 7th day. *Left:* Intense calcium deposition in nuchal skin and underlying striated musculature of intact control. *Right:* Lesion prevented by hypophysectomy. (von Kóssa, ×75.)

Fig. 227. **Papillary nephrocalcinosis produced by hypophysectomy + DHT.** Rat
(100 g. ♀): Hypophysectomy 1st day + triamcinolone (100 μg. in 0.2 ml. water, s.c., for life
maintenance) 1st–14th day + DHT (150 μg. p.o./day) 1st–14th day; killed 15th day. *Top:*
Fresh. *Bottom:* AgNO₅-stained specimens. Calcification (white on fresh, black on stained, specimen) virtually limited to renal papilla in hypophysectomized animal. (In intact rat, nephrocalcinosis is always predominantly cortical.)

It is particularly difficult to appraise the influence of adrenalectomy upon *systemic calciphylaxis*, because very large doses of glucocorticoids must be administered to protect the adrenalectomized animal against the intense stress of DHT + systemic challengers, and some of the systemic syndromes are prevented by glucocorticoid overdosage.

Preliminary observations suggest that the severe calciphylactic dermatomyositis which develops in intact rats (100 g. ♀) treated with DHT (1 mg. p.o.) 1st day + Fe-Dex (1 ml. = 1 mg. Fe, i.v.) 2d day + PMX (2 mg. in 0.2 ml. water, s.c.) 2d day is only partially prevented by pretreatment with triamcinolone (200 µg. in 0.5 ml. water, s.c./day) during one week. If, on the other hand, the rats are adrenalectomized on the day on which triamcinolone treatment begins, the inhibition is virtually complete. Possibly some adrenal principle (perhaps a mineralocorticoid) normally antagonizes the anticalciphylactic action of triamcinolone. Further evidence in support of this view was obtained in adrenalectomized rats

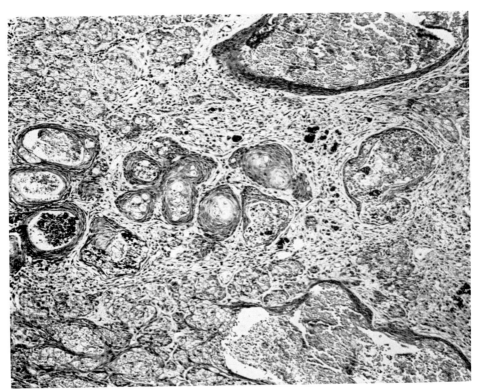

Fig. 228. Calcification and sclerosis of preputial glands produced by DHT + lyophilized anterior pituitary powder (LAP) s.c. (100 g. ♀): DHT (1 mg. p.o.) 1st day + LAP (20 mg. in 0.5 ml. of water, s.c.) 1st–10th day; killed 11th day. Intense sclerosis and moderate calcium deposition in stroma of preputial gland. Small amounts of calcium within ducts and acini. (von Kóssa, ×135.)

which, under otherwise similar circumstances, received DOC (1 mg. in 0.5 ml. water, s.c./day) in addition to the same dose of triamcinolone. Here, the effect of the glucocorticoid was antagonized and the animals responded approximately as markedly as intact controls given triamcinolone alone. Thus, there appears to be a mutual antagonism between triamcinolone and DOC with regard to their influence upon the development of calciphylactic dermatomyositis.[829a]

In intact rats overdosage with **glucocorticoids** (e.g., triamcinolone), far from inhibiting *topical calciphylaxis*, actually tends to aggravate it.[491, 829a]

The effect of glucocorticoids upon *systemic calciphylaxis* has not yet received much attention, but as we have just outlined, the calciphylactic dermatomyositis is inhibited by heavy overdosage with triamcinolone not only in the adrenal-ectomized but to some extent also in the intact rat. However, the antagonism between gluco- and mineralocorticoids, which is so obvious after adrenalectomy, is not evident in the presence of the adrenals, perhaps because the latter normally produce near-optimal amounts of mineralocorticoids.

It should be mentioned, incidentally, that *nonspecific calcinosis*, particularly the calcification of the ascending aorta that is induced by various vitamin-D deriva-tives including DHT, is aggravated by glucocorticoids.[821, 823]

Finally, various glucocorticoids—particularly triamcinolone and 9α-fluorocor-tisol—can cause selective *thymic calcification* if the hormones are given during a sharply limited critical period just before or after a sensitizing dose of DHT.[863] In this respect the effects of glucocorticoids resemble those of stress, presumably be-cause the latter acts upon the thymus through the stimulation of glucocorticoid production.

The effect of sex hormones upon calciphylaxis has likewise not yet received much attention. It could be demonstrated, however, that **estradiol** and **methyl-testosterone** can inhibit the *topical calciphylaxis* produced in the DHT-sensitized rat by plucking of the scalp hair.[491]

Among the *systemic calciphylactic syndromes*, only the uterine calcification pro-duced by DHT + Fe-Dex i.p. has been investigated from this point of view. This lesion is not inhibited by ovariectomy and hence does not appear to depend upon the maintenance of a fully developed uterus. Even in spayed females DHT + Fe-Dex i.p. produces extensive uterine calcinosis often with great dilatation of the lumen owing to the accumulation of a milky fluid rich in calcium (Fig. 229).

Parathyroidectomy does not prevent any form of calciphylactic syndrome produced after sensitization with DHT or parathyroid hormone.[840] But prelimi-nary experiments indicate that the calciphylactic responses that normally develop after sensitization by bilateral nephrectomy and challenge by Thorotrast® i.v. or Fe-OS i.v. are prevented by parathyroidectomy, presumably because here uremia sensitizes through the stimulation of parathyroid hormone secretion.

Fig. 229. Uterine calcification produced by ovariectomy + DHT + Fe-Dex i.p. Rat (190 g. ♀): ovariectomy 1st day + Fe-Dex (1 ml. = 1 mg. Fe, i.p.) 7th day + DHT (1 mg. p.o.) 8th day; killed 13th day. *Left:* Fresh. *Right:* AgNO$_3$-stained specimens. Uterus greatly dilated, filled with milky fluid and completely petrified by massive calcium deposition in its walls.

Nervous Stimuli

Many observations suggest that nervous stimuli play a part in calciphylactic reactions. We have seen that **stress** is an extremely potent regulator of calciphylaxis and, of course, the nervous system is involved in the mediation of stress responses. Furthermore, **neurohumoral substances** and their close derivatives (e.g., IPR, 5HT) can evoke certain calciphylactic syndromes. On purely theoretic grounds it is also probable that **vasomotor nerves** may affect the distribution of blood-borne challengers and thereby influence the pattern of the lesions that these compounds produce.

However, we did not succeed in preventing the DHT + 5HT-induced muscular lesions or topical calciphylactic responses in an extremity by transecting the **spinal cord** or the regional **central nerves**.[865b] Corresponding experiments with autonomic denervation have not yet been performed.

The scleroderma-like lesions normally induced by parathyroid-hormone injections in young rats can be prevented by operations in the thyroid region. This protective effect was ascribed to interference with the **nerves of the thyro-parathyroid apparatus;** but since control operations in other regions were not performed, the stress effect of the intervention could not be excluded.[3]

Removal of the left **superior cervical sympathetic ganglion** protected the left carotid body from calcification in rats subsequently treated with DHT + CrCl$_3$ i.v. Dummy operations had no such effect except when they caused atrophy of the glomus, presumably owing to accidental injury to the organ or its nerves[829a] (Fig. 230). Thyro-parathyroid calcification was not influenced by this operation.

Renal Lesions

As previously stated, **nephrectomy** can sensitize experimental animals for the production of various topical and systemic calciphylactic reactions. We shall see furthermore—in discussing the actions of drugs—that ***nephrotoxic substances,*** such as thallium acetate, can greatly augment the sensitizing action of DHT, for example as regards the production of cutaneous calcinosis by plucking of the scalp hair.[859] Calcinosis may also develop in man as a consequence of ***spontaneous renal diseases,*** particularly if the latter result in uremia. (Cf. p. 397.)

The mechanism through which renal lesions affect calciphylactic responsiveness has not yet been clarified, but it is highly probable that they do so through interference with the urinary elimination of calcium and phosphorus with a concomitant stimulation of parathyroid secretion.

GASTRIC AND ESOPHAGEAL FISTULAS

We have seen that the loss of the gastric or salivary secretions through fistulas sensitizes for the production of calciphylactic reactions by challengers. It is probable that this effect—like that of nephrectomy—is due to a stimulation of parathyroid hormone secretion, although only metabolic changes (e.g., loss of electrolytes, induction of metabolic alkalosis) may also act directly.

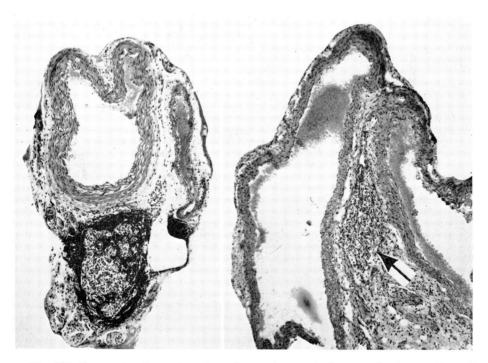

Fig. 230. **Prevention by extirpation of superior cervical sympathetic ganglion of carotid body calcification produced by DHT + CrCl₃ i.v.** Two rats (100 g. ♀): DHT (1 mg. p.o.) 10th day + CrCl₃ (10 mg. in 1 ml. water, i.v.) 11th day + (right) extirpation of superior cervical sympathetic ganglion 1st day; killed 7th day. *Left:* Intense calcification of stroma and capsule of carotid body. *Right:* Calcinosis in carotid body (arrow) completely inhibited by extirpation of ganglion. (von Kóssa, ×80.)

Drugs

Lathyrogenic compounds.—The cutaneous calcinosis induced in DHT-sensitized rats by plucking of the scalp hair—as well as the cardiovascular lesions produced by DHT itself—can be inhibited by pretreatment with comparatively small doses of lathyrogenic compounds, such as aminoacetonitrile (AAN).[833] AAN produces not only pronounced skeletal lesions but also important structural changes in the connective tissue throughout the body; it is not yet clear which one of these actions is responsible for the anticalciphylactic potency.

Thallium salts.—We have seen that in the DHT-sensitized rat thallium salts can induce a nephrocalcinosis sharply limited to the cortico-medullary junction line. Rats so treated also become unusually sensitive to the production of topical cutaneous calcinosis at sites where the hair is plucked.[859] These two effects of thallium salts are probably interrelated in that thallium produces a selective predisposition for nephrocalcinosis and the resulting renal lesion (like nephrectomy and other forms of kidney damage) further increases calciphylactic sensitivity.

2:4-dinitrophenol.—This compound has been found to exert an inhibitory effect on soft tissue calcification induced by calciferol in the rat. It was suggested that this effect of the drug "may be in part at least due to its known effects on adenosine-triphosphate synthesis and adenosine-triphosphatase activity." The authors believe that a similar mechanism might explain our observation that the cardiovascular calcification produced by DHT + sodium phosphate[823] can be prevented by $MgCl_2$, since Mg ions increase adenosine-triphosphatase activity.[400] It must be kept in mind, however, that 2:4-dinitrophenol is a toxic substance and that stress itself can prevent soft-tissue calcification.

Mastocyte dischargers.—Several mastocyte and histamine dischargers have been found to influence calciphylactic syndromes in a decisive manner, but we have no evidence that this effect is actually due to their influence upon histamine metabolism.

The mastocyte granules probably contain many substances in addition to histamine (e.g., 5HT, mucopolysaccharides) and it is uncertain which of these metabolites is principally involved in the regulation of calciphylactic reactions. It is quite clear, however, that pretreatment with large doses of mastocyte dischargers protects the rat against both the topical and the systemic calciphylaxis produced by various challengers. Conversely, even moderate doses of mastocyte dischargers given after calciphylactic sensitization can actually elicit calciphylactic responses. Mastocyte granules are apparently indispensable for the production of various forms of calciphylaxis: if the body is deprived of them by pretreatment with a mastocyte discharger, it fails to react; on the other hand, if an unusually large number of mastocytes are forced to release their granules after sensitization, calciphylactic reactivity increases.

Our most instructive experiments on the prevention (Tables 9 and 10) and the production or aggravation (Tables 11 and 12) of calciphylactic responses are presented in tabular form. As in the preceding tables, only the principal targets selected for the characterization of each syndrome are listed. The mean intensity of the change is gauged in terms of our arbitrary four-grade scale (0–3), except for cutaneous wheals indicative of topical calciphylactic responses for which the magnitude is indicated by their mean diameter (mm.). For calculations of statistical significance and other details the reader is referred to a forthcoming original publication,[837c] but inhibitions to less than half and aggravations to more than double the control values are emphasized by bold numerals.

The data in Table 9 suggest that five days' pretreatment with moderate doses of PMX inhibits some calciphylactic syndromes completely, while in others it prevents only the response of certain target organs or exhibits no inhibitory effect at all. In the DHT + albumen i.p. syndrome (Group 1) both the pancreatic and the cutaneous calcinosis were virtually abolished. The topical calciphylactic wheals produced after DHT sensitization by Fe-Dex and albumen (Group 2), CrCl₃ and

TABLE 9

PREVENTION OF VARIOUS CALCIPHYLACTIC RESPONSES BY PMX (LARGE DOSES)

			RESULTS	
GROUP	TREATMENT	TARGETS	Calci-phylactic Treatment	Same Treatment +PMX
1	**DHT p.o.+albumen i.p.:** Rat (100 g. ♀): DHT (1 mg. p.o.) 1st day+albumen (50%, 5 ml. i.p.) 2d day; killed 6th day	Pancreas Skin Mortality	2.5 1.1 0	**0.2*** **0** 0
2	**DHT p.o.+albumen s.c.+Fe-Dex s.c.:** Rat (100 g. ♀): DHT (1 mg. p.o.) 1st day+albumen (50% 0.2 ml. s.c.) 2d day+Fe-Dex (50 μg. in 0.2 ml. water, s.c.) 2d day; killed 6th day	Skin{Fe-Dex–site {Albumen-site Mortality	20.0 24.2 0	**8.7*** **12.0** 0
3	**DHT p.o.+CrCl₃ s.c.+hemostat:** Rat (100 g. ♀): DHT (1 mg. p.o.) 1st day+CrCl₃ (20 μg. in 0.2 ml. water, s.c.) 2d day+hemostat (applied 20 seconds) 2d day; killed 7th day	Skin{CrCl₃–site {Hemostat-site Mortality	18.4 18.8 0	**5.4†** 3.4 0
4	**DHT p.o.+FeCl₃ s.c.+plucking:** Rat (100 g. ♀): DHT (1 mg. p.o.) 1st day+FeCl₃ (25 μg. in 0.2 ml. water, s.c.) 2d day+plucking of scalp hair, 2d day; killed 7th day	{FeCl₃–site Skin{Site of pluck- { ing Mortality	7.6 2.6 0	**3.2†** 3.0 0
5	**DHT p.o.+5HT i.p.:** Rat (100 g. ♀): DHT (1 mg. p.o.) 1st day+5HT (5 mg. in 0.5 ml. water, i.p.) 2d day; killed 6th day	Salivary gland Muscles Mortality	1.6 0.8 0	**0.9*** 0.1 0
6	**DHT p.o.+yolk i.v.:** Rat (100 g. ♀): DHT (1 mg. p.o.) 1st day+yolk (50%, 3 ml. i.v. ×2) 2d day; killed 4th day	Spleen Liver Mortality	1.3 1.1 0	**0.3†** **0.2** 0

* PMX (300 μg. in 0.2 ml. water, s.c.) on −5th and −4th day + (1 mg. in 0.2 ml. water, s.c. ×2/day) on −3d to 1st day.
† PMX (1 mg. in 0.2 ml. water, s.c. ×2/day) on −5th to 1st day.

trauma with a hemostat (Group 3) or FeCl$_3$ and plucking of the hair (Group 4) were all markedly inhibited but not completely prevented; the same was true of the systemic syndromes produced py DHT + 5HT i.p. (Group 5) or DHT + yolk i.v. (Group 6).

In a second series of experiments in which smaller doses of PMX were given, the inhibitory effect of the mastocyte discharger was sometimes even more obvious (Table 10).

The topical calciphylaxis produced after sensitization with DHT by FeCl$_3$ or albumen s.c. (Group 1) was only moderately (and not statistically significantly) inhibited. The systemic calciphylactic syndrome produced by DHT + CrCl$_3$ i.v. (Group 2) was likewise not significantly affected. The action of DHT + Fe-Dex i.v. (Group 3) upon the pancreas was not affected but here the attendant cutaneous lesions were almost completely prevented. The calciphylactic dermatomyositis induced by DHT + Fe-Dex i.v. + PMX s.c. (Group 4) was virtually abolished. The action of DHT + Fe-Din i.v. (Group 5) upon the esophagus was hardly diminished but the concomitant calcification in the joints, skin, and lips was totally prevented. The DHT + Fe-OS i.v. syndrome (Group 6) was only moderately suppressed while the DHT + Thorotrast® i.v. syndrome (Groups 7 and 8) was almost completely prevented (in two experiments with different doses of Thorotrast®). The DHT + yolk i.v. syndrome (Group 9) was totally abolished as regards both splenic calcinosis and mortality. All these experiments show that certain calciphylactic syndromes, and sometimes within these individual target organ responses, are more readily abolished by PMX pretreatment than others.

Two important problems remain to be solved: (1) whether the apparent refractoriness of certain targets could be overcome by still higher doses of PMX and (2) whether the action of PMX is specific or merely due to its stressor effect. A priori it is conceivable that calcification depends only in certain targets upon a PMX-inhibitable chemical response (e.g., mastocyte discharge). This would explain its selective action. It is also conceivable that PMX acts merely as a stressor, although the amounts given produced much less evidence of stress than would appear to be necessary for the inhibition of calciphylaxis. For example, in control experiments short-term restraint periods (that appeared to induce a degree of stress comparable to that of PMX treatment) proved to be ineffective in preventing calciphylaxis. Yet these findings do not exclude the possibility that PMX may in part act through its stressor action.

If PMX prevents calciphylaxis by virtue of its mastocyte discharging effect, it follows that a sudden discharge of mastocytes after sensitization should have an inverse (sensitizing) effect. To test this possibility we used single doses of 1 or 2 mg. of PMX, given 24 to 48 hours after sensitization.

The results of the experiments with 1 mg. of PMX are summarized in Table 11. As previously stated, normally DHT + CrCl$_2$ i.v. (Group 1) produces no cal-

TABLE 10

Prevention of Various Calciphylactic Responses by PMX (Small Doses)

Group	Treatment	Targets	Results	
			Calci- phylactic Treatment	Same Treatment +PMX*
1	**DHT p.o.+albumen s.c.+FeCl₃ s.c.:** Rat (100 g. ♀): DHT (1 mg. p.o.) 1st day+albumen 10%, 0.2 ml. s.c.) 2d day+FeCl₃ (25 μg. in 0.2 ml. water, s.c.) 2d day; killed 6th day	Skin { FeCl₃-site / Albumen-site } Mortality	18.6 20.0 0	15.0 16.0 0
2	**DHT p.o.+CrCl₃ i.v.:** Rat (100 g. ♀): DHT (1 mg. p.o.) 1st day+CrCl₃ (10 mg. in 1 ml. water, i.v.) 2d day; killed 6th day	Thyroid Parathyroid Carotid body Heart Lung Mortality	1.3 2.2 2.2 1.5 2.2 0	2.1 3.0 2.8 2.0 2.5 0
3	**DHT p.o.+Fe-Dex i.v.:** Rat (100 g. ♀): DHT (1 mg. p.o.) 1st day+Fe-Dex (1 ml.=50 mg. Fe, i.v.) 2d day; killed 6th day	Pancreas Skin Mortality	2.0 2.2 30%	2.2 **0.2** 60%
4	**DHT p.o.+Fe-Dex i.v.+PMX s.c.:** Rat (100 g. ♀): DHT (1 mg. p.o.) 1st day+Fe-Dex (1 ml.=1 mg. Fe, i.v.) 2d day+PMX (2 mg. in 0.2 ml. water, s.c.) 2d day; killed 6th day	Calciphylactic der- matomyositis Mortality	2.4 0	**0.2** 0
5	**DHT p.o.+Fe-Din i.v.:** Rat (100 g. ♀): DHT (1 mg. p.o.) 1st day+Fe-Din (0.5 ml. i.v.) 2d day; killed 6th day	Esophagus Joints Skin Lips Mortality	1.8 1.3 1.6 1.5 50%	1.4 **0** **0** **0** 0
6	**DHT p.o.+Fe-OS i.v.:** Rat (100 g. ♀): DHT (1 mg. p.o.) 1st day+Fe-OS (1 ml.=20 mg. Fe, i.v.) 1st day; killed 6th day	Bile ducts Auricle Mortality	1.2 2.7 0	0.8 1.8 0
7	**DHT p.o.+Thorotrast® i.v.:** Rat (100 g. ♀): DHT (1 mg. p.o.) 1st day+Thorotrast® (100%, 0.4 ml. i.v.) 2d day; killed 6th day	Esophagus Joints Skin Mortality	2.6 1.6 1.0 0	**0** **0** **0.8** 0
8	Rat (100 g. ♀): DHT (1 mg. p.o.) 1st day+Thoro- trast® (100%, 0.3 ml. i.v.) 2d day; killed 6th day	Esophagus Joints Skin Lips Mortality	1.2 0.8 2.0 1.2 0	**0** **0** **0.6** **0.4** 0
9	**DHT p.o.+yolk i.v.:** Rat (100 g. ♀): DHT (1 mg. p.o.) 1st day+yolk (50%, 5 ml. i.v.) 2d day; killed 6th day	Spleen Mortality	2.7 50%	**0** 0

* PMX (300 μg. in 0.2 ml. water, s.c. ×2/day) on −5th to 1st day.

ciphylactic dermatomyositis, yet it can sensitize for the subsequent production of this lesion by PMX. Treatment with DHT + CrCl$_3$ i.v. (Group 2) did not sensitize for the evocation of dermatomyositis by PMX nor were the (thyroid, parathyroid, cardiac, carotid body, and pulmonary) lesions, usually produced by this treatment, consistently altered, but mortality was increased by subsequent administration of the mastocyte discharger. It is especially noteworthy that several other treatments which normally produce calciphylactic lesions other than dermatomyositis can sensitize the rat for the subsequent production of typical dermato-

TABLE 11

PRODUCTION OR AGGRAVATION OF VARIOUS CALCIPHYLACTIC
RESPONSES BY PMX (SMALL DOSES)

| | | | RESULTS | |
GROUP	TREATMENT	TARGETS	Calciphylactic Treatment	Same Treatment +PMX*
1	**DHT p.o.+CrCl$_2$ i.v.:** Rat (100 g. ♀): DHT (500 μg. p.o.) 1st day+CrCl$_2$ (1 ml.=500 μg. Cr, i.v.) 3d day; killed 8th day	Calciphylactic dermatomyositis Mortality	0 10%	**2.7** 60%
2	**DHT p.o.+CrCl$_3$ i.v.:** Rat (100 g. ♀): DHT (500 μg. p.o.) 1st day+CrCl$_3$ (1 ml.=500 μg. Cr, i.v.) 3d day; killed 8th day	Thyroid Parathyroid Heart Carotid body Lung Mortality	0 1.0 0.4 0.9 0.6 0	0 0.5 **1.4** 0.3 **1.7** 70%
3	**DHT p.o.+FeCl$_2$ i.v.:** Rat (100 g. ♀): DHT (500 μg. p.o.) 1st day+FeCl$_2$ (1 ml.=500 μg. Fe, i.v.) 3d day; killed 8th day	Calciphylactic dermatomyositis Mortality	0 0	**1.7** 30%
4	**DHT p.o.+FeCl$_3$ i.v.:** Rat (100 g. ♀): DHT (500 μg. p.o.) 1st day+FeCl$_3$ (1 ml.=500 μg. Fe, i.v.) 3d day; killed 8th day	Calciphylactic dermatomyositis Mortality	0 0	**2.4** 20%
5	**DHT p.o.+Fe-Dex i.v.:** Rat (100 g. ♀): DHT (500 μg. p.o.) 1st day+Fe-Dex (1 ml.=500 μg. Fe, i.v.) 3d day; killed 8th day	Calciphylactic dermatomyositis Mortality	0 0	**0.6** 0
6	**DHT p.o.+Fe-Din i.v.:** Rat (100 g. ♀): DHT (500 μg. p.o.) 1st day+Fe-Din (1 ml.=500 μg. Fe, i.v.) 3d day; killed 8th day	Calciphylactic dermatomyositis Lips Mortality	0 0 10%	**0.1** **1.1** 10%
7	**DHT p.o.+Fe-OS i.v.:** Rat (100 g. ♀): DHT (500 μg. p.o.) 1st day+Fe-OS (1 ml.=500 μg. Fe, i.v.) 3d day; killed 8th day	Calciphylactic dermatomyositis Lips Mortality	0 0 10%	**0.3** **0.2** 10%
8	**DHT p.o.+Fe-Sol i.v.:** Rat (100 g. ♀): DHT (500 μg. p.o.) 1st day+Fe-Sol (1 ml.=500 μg. Fe, i.v.) 3d day; killed 8th day	Calciphylactic dermatomyositis Mortality	0 0	**0.2** 0

* PMX (1 mg. in 0.2 ml. water, s.c.) 3d day.

myositis by PMX (Groups 3 to 5). Fe-Din, Fe-OS, and Fe-Sol (Groups 6 to 8) had no such sensitizing effect, the occasional trace of dermatomyositic change not being in excess of what might have been expected from treatment with DHT and PMX alone.

We then proceeded to explore the possibility of producing more clear-cut results by doubling the dose of PMX; our relevant experiments are summarized in Table 12.

A single dose of 2 mg. of PMX given on the second or third day after DHT greatly aggravated at least some of the lesions otherwise obtained by DHT + albumen i.p. (Groups 1 and 2), DHT + albumen i.v. (Groups 3 and 4), DHT + $CrCl_2$ i.v. (Group 5), DHT + $CrCl_3$ i.v. (Group 6), DHT + $FeCl_2$ i.v. (Group 7) and DHT + $FeCl_3$ i.v. (Group 8). In addition to the accentuation of the lesions that are characteristic of treatment with these agents, severe calciphylactic dermatomyositis occurred following the administration of various compounds which normally do not produce such lesions (Groups 5, and 7 to 14). It may be concluded therefore that the so-called "calciphylactic dermatomyositis" does not necessarily depend on what we have called siderocalciphylactic treatment; in the present series of experiments not only a great variety of iron compounds but even $CrCl_2$ (Group 5) or yolk (Group 14) proved to be highly effective in preparing the rat for the subsequent production of dermatomyositis by a subsequent single injection of PMX.

AGE AND SEX

Age.—Many of the observations reported in this volume have shown that sensitivity to calcifying agents (e.g., DHT, parathyroid hormone) in general and to calciphylactic responses in particular largely depends upon the age of the experimental animal. It would be redundant to describe these findings again in detail here, but it may be well to enumerate them synoptically.

Our earliest observations have shown that the administration of irradiated ergosterol to mother rats during pregnancy or lactation produces much severer osseous lesions in the embryo or newborn than in the maternal organism.[806, 811] Young rats also proved more sensitive to the production of osteitis fibrosis by parathyroid hormone than adults.[808] Moreover it was noted even before we knew that *topical challenge* is necessary for the production of cutaneous calcinosis that scleroderma-like skin lesions can be produced by parathyroid hormone[809, 810] or DHT,[819] without intentional challenge, only if the animals are very young. In retrospect we realize that even here accidental local challenge probably played a role (e.g., the *trauma* incident to holding the young rat by the nape of the neck), but in any event, comparable injuries were ineffective in adults.

More recently, it was found that sensitivity to the cutaneous calcinosis induced by *epilation* or $FeCl_3$ s.c. is inversely proportional to sensitivity to the nonspecific calcinosis (e.g., cardiovascular or renal calcification) produced by DHT overdosage

TABLE 12

PRODUCTION OR AGGRAVATION OF VARIOUS CALCIPHYLACTIC
RESPONSES BY PMX (LARGE DOSES)

GROUP	TREATMENT	TARGETS	RESULTS	
			Calciphylactic Treatment	Same Treatment +PMX
1	**DHT p.o.+albumen i.p.:** Rat (100 g. ♀): DHT (1 mg. p.o.) 1st day+albumen (25%, 4 ml. i.p.) 2d day; killed 6th day	Pancreas Skin Mortality	0 0.8 0	1.0* 2.4 0
2	Rat (100 g. ♀): DHT (1 mg. p.o.) 1st day+albumen (50%, 5 ml. i.p.) 2d day; killed 6th day	Pancreas Skin Mortality	1.0 0.2 0	2.5* 1.4 10%
3	**DHT p.o.+albumen i.v.:** Rat (100 g. ♀): DHT (1 mg. p.o.) 1st day+albumen (25%, 5 ml. i.v.) 2d day; killed 6th day	Pancreas Skin Mortality	0 0.4 0	0* 1.6 0
4	Rat (100 g. ♀): DHT (1 mg. p.o.) 1st day+albumen (50%, 2 ml. i.v.) 2d day; killed 6th day	Pancreas Skin Mortality	0 0.1 10%	0* 1.0 0
5	**DHT p.o.+$CrCl_2$ i.v.:** Rat (100 g. ♀): DHT (500 μg. p.o.) 1st day+$CrCl_2$ (1 ml.=1 mg. Cr, i.v.) 3d day; killed 7th day	Calciphylactic dermatomyositis Thyroid Parathyroid Carotid body Heart Mortality	0 0 0 0 0.1 0	2.6† 0.5 1.5 0 0.3 30%
6	**DHT p.o.+$CrCl_3$ i.v.:** Rat (100 g. ♀): DHT (1 mg. p.o.) 1st day+$CrCl_3$ (1 mg. in 1 ml. water, i.v.) 2d day; killed 6th day	Thyroid Parathyroid Carotid body Heart Lung Mortality	0.6 1.6 0.6 0.4 0.4 0	1.5* 2.1 1.4 1.3 0.7 20%
7	**DHT p.o.+$FeCl_2$ i.v.:** Rat (100 g. ♀): DHT (500 μg. p.o.) 1st day+$FeCl_2$ (1 ml.=1 mg. Fe, i.v.) 3d day; killed 7th day	Calciphylactic dermatomyositis Thyroid Parathyroid Carotid body Heart Lung Mortality	0 0 0 0 0 0 40%	1.5† 1.0 0 0 1.5 2.2 80%
8	**DHT p.o.+$FeCl_3$ i.v.:** Rat (100 g. ♀): DHT (500 μg. p.o.) 1st day+$FeCl_3$ (1 ml.=1 mg. Fe, i.v.) 3d day; killed 7th day	Calciphylactic dermatomyositis Heart Mortality	0 0.3 0	1.5† 1.5 0
9	**DHT p.o.+Fe-Dex i.v.:** Rat (100 g. ♀): DHT (500 μg. p.o.) 1st day+Fe-Dex (1 ml.=1 mg. Fe, i.v.) 3d day; killed 7th day	Calciphylactic dermatomyositis Mortality	0 30%	1.4† 70%
10	**DHT p.o.+Fe-Din i.v.:** Rat (100 g. ♀): DHT (500 μg. p.o.) 1st day+Fe-Din (1 ml.=1 mg. Fe, i.v.) 3d day; killed 7th day	Calciphylactic dermatomyositis Esophagus Lips Mortality	0 0 0 0	2.4† 0 2.1 0

* PMX (2 mg. in 0.2 ml. water, s.c.) 2d day.　　　　† PMX (2 mg. in 0.2 ml. water, s.c.) 3d day.

TABLE 12—*Continued*

Group	Treatment	Targets	Calci-phylactic Treatment	Same Treatment +PMX
			Results	
11	**DHT p.o.+Fe-OS i.v.:** Rat (100 g. ♀): DHT (500 μg. p.o.) 1st day+Fe-OS (1 ml.=1 mg. Fe, i.v.) 3d day; killed 7th day	Calciphylactic dermatomyositis	0	**1.0†**
		Lips	0	**0.4**
		Mortality	0	0
12	Rat (100 g. ♀): DHT (1 mg. p.o.) 1st day+Fe-OS (1 ml.=5 mg. Fe, i.v.) 2d day; killed 6th day	Calciphylactic dermatomyositis	0.1	**2.7***
		Auricle	1.1	0
		Mortality	0	10%
13	**DHT p.o.+Fe-Sol i.v.:** Rat (100 g. ♀): DHT (500 μg. p.o.) 1st day+Fe-Sol (1 ml.=1 mg. Fe, i.v.) 3d day; killed 7th day	Calciphylactic dermatomyositis	0	**2.3†**
		Mortality	0	50%
14	**DHT p.o.+yolk i.v.:** Rat (100 g. ♀): DHT (1 mg. p.o.) 1st day+yolk (25%, 1.5 ml. i.v.) 2d day; killed 6th day	Calciphylactic dermatomyositis	0.4	**2.8***
		Mortality	0	20%

in different age groups: the younger the animal, the more sensitive it is to cutaneous calcinosis and the less sensitive to nonspecific calcinosis.[491]

In the preceding chapter we met with numerous examples that illustrate the importance of the age factor in **systemic calciphylaxis.** Thus, *albumen i.p.* produced the three characteristic (sternal and costovertebral) cutaneous calciphylactic plaques only in young animals presumably because the challenger cannot readily diffuse to the skin through the thick abdominal musculature of fully grown rats. Conversely, *Fe-Dex i.p. or i.v.* produces uterine calcification only in older rats, and *Thorotrast® i.v.* causes more intense calcinosis of the joints in fully grown than in young animals. The older rat is also more sensitive to the production of calciphylactic muscular dystrophy by *5HT* or bile-duct calcinosis by Fe-OS.

The participation of the age factor in calciphylactic sensitization by bilateral *nephrectomy* is more difficult to assess because young rats do not survive this intervention as long as older animals; however, the severity of calcinosis produced by this operation (with or without calciphylactic challenge) increases with progressing age.

All these observations illustrate the importance of the age factor but they also show that no general statement can be made in this respect, since some forms of calcinosis can be produced more readily in young, others in old, animals.

It may be mentioned, incidentally, that even the cutaneous calcification produced by *direct calcifiers* (e.g., KMnO₄ s.c.) depends upon age. Young rats (50 g.) are particularly sensitive; old animals (300 g. or more), totally refractory.[863a]

Sex.—Most of our work has been performed on female rats, but as far as available evidence goes, both sexes are approximately equally sensitive to calciphy-lactic reactions. Yet, sex undoubtedly plays a role, since some forms of calciphy-laxis affect sex organs (e.g., the uterus, preputial glands) selectively and over-dosage with sex hormones (e.g., estrogens, androgens) can influence calciphylactic reactivity. (Cf. p. 281.)

SPECIES

Most of our work was performed on a single species—the rat—in order to obtain strictly intercomparable results; we had to show, however, that calciphylactic re-activity is not limited to this rodent. Comparative pathologic studies were per-formed only on eight to twelve animals of each species, without much regard to age, breed, or sex, using but a few of those calciphylactic techniques that most reliably produced very intense changes and did not exhibit a sharply limited "critical period." Since nothing was known about the calciphylactic sensitivity of species other than the rat or of the "critical period," which may well be different in diverse species, we merely wanted to perform a few tests under what a priori appeared to be the most favorable experimental conditions.[866a]

The experimental techniques used were essentially the same as those employed for the rat except that the dosages of both the active ingredients and the solvents had to be adjusted to the vastly varying body weight. Hence, in this section we shall register even such details as the amount of oil employed as a solvent for DHT.

Topical calciphylaxis of the skin could be produced in many species.

In the *cat* (2,010–2,820 g. ♂ or ♀ treated with DHT, 4 mg. in 0.5 ml. corn oil/100 g., p.o., subcutaneous challenge with 2 ml. of a 50% yolk solution, Fe-Dex, 2 ml. = 100 mg. Fe, or $FeCl_3$, 2 mg. in 2 ml. water, 2d day; killed 6th day) cal-cification at the injection sites was detectable. On the other hand, no response could be obtained under otherwise similar circumstances at subcutaneous sites challenged by albumen (50%, 2 ml.).

In the *dog* (4,320–7,800 g. ♂ or ♀ sensitized with DHT, 2 mg. in 0.5 ml. corn oil/100 g., p.o., 1st day and challenged by subcutaneous injection of Fe-Dex, 2 ml. = 50 mg., and $FeCl_3$, 2 mg. in 2 ml. water, or 2 ml. of a 50% yolk solution, 2d day; killed 6th day) calciphylactic responses were also obtained at all injection sites; but in this species calcium deposition was comparatively mild, while necrosis of the subcutaneous and dermal collagen with subsequent polynuclear leukocytic infiltration was quite evident. Thus, the skin lesions here assumed a predomi-nantly acute, inflammatory character. Challenge by albumen (50%, 2 ml.) pro-duced no obvious local reaction in these dogs.

In the *golden hamster* (80 g. ♀, sensitized with DHT, 2 mg. in 0.5 ml. corn oil/100 g., p.o., 1st day + Fe-Dex, 0.2 ml. = 10 mg. Fe, 2d day; killed 6th day) the cutaneous histologic changes were almost exactly the same as those elicited under comparable conditions in the rat (Fig. 231). Similar lesions were obtained under the same circumstances by s.c. challenge with $FeCl_3$ (200 µg. in 0.2 ml. water) and yolk (50%, 0.2 ml.).

In the *monkey* (2,310–2,340 g. ♂ or ♀, sensitized with DHT, 10 mg/100 g., p.o., 1st day and subcutaneously challenged by $FeCl_3$, 2 mg. in 2 ml. water, and Fe-Dex, 2 ml. = 50 mg. Fe, or 2 ml. of a 50% solution of yolk or albumen 2d day) topical calcinosis was very mild but present at all injection sites. Thus, it appears that even the primate is sensitive to calciphylaxis.

In the *mouse* (20 g. ♂ or ♀ sensitized with DHT, 2 mg. in 0.5 ml. corn oil/100 g., p.o., 1st day + Fe-Dex, 0.1 ml. = 5 mg. Fe, 2d day; killed 6th day) the result was the same, although here calcinosis was almost completely limited to the subcutaneous tissue and did not tend to penetrate into the derma (Fig. 232). Similar though less constant lesions were produced after this form of sensitization by $FeCl_3$ (100 µg. in 0.1 ml. water, s.c.) or yolk (50%, 0.1 ml. s.c.).

Systemic calciphylaxis can likewise be elicited in a variety of laboratory animals besides the rat.

This proved to be possible, for example, in the *cat* (2,200–4,800 g. ♂ or ♀ by sensitization with DHT, 4 mg. in 0.5 ml. corn oil/100 g., p.o., 1st day + $CrCl_3$, 10 mg/100 g. in 1 ml. water, i.v., 2d day). Although most of the animals died during

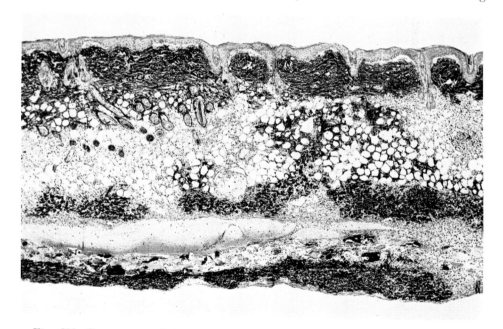

Fig. 231. Cutaneous calcinosis produced by DHT + Fe-Dex s.c. in the hamster. Golden hamster (80 g. ♀): DHT (2 mg. in 0.5 ml. corn oil/100 g. body weight, p.o.) 1st day + Fe-Dex (0.2 ml. = 10 mg. Fe., s.c.) 2d day; killed 6th day. Intense cutaneous calcinosis, especially affecting horizontal collagen fibers underneath epidermis but subcutaneous connective and fat tissue also affected. (von Kóssa, ×39.)

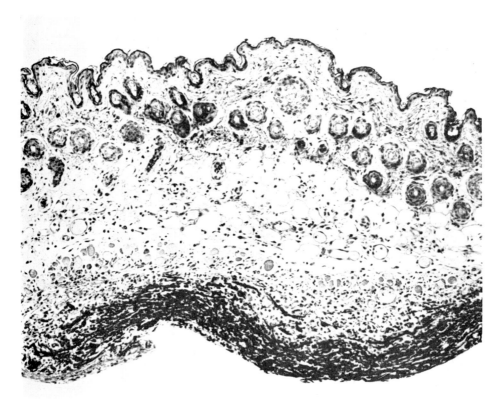

Fig. 232. Cutaneous calcinosis produced by DHT + Fe-Dex s.c. in the mouse. Swiss mouse (20 g. ♀): DHT (2 mg. in 0.5 ml. corn oil/100 g. body weight, p.o) 1st day + Fe-Dex (0.1 ml. = 5 mg. Fe, s.c.) 2d day; killed 6th day. Calcium deposition is predominantly subcutaneous and appears to follow horizontal connective-tissue fibers. (von Kóssa, ×135.)

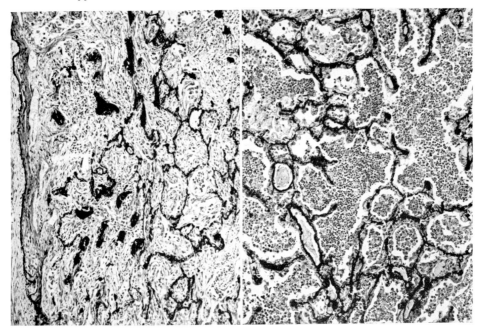

Fig. 233. Pulmonary calcinosis with suppuration and fibrosis produced by DHT + CrCl₃ i.v. in the cat. Cat (2390 g. ♀): DHT (10 mg/100 g. p.o.) 1st day + CrCl₃ (10 mg/100 g., i.v.) 2d day; died 4th day. *Left:* Marked calcification of pulmonary septa with intense reactive fibrosis in one region. *Right:* Calcinosis with suppuration in another region. (von Kóssa, ×70.)

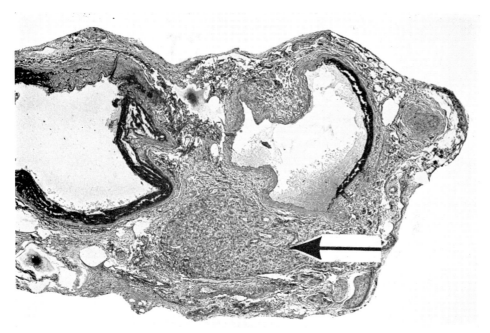

Fig. 234. Calcinosis of carotid bifurcation produced by DHT + CrCl₃ i.v. in the cat.
Cat (4530 g.♂) DHT (10 mg/100 g., in 0.5 ml. corn oil, p.o.) 1st day + CrCl₃ (10 mg/100 g., in 1.0 ml. water, i.v.) 2d day; died 3d day. Calcification of internal and external carotid artery, while carotid body (arrow) remains intact. (von Kóssa, ×41.)

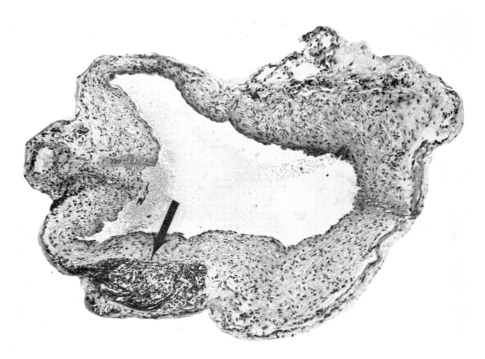

Fig. 235. Calcinosis of carotid body produced by DHT + CrCl₃ i.v. in the guinea pig.
Guinea pig (230 g. ♀): DHT (2.5 mg/100 g., in 1 ml. corn oil, p.o.) 1st day + CrCl₃ (10 mg. in 0.5 ml. water, i.v.) 2d day; died 5th day. Carotid body (arrow), embedded in arterial wall, exhibits selective calcification of stroma. (von Kóssa, ×120.)

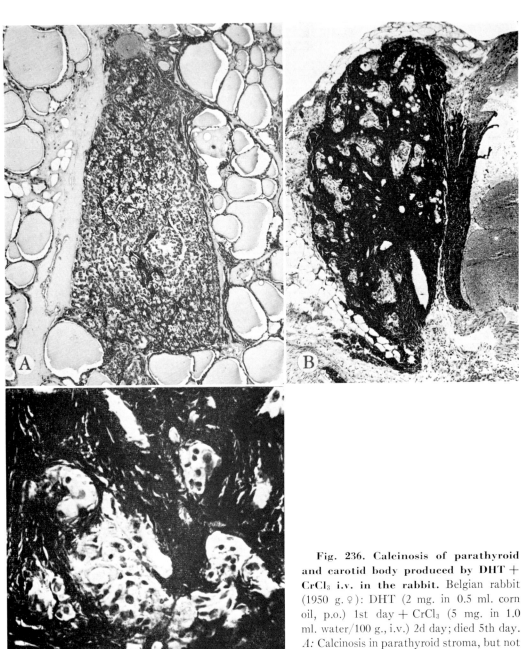

Fig. 236. Calcinosis of parathyroid
and carotid body produced by DHT +
CrCl₃ i.v. in the rabbit. Belgian rabbit
(1950 g. ♀): DHT (2 mg. in 0.5 ml. corn
oil, p.o.) 1st day + CrCl₃ (5 mg. in 1.0
ml. water/100 g., i.v.) 2d day; died 5th day.
A: Calcinosis in parathyroid stroma, but not
in surrounding thyroid. (von Kóssa, ×120.)
B: Intense calcinosis of carotid body and
adjacent arterial wall. (von Kóssa, ×100.)
C: Necrosis without calcinosis in specific cells
of carotid body, combined with intense calcification of surrounding stroma. (von Kóssa,
×360.)

296

the first week, obvious calcification of the pulmonary septa was seen as early as the 4th day. The calcinosis led to suppuration in some regions and to fibrosis in other portions of the lung, so that the picture was quite varied even in the same animal (Fig. 233). The intense reactive fibrosis elicited in this manner greatly resembled that seen in some cases of essential pulmonary fibrosis in man. There were also a few calcium casts in the kidney, but no noteworthy calcinosis was found in the heart, pancreas, or the carotid body (even when the adjacent carotid arteries were severely calcified) (Fig. 234). Brunner's glands were almost invariably very heavily calcified in this species.

In the *dog* (4,410–7,960 g. ♂ or ♀, treated with DHT, 4 mg. in 0.5 ml. corn oil, p.o., 1st day + $CrCl_3$, 10 mg. in 0.5 ml. water/100 g., i.v., 2d day; killed 5th day) there was moderate calcification of the parathyroids and thyroids, but not of the carotid body.* Other organs merely showed evidence of nonspecific calcinosis owing to DHT overdosage.

In the *golden hamster* (140–145 g. ♂ or ♀ given DHT, 2 mg/100 g., p.o., 1st day + $CrCl_3$, 10 mg. in 0.5 ml. water/100 g., i.v., 2d day; killed 5th day) there was usually pronounced calcification of the parathyroids, stomach, heart, and kidney (cortical) with less marked calcinosis in the thyroid, duodenum, and trachea.

In the *guinea pig* (200–250 g. ♂ or ♀ given DHT, 3 mg. in 1 ml. corn oil/100 g., p.o., 1st day + $CrCl_3$, 10 mg. in 0.5 ml. water, i.v., 2d day) calcinosis of the carotid body and pulmonary septa was virtually constant and usually very intense (Fig. 235). In other organs calcification was much more irregular.

In the *rabbit* (1,700–2,100 g. ♂ or ♀ treated with DHT, 2 mg. in 0.5 ml. corn oil/100 g., p.o., 1st day + $CrCl_3$, 5 mg. in 1 ml. water/100 g., i.v., 2d day) there was always very pronounced calcification of the parathyroid (Fig. 236), cardiovascular system, kidney, diaphragm, pulmonary septa, and Brunner's glands. The thyroid itself was rarely calcified except occasionally in the immediate surroundings of the parathyroid.

Even these few observations suffice to show that calciphylaxis is not merely a species-specific peculiarity of the rat.

---

* Pronounced carotid body calcinosis was obtained, however, in dogs when, under otherwise similar conditions, $CrCl_3$ (3 mg/100 g., i.v.) was given on the −3d and again on the 1st day.

V

Direct Calcifiers

We have defined direct calcifiers as substances which produce topical tissue calcification at the site of administration even without previous sensitization. Many
substances can act as challengers for topical calcinosis in the DHT-sensitized animal, but until quite recently only KMnO$_4$ had been shown to act in this manner
even in unsensitized rats[865] (Fig. 237). We now know that numerous inorganic and
some organic compounds share this property,[864] but in most of the relevant work
KMnO$_4$ is used as a standard test substance because it is comparatively free of
local or systemic toxic effects at the dose levels required to produce direct tissue
calcification. Accordingly, in our description we shall consider KMnO$_4$ as the pro-
totype of the direct calcifiers; what we have learned about its actions probably
also applies to most other inorganic salts of this series.

KMnO$_4$.—In the rat, as little as 5–10 μg. of KMnO$_4$ (in 0.2 ml. of water, s.c.)
suffices to produce a readily visible wheal of local calcification. Young animals are
particularly suitable for this type of study because of their great sensitivity to
direct calcifiers and because the development of the calcified white patch can easily
be seen through their translucent skin if the hair is removed by shaving or
plucking.

To study the **histogenesis** of this lesion, KMnO$_4$ (100 μg. in 0.2 ml. water, s.c.)
was injected at different points on the back of 100 g. rats every second day between the 1st and 11th days. The animals were killed on the 12th day. Specimens
of the skin at each injection site were fixed in alcohol-formol for subsequent staining with the von Kóssa procedure.

Twenty-four hours after the injection the treated region merely revealed some
edema and a slight infiltration with histiocytes and polymorphonuclear leukocytes.
Eosinophils were rare. The mastocytes swelled and discharged their granules, but
did not tend to accumulate within the injection sites, although many mastocytes
were seen in the periphery of these foci. Precipitation of calcium salts could be
detected at this time only in 20 per cent of the animals; these appeared to have
responded somewhat more rapidly than the rest and revealed the very first stages
of KMnO$_4$-induced tissue calcification. In these animals the inflammatory exudate
became more cellular with a definite predominance of polymorphonuclear leukocytes; it was rich in basophilic nuclear debris and contained a slightly granular

298

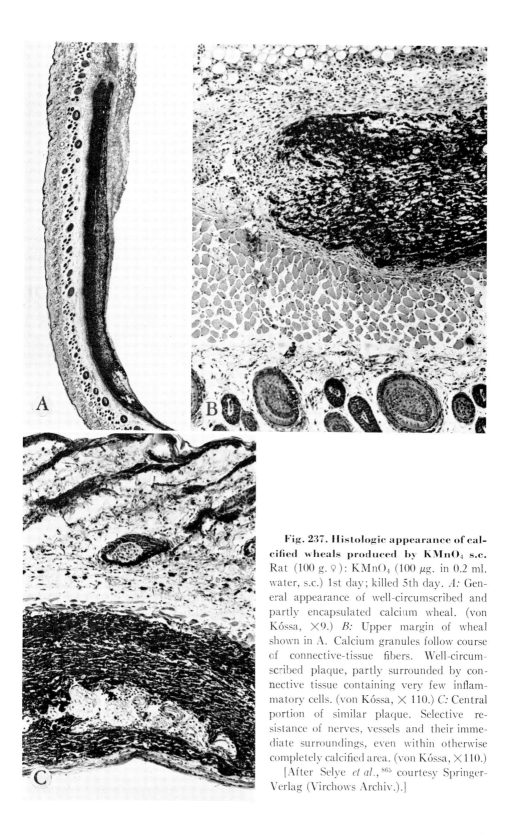

Fig. 237. Histologic appearance of calcified wheals produced by KMnO₄ s.c. Rat (100 g. ♀): KMnO₄ (100 μg. in 0.2 ml. water, s.c.) 1st day; killed 5th day. *A:* General appearance of well-circumscribed and partly encapsulated calcium wheal. (von Kóssa, ×9.) *B:* Upper margin of wheal shown in A. Calcium granules follow course of connective-tissue fibers. Well-circumscribed plaque, partly surrounded by connective tissue containing very few inflammatory cells. (von Kóssa, × 110.) *C:* Central portion of similar plaque. Selective resistance of nerves, vessels and their immediate surroundings, even within otherwise completely calcified area. (von Kóssa, ×110.)

[After Selye *et al.*,[865] courtesy Springer-Verlag (Virchows Archiv.).]

eosinophilic precipitate. At this stage the mastocytes disappeared completely from the foci and the first traces of calcium appeared on the collagen fibers.

By the third day the injected spots were fully calcified in all cases. The calcium deposits formed a regular meshwork of calcified collagen fibers; the interstices between these were occupied by fibroblasts and a few inflammatory cells. However, by this time the inflammatory response had largely subsided and only occasional polymorphonuclear leukocytes and histiocytes remained, particularly at the edges of the wheals just outside the calcified areas.

During the next few days calcification progressed slowly, having almost reached its maximum by the third day. However, the lesions became increasingly more solid owing to the gradual absorption of both the cellular and liquid exudates within and around the calcified plaque.

Between the sixth and twelfth days, organization and absorption of the focus had begun. The calcified fibers tended to break up into small fragments, the interstices between the fibers being invaded by fibroblasts; concurrently, smaller particles of calcium were ingested by polynuclear foreign-body giant cells of different sizes (Fig. 238).

It is still uncertain whether there is any fundamental ***relationship between this direct calcifying effect and calciphylaxis.*** Histologically, the cutaneous calcinosis induced by these two techniques is very similar, but not identical. Calcification of the skin, whether elicited by calciphylaxis or by $KMnO_4$, affects primarily the connective-tissue fibers. However, in most forms of calciphylaxis the outlines of the wheals are less sharply limited and there is a greater tendency for involvement of the dermis with subsequent ulceration than if a calcinosis of equal intensity is produced by $KMnO_4$. This difference is especially obvious in the case of extensive subcutaneous infiltrations conducive to widespread calcinosis of the skin; when induced by calciphylactic challengers after sensitization this procedure invariably results in generalized exfoliation of the affected skin regions, while extensive or frequently repeated injections of $KMnO_4$ can produce a subcutaneous calcified layer involving virtually the entire body without affecting the dermis. Here, the most superficial layers of the skin remain well nourished (indeed they tend to be hyperemic) and even accidental wounds heal promptly. There is no scaling and little or no hardening of the skin with inflammation and sclerosis, such as characterize calciphylactic and particularly siderocalciphylactic reactions. Furthermore, in the case of repeated treatment, sensitivity to $KMnO_4$ is well maintained without obvious signs of the acquired resistance characteristic of calciphylaxis.[865] If $KMnO_4$ is used as a subcutaneous challenger in DHT-sensitized rats, the resulting calcified plaques are not only larger than otherwise but they also assume the typical characteristics of calciphylactic wheals (involvement of the dermis, scaling and ulceration).

In comparing directly induced calcification with calciphylaxis, we must also

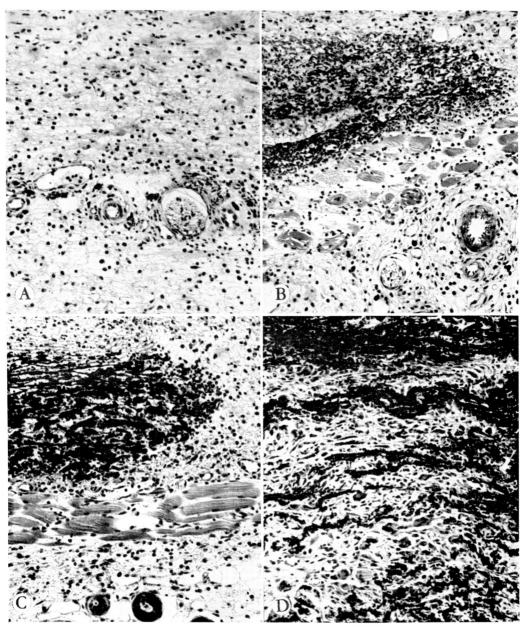

Fig. 238. Histogenesis of direct calcification produced by KMnO₄ s.c. Rat (100 g. ♀):
KMnO₄ (100 μg. in 0.2 ml. s.c. at various sites on back) injected in *A:* 6th day; *B:* 5th day;
C: 4th day and *D:* 1st day; killed 7th day. Initial mild inflammatory reaction, rapidly followed
by more or less diffuse calcium precipitation, gradually leading to selective incrustation of
collagen fibers and eventually to sclerosis with giant-cell formation. (von Kóssa, ×160.)

keep in mind that both these reaction forms have a definite protective or "phylactic" value. The **topical resistance** induced by calciphylactic means will be discussed later. Let us point out here, however, that a circumscribed subcutaneous calcinotic wheal produced by a direct calcifier in the absence of sensitization also offers considerable protection against the subsequent induction of necrosis by a strong irritant[863a] (Figs. 239, 240). This type of protection is by no means a specific attribute of the calcinotic reaction forms; many types of non-specific tissue injury can either increase or decrease topical resistance to subsequently applied agents.[825] Yet, in evaluating the functional significance of calcinosis, it is noteworthy that calcium incrustation of tissues can augment their capacity to protect adjacent structures against injury.

We have seen that **hypophysectomy,** exposure to **stress** at the proper time, and in some instances even **glucocorticoid** treatment, can prevent calciphylactic reactions. The $KMnO_4$-induced calcinosis is likewise inhibited by hypophy-

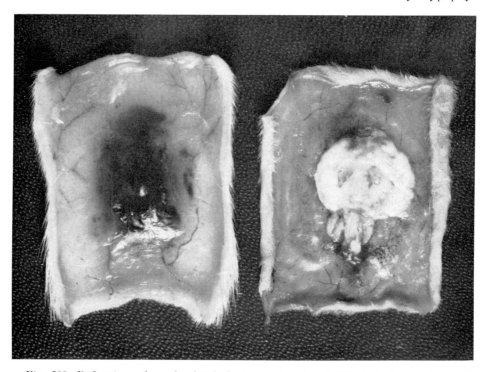

Fig. 239. Defensive value of calciphylaxis produced by DHT + CrCl₂ s.c. Two rats (100 g. ♀): DHT (1 mg. p.o.) 1st day + croton oil (5%, 0.2 ml. olive oil, s.c. in dorsal region) 6th day + (right) $CrCl_2$ (50 μg. in 0.5 ml. water s.c. on back) 2d day; killed 10th day. Sub-cutaneous aspect of dorsal skin. *Left:* Croton oil produced marked hemorrhagic necrosis and edema in unpretreated rat. *Right:* The experimental animal developed a typical white calciphylactic wheal, but it was virtually insensitive to topical action of irritant, in spite of heavy calcium incrustation.

sectomy, but it is not markedly influenced by stress or glucocorticoids[865] (Fig. 241).

Parathyroidectomy does not significantly alter responsiveness to direct calcifiers such as $KMnO_4$; these apparently can attract calcium into the tissues even in the presence of hypocalcemia.[865]

The **age** factor plays a particularly important role in determining the reactivity of experimental animals to direct challengers. For example, the subcutaneous injection of $KMnO_4$ (100 μg.) produces calcified wheals most readily in rats weighing 50–100 g., less effectively in animals within the weight range of 150–250 g., while in rats of 300 g. or more it is completely ineffective (Fig. 242).

In view of all these observations we feel that direct calcification cannot be designated either as metastatic or—in the classical sense—as dystrophic.

Evidently, direct calcification is not due to hypercalcemia, such as occurs in metastatic calcification owing to calcium liberation from the bones or inhibition of calcium excretion. However, this form of calcinosis cannot be ascribed to a mere

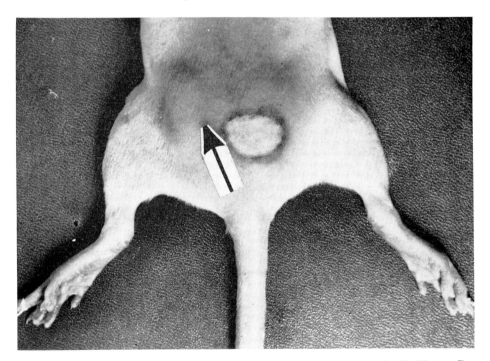

Fig. 240. **Protective value of direct tissue calcification produced by $ZnCl_2$ s.c.** Rat (100 g. ♀): $ZnCl_2$ (500 μg. in 0.2 ml. water, s.c.) 1st day + $ZnCl_2$ (5 mg. in 0.2 ml. water, s.c. underneath previous injection site and in corresponding unpretreated area on right side) 7th day. Only small calcified nodule at pretreated site (arrow). At unpretreated site, central necrosis (white disc) surrounded by hyperemic halo.
(After Selye and Padmanabhan.[863a])

nonspecific or "dystrophic" tissue damage either: the highly calcifying, small doses of KMnO$_4$ induce no significant nonspecific tissue injury, while many compounds that produce much local damage (e.g., inflammation and necrosis) cause no calcification. We therefore proposed to drop the old concepts of dystrophic and metastatic calcification and merely distinguish between locally induced, or "topogenic," calcification (which does not exclude a specific pathogenesis) and "systemogenic calcification" (which does not specifically imply a strictly metastatic origin).[865]

KMnO$_4$ can also produce direct *calcification in tissues other than the subcutis.* For example, in 100 g. rats 100 μg. of KMnO$_4$ injected in and around the

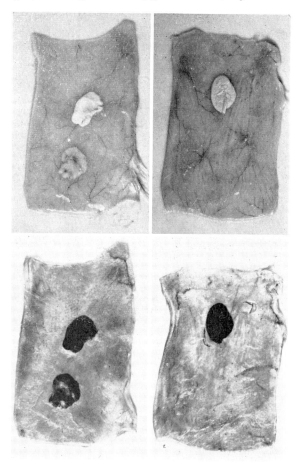

Fig. 241. **Prevention by hypophysectomy of calcified wheals produced by KMnO$_4$ s.c.** Two rats (100 g. ♀): KMnO$_4$ (100 μg. in 0.2 ml. water, s.c.) cranial wheal 3d day, caudal wheal 5th day + (right) hypophysectomy 1st day; killed 10th day. *Top:* Fresh. *Bottom:* AgNO$_3$-stained specimens. KMnO$_4$ produced wheal on 3d day but not on 5th day after hypophysectomy.

[After Selye *et al.*,[865] courtesy of Springer-Verlag (Virchows Arch.).]

kidney, adrenals, thyroid, parathyroid, pancreas, salivary glands, blood vessels, or muscles induces calcinosis in all of these sites, though always predominantly in the stroma. If 500 μg. of $KMnO_4$ are injected into one common iliac artery of the rat, the muscles of the ipsilateral limb undergo severe progressive atrophy with signs of subsequent regeneration, although the local calcinosis is relatively mild (Figs. 243, 244, 245). At the same time osteoporosis develops in the shaft of the corresponding femur, the junction cartilage disintegrates and islands of new-bone tissue appear in the medullary cavity[863a] (Figs. 246, 247).

When extensive subcutaneous calcinosis is induced by very large or frequently repeated doses of $KMnO_4$ *systemic manifestations* may accompany the topical calcinosis. For example, in 100 g. rats given a total of 12.5 mg. of $KMnO_4$ in 20 ml.

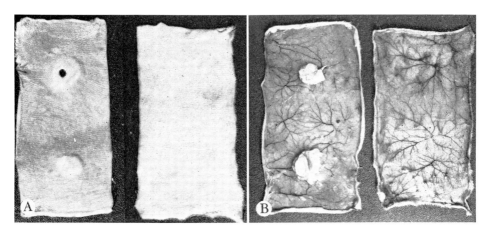

Fig. 242. Age-dependence of the topical response to $KMnO_4$ s.c. Two rats [50 g. (left) and 300 g. (right) ♀]: $KMnO_4$ [100 μg. (bottom) and 1 mg. (top) in 0.2 ml. water, s.c.] 1st day; killed 10th day. *A:* Outside of shaved skins. *B:* Subcutaneous aspects of same skins. In young animal (left side of each picture) both injections produced disc-shaped local calcium deposits visible through skin from the outside (A) (larger dose even led to small central ulceration). This is even more clearly visible from subcutis (B). Same dosages produced no detectable change in older rat.

of water over a period of 2 days in 10 divided doses, there developed pronounced osteitis fibrosa with severe bone absorption, presumably as a consequence of the precipitous attraction of calcium into the treated subcutaneous area (Fig. 248). Under similar circumstances calcification may also occur in the liver, perhaps as a consequence of the direct effect of absorbed $KMnO_4$ upon hepatic cells (Figs. 249, 250).

Other salts.—A large number of metallic salts—especially those that act as challengers after DHT sensitization—have been tested at doses of 1 μg. to 8 mg. given subcutaneously for possible direct calcifying activity in rats (100 g. ♀) with-

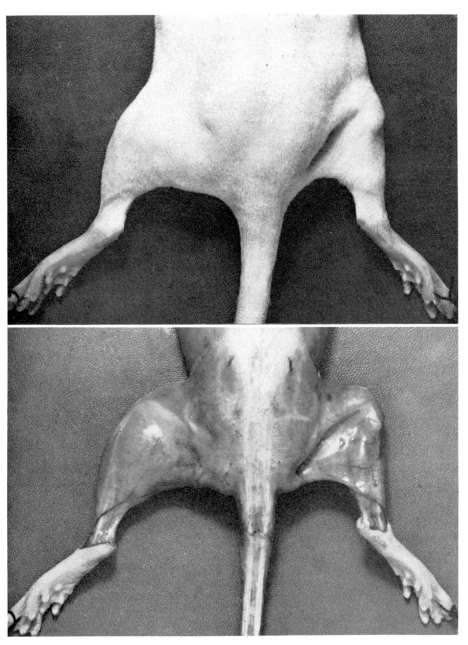

Fig. 243. Muscular atrophy produced by KMnO₄ intra-iliac. Rat (150 g. ♀): KMnO₄ (500 μg. in 1 ml. water, into right common iliac artery) 1st day; killed 14th day. *Top:* Intense muscular atrophy and contracture. *Bottom:* This is even more obvious after skin removal. Paradoxically, direct calcifier caused much fibrosis and atrophy with comparatively little calcification in affected muscles, while after DHT sensitization intra-iliac challenge (e.g., by CrCl₃) results in massive local calcinosis. (Cf. Plate XII, *E*.)

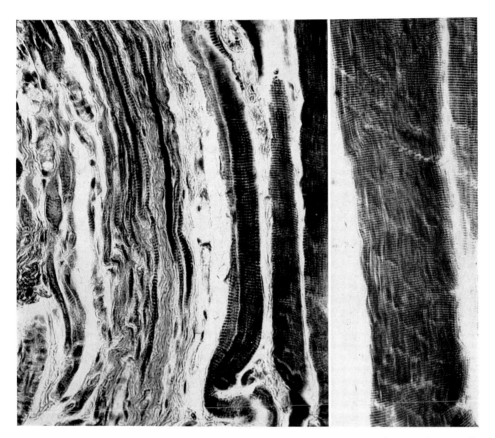

Fig. 244. Muscle lesions produced by KMnO₄ intra-iliac. Rat (150 g. ♀): KMnO₄ (500 μg. in 1 ml. water, intra-iliac) 1st day; killed 50th day. *Left:* Extremely thin (presumably regenerating) muscle fibers with obvious cross-striation between edematous tissue (near left margin) and larger, but still subnormal muscle fibers (near right margin). *Right:* Normal muscle fiber taken from another region of the same thigh for comparison. (Phosphotungstic acid, ×400.)

Fig. 245. Muscular fibrosis produced by KMnO₄ intra-iliac. Rat (150 g. ♀): KMnO₄ (500 μg. in 1 ml. water, into right common iliac artery) 1st day; killed 51st day. Extraordinarily intense sclerosis with comparatively slight calcinosis (arrows) in right quadriceps. (von Kóssa, ×100.)

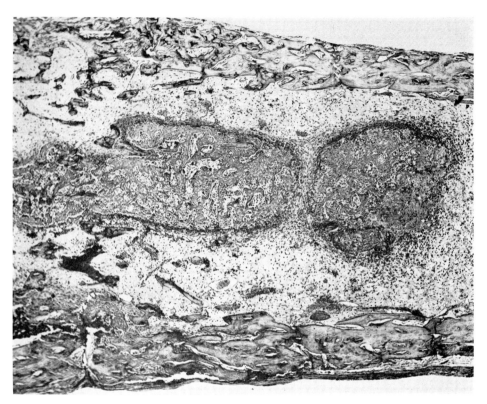

Fig. 246. Osseous lesions produced by KMnO₄ intra-iliac. Rat (150 g. ♀): KMnO₄ (500 μg. in 1 ml. water, into right common iliac artery) 1st day; killed 50th day. Longitudinal section through entire thickness of femur near its distal extremity. Extreme porosis of shaft. Marrow replaced by gelatinous tissue. Two newly formed osteogenic centers occupy middle of marrow cavity. (Hematoxylin-phloxine, ×39.)

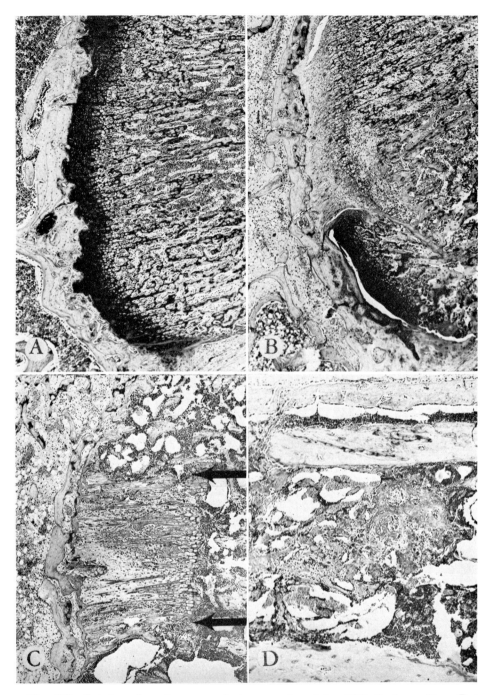

Fig. 247. **Epiphyseal and osseous lesions produced by KMnO₄ intra-iliac.** Rat (100 g. ♀): KMnO₄ (500 μg. in 1 ml. water, into right common iliac artery) 1st day; killed 50th day. *A:* Normal epiphyseal cartilage plate at distal end of left femur. *B:* Corresponding epiphyseal plate on right side. Only small, partially encapsulated, degenerating remnant of basophilic growth cartilage persists. Rest of cartilage plate lost staining properties and exhibits structural disorganization and formation of several slits. *C:* Other region of same cartilage plate. There remains only a small, square area of elongated growth cartilage columns (between arrows), without trace of growth cartilage either above or below. Marrow is almost normal in diaphysis but completely degenerated in epiphysis. *D:* Axial section through femur near distal extremity. Beginning new-bone formation in marrow. (Hematoxylin-phloxine, ×35.)

out previous sensitization.[863a] The following compounds were found to be *active* at one or more dose levels within this range:

Ca-acetate	$CuSO_4$	K_2MnO_4
$CaCl_2$	$Ga_2(SO_4)_3$	$LaCl_3$
$CdCl_2$	$Ga(NO_3)_3$	$NaMnO_4$
$CeCl_3$	$InCl_3$	$PbCl_2$
$CoCl_2$	$KMnO_4$	$ZnCl_2$

On the other hand, the following compounds were *inactive:*

$AgNO_3$	K_2CrO_4	$NbCl_5$
$AlCl_3$	$K_2Cr_2O_7$	$PdCl_2 \cdot 2KCl$
$CrCl_3$	$MnCl_2$	$SnCl_2$
$FeCl_2$	$Mn(NO_3)_2$	$TiCl_3$
$FeCl_3$	$MnSO_4(NH_4)_2SO_4$	$ZrOCl_2$
Hg-acetate	$NaClO_4$	
H_2O_2	Na_2SnO_3	

It is evident that a number of inorganic salts share with $KMnO_4$ the property of changing living connective tissue, so that it will trap calcium, somewhat as mordants prepare inanimate tissues for the uptake of dyes. As judged by histologic studies, the connective-tissue fibers and adipose cells represent the most appropri-

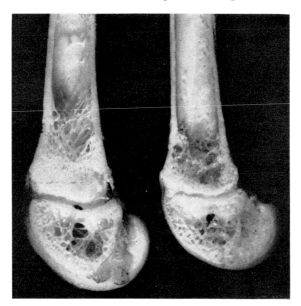

Fig. 248. Bone absorption produced by $KMnO_4$ s.c. Rat (100 g. ♀): $KMnO_4$ (1.25 mg. in 2 ml. water, s.c. at ten different sites) throughout 1st and 2d day; killed 5th day. *Left:* Untreated control for comparison. *Right:* Pronounced absorption of trabeculae in region just above growth cartilage of lower end of femur.

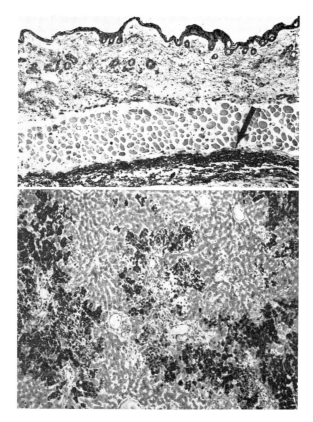

Fig. 249. **Cutaneous and hepatic calcinosis produced by KMnO₄ s.c.** Rat (60 g. ♀):
KMnO₄ (1.25 mg. in 1.5 ml. water, s.c. in ten widely separated sites) 1st day; killed 3d day.
Top: Typical cutaneous calcinosis as produced by direct calcifiers. Heavy calcification of injection area (arrow) underneath cutaneous muscle; derma itself remains unaffected. (von Kóssa, ×80.) *Bottom:* Calcification and necrosis, especially near periphery of hepatic lobules. (von Kóssa, ×80.)

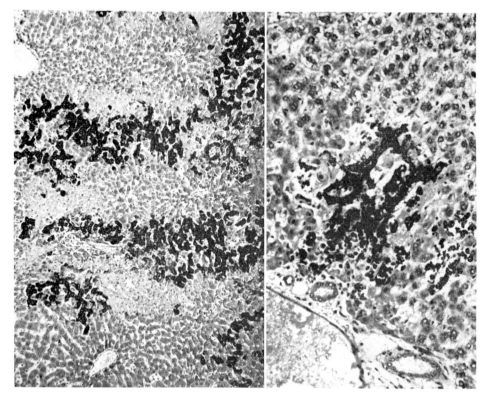

Fig. 250. Hepatic calcification produced by KMnO₄ s.c. Rat (80 g. ♀): KMnO₄ (1.25 mg. in 2 ml. water, s.c. in ten different sites of body surface in course of 24 hours) 1st day; killed 5th day. There was calcification of entire body surface, osteoporosis and, simultaneously, calcium deposition with subsequent focal necrosis of liver. Here, cytoplasm of parenchymal cells is seen to undergo calcification, while space occupied by nucleus is refractory. In this respect, the lesion differs from the selective nuclear calcification produced by calciphylaxis in the salivary glands (Fig. 120), as well as from most other types of calciphylaxis predominantly affecting the stroma. (von Kóssa, left ×105, right ×155.)

ate sites for this type of calcium precipitation. There appears to be no proportionality between the ability of these salts to cause tissue injury with necrosis or inflammation and their efficacy in eliciting topical calcinosis. Hence, it was "concluded that the induction of topical tissue calcification by contact with direct calcifiers is not merely due to damage, but results from certain highly specific properties of drugs, quite independently of their ability to produce inflammation, necrosis, or other signs of nonspecific tissue injury."[864]

Calcium salts.—Especially careful histogenetic studies were carried out concerning the development of the tissue calcification induced by the injection of calcium itself.

Subcutaneous injection of $CaCl_2$ (2 mg. in 0.2 ml. water) in 100 g. rats induces local calcification very similar to that produced either by calciphylactic challenge or by contact with $KMnO_4$. Although the calcium solution impregnates the entire injection area fairly evenly, precipitates develop predominantly in adipose cells within the thin rim of cytoplasm that surrounds the central fat vacuole, but never in the vacuole itself. At the injection site calcification also occurs in the walls of blood vessels and in the sheaths of nerves, but not in the nerves themselves. Occasional mast cells likewise undergo calcification, their discharged granules forming calcified clusters in the interstices between the calcified fat cells (Fig. 251).

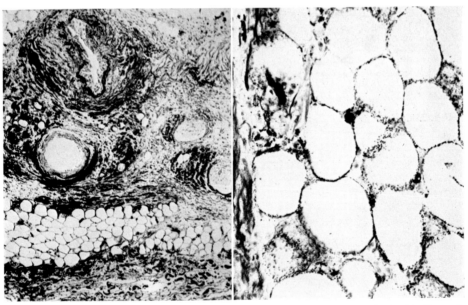

Fig. 251. **Direct calcification produced by CaCl₂ s.c.** Rat (100 g. ♀): CaCl₂ (2 mg. in 0.2 ml. water, s.c.) 1st day; killed 5th day. *Left:* General aspect of injection site. Calcium deposition along collagen fibers in wall of blood vessels; perineurium of subcutaneous nerves and adipose tissue. (von Kóssa, ×75.) *Right:* Higher magnification of beginning calcification in adipose tissue. Calcium granules along cell membranes. (von Kóssa, ×300.)

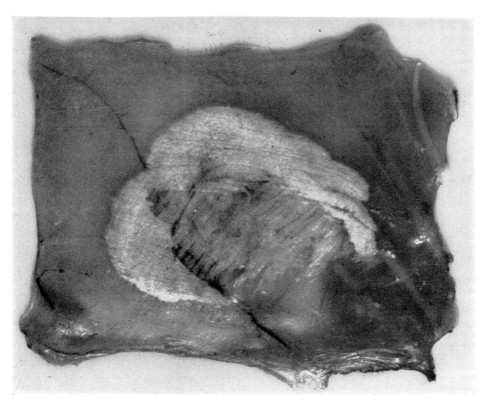

Fig. 252. Typical "asbestos-like" muscle calcification produced by DHT + PMX s.c. Rat (100 g. ♀): DHT (1 mg. p.o.) 1st day + PMX (2 mg. in 0.2 ml. water, s.c.) 2d day; killed 6th day. In flank region just underneath PMX-treated subcutis, there is an "asbestos-like," fibrous, roughly circular disk of calcification within muscle fibers. White lines (corresponding to muscle fibers) are slightly elevated above surface of surrounding normal muscle; they follow intersecting pattern of muscle fibers in different layers.

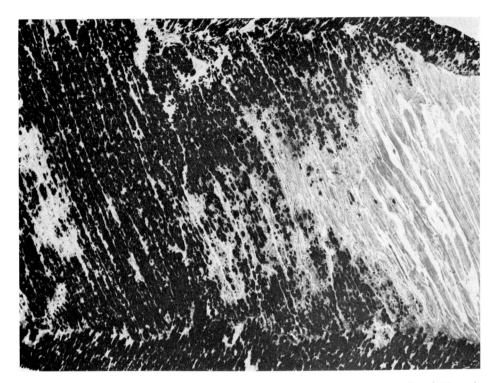

Fig. 253. Topical muscle calcification produced by DHT + PMX s.c. Rat (100 g. ♀): DHT (1 mg. p.o.) 1st day + PMX (2 mg. in 0.2 ml. water, s.c. in flank region) 2d day; killed 7th day. On this flat section through lateral abdominal wall musculature, the selective deposition of calcium appears as an "asbestos-like" patch owing to selective calcification of muscle fibers. (von Kóssa, ×17.) Muscle calcification of the type shown here and in Fig. 252 is produced by PMX even without pretreatment by DHT, although in the absence of sensitization the calcinosis is less severe.

It may be concluded that these tissues have an inherent affinity for calcium salts whether these be provided through calciphylactic challenge, treatment with a direct calcifier, or treatment with a calcium salt. Curiously, even in the latter case tissue calcification occurs only after the injected calcium salt is absorbed.

Organ-specific direct calcifiers.—A few observations imply that there are direct calcifiers which, like those previously mentioned, act without the need of special sensitization, though not on connective tissue, but only on certain other structural elements. For example, **PMX** (Figs. 252, 253) can cause local calcification when applied to striated muscle and, of course, various agents—including HgCl₂ (Fig. 254), mechanical **trauma** and **ligature** of **blood vessels**—can produce calcinosis in the kidney.

Apparently, in all these instances the receptive target organ itself contains the prerequisites (enzyme systems, calcifiable substrates?) for the ready induction of local calcification. Only KMnO₄ and similarly acting, classical direct calcifiers possess the singular property of causing calcification in connective tissue virtually anywhere.

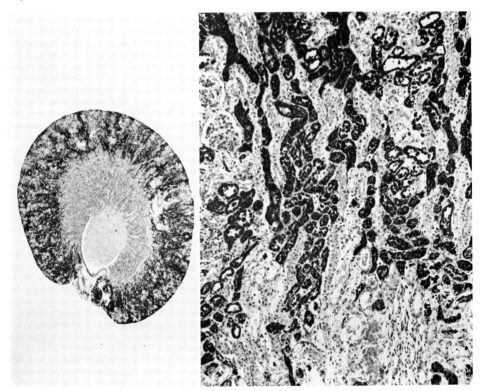

Fig. 254. Selective calcification of the renal cortex produced by HgCl₂ s.c. (For comparison with Fig. 95.) Rat (100 g. ♀): HgCl₂ (1 mg. in 0.2 ml. water, s.c.) 1st day; killed 4th day. Although here calcification is also limited to renal cortex, only the tubules themselves are affected. (von Kóssa, left ×7, right ×105.) (Cf. Plate IX, *B*, *E*.)

VI
Clinical Implications

As this book goes to press we still have no definite proof that any spontaneous disease of man depends upon calciphylaxis. It is a priori improbable, however, that such a fundamental reaction form of connective tissue—proven to be operative in the most diverse mammals, including the monkey—should not exist in man. Therefore, as a guide to future clinical research, it may be useful to survey briefly those morbid entities of human pathology that resemble one or the other experimental calciphylactic reaction. In the two final chapters we shall also consider the possible uses that could be made of induced calciphylaxis as a form of treatment.

To begin with, any speculations along these lines must take into account that:

1. *Not all calcinoses are necessarily due to calciphylaxis.*
2. *Not all forms of calciphylaxis are accompanied by a lasting and readily detectable calcinosis.*

For example, topogenic calcification (due predominantly to local causes) may be induced either by calciphylactic challenge or by the local action of a direct calcifier. Systemogenic calcification (due predominantly to general metabolic derangements, e.g., increased calcium liberation from the skeleton, increased absorption, or decreased excretion of calcium) may also occur with or without the participation of a topical calciphylactic challenge. Finally, an evanescent shower of fine calcium precipitation may elicit connective-tissue reactions which greatly outlast the presence of histologically demonstrable calcium.

The Calcinoscleroses

The basic concept of the calcinoscleroses was first formulated in 1932, when it was observed that simultaneously with osteolysis, parathyroid hormone may produce scleroderma-like lesions. Here, the transfer of calcium from the skeleton to the skin was accompanied by intense inflammatory and sclerotic changes, both in the bones and in the derma. Indeed, mild lesions of the same kind occurred in various tissues throughout the organism. For example, slight inflammation and sclerosis, often with intense mastocyte accumulation, were seen in and around the sheaths of muscular arteries and nerves. These findings drew our attention to the role of hormones in inflammation long before we made our first observations on the prophlogistic effects of mineralocorticoids and STH or formulated the concept of hormonal conditioning in relation to the "pluricausal diseases" in general. The conclusion was reached that hyperparathyroidism can result in a "systemic connective tissue disease and that a hormone, which is a fundamentally physiologic substance, is capable of producing true inflammation."[810]

The concept as we saw it then was summarized as follows:

"Up to now, we were accustomed to consider diseases caused by an excessive secretion of a certain endocrine gland as more or less well defined morbid entities. . . . In the light of our findings it appears, however, that under different circumstances, flooding of the organism with one and the same hormone can produce lesions that are fundamentally different, at least as regards their morphologic manifestations."[810]

The group of maladies now known as "collagen diseases" (particularly scleroderma, endarteritis obliterans, periarteritis nodosa)—as well as osteitis fibrosa, marble-bone disease, and other morbid entities characterized by systemic inflammatory and proliferative connective-tissue reactions—were thought to be interrelated in some way. As a working hypothesis it was postulated that all these diseases are at least in part dependent upon parathyroid function and variations in calcium metabolism. *"Diverse, largely still unidentified, conditioning factors may be responsible for the fact that an increase in parathyroid hormone secretion produces one or the other disease under different circumstances."*[810]

Subsequent work on stress led us to a rather similar concept which regards pituitary and adrenocortical hormones as regulators of inflammatory and sclerotic responses to injury. We came to believe that the hormones of the pituitary-adrenal system can play a decisive "conditioning" role in determining the body's susceptibility to various potential pathogens and particularly to those which affect connective tissue.[813, 814, 816, 853, 854, 855, 856]

The fact that the same hormone (e.g., a corticoid) can condition for the most diverse diseases has perhaps been demonstrated most clearly by the work on the experimental "pluricausal cardiopathies," in which the endocrine component is but one factor in a complex pathogenic situation.[821, 823] Here, as in many other diseases, the hormone acts more or less nonspecifically; it merely determines disease susceptibility to potential pathogens.

Calciphylaxis may well represent the connecting link between the parathyroid and the pituitary-adrenocortical concepts of connective-tissue disease. There are substances normally manufactured by the body which can act as sensitizers (e.g., parathyroid hormone, possibly compounds of the vitamin-D group) and challengers (e.g., iron and mastocyte granules) for systemic responses; these substances are capable of selectively depositing calcium in different target areas. In the overt typical calcinoses, calcification itself is the "disease," while in other connective-tissue maladies it may merely act as a stimulant for subsequent inflammation and sclerosis.

In our experiments we have often seen that under certain circumstances calciphylaxis produces only an evanescent, extremely fine shower of dustlike calcium precipitates; these are rapidly absorbed but they give rise to lasting inflammation and sclerosis, sometimes followed by hyalinization. All these connective-tissue reactions are demonstrably dependent upon the balance between the pro- and anti-inflammatory hormones. Thus calcification (with subsequent inflammation, sclerosis, and hyalinization) regulated by the parathyroids and the pituitary-adrenocortical system may well play a decisive role in many collagen diseases.

All these facts have been demonstrated in animal experiments, but their *implications for human pathology are meanwhile based only on speculation;* hence it would seem particularly fruitful at this time to initiate systematic clinical research along these lines. It was to facilitate this task that we compiled a list of all those diseases in which calcification and/or inflammation with sclerosis are sufficiently prominent to raise the suspicion that they may depend upon calciphylactic responses. However, their mention here should not be taken to suggest that we consider them to be dependent upon calciphylaxis.

During the past twenty years we have collected over 50,000 references (books, reprints, photocopies) on diseases of this group. Among these we shall discuss here only those that describe observations of special interest in connection with calciphylaxis. Thus our bibliography is chosen with a particular point of view: it is by no means a representative "random sample," nor is it intended to cover the entire field of the collagen diseases.

Every relevant morbid condition will be briefly defined and documented with a few key references, but many important data of practical interest, such as diagnostic and therapeutic procedures (including the use of corticoids), will have to be neglected. By contrast, we shall give considerable attention to some apparently quite trivial, incidental observations merely because they appear to be particularly pertinent to the concepts of calciphylaxis and calcinoscleroses. Prominent among these points are: (1) calcium and iron deposition in tissues, (2) the possible pathogenic importance of changes in elastic fibers and mastocytes, (3) challenge by trauma or metals, (4) the effects of calcium chelators and stressors, (5) similarities between these various spontaneous diseases that suggest their belonging to a single group, the "calcinoscleroses," (6) similarities between the experimental calciphylactic syndromes and any of the spontaneous maladies of man and (7) possible relationships between the calcinoscleroses and neoplasia.

Acrodermatitis Chronica Atrophicans

This is a rare disorder which predominantly affects the dorsa of the hands and feet as well as the extensor surfaces of the elbows and knees, usually occurring in women over 40 years of age.

The disease is probably a simple clinical variant of diffuse idiopathic skin atrophy. Immediately beneath the epidermis there is a thin but definite zone of homogenized collagen and there may be calcification.[16, 971] The lesions begin as red or purple edematous macules, nodules or plaques, which after several months tend to become wrinkled, thin, atrophic, and covered by fine scales. Sometimes fibrous "pseudo-sclerodermatous" nodules and bands develop along the length of the ulna and tibia, occasionally with ulcerations over bony prominences. The affected skin areas are said to be especially susceptible to the development of carcinomas.[781]

Acrodermatitis atrophicans is frequently combined with scleroderma,[132, 496, 750, 798] but the literature is divided regarding the question whether this dermatosis is or is not merely a variant of scleroderma.[16, 85, 90, 199, 450, 740]

Acrosclerosis

Syn., sclerodactyly.

Acrosclerosis is almost invariably accompanied and usually preceded by Raynaud's syndrome. It occurs most frequently in adult women as a slowly progressive disorder and is generally considered to be a form of scleroderma which affects predominantly the extremities, particularly the fingers, but may spread to the face and other parts of the body. The fingers are characteristically pointed and atrophic, the fingernails bowed. The skin of the hands and feet feels cold, presumably as a consequence of vascular disturbances.

Calcific foci may replace altered collagen in the dermis and subcutis. Like scleroderma, acrosclerosis may be accompanied by arthralgia, osteoporosis, and esophageal lesions.[16, 173, 185] In addition to the cutaneous calcification, the larger arteries may be sclerosed, calcified and occluded[173] (Figs. 255, 256).

Sometimes the disease was elicited by a topical injury.[211] Emotional factors and other stressful experiences tend to cause exacerbations and the condition has been considered to be a disease of adaptation.[605] (Cf. also "Scleroderma.")

Adiponecrosis Neonatorum

This lesion is characterized by necrosis with consequent fibrosis of subcutaneous tissue elicited by trauma at birth. It may be associated with calcification, presumably as a consequence of calcium-soap formation in damaged fat tissue. It resembles the so-called "lipophagic granuloma" of the newborn, fat-sclerema, and scleroderma, but is not considered to be identical with the latter conditions.[181, 261, 538]

Anetoderma Erythematodes

This dermatosis is characterized by degeneration and disappearance of the dermal elastic fibers with consequent wrinkling and flabbiness of the skin. In certain instances, differential diagnosis between anetoderma and scleroderma, particularly "white spot disease," may be virtually impossible.[593]

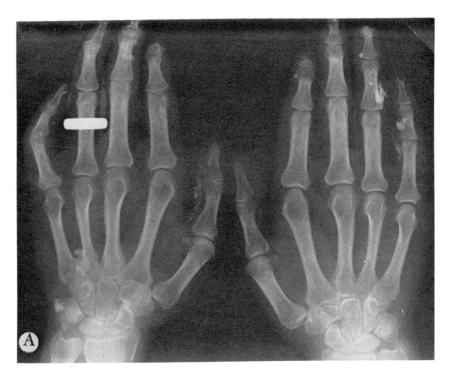

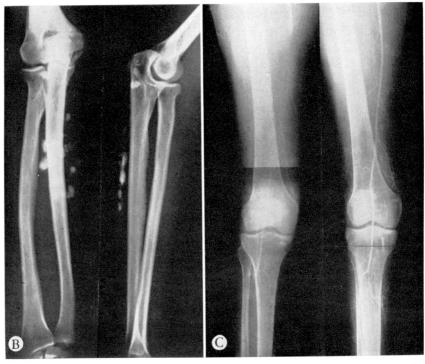

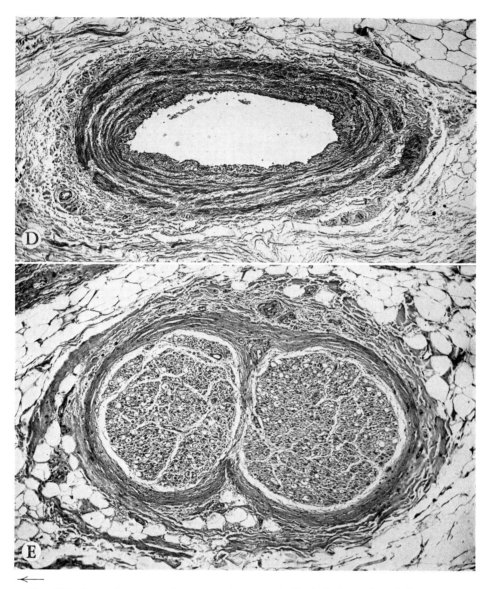

Fig. 255. Acrosclerosis with arterial lesions. *A:* Typical absorption of the tips of the phalanges and soft-tissue calcification in the hands. *B:* Calcinosis in the right forearm. *C:* (Left) Arteriogram of the right leg, showing block in femoral artery. Popliteal artery is filled by collaterals but there is no filling of anterior and posterior tibial arteries. *C:* (Right) Arteriogram of left leg fails to visualize posterior tibial artery. *D:* Mural edema in a subcutaneous artery. The adventitial collagen proliferation is characteristic of scleroderma. *E:* Posterior tibial nerve with sclerodermatous proliferation of connective tissue particularly in perineurium (note similarity to calciphylactic perineuritis).

[After Calvert *et al.*,[173] courtesy Williams & Wilkins Co. (Angiology).]

323

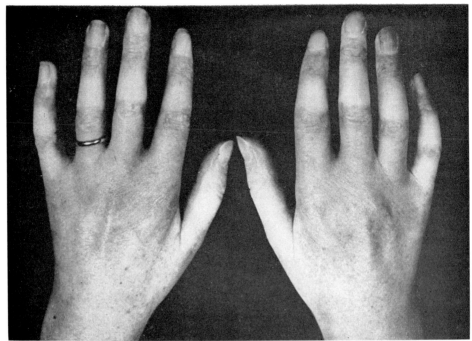

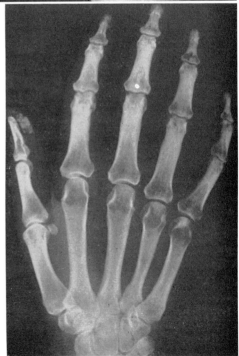

Fig. 256. Acrosclerosis. *Top:* Atrophic changes in fingers with slight edema distally. *Bottom:* Calcium deposit in pulp of right thumb and osteoporosis.

(After Caughey and Richardson,[185] courtesy New Zealand Medical Journal.)

324

Arteriosclerosis

The term "arteriosclerosis" is used here as a generic designation for various arterial lesions. It includes not only the common degenerative and proliferative changes in the intima of the larger arteries which result in fibrous and lipoid-containing, often calcified plaques, but also the medial calcification of Mönckeberg and arteriolar sclerosis. The term "atherosclerosis" designates only the fatty degenerative and sclerotic changes in arteries.[22, 781]

Arteriosclerosis is listed here because arterial calcification plays an important part in many forms of calciphylaxis. The Mönckeberg type of medial calcification can occur after simple overdosage with parathyroid hormone or vitamin-D compounds. However, with calciphylactic techniques, intima proliferation and periarteritis nodosa can also be produced. Hence, calcification is not necessarily always a secondary phenomenon and the possible role of calcium in the initiation of diverse arterial diseases appears to deserve careful study.

Among 92 cardiac aneurysms observed at the Massachusetts General Hospital, 11 showed calcification of the aneurysmal wall.[458]

While calcinosis frequently accompanies obliterative arterial diseases of various kinds, ossification in the arterial walls occurs almost exclusively in patients of 60 years and more.[331]

In rare instances, widespread and often fatal calcinosis affecting primarily the cardiovascular system and the kidney may be combined with osteosclerosis and dwarfism. Although the syndrome strikingly resembles that of vitamin-D intoxication, it can occur in the absence of any vitamin-D medication.[154, 523, 602] As early as 1815, Hodgson spoke in his "Treatise on Diseases of the Arteries" about "a temporal artery removed from an infant 18 months old, in which the coats of the vessel were covered with a complete tube of calcareous matter."

Chemical studies on the cholesterol, phosphatide, fatty acid and calcium content of atheromatous aortas have led to the rejection of the hypothesis that calcium is captured by the fatty acids of cholesterol esters. If, as the hypothesis postulates, calcium were bound to fatty acids liberated from cholesterol esters, the proportion of free cholesterol (as compared with the esterified) should be higher in the heavily calcified parts of the aorta than in the not heavily calcified areas. This was not the case.[795]

Bone Diseases in General

Various destructive bone diseases, including primary or metastatic neoplasms and osteomyelitis, may occasionally cause cutaneous calcinosis.[16] Generalized soft-tissue calcification has also been observed in patients with the most diverse types of destructive bone lesions, such as tumors, syphilitic osteitis, senile osteoporosis, and osteomyelitis.[265, 524, 800] Multiple myelomas that cause extensive bone destruction may produce particularly severe generalized calcinosis.[934] However, calcinosis as a result of bone destruction is most common in osteitis fibrosa (cf. "Hyperparathyroidism") and skeletal neoplasia.

Like parathyroid hormone or vitamin-D compounds, destructive bone diseases cause "metastatic calcification" predominantly in the lungs, stomach, kidneys, and cardiovascular system. The walls of the left auricle and the aorta are especially predisposed.[65, 66]

In a boy of 12 with extensive osteomyelitis and generalized calcinosis affecting the heart, lungs, kidneys, arteries, and skin, it was noted that the elastic fibers (especially in the skin and arteries) were particularly predisposed for calcification. The cutaneous striae that develop in the vicinity of joints allegedly tend to undergo calcification because here the degenerating and ruptured elastic fibers attract calcium. In another case of osteomyelitis with purulent dermatitis, calcium impregnation of the affected skin was assumed to have been caused by substances arising in the infected skin.[484] These interpretations come very close to the concept of vital mordanting, or calciphylaxis, and may show the way to its clinical application.

Buerger's Disease

Syn., thromboangiitis obliterans.

This is an inflammatory panarteritis and panphlebitis, usually affecting the medium-sized and small vessels of the extremities and resulting in thrombosis with organization. As the occlusion progresses there develops ischemia, and finally gangrene of the affected part. The lower extremities are most commonly affected, but visceral blood vessels may occasionally also be involved. Atheromatous plaques and calcification are not characteristic of this condition,[22] but nothing is known about the possible participation of transient minimal calcium precipitations in the vessels, such as occur in those forms of calciphylaxis that lead to thromboembolic processes.

Buerger's disease is often combined with **Raynaud's phenomenon** and in advanced stages there may be obstruction of digital arteries, especially in the case of sclerodactyly with necrosis of the fingers.[596] **Giant cells** (similar to those seen in calciphylactic lesions) are quite common in the thrombi of vessels affected by Buerger's disease.[781]

Thromboangiitis-obliterans-like lesions are frequently observed not only in the skin but also in internal organs of patients suffering from **scleroderma,**[631] and even typical Buerger's disease may be associated with scleroderma.[311, 756]

On the basis of predominantly theoretic considerations, Buerger's disease was interpreted as a stress-induced **"disease of adaptation,"**[742] but this claim requires confirmation.

Burnett's syndrome, cf. "Milk-Alkali Syndrome of Burnett *et al.*"

Calcinosis

We shall employ the term "calcinosis" as a generic designation for any type of pathologic calcification. It has been customary to distinguish between calcinosis universalis and circumscripta.[971] According to dictionary definitions we should speak of: (1) *calcinosis universalis* when there are widespread calcified nodules which tend to ulcerate, heal slowly, and involve subcutaneous tissues, muscles, tendons, and nerve sheaths; (2) *calcinosis circumscripta* when calcified nodules are limited to the skin and subcutaneous tissues of the upper extremities, particularly the hands, most common in sclerodactyly.[397] However, in practice the two conditions overlap and many investigators have emphasized that such a distinction is quite artificial.[971]

The connective-tissue lesions, both in circumscribed and in generalized calcinosis, exhibit so many similarities to the changes characteristic of the *collagen diseases,* particularly scleroderma, that some investigators came to the conclusion that "calcinosis is a syndrome characterized by calcareous concretions in subcutaneous or deep connective tissue which may be considered as a variant of the diseases of the scleroderma group. Calcifications develop always on a sclerodermatous terrain."[32]

It is debatable whether all forms of circumscribed and generalized tissue calcification that develop suddenly in the form of goutlike attacks should be grouped under the name of *acute soft-tissue calcinosis* (calcinosis acuta).[316]

We shall discuss calcinosis universalis in a separate section, but calcinosis circumscripta, which may occur almost anywhere in the body, will be dealt with in connection with each affected site under "Calcinosis Cutis," "Calcinosis of the Lung," "Calcinosis of the Thyroid," etc.

It is particularly interesting in connection with our problem that a close relationship between calcification and *iron* deposition has repeatedly been observed in various forms of clinical calcinosis[157, 524, 799] and that calcification frequently begins with the incrustation of *elastic* fibers.[465, 799] (Cf. also "Speculations.")

Calcinosis of the Adrenals

Calcinosis of the adrenals occurs quite frequently following tissue damage by hemorrhage, tumors, tuberculosis, etc.[898] It may occur in hyperparathyroidism[988] and in hypervitaminosis D.[982] Pronounced bilateral calcification with bone and bone-marrow formation has been observed in a patient who died of diphtheric myocarditis.[541] Massive calcinosis in the inner fasciculata and the reticularis of the adrenals was observed in a case of familial xanthomatosis without any calcification elsewhere in the body.[986]

Calcinosis of Bursae

Syn., bursitis calcificans, subacromial or subdeltoid bursitis, bursitis chronica calcarea, periarthritis humeroscapularis, painful shoulder with calcification, calcareous tendovaginitis, maladie de Duplay.

Calcareous bursitis, usually accompanied by tendinitis, is a symptomatic inflammatory involvement of one or more of the rotator tendons, due to inflammation with deposition of calcium in and about the tendon, most often the supraspinatus.

The calcifying bursitis of the shoulder joint is not only of great practical importance but also poses many intriguing theoretical problems regarding the biochemical and mechanical factors that may be responsible for its development.
Ever since its first description by Emanuel Simon Duplay in 1896, the etiology and
pathogenesis of this common and often disabling condition has been the subject of
intense investigation. Various authors considered trauma, "wear and tear," over-
exertion, lack of activity, infection, allergy, "rheumatism," derangements in calcium metabolism, collagen disease or other factors to be primarily responsible,[10, 204, 219, 257, 659, 670, 896] but "in spite of many explanations . . . the exact
method by which calcium is deposited remains obscure."[896]

This condition is of special importance in connection with the study of calciphylaxis, since it has been reproduced by DHT + Thorotrast® i.v. and DHT +
Fe-Din i.v. Occasionally calcification in and about the joints occurs also in the
siderocalciphylactic syndromes, particularly that induced by DHT + Fe-Dex
i.v. + mastocyte depletors s.c. (Cf. also "Calcinosis of the Joints.")

Calcinosis of the Choroid Plexus

Calcium deposition, quite similar to that induced by calciphylaxis, can occur
spontaneously in the choroid plexus of man[79] (Fig. 257).

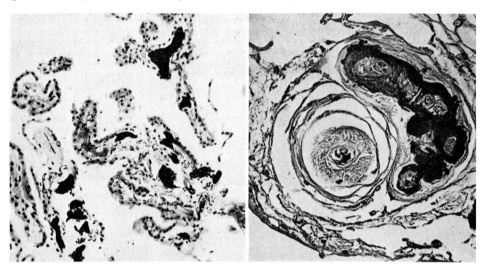

**Fig. 257. Calcification and formation of corpora amylacea in choroid plexus of
man.** *Left:* Several calcified concretions in and around the vessels of the choroid plexus. *Right:*
Confluescent corpora amylacea showing different stages of their development. Calcium is deposited around small vessels in the lumen of which some erythrocytes are still distinguishable.
(After Becker,[79] courtesy Beitr. path. Anat. u. allg. Path.)

Calcinosis Cutis

In man, as in experimental animals subjected to calciphylactic treatment, one
of the most common sites of calcinosis is the skin. Only the "nonspecific calcinoses"

produced by a simple excess of an indirect calcifying agent (parathyroid hormone, vitamin-D compounds) form an exception; in these, cutaneous calcinosis is usually absent or at least negligible in proportion to calcium deposition elsewhere.

Calcification of the skin—as it occurs spontaneously in man—is hardly ever due to the topical action of a direct calcifier; it is virtually always but one manifestation of a systemic disease. Most frequently, the calcium is deposited in amorphous form within the **subcutaneous tissue** but it may penetrate to the **derma** and eventually lead to the formation of ulcers, from which gritty calcified material is eliminated. On the other hand, if the deposit is deep-seated and well encapsulated by subcutaneous connective tissue, it may eventually give rise to bone formation (cf. "Osteosis Cutis").[16, 781] The **axillary region** appears to be especially predisposed for cutaneous calcinosis[524, 929, 946] perhaps because of the constant irritation by friction and sweat.

Calcification and even true ossification may occur in the wall of **sebaceous cysts.**[336] In some of these cases, the epithelium is no longer recognizable and the diagnosis is based merely upon the cystic nature and cutaneous location of the lesions. It should be remembered, however, that calcified cutaneous cysts can also be produced through calciphylaxis, quite independently of the sebaceous glands. Occasionally, calcification occurs even in **hair follicles.**[524]

In all these respects, experimentally induced calciphylactic cutaneous calcinosis resembles its clinical counterpart. On the other hand, the purely topogenic experimental calcification (e.g., that induced by subcutaneous injection of $KMnO_4$) differs, in that it exhibits no tendency to exulcerate.

In comparing clinical cutaneous calcinosis to that produced by calciphylaxis in experimental animals, it is also noteworthy that in many patients the calcification occurs as a consequence of **topical trauma.**[50, 281] (Cf. also "Topical Tissue Injury.")

Calcinosis cutis can allegedly also develop as a result of **infection.** For example, in a boy repeated attacks of fever, diarrhea, vomiting, facial edema, and pains in the limbs were invariably associated with massive calcium deposits in the subcutis, buttocks, and joint regions. Treatment with penicillin permanently stopped these attacks.[712] Sometimes the **systemic stress** of a psychic trauma appears to aggravate the condition.[326]

The **blood calcium and phosphorus** values may be normal even in the presence of extensive "idiopathic" cutaneous calcinosis.[305]

In an adipose elderly woman, allegedly "the blood chemistry tended to show that the deposits of calcium phosphate in the fingers may be due to an endogenous hypervitaminosis D, caused by an unusually high blood cholesterol (480 mg. per 100 ccm.) superimposed on an old, remitted Raynaud's disease,"[981] but this view requires confirmation.

The incidence of macroscopically obvious cutaneous calcinosis in **scleroderma** is not very high, but conversely, among patients with evident cutaneous calcinosis, indications of scleroderma are so common[8, 41, 118, 142, 169, 274, 285] that skin calcification has been considered to be merely one manifestation of scleroderma. The so-called "sclérodermie calcaire" of Thibierge and Weissenbach is a type of scleroderma in which cutaneous calcinosis is particularly prominent. According to current opinion "lime salt infiltration is a terminal stage,"[389] since in early cases of scleroderma visible calcium deposits are rarely found. However, in the light of recently acquired knowledge this concept should be re-examined. (Cf. "Scleroderma.")

Not infrequently, cutaneous calcinosis is accompanied by classical signs of **dermatomyositis;**[136, 528] this is hardly surprising, since scleroderma and dermatomyositis are presumably only two forms of the same disease. (Cf. "Dermatomyositis.")

The fact that cutaneous calcinosis is usually only one particularly prominent manifestation of a **systemic disturbance** is well illustrated by the many observations showing associated lesions in other organs, e.g.: **myositis** and muscle fibrosis,[169] **renal insufficiency,**[528] **rheumatoid arthritis** and other collagen diseases,[528] as well as **calcification in other sites such as joints and tendons** (particularly around the shoulder joint),[41, 118, 274, 285] the **lung,**[281] the **thyroid,**[8] the Hassall bodies of the **thymus,**[8] and the **cardiovascular system.**[8]

Postphlebitic subcutaneous calcinosis occurs usually in postmenopausal women with chronic varicose ulcerations and eczematous skin lesions. The calcific plaques are not necessarily in direct contact with the veins and have been ascribed to local hypoxia, although phleboliths may also occur. These concretions are not necessarily in the vicinity of the calcified subcutaneous plaques. The latter are always associated with subcutaneous adipose tissue and may undergo ossification[476] (Fig. 258).

Intense calcinosis and ossification of the skin have been noted in two elderly **diabetic** patients,[248] although a causal connection between the cutaneous lesions and the diabetes could not be definitely proven.

Finally, the occasional occurrence of calcium deposits in **chronic eczema** and **dermatitis**[265] suggests that even superficial dermatoses may be associated with calcification.

Sometimes calcinosis cutis improves under the influence of **EDTA.**[983]

Calcinosis of the Ear

Calcification of the ear cartilages has been reported in patients who were otherwise well,[191, 532, 629, 787] but also in combination with various metabolic disorders[787] especially in acromegaly,[679a] Addison's disease,[490] and sarcoidosis.[74] Sometimes calcinosis of the ear cartilage or ear lobe results from mechanical trauma or frostbite.[268, 342, 759]

Calcinosis of the Gallbladder

The wall of an inflamed gallbladder may undergo calcification with giant-cell formation[332] (Fig. 316). The resulting structural changes may be very similar to those of the experimental calciphylactic biliary tract lesions produced by DHT (or parathyroid hormone) +Fe-OS i.v.

Calcinosis of Intervertebral Discs

Selective calcium deposition in the nucleus pulposus has been considered to represent a special disease entity.[63] It is common in adults but only a few cases have been described in children[207] (Fig. 259). Nothing is known about the pathogenesis

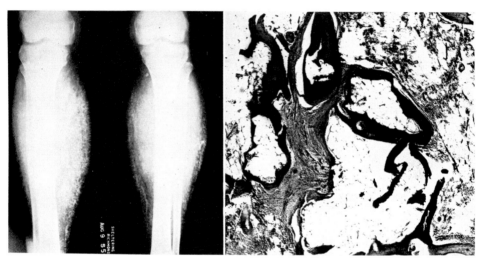

Fig. 258. Postphlebitic subcutaneous calcinosis. *Left:* X-ray appearance of the legs in a case of unusually severe postphlebitic calcinosis. *Right:* Dark calcified (ossified?) areas with fatty marrow formation in subcutaneous tissue.

(After Irby and Freed,[476] courtesy Virginia Medical Monthly.)

of this condition, and up to now it has not been possible to reproduce it experimentally.

Calcinosis of the kidney, cf. "Renal Disease."

Calcinosis of the Joints

Calcium deposition in joints is extremely common in connection with various forms of calcinosis. (Cf. "Calcinosis of Bursae," "Calcinosis Universalis," "Chondrodystrophia Calcificans Congenita Punctata.") Sometimes it may assume enormous proportions without there being any significant change in blood calcium or phosphate and without much soft-tissue calcification in other locations[24] (Fig. 260).

Here again *trauma* may be the eliciting factor. In a woman who fell on her overextended right hand, a rapidly growing, para-articular mass developed in which calcium could be demonstrated by X-ray photography 48 hours after the injury, while 7 days later the calcium was seen to wander proximad, presumably through the lymph channels. After an additional week, calcium could no longer be demonstrated on X-ray pictures. This case clearly demonstrates the often evanescent nature of traumatically induced para-articular calcinosis in man.[700] An almost identical, evanescent, posttraumatic, para-articular calcium deposit with subsequent lymphatic removal was seen near the left elbow joint in a man immediately after trauma.[700]

In a woman severe calcification on the flexor side of both knee joints developed (in combination with an acute psychosis) following infection with ***Toxoplasma***.[6]

Under the name of ***chondrocalcinosis polyarticularis (familiaris)*** a disease was described in which calcified shadows lining the articular surfaces of both large and small joints can be demonstrated radiographically. Calcification in the menisci of the knee joints is also constant in this familial disease of unknown etiology

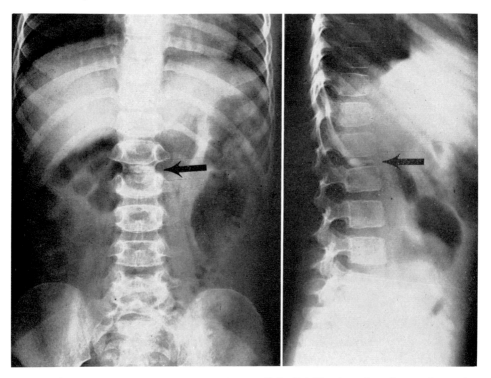

Fig. 259. Calcinosis of intervertebral disc. *Left:* Calcification of nucleus pulposus between 12th thoracic and 1st lumbar vertebrae in a girl, aged 6. *Right:* Lateral view of same disc (arrow).

(After Cohen *et al.*,[207] courtesy Ann. West. Med. and Surg.)

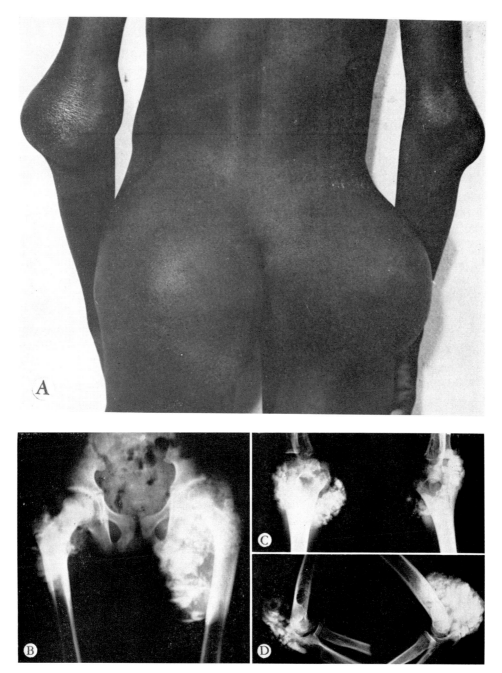

Fig. 260. Calcinosis of the joints. *A:* Tumorous calcinosis of the elbows and hips. *B:* X-ray appearance of hips. *C* and *D:* X-ray appearance of elbows.
(After Annamunthodo,[24] courtesy Am. J. Surg.)

which clinically resembles rheumatoid arthritis.[997] (Cf. also "Calcareous Bursitis.")

Calcinosis of the Lung

The pulmonary calcification which occurs with some regularity in severe cases of **hyperparathyroidism, hypervitaminosis D** and other forms of **generalized** (**"nonspecific"**) **calcinosis** need not be discussed here; the lung (like the kidney, gastrointestinal tract, and skin) is particularly predisposed for calcification.

Pulmonary calcification may occur in association with **calcinosis cutis**[281] and sometimes results in **ossification of the lung.**[487, 488]

Calcification of the pulmonary septa is comparatively common even in the absence of detectable destructive bone lesions. It occurs with particular frequency in **pulmonary stasis,**[614] perhaps because the accumulated iron pigments act as mordants for calcium.

Calcification has not been described in the **"acute, diffuse interstitial pulmonary fibrosis"** also known as the Hamman-Rich syndrome,[418] but the sclerosis of the pulmonary septa is rather reminiscent of that seen in certain types of calciphylaxis and, like the latter, may induce hyalinization, infiltration with eosinophils, and the formation of patches of squamous metaplasia.[319] Although the condition is often regarded as a form of virus pneumonia, a causative microorganism has not been demonstrated and many investigators believe this to be merely an acute form of **progressive interstitial pulmonary** fibrosis.[781] Further studies on the possible relationship between this condition and pulmonary calcinosis may, therefore, be profitable.

A special type of pulmonary calcinosis has been described as an **"alveolar microlithiasis"** or "Puhr's disease." The condition is often familial and it may be due to the secondary calcification of intra-alveolar hyaline exudates.[922]

Although calcinosis of the lung is common in **tuberculosis,** it has been pointed out that "pulmonary calcifications are apparently nonspecific reactions to a variety of organisms."[888] **Histoplasma capsulatum** was observed in 67 per cent of 105 consecutive cases of pulmonary calcification.[801, 901] In another series of 138 surgically excised pulmonary granulomas, organisms resembling Histoplasma capsulatum or **Coccidoides immitis** could be identified in 55.9 per cent of the cases.[802] Indeed, several authors accept the statement of Furcolow[358] that "tuberculosis is an exceedingly infrequent cause of disseminated pulmonary calcinosis. Histoplasmosis or some closely related infection is the cause in most cases"[195a, 630] (Figs. 261, 262, 263).

A very unusual case of pulmonary calcinosis was described as a distinct disease entity due to a **"constitutional anomaly or metabolic disturbance of unknown nature."**[419a] It appeared without any obvious ectopic calcification in other organs or possibly related changes in the skeleton, gastrointestinal tract or kidney. Here, the lung was so solidly calcified that it "could be cut only with difficulty and felt

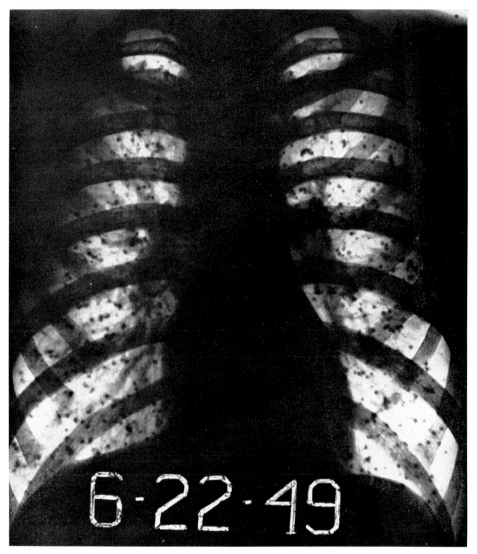

Fig. 261. Pulmonary calcinosis in histoplasmosis. Miliary calcified nodules throughout both lungs.

(After Furcolow,[358] courtesy Postgrad. Med.)

like porous bone. Passing the finger over the surface felt like rubbing it over sand-paper." The lungs weighed nearly six times as much as normally and throughout the stroma they contained concentrically lamellated psammoma-like calcified concretions which encroached upon the alveolar lumina. In view of what has been learned since, the possibility of a microbial (Histoplasma, Coccidoides?) or calciphylactic pathogenesis must also be considered; indeed, these two mechanisms may have coexisted in that perhaps microorganisms can also act as calci-phylactic challengers.

Calcinosis of the Nose

Calcium deposition occurs sometimes in rhinoscleroma.[190, 524]

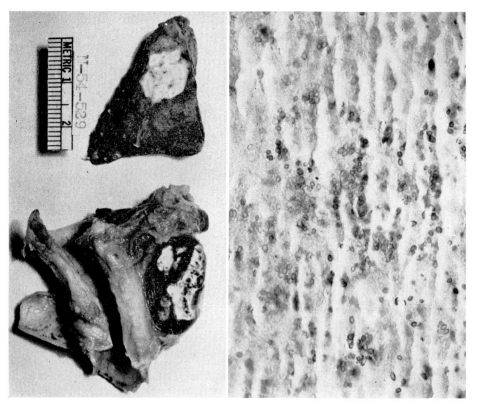

Fig. 262. Pulmonary calcinosis in histoplasmosis. *Left:* Large fibrocaseous and chalky primary focus in left lower lobe and left tracheobronchial lymph nodes in identical conditions. *Right:* Center of primary focus with numerous yeast cells, single and in clusters. (Gridley stain, ×580.)

(After Straub and Schwarz,[901] courtesy Am. J. Clin. Pathol.)

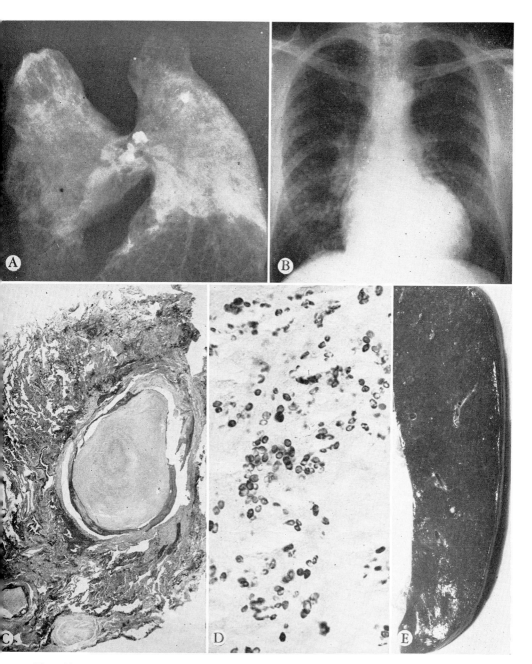

Fig. 263. Pulmonary calcinosis in histoplasmosis. *A:* X-ray of left lung illustrates typical "primary Ghon complex." *B:* X-ray showing typical miliary pattern of pulmonary calcinosis. *C:* Calcified focus in the lung without evidence of inflammation. (Hematoxylin-eosin.) *D:* Appearance of organisms resembling Histoplasma capsulatum in a partially calcified pulmonary lesion. Note tendency to cluster in small groups. (Methenamine-Silver method.) *E:* Gross specimen of spleen showing several calcified nodules on section plane. In all foci, organisms resembling Histoplasma capsulatum were demonstrable.

(After Mashburn *et al.*, [630] courtesy Am. Rev. Resp. Dis.)

Calcinosis of the Ovary

Dermoid cysts of the ovary are particularly common sites of massive calcification which may or may not be associated with ossification[332] (Fig. 264).

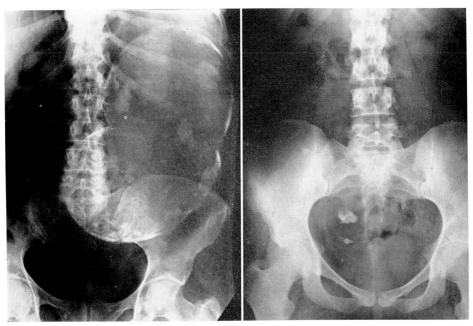

Fig. 264. Calcified ovarian dermoid cysts. *Left:* Relative lack of density in a large calcified abdominal cyst indicates oleaginous nature of contents which suggests dermoid cyst. *Right:* Cystlike mass arising in pelvis and containing radiolucent oleaginous material often associated with hair, vestigial teeth and bone is diagnostic of ovarian dermoid cyst.

(After Bartholomew *et al.*,[68] courtesy Postgrad. Med.)

Calcinosis of the Pancreas

Pancreatic calcinosis occurs quite frequently in connection with generalized calcinosis (cf. "Hyperparathyroidism," "Hypervitaminosis D"). It may also develop in combination with "idiopathic" chronic relapsing pancreatitis[68] (Fig. 265). It is not yet clear to what extent hyperparathyroidism participates in the production of the latter condition and whether calcinosis is the result or the cause of this disease.

Calcinosis of the Pericardium

The so-called calcifying pericarditis may develop in association with various pericardial lesions and is frequently detectable by X-ray examination.[332]

Calcinosis of the Pineal Body

The pineal body is also subject to calcification. Brain-sand granules (acervulus, corpora arenacea) are almost invariably present in this gland, especially in adults.

These granules are composed mainly of calcium phosphates and carbonates but may also contain traces of magnesium and are thought to result from "degenerative changes."[781] Massive calcification of the pineal body is rare.[110]

Calcinosis of the Pleura

In patients with pleuritis, intense calcification of the inflamed regions occurs quite frequently.[332]

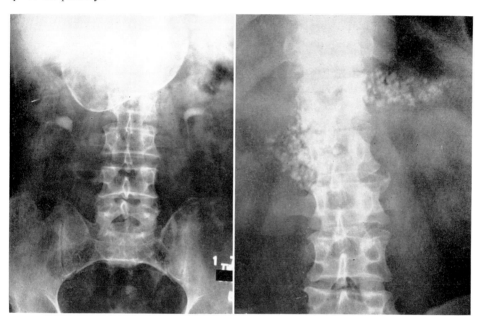

Fig. 265. Calcinosis of pancreas. *Left:* Calcified pseudocyst in pancreas. *Right:* Conglomerate punctate calcification distributed throughout pancreas is characteristic of chronic relapsing pancreatitis.

(After Bartholomew *et al.,*[68] courtesy Postgrad. Med.)

Calcinosis of the Scrotum

Calcification of the scrotum may represent merely a special localization of cutaneous calcinosis, but it often occurs as an isolated condition without any pronounced calcinosis elsewhere.[305, 380, 613, 911] Possibly here, degenerating elastic fibers or small xanthomatous and atheromatous plaques may serve as "mordants" for calcium.[265, 524, 613]

A study of relevant cases led to the conclusion that "fat and lipid-containing tissue in general are predisposed for calcification. Chemically, we may imagine the process so that the fatty acids liberated from cholesterol-fatty-acid-esters combine with the calcium of the blood and tissue fluids to form calcium soaps; and that subsequently the fatty acid radicals are substituted by carbonic and phosphoric acid."[105]

Calcinosis Segmentalis Congenita

This is an exceedingly rare disease which suggests the participation of nervous factors in calcification. For example, in one newborn baby, intense calcium deposition was wholly limited to the territory innervated by the second to seventh cervical nerve segments.[513]

Calcinosis of the Spleen

Calcinosis of the spleen is not infrequently the result of infection with Histoplasma capsulatum and similar organisms [451, 630, 801, 987a] but it may also occur as one manifestation of calcinosis universalis.[891]

Calcinosis of the Thyroid

Thyroid calcification or ossification is comparatively common in nodular colloid goiters with repeated cycles of involution and hyperplasia, as well as in the walls of thyroid cysts and in areas of old hemorrhages.[332, 781] In one case, the entire right lobe of the thyroid became calcified without producing any obvious symptoms.[208]

Psammoma bodies or "calcospherites" are rare in normal thyroid tissue but quite common in various types of thyroid tumors[72] and particularly in goitrous thyroids,[59] where they are frequently associated with ossification.[332]

Calcinosis Universalis

As previously stated (cf. "Calcinosis") there are imperceptible transitions between the generalized and the strictly limited calcinoses; yet it may be useful to retain the term "calcinosis universalis" for cases in which soft-tissue calcification is very widespread and shows no particular predisposition for any one organ. Here the term "interstitial calcinosis," originally recommended by Krause in 1909,[548] is appropriate because, even in massive calcinosis involving the skin, muscles, mesenteric lymph nodes, etc., as a rule only the connective tissue is incrustated with calcium.[794] Frequently, calcinosis universalis affects fascial layers between muscles selectively, often forming a thick envelope around the sciatic nerves.[625] Universal calcinosis in a two-month-old boy (ascribed to a metabolic acidosis resulting from a congenital cardiac anomaly) was attended by calcium deposits in the kidneys, spleen, and epiglottis.[891] Cases of calcinosis with predominantly periarticular localization were described as *"calcium gout,"*[939, 972a] but this localization is not unusual in universal calcinosis[104] and there appears to be no basis for a comparison with gout. These changes are very similar to those seen in the DHT + Thorotrast® type of calciphylaxis. The clinical disease also resembles experimental calciphylaxis in that it exhibits a great tendency to affect the elastic fibers predominantly.[946]

It has been said that in calcinosis universalis there is an increased *retention of orally administered calcium* even when the blood calcium levels are normal.[353] Although the *blood calcium and phosphorus* values are usually normal, the *blood cholesterol* may be very high.[405]

In a child of ten who developed calcinosis universalis in the course of a chronic febrile disease of unknown origin, considerable improvement was allegedly obtained by **partial thyroparathyroidectomy.**[733] In another patient with pronounced renal and muscle calcification, **EDTA** (i.v.) accelerated the removal of the calcium deposits.[200] (Cf. also EDTA treatment in the sections "Scleroderma," "Calcinosis Cutis," etc.)

Calcinosis of the Uterus

Calcification of the uterus is extremely rare, but it may occur even in combination with metaplastic bone formation.[141] Occasional instances of uterine calcification have been observed, for example, in a patient with hyperparathyroidism associated with discoid lupus erythematosus,[660] and also in a woman with multiple myeloma.[355] It is perhaps relevant that the calcium content of the fluid in an artificial hydrometra was extraordinarily high.[88]

Uterine fibroids quite frequently undergo calcification,[65] especially in women more than 50 years of age[662] (Fig. 266). An embryo, if retained in utero after death, may be transformed into a "lithopedion" through extensive calcification[50a, 65] (Fig. 267).

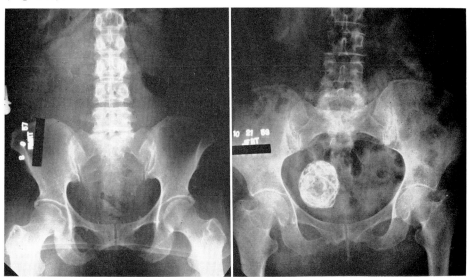

Fig. 266. Calcified uterine fibromyomas. *Left:* Spheroid mass displaying calcification in irregular whorls is the hallmark of uterine fibromyomas regardless of an atypical location of the shadow within the abdomen. *Right:* Despite density of calcification, the whorl-like pattern of uterine fibromyoma is evident.

(After Bartholomew *et al.*,[68] courtesy Postgrad. Med.)

Calculi

Concretions—such as are commonly found in the bile ducts, gallbladder, pancreas, salivary glands, or tonsils—frequently contain large amounts of calcium.[781]

It would not be rewarding to discuss the extensive literature on this subject here, but it may be interesting in the future to explore the possible relationships between these clinical diseases and the calciphylactically induced calcium deposits in the biliary passages, salivary glands, urinary tract, and fauces.

Chondrodystrophia Calcificans Congenita Punctata

Syn., dysplasia epiphysiaria punctata or puncticularis, chondrodystrophia fetalis calcarea or hypoplastica, chondroangiopathia calcarea or punctata, calcareous chondrodystrophy, congenital stippled epiphyses.

This is a rare congenital skeletal defect recognizable by the roentgenographic demonstration of multiple punctate epiphyseal calcific deposits. Other skeletal defects (e.g., shortening of limbs, semiflexion, and limitation of extension in large

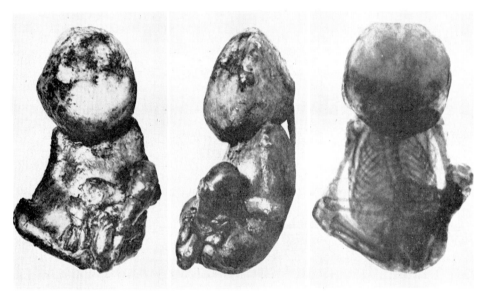

Fig. 267. Lithopedion. Typical aspect of a lithopedion seen from the front, side and on X-ray picture. "Inasmuch as the woman (of whose moral status there is no question) had been a widow for 14 years, the lithopedion had been carried for at least that length of time."
(After Bainbridge,[50a] courtesy Am. J. Obst.)

joints), bilateral congenital cataracts, and mild mental deficiency are also common.[502]

The skin is sometimes markedly thickened, deeply furrowed, and adherent to the deep tissues. Abnormal calcification usually disappears during the third or fourth year of life. The etiology of the disease is unknown, but it is probably transmitted by simple, recessive Mendelian inheritance.[34, 144, 900] Maternal hypothyroidism during pregnancy may also play a predisposing role.[502]

A systematic study of the literature brought out the interesting fact that, contrary to earlier opinion, the cartilage changes are only one manifestation of a general syndrome which involves also the skin and subcutaneous tissue as well as the heart, gastrointestinal tract, central nervous system, and eyes. "Such findings take this syndrome out of the limited category of chondrodystrophies into that of a more generalized disturbance, which can interfere with normal growth, and the development of mesodermal as well as ectodermal structures"[34] (Fig. 268).

Collagen Diseases in General

Some degree of calcinosis may occur in various collagen diseases, although its intensity and frequency are subject to considerable variation. Apart from the "idiopathic calcinoses," calcification is most common in dermatomyositis and scleroderma.

Any type of calcinosis that affects the connective tissue is, of course, essentially a collagen disease, and it has been pointed out—to our mind with great justification—that "the descriptive adjectives calcinosis circumscripta and universalis, though widely used, are equivocal terms. It is impossible to know where circumscript calcinosis ends and universal calcinosis begins in a spectrum of disease states associated with all degrees of calcification from two or three deposits to almost complete encasement in a shell of lime."[971] There exist many transitional forms between scleroderma, Raynaud's syndrome, dermatomyositis, lupus erythematosus, and related collagen diseases. Hence, an unequivocal classification of individual cases with a mixed symptomatology is often impossible.[518, 907, 908, 909, 971]

It has generally been assumed that calcification in collagen disease is a secondary "dystrophic" phenomenon, but our experiments suggest that in many instances the reverse may be true. A stepwise study of the histogenesis of the lesions induced either by calciphylaxis or by direct calcifying compounds strongly intimates that here the diffuse infiltration of connective tissue with a fine calcium precipitate secondarily stimulates inflammatory lesions, sclerosis, and eventually hyalinization; thus, it can be the cause rather than the consequence of collagen disease. It may be more appropriate, therefore, to designate the clinical as well as the experimental collagen diseases in which calcification is a prominent and perhaps even a primary phenomenon as the "calcinoscleroses."[826] (Cf. also individual collagen diseases.)

In this connection it is noteworthy that the metal chelator EDTA can produce beneficial results in a large variety of diseases that fit into our concept of the calcinoscleroses but are otherwise apparently unrelated, such as: coronary artery disease, valvular heart disease, calcinosis universalis, dermatomyositis, rheumatoid arthritis and spondilitis, and scleroderma. Allegedly "it would be ludicrous to believe that [these] diseases are solely metal disturbances," but "it is conceivable that the lowering of ionic calcium in the blood, brought about by Na_2EDTA, could produce a parathyroid response within physiological limits which would result in a more dynamic exchange of calcium throughout the organism. Such exchange would

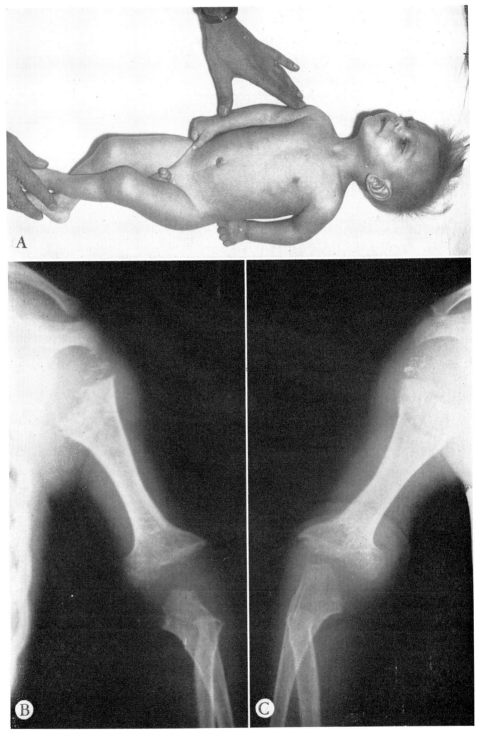

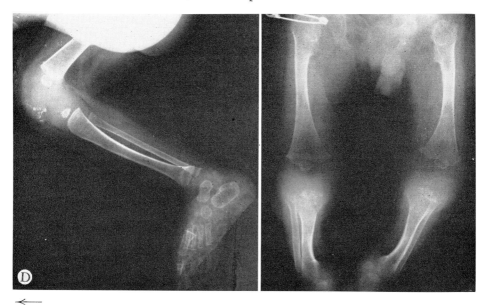

Fig. 268. Chondrodystrophia calcificans congenita punctata. *A:* Shortness of the arms and thighs, enlargement of the knee and elbow joints, with flexion contractures and "scissors legs," extension of neck. *B* and *C:* X-ray of upper extremities. Shortness of both humeri, marked mushrooming of both epiphyseal ends, and fine "stippling" due to calcification in the epiphyseal region. *D:* X-ray of lower extremities (lateral and postero-anterior views). Marked mushrooming of both ends of femora and those of tibias with fine discrete "stippling" in epiphyseal regions. In lateral view, we see also abundant fine stippling around patella and in synovial membrane. There was optic atrophy with bilateral cataracts.

[After Armaly,[34] courtesy A.M.A. Specialty Journals (A.M.A. Arch. Ophth.).]

eventually lead to increased calcium loss and a reduction of net metastatic calcium."[128]

Congenital Ectodermal Defect

This condition, also known as anhidrotic ectodermal dysplasia, is characterized by a dry, grayish, smooth, shiny skin with intolerance to heat because of anhidrosis and hypotrichosis. In addition, there may be saddle nose, chronic rhinitis or ozena, and skeletal defects (e.g., underdeveloped mandible, malformations of the teeth), dysphonia, dysphagia, radiating furrows about the mouth, deformities of the ears, dystrophy of the nails, and mental retardation. The condition is probably related to several other congenital cutaneous anomalies which affect the skin and skeleton. One variant—characterized by leukoplakia of the mouth, dyskeratosis with pigmentation and dystrophy of the nails—may be associated with multiple carcinoma formation.[16] (Cf. also "Werner's Disease," "Rothmund's Disease.")

Dermatofibrosis Lenticularis Disseminata

This may be a kind of capillary angiomatosis. It affects chiefly the extremities and produces elevated nodules averaging up to 1 cm. in diameter whose cut surface is yellowish-brown because they contain fat and hemosiderin. The capillary lumina may be very small and hardly visible, but around them there is intense connective and adipose tissue proliferation, often with lipid-filled macrophages and slits of cholesterol crystals. The overlying epidermis may be normal, atrophied, or acanthotic. Occasionally, "seborrheic keratoses and even basal cell carcinomas are superimposed unto the sclerosing angiomas as if provoked by them."[16] The disseminated form is sometimes accompanied by rheumatoid arthritis, marble-bone disease, and scleroderma.[290]

Dermatomyositis

Syn., polymyositis, pseudotrichinosis. A careful study of the literature led to the conclusion that the following terms have also been used to designate what appears to have been cases of dermatomyositis: dermatomucomyositis, angiomyositis, adenomyositis, neuromyositis, poikiloderma, and poikilodermatomyositis.[153a]

Dermatomyositis is a nonsuppurative, nonspecific inflammatory disease of the striated muscles and the surrounding connective tissue which frequently involves the skin and occasionally the mucous membranes. It manifests itself clinically by pain, fever, and edema and may take an acute, subacute, or chronic course (Figs. 269, 270, 271, 271*a*, 271*b*).

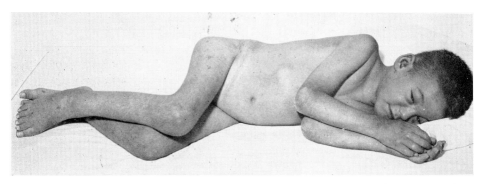

Fig. 269. Dermatomyositis. Edema and erythema of face, eyelids, and extensor surfaces of joints, accompanied by muscular atrophy.
[After Winkelmann,[985] courtesy C. V. Mosby Co. (J. of Chronic Dis.).]

Minor degrees of soft-tissue *calcification* are almost always demonstrable in dermatomyositis by sensitive histochemical techniques. In some comparatively rare cases there are even massive subcutaneous deposits of calcium salts throughout the body, particularly in the connective tissue, the musculature of the pelvis and around the joints[519, 531, 647, 725, 771, 889] (Fig. 271). Dermatomyositis was accompanied by calcinosis cutis in 40 per cent of the children studied at the Mayo Clinic. Extrusion of these calcified masses may cause great discomfort and high fever.[985] A case of "polydermatomyositis haemorrhagica" was also associated with severe calcinosis of the subcutaneous tissue, especially in the forearms.[510]

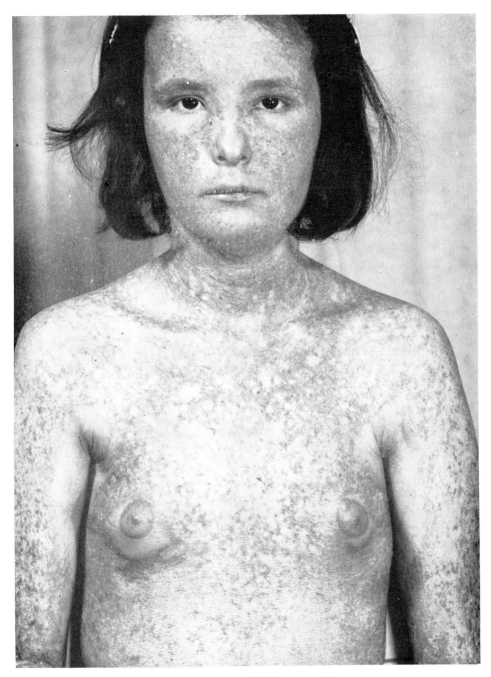

Fig. 270. Dermatomyositis. Extensive poikilodermatous changes.
[After Winkelmann,[985] courtesy C. V. Mosby Co. (J. of Chronic Dis.).]

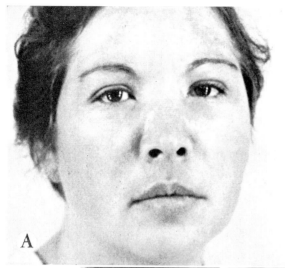

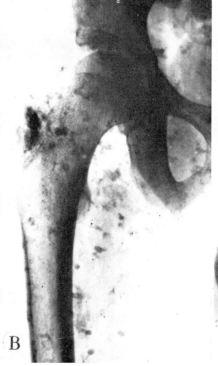

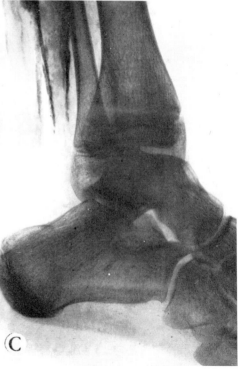

Fig. 271. Dermatomyositis. *A:* Typical facial edema and pigmentation of forehead at onset of disease. *B:* Interstitial calcinosis in musculature of pelvis and thigh. *C:* Calcified envelopes surround attachments of peroneus and gastrocnemius muscles.

(After Kirchhof and Klingmüller,[531] courtesy Springer-Verlag, Berlin.)

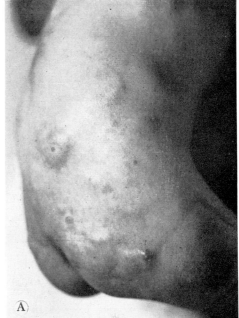

Fig. 271a. Dermatomyositis with generalized calcinosis. Female patient in whom dermatomyositis began at the age of four, gradually worsened until puberty, and after that virtually disappeared. *A:* Sub-cutaneous nodules with abscess formation at the age of nine. *B:* Maximal calcinosis at the age of eight. *C:* Almost complete disappearance of calcium deposits at the age of twelve.

(After Spahr and Brenn,[889] courtesy Helvet. Paediatr. Acta.)

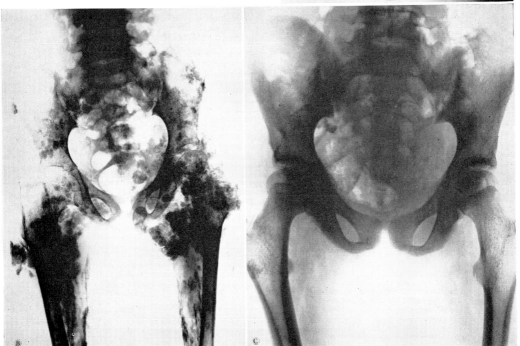

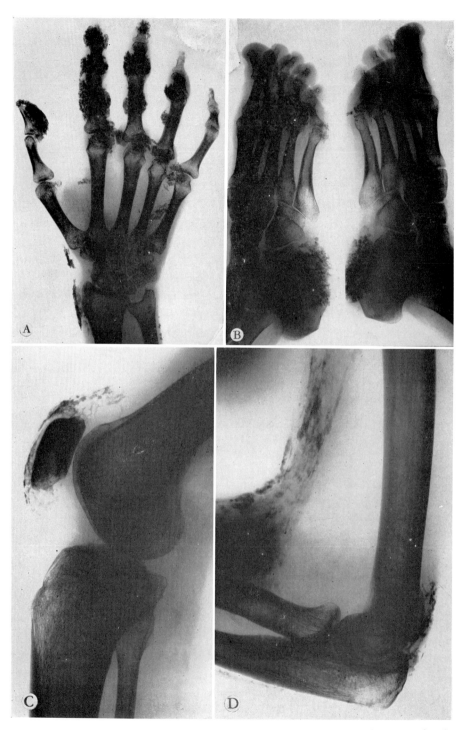

Fig. 271b. Dermatomyositis with generalized calcinosis. 34-year-old woman in whom
dermatomyositis began to develop two years earlier with infiltration of the skin around the eyes
and nose, muscular weakness, tachycardia, and fever. *A:* Soft-tissue calcification in right hand.
B: Dense calcium deposits in both feet. *C:* Right knee with prepatellar calcinosis. *D:* Left elbow
with subcutaneous, intramuscular and particularly periarticular calcinosis.

(After Spahr and Brenn,[889] courtesy Helvet. Paediatr. Acta.)

The blood calcium levels are usually normal or actually subnormal in dermatomyositis,[519] although sometimes elevated values have been observed and these were considered to be manifestations of hyperparathyroidism.[716] Yet in dermatomyositis the blood calcium may remain normal even when intense soft-tissue calcification is present;[372] evidently, hypercalcemia is not indispensable for the production of the lesions.

In two patients with dermatomyositis, the *urinary excretion of calcium* was determined and found to be normal.[654]

Concurrently with the soft-tissue calcification, there may be *"metaplastic ossification,"* the published pictures of which greatly resemble what we call "preosseous tissue."[360, 561, 909, 971] Occasionally there is even true ossification and in this case the distinction from *polymyositis ossificans* may become difficult.[511] In one case dermatomyositis involving the entire body developed following a local *traumatic myositis;*[45] it is possible, of course, that here the original local myositis already reflected a general tendency to develop the systemic disease. *Osteoporosis* is common.[647]

The *serum iron* level is usually low in dermatomyositis, while in most other types of acute muscle disintegration the reverse is true because the discharged muscle iron reappears in the blood. The tendency to bind iron within the affected muscle fibers is assumed to be a specific characteristic of dermatomyositis.[399] This interpretation receives support from histochemical observations indicating that the iron liberated from damaged muscle cells remains fixed locally in dermatomyositis.[719] These findings are of special interest to us in view of the high challenging potency of iron especially in calciphylactic dermatomyositis.

In clinical dermatomyositis—as in the calciphylactic model—a *metachromatic substance* (tingible with mucicarmine or cresyl violet) appears in the affected cutaneous and muscular regions[409] and sometimes mucinous infiltration of the subcutis may be extremely prominent.[519] Simultaneously, the affected muscular and cutaneous regions are infiltrated by an unusually large number of *mastocytes.*[112, 150, 611, 612]

Dermatomyositis is so frequently associated with *scleroderma* that the two conditions are generally considered to represent variants of the same fundamental morbid process.[140, 276] The term "sclerodermatomyositis" was applied to a case of dermatomyositis with scleroderma and particularly intense universal calcinosis unaccompanied by any detectable anomalies in blood calcium and phosphate values.[220] Allegedly "histological changes in skin and muscles in generalized scleroderma and dermatomyositis show no essential difference."[348] "Apparently, the difference between dermatomyositis and scleroderma lies in the observer"; the same case may be described as scleroderma by dermatologists and as myositis by internists.[15] In any event, dermatomyositis has many features in common with scleroderma[597, 647] and may be indistinguishable from the latter.[278, 536] In one of the first cases of dermatomyositis to be published in England, "it was noticed that as each muscle became involved, the skin over it assumed a sclerodermatous character—i.e., it could not be separated from the muscle and it lost its elasticity."[927]

Like scleroderma, dermatomyositis may affect the **buccal mucous membranes and conjunctivas** and such cases have been called "dermatomucopolymyositis."[674] **Ocular lesions** such as retinitis, conjunctivitis, iritis, and paralysis of the ocular muscles are quite common in dermatomyosis.[148, 689] In one typical case of dermatomyositis with a singular retinopathy "cytoid bodies were lying in the nerve-fiber layer (varicose or ganglion-like swelling of fibers). This area obviously corresponded to the patch of retinopathy seen ophthalmoscopically. It also contained an albuminous deposit and showed separation of paralleling nerve fibers." Several previously published cases with similar features are quoted.[947] Focal lesions of the retinal nerve fibers may also occur in dermatomyositis.[926]

The **muscle changes** in dermatomyositis are not specific. There may be necrosis, inflammation, and foreign-body giant-cell formation;[406] but similar lesions are seen in rheumatoid arthritis, pneumonia, thyrotoxicosis, and various other disorders.[486] The changes are particularly reminiscent of those seen in thyrotoxicosis.[276, 278] Let us recall in this connection that thyroxin greatly sensitizes the rat for the lethal effect of calciphylactic "dermatomyositis."

"Edematous polymyositis" is presumably a variant of dermatomyositis in which the skin manifestations are absent or negligible. The disease is usually accompanied by eosinophilia and lesions in the esophagus or soft palate, sometimes with a periorbital "spectacle erythema." There may be hyperthyroidism.[757]

The **cardiac musculature** may also be affected[511, 612, 627] and this can lead to **pulmonary hypertension.**[171] In all these respects dermatomyositis resembles scleroderma.

The relationship with systemic lupus erythematosus is less obvious, but "butterfly erythema" around the cheeks and eyelids may occur in patients with typical dermatomyositis in combination with cutaneous calcinosis.[360] Observations of this type further emphasize the inherent similarities between the collagen diseases and the calcinoses.

There are also similarities between dermatomyositis and **sclerema neonatorum,** but, allegedly, even true dermatomyositis can occur in the newborn.[203]

Hypertrichosis and pigmentation of the skin are not uncommon in dermatomyositis,[318, 741] and the disease may be associated with **psoriasis** and various forms of vesicular and bullous skin lesions.[318]

Not infrequently, dermatomyositis occurs during, or more often after, a systemic **infection,**[140, 511, 628] rheumatic fever,[522, 536] or intoxication.[511] Allegedly it has been possible to reproduce dermatomyositis-like changes in guinea pigs and mice by inoculation with exudate from the lesions of patients suffering from dermatomyositis.[89] However, these observations have not yet been confirmed and, in any event, there is no reason to believe that any particular microorganism or poison is the specific cause of this malady. It is much more probable that dermatomyositis is one of the "pluricausal diseases" in which various potential pathogens can act as immediate eliciting agents after exposure to some predisposing sensitizer.

The occasional occurrence of pronounced *lymphadenitis* in dermatomyositis has also been interpreted as an indication that infection plays an important pathogenic role, especially since certain cases respond well to penicillin.[271, 372] However, responsiveness to antibiotics does not prove a microbial etiology and there seems to be a special tendency for hyperplasia of the lymphatic system, since dermatomyositis can occur in combination with *status thymicolymphaticus*.[252]

The fact that dermatomyositis often responds very favorably to *penicillin* treatment[372] has been thought to indicate that we are dealing "with an allergic response of the organism which yields to penicillin treatment when the causative germ is sensitive to this antibiotic"[271] or with an "allergic-hyperergic response of the rheumatic type."[113]

It has been claimed "that dermatomyositis and *rheumatism* develop on the same toxic-allergic basis."[546] In any event the view that dermatomyositis is essentially a *hypersensitivity reaction* appears to receive support from the observation that it is frequently accompanied by intense *blood eosinophilia*.[9, 38, 60, 317, 406, 432, 639, 741] Occasionally, the blood eosinophil count may be as high as 20 per cent[980] or even 31 per cent.[642]

Dermatomyositis is frequently attended by a variety of *nervous complications*[531] and this fact has been taken to suggest a neural etiology.[616] There may be electroencephalographic changes,[652] but lesions are particularly obvious in the peripheral nerve endings.[529] The term "neuromyositis" has been suggested for cases of dermatomyositis combined with prominent manifestations of polyneuritis.[150, 194, 334]

In rare instances dermatomyositis is completely limited to one side of the body,[433] which allegedly also suggests a nervous participation in the etiology of the disease.

Although a detailed review of the literature confirmed that nervous involvement—particularly perineuritis—is very common in dermatomyositis, there is no evidence that the disease is primarily due to a nervous derangement.[153a]

Special emphasis has been placed upon the comparatively common association of dermatomyositis with *malignant tumors*.[170, 237, 604] There appears to be no particular predisposition for any one kind of neoplasm: dermatomyositis has been observed in association with carcinoma of the lung,[230, 640] gallbladder,[117] mammary gland,[884] ovary,[152, 273, 334] kidney,[230] prostate,[106] and many other organs. There may also be leukemia, "pseudoleukemia," or reticuloendotheliosis.[878]

A woman with dermatomyositis and metastatic pulmonary cancer was shown to be sensitive to her own tumor tissue. "It is postulated that dermatomyositis in cancer may represent an autosensitivity to malignancy."[238] Yet, in one series of 270 cases, the incidence of carcinoma was only 6 per cent.[195]

In dermatomyositis with extensive calcinosis of the muscles, deep ***X-irradiation of the diencephalon*** allegedly produced improvement and occasionally even a "complete cure" with resorption of the calcium deposits. These findings were again thought to indicate the participation of a nervous derangement in the development of the disease.[624]

In connection with the possible role of calcium in the pathogenesis of dermatomyositis it is noteworthy that treatment with the calcium chelator ***EDTA*** is allegedly beneficial.[983]

In cases of poikilodermatomyositis[882] or ordinary dermatomyositis with calcinosis cutis and generalisata[136] ***ACTH*** produced remissions (Fig. 272).

Curiously, ***vitamin-E*** treatment allegedly produced remissions in several cases of dermatomyositis,[48, 81, 654] but in other cases this treatment produced no obvious improvement.[46]

Dupuytren's Contracture

This is an affection of the palmar fascia of one or both hands that leads to permanent flexion-contracture of the fingers. The lesions are frequently nodular and consist of a proliferating, rather cellular, dense, connective tissue which replaces the fat. The cutaneous appendages disappear from the overlying dermis. There may be accumulation of iron pigment and occasional hemorrhages in the palmar aponeurosis, but these changes have been interpreted as the results of ruptures in the hardened connective tissue.[564]

The histologic features of Dupuytren's contracture resemble those of ***keloids, fascial desmoids, induratio penis plastica or "Peyronie's disease,"*** and other fibroplasias to which it may well be related.[156, 462, 471] Dupuytren's contracture has been observed in combination with ***Raynaud's syndrome,***[124] the ***shoulder-hand syndrome*** of Steinbrocker,[895] and ***scleroderma,*** particularly the acrosclerotic form.[236, 282, 560, 574, 688, 959]

Dupuytren's contracture has repeatedly occurred following ***myocardial infarction;*** allegedly here, as in pulmonary hypertrophic osteoarthropathy, derangements in sympathetic innervation and the blood supply may be of a pathogenic importance.[516]

The ***blood calcium*** levels have been claimed to be usually below normal in Dupuytren's contracture,[505] yet ***EDTA*** is allegedly beneficial.[925]

Ehlers-Danlos Syndrome

Syn., cutis hyperelastica, rubber-man syndrome.

This is an inheritable disease characterized by hyperelasticity of the skin and overdistensibility of the joints, with frequent subluxations and sprains. Cutaneous

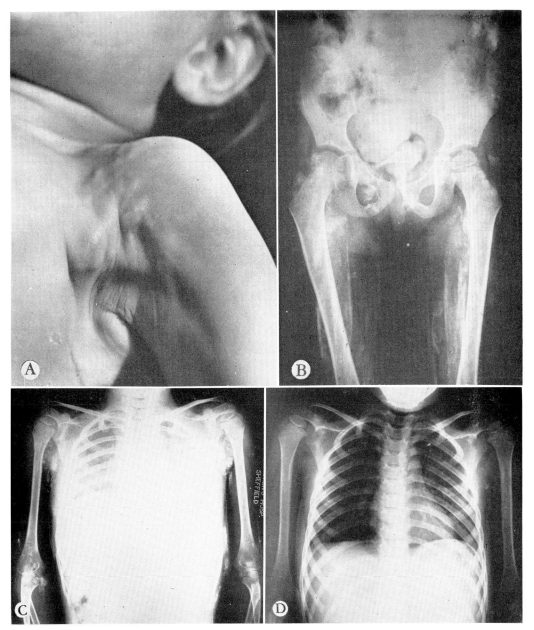

Fig. 272. Dermatomyositis and calcinosis universalis treated with ACTH. *A:* Subcutaneous calcium deposits in shoulder region of girl, aged 4. *B:* Calcium deposits in tissues of lower limbs *C:* Calcinosis of soft tissues especially in axilla before ACTH. *D:* Same patient after ACTH treatment. Calcinosis shown in A and B likewise disappeared following this therapy.

(After Briggs and Illingworth,[136] courtesy Lancet.)

fragility predisposes to the development of cicatricial, often brownish, cutaneous and subcutaneous "pseudomolluscoid tumors" which are nodules containing fibrous tissue, fat, and calcified deposits. The syndrome may also be associated with dental anomalies, club foot, and a characteristic facial type with widely spaced eyes and a broad-bridged nose.[16] A possibly related condition is cutis laxa (*syn.*, dermatochalasis, dermatolysis, cutis pendulum).[797]

Facial hemiatrophy, cf. "Scleroderma."

Heberden's Nodules

These are painless, usually bilateral and symmetrical subcutaneous nodosities, less than 1 cm. in diameter, located around the joints of the terminal phalanges of the digits of the hands. Gradually they tend to become radiopaque and often show histologic evidence of calcification within a hyalinized collagen matrix. These bodies are probably related to rheumatic and rheumatoid nodules, which likewise tend to undergo calcification and sometimes even ossification.[16, 971]

Hemochromatosis and Hemosiderosis

Hemochromatosis.—This disease is characterized by excessive deposition of iron-containing pigments in parenchymal tissues, particularly the liver and pancreas. It is usually accompanied by diabetes mellitus, hepatic cirrhosis, and an intense cutaneous pigmentation, which is only partly due to iron-containing pigments. Most of the affected tissues show a definite increase in their calcium content and apparently "the increase of both calcium and iron are in some way related to each other."[876] It will be recalled that a similar association of iron and calcium deposition in connective tissue is also characteristic of the "sideroscleroses."[515]

Hemosiderosis.—In patients with chronic pancreatitis and pancreatic calcification, the intestinal absorption of Fe^{59} is accelerated and the histochemically detectable iron is greatly augmented in both the parenchymal and the Kupffer cells of the liver. Allegedly, "in man as in animals, iron absorption is enhanced by pancreatic damage; and the study of the literature suggests that absorption of iron may increase whenever the pancreas is severely damaged and that pancreatic failure may be the prime cause of hemosiderosis in man."[247]

Hemochromatosis and hemosiderosis are of special interest in connection with calciphylaxis because of the intense challenging potency of various iron compounds.

Hyperparathyroidism

In man hyperparathyroidism causes osteitis fibrosa, nephrolithiasis, and calcium deposition in predisposed organs (e.g., cardiovascular system, kidney, intestine, lungs, stomach). All these changes are readily duplicated in experimental animals by exogenous parathyroid hormone, which also sensitizes for calciphylaxis. Hence, clinical hyperparathyroidism deserves special consideration here.

Calcification may develop, even in clinical hyperparathyroidism, at sites at which it would rarely occur in animals except as a consequence of calciphylaxis. For example, **cutaneous calcinosis** was observed in a sixteen-year-old boy who developed osteitis fibrosa with hyperplasia of all four parathyroids. Here, the calcification was most intense in the dermal and subcutaneous tissue of the axillae and was described as a "Kalkpanzerhaut" ("calcium-armor skin"). Histologically, the cutaneous lesions were virtually identical with those produced in animals after sensitization by topical calciphylactic challenge (Fig. 273). Simultaneously, there was symmetrical gangrene of both big toes and a pronounced hypercalcemia (14.2 mg. %) which was unexpectedly accompanied by hyperphosphatemia (9.1 mg. %). Since this boy also had a basophilic adenoma of the anterior pituitary, an interaction between the hypophysis and the parathyroids was considered to be of possible pathogenic significance.[454] However, in view of the selective localization of the cutaneous lesions in the axillae and the toes, the role of local challenge by trauma or sweat should perhaps also be considered.[568] In another patient hyperparathyroidism (diagnosed by clinical and radiologic findings without anatomic proof) was found in association with **scleroderma** and was considered to be its cause.[573]

While calcinosis cutis is rare in clinical hyperparathyroidism, **nephrocalcinosis, urolithiasis, calcinosis of the cardiovascular system, lung, stomach, intestines, and other soft tissues, pancreatitis, and pancreatic calcification** with sclerosis are quite common[103, 205, 218, 296, 428, 429, 661] (Figs. 274, 275).

In a patient with a large parathyroid adenoma there developed calcinosis of the cardiovascular system, kidney, lungs, stomach, spleen, adrenals, and lymph nodes.[988] In another case fatal hyperparathyroidism was associated with necrotizing pancreatitis, multiple thrombi in the arteries of the kidneys, parathyroids, and pancreas as well as hypertension and cholecystitis.[440] It was pointed out that the calcium ion enhances the conversion of trypsinogen to trypsin in pancreatic juice and that this may explain the association of pancreatitis and pancreatic calcification with hyperparathyroidism.[429] In any event, it is quite probable that some local challenging factor plays an eliciting role here, since pancreatic adiponecrosis with calcification, though not rare,[36] is by no means a constant accompaniment of clinical hyperparathyroidism. In hyperparathyroidism with pancreatitis, the hypercalcemia is frequently associated with a high or at least normal blood phosphorus level.[320]

In a pregnant woman with **discoid lupus erythematosus** of the face, hyperparathyroidism was attended by calcification of the decidua, the myometrial vessels, and the chorionic villi as well as liponecrosis of the pancreas.[660]

Certain **ocular lesions** (especially in the conjunctiva and cornea) are allegedly quite characteristic of hypercalcemia such as occurs in hyperparathyroidism.[954] Band keratitis, a separate entity, may also be induced by hypercalcemic states.[42, 328, 954]

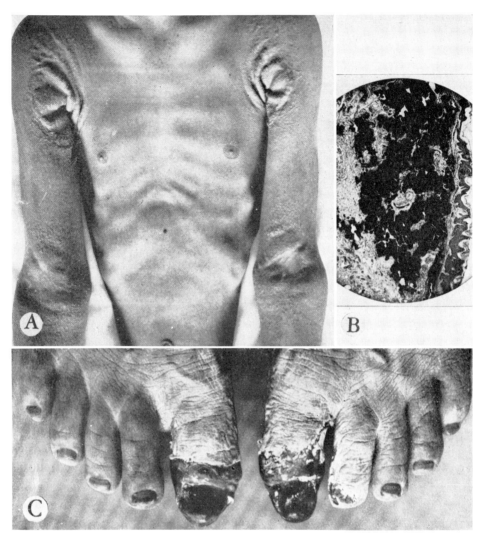

Fig. 273. Hyperparathyroidism conducive to cutaneous calcinosis. *A:* Armor-like thickening of skin especially in axillary and elbow regions. *B:* Histologic picture of dermal calcinosis which appears to be identical with that produced in the rat by calciphylaxis. *C:* Symmetrical gangrene of both big toes presumed to result from vascular calcification.

[After Hoff,[454] courtesy J. F. Bergmann Verlag (Verhandl. Deutsch. Ges. f. innere Med.).]

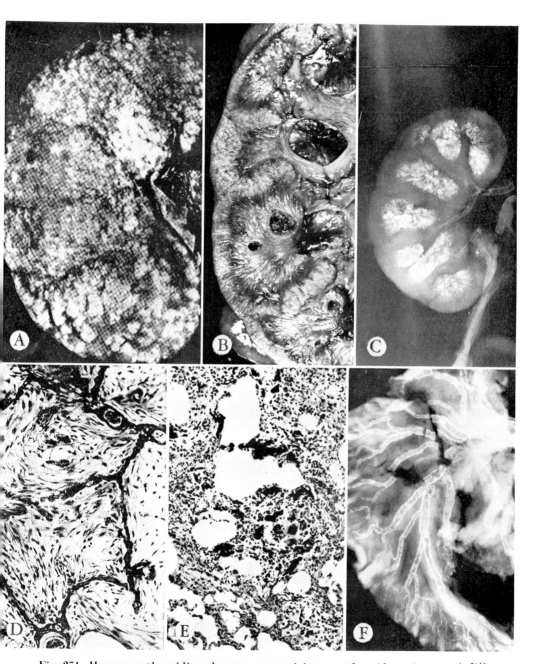

Fig. 274. Hyperparathyroidism due to metastasizing parathyroid carcinoma. *A:* Diffuse granularity of kidney surface with larger depressed scars. *B:* Cut surface of kidney with diffuse cortical calcification, linear streaks of calcium in medullary rays and medullary cysts. Renal pelvis normal. *C:* X-ray picture of kidney showing calcium deposits predominantly in medulla. Renal arteries are diffusely outlined by calcium. *D:* Pulmonary calcinosis largely restricted to alveolar walls and capillaries. Fibrosis was ascribed to an organizing infarct. (Hematoxylin-eosin, ×145.) (Note similarity to calciphylactic pulmonary fibrosis in cat, Fig. 233.) *E:* The type of calcification that was found scattered diffusely throughout the lungs. Multinucleated giant cells and alveolar fibrosis. (Hematoxylin-eosin, ×95.) *F:* Roentgenogram showing diffuse calcification of the superior mesenteric artery and its branches.

(After Ellis and Barr,[296] courtesy Am. J. Path.)

Hyperparathyroidism is frequently associated with **peptic ulcers.**[36, 42, 103, 973] In such cases, it is often difficult to decide whether the peptic ulcer is the result of a primary hyperparathyroidism or whether the metabolic derangements conducive to the ulcer (as well as the ulcer treatment with milk and alkali) have induced a secondary hyperparathyroidism.

Many accompaniments of clinical hyperparathyroidism strikingly resemble some of the experimental calciphylactic syndromes. Of course, in man severe progressive primary hyperparathyroidism (due to idiopathic parathyroid hyperplasia

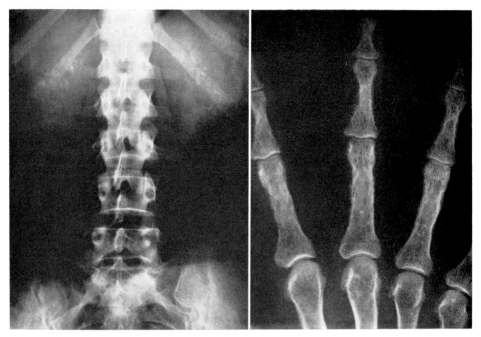

Fig. 275. Hyperparathyroidism with nephrocalcinosis. *Left:* Nephrocalcinosis. *Right:* Associated subperiosteal bone resorption characteristic of hyperparathyroidism.
(After Bartholomew *et al.*,[68] courtesy Postgrad. Med.)

or neoplasia) is rare; it could account for calciphylactic sensitization only in exceptional cases. Yet allegedly, **"masked hyperparathyroidism,"** with hypercalcemia but without hypercalciuria or hypophosphatemia, often leads to calcinosis and renal insufficiency in patients with peptic ulcers.[42] (Cf. "Milk-Alkali Syndrome of Burnett *et al.*")

Secondary hyperparathyroidism can also result from renal disease and "pluricausal pathogenic situations"; hence, excessive parathyroid activity is by no means so rare as is commonly thought.[658] A uremic patient, who probably belonged to this category, developed enormous periarticular calcium deposits around the shoulder and hip joints following prolonged and excessive alkali intake for a duodenal ulcer. There was also intense nephrocalcinosis. Here, uremia was thought to have contributed to the induction of a secondary hyperparathyroidism. However, the blood calcium and phosphorus levels were essentially normal and it was "especially pointed out that hypercalcemia is not necessary for the development of even a very marked calcinosis"[461] (Fig. 276).

It should be kept in mind that *hyperparathyroidism may take an interrupted course* with severe gastrointestinal attacks and prolonged, virtually complete remissions during which the disease is difficult to diagnose.[43]

Usually, all the manifestations of hyperparathyroidism are ascribed to the mobilization of excess calcium and phosphorus from the bones. As we shall see, however (cf. "Speculations"), there is evidence in favor of the suggestion that the mobilization of calcifiable organic matter, particularly *mucopolysaccharides,* is equally important.[301]

Hypervitaminosis D

Although hypervitaminosis D is not a spontaneous disease, we mention it here because it comes closest to the conditions of sensitization used in the majority of our experiments. The literature on the subject has been summarized elsewhere;[514, 739] suffice it here to mention a few instructive case reports.

In man—as in the experimental animal—cardiovascular, renal, and intestinal calcifications are the most common changes induced by overdosage with vitamin-D compounds; however, even without recognizable calciphylactic challenge, patients may also respond with lesions very similar to those induced in animals by calciphylaxis.

For example, in patients given large amounts of the vitamin-D preparation Ertron,® calcification appeared sometimes in the pancreas, parathyroids, joints, and lymph nodes; this was usually accompanied by granuloma formation, presumably as a consequence of irritation by calcium precipitates. Occasionally there was also calcification of the subcutis with intense pruritus.[514]

Several other cases of Ertron®-intoxication (some fatal) have been published. In most of these there was marked periarticular, subcutaneous, cardiovascular, renal, pancreatic, gastric, and pulmonary calcification,[101, 644, 673, 921, 936] sometimes with multiple subcutaneous calcific deposits.[469]

In a woman with long-standing scleroderma and Raynaud's disease, treatment with excessive amounts of a vitamin-D preparation (intended as a cure for her arthritis) resulted in extraordinarily intense calcification in the skin, pelvis, buttocks, lung, hands, and feet[606] (Fig. 277).

In a child chronic overdosage with vitamin D produced osteosclerosis accompanied by calcinosis in the kidney, lung, gastrointestinal tract, and adrenals.[982]

In a patient who received Ertron® (as a treatment for bursitis!), intense calcification developed not only in the affected shoulder but also under the skin and in the soft tissues of the shoulder region. This was accompanied by exfoliative

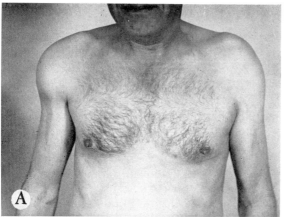

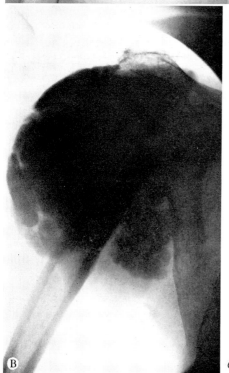

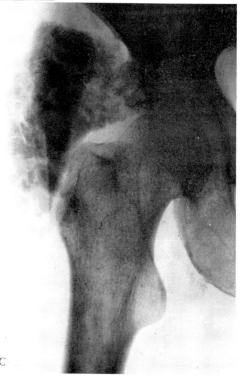

Fig. 276. Renal insufficiency with severe calcinosis due to excessive alkali-intake. *A:* Swelling at right shoulder. *B:* X-ray of right shoulder region. *C:* X-ray of right hip region. *D:* Tumor of right shoulder at autopsy after removal of cutaneomuscular covering. *E:* Tumor excised and cut open after evacuation of its white, "toothpaste-like" contents. *F:* Very small, contracted granular kidneys.

(After Holten and Lundbaeck,[461] courtesy Acta Med. Scandinav.)

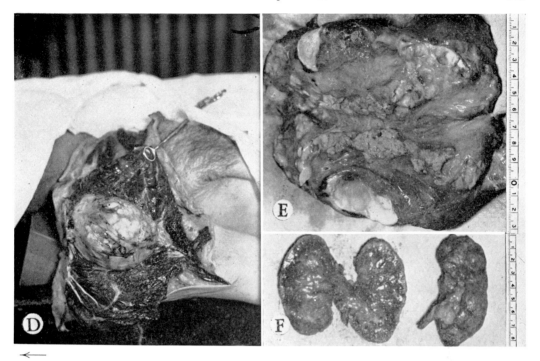

dermatitis and pigmentation of the skin (pityriasis rubra). "Connective tissue or fat deposits" appeared on the conjunctivas and eventually X-ray shadows developed indicating calcification about numerous joints. Almost all these disturbances disappeared upon cessation of Ertron® therapy. Another patient observed by the same investigator developed a maculopapular eruption about the face, his eyes became bloodshot, and his teeth extremely sensitive to temperature.[346] Sometimes there develop occlusive arterial lesions (Figs. 278, 279).

Hypervitaminosis D undoubtedly can lead to calcium deposition in the sclera, cornea,[356] and sometimes the conjunctiva, in man.[954]

Hypervitaminosis D in a patient with Paget's disease led to calcification in the kidney, cardiovascular system (particularly the left atrium), lung, and gastric mucosa. In addition there was a "heavy focal calcium deposit in the subcutaneous tissue surrounded by marked fibroplastic reaction in which young fibroblasts and foreign-body cells were numerous."[964] It is possible that in this case the metabolic disturbances characteristic of Paget's disease induced a special hypersensitivity to vitamin D.

In a child hypervitaminosis D led to skin induration which was clinically diagnosed as scleroderma, but histologically consisted of a granuloma with foreign-body giant cells and cholesterol crystals. At the same time there was nephrocalcinosis.[731]

As a rule hypervitaminosis D produces essentially the same kind of "non-

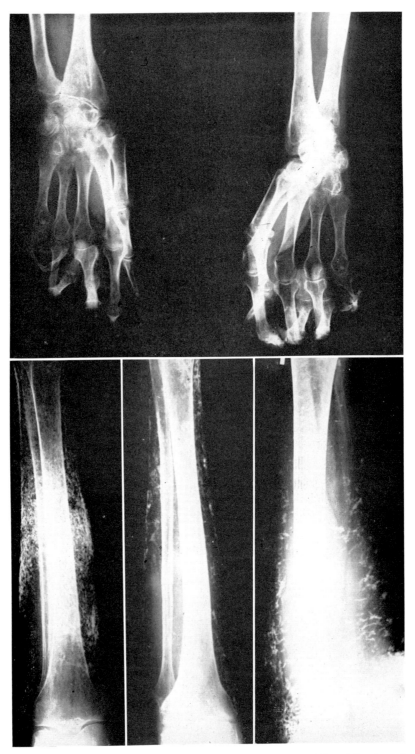

Fig. 277. Hypervitaminosis D. Forty-eight-year-old woman with calcinosis universalis and scleroderma. *Top:* Hands with contractures and rheumatoid type of atrophic arthritis. *Bottom:* X-rays of thigh and legs showing diffuse soft-tissue calcification.

(After Livingstone and Walker,[606] courtesy Royal Medico-Chirurgical Society of Glasgow.)

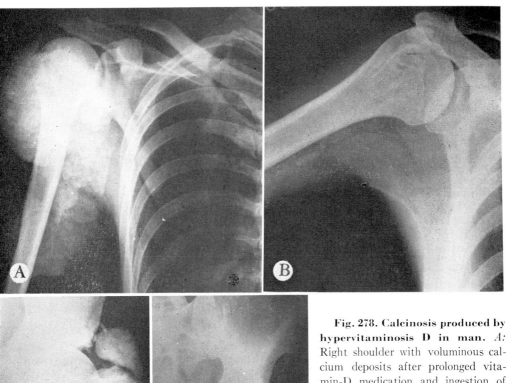

Fig. 278. Calcinosis produced by hypervitaminosis D in man. *A:* Right shoulder with voluminous calcium deposits after prolonged vitamin-D medication and ingestion of high milk diet. *B:* Same shoulder six months after discontinuation of medication. *C:* Left hip joint of same patient with intense peri-articular calcium deposition. *D:* Same hip joint six months after discontinuation of medication.

(After Freeman *et al.,*[345] courtesy J.A.M.A.)

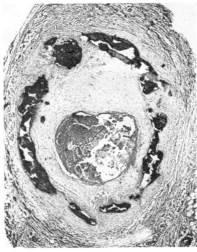

Fig. 279. Calcinosis produced by hypervitaminosis D in man. Cross section through dorsalis pedis artery of a woman with severe vitamin-D poisoning whose leg had to be amputated because of inadequate circulation. [Courtesy S. Freeman (unpublished observation).]

specific" generalized soft-tissue calcification and bone lesions in man as in the experimental animal; however, when hypervitaminosis-D-induced calcification develops in unusual locations, possibly some topical trauma or pre-existent disease may act as a calciphylactic challenger.

Hypervitaminosis D may even develop in the absence of an exogenous intoxication. In cases of the so-called "idiopathic hypercalcemia of infancy" nephrocalcinosis and ectopic calcification in other tissues are not uncommon. "Although it is not proved, it seems probable that the disease is due to vitamin-D overactivity in the presence of a milk diet, and that only those infants who are unusually sensitive to the effects of vitamin D are likely to develop it."[288] (Cf. also "Sarcoidosis.")

Hypoparathyroidism

While acute destruction of the parathyroids merely produces a rapidly fatal tetany, the chronic variety of either parathyroprival or "idiopathic" hypoparathyroidism elicits a rather complex progressive syndrome. In addition to tetany, convulsions and muscle cramps, there are *paresthesias, mental changes, vomiting, constipation, soft-tissue calcification, cataracts, dental defects, and ectodermal changes involving the hair, nails, and skin.*[145, 571, 727]

The calcium content of the *lens* increases considerably in parathyroidectomized rabbits at the time the lenticular opacities develop. A similar increase in calcium concentration has been noted in senile cataracts of man.[753]

Calcific deposits may form in the *basal ganglia* and cause epileptiform fits.[22, 894] The condition is sometimes familial.[683] The mechanism of this type of calcification has not yet been clarified; it could be due to the hyperphosphatemia characteristic of hypoparathyroidism, since an excess of phosphate tends to enhance calcium precipitation.

Occasionally, hypoparathyroidism with calcinosis is accompanied by *Raynaud's* phenomenon and *scleroderma.*[327, 362, 375] Some connection between *gout* and hypoparathyroidism has been suggested by the observation that hyperuricemia and even classical gout occur in a fairly high percentage of patients with hyperparathyroidism. However, surgical correction of the hyperparathyroidism did not restore the elevated serum uric acid levels to normal.[660a] One patient passed a uric acid stone after removal of a parathyroid adenoma,[463a] while in three cases of hyperparathyroidism with articular manifestations an unexplained hyperuricemia was noted.[997a]

In rare instances idiopathic hypoparathyroidism appears to have developed as a result of some *stressful* experience, such as physical fatigue or emotional excitement,[300] and tetany is quite frequently aggravated by exertion.[12]

True hypoparathyroidism responds readily to treatment with parathyroid hormone and can thereby be distinguished from *pseudohypoparathyroidism* (cf. p. 395) which is parathyroid-hormone insensitive.[300]

Ichthyosis and Other Types of Hyperkeratosis

Intense cutaneous scaling reminiscent of ichthyosis occurs very rarely in scleroderma.[338] In one case of generalized ichthyotic hyperkeratosis, parathyroidectomy was allegedly beneficial,[446] but this finding requires confirmation.

Actually, we have no convincing evidence to suggest any relationship between ichthyosis or other exfoliative dermatoses and the parathyroids or calcium metabolism in general; but up to now there has been no special reason to suspect such interrelations. In view of the great frequency of exfoliative dermatoses in experimental calciphylaxis the calcium content of the skin in the corresponding clinical conditions should be examined.

Impetigo Herpetiformis

Most investigators consider impetigo herpetiformis to be a particularly severe variety of dermatitis herpetiformis (Duhring's disease). Like the latter, it is characterized by vesicle formation at the epidermo-dermal junction with the accumulation of leukocytes (chiefly eosinophilic) within these vesicles. The mucous membranes, including those of the oropharynx and esophagus, are frequently also affected. The disease may be of bacterial origin, especially since many cases respond favorably to antibiotics,[16] but even if this were so, humoral factors could still exert a decisive conditioning influence in determining susceptibility to this effect of the causative organism.

Considerable evidence has accumulated in favor of the concept that impetigo herpetiformis develops with particular frequency in patients with chronic *parathyroid insufficiency,* especially during *pregnancy,* which represents an additional strain on calcium metabolism[116, 243, 244, 302, 354, 376] (Fig. 280). In several such cases remissions were obtained by treatment with parathyroid hormone or DHT.[315, 591, 791]

One case of impetigo herpetiformis with pronounced hypocalcemia resembled *psoriasis.*[544] (Cf. also "Psoriasis.")

Keloids

Keloids are foci of fibrous hyperplasia that usually develop at the site of a scar. They form elevated, rounded, white, sometimes pink, firm bodies which essentially correspond to proliferating scar tissue and consist of parallel bundles of hyalinized connective tissue covered by a thin epidermis with an atrophic interpapillary epithelium. Keloids are more common in Negroes than in Caucasians and occur with particular frequency in young adult females.

The histologic resemblance between keloid and hypertrophic *scleroderma* tissue is striking; indeed, often a differential diagnosis between extensive flat keloids and scleroderma may be difficult.[559]

In cases with spontaneous keloids the *blood calcium* is said to be often elevated, while it is normal in patients with cicatricial keloids.[505]

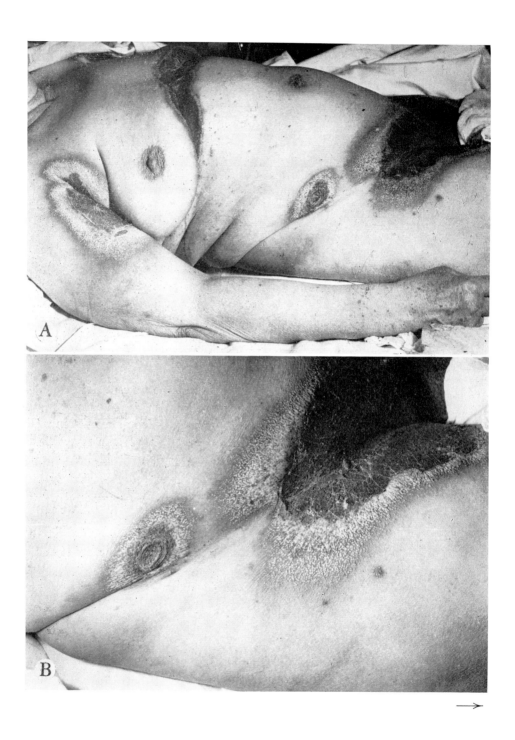

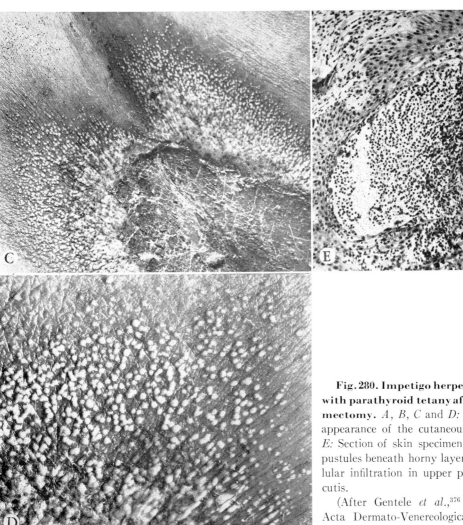

Fig. 280. Impetigo herpetiformis
with parathyroid tetany after strumectomy. *A*, *B*, *C* and *D:* External
appearance of the cutaneous lesions.
E: Section of skin specimen showing
pustules beneath horny layer and cellular infiltration in upper portion of
cutis.

(After Gentele *et al.*,[376] courtesy
Acta Dermato-Venereologica, Stockholm.)

The mastocyte count of keloids is usually high, especially in the peripheral zone, and this is accompanied by metachromasia of the ground substance during active growth. However, as the keloids involute, the mastocyte count diminishes; and then the intensity of tissue mastocytosis is not very different in keloids and ordinary scar tissue.[172, 710, 972]

Apparently, in some types of keloids *EDTA* has given favorable results.[925]

Leukoplakia and Kraurosis Vulvae

Leukoplakia is a disease characterized by whitish thickening of the epithelium of a mucous membrane. One of its common varieties is apparently the mucosal analogue of cutaneous senile keratosis. The condition tends to develop at the site of chronic local irritation (e.g., by smoking or ill-fitting pessaries and dentures). It is often precancerous, but whitish patches of leukoplakia may also occur in psoriasis, mycosis, lichen planus, and many types of stomatitis which do not lead to malignancy.

One form of leukoplakia, *kraurosis vulvae,* may show features reminiscent of scleroderma;[365] indeed, "some cases, at least, which are diagnosed leukoplakia are examples of white spot scleroderma of the vulva"[525] and kraurosis vulvae may merely be one form of scleroderma.[594]

Libman-Sacks Syndrome

This is merely a variety of lupus erythematosus in which verrucous endocarditis is prominent. (Cf. "Lupus Erythematosus Disseminatus.")

Lichen Sclerosus

Syn., lichen sclerosus et atrophicus, dermatitis lichenoides chronica atrophicans, lichen albus of Zumbusch, Csillag's disease, lichen sclerosus of Hallopeau, leucodermie atrophique ponctuée of Millian.

Lichenification is a thickening of the skin with exaggeration of its normal markings, so that the striae form a crisscross pattern. It follows chronic irritation, for example, in pruritic skin. The form known as lichen sclerosus is a chronic, not or only slightly pruritic, localized eruption characterized by ivory white, firm macules and slightly elevated papules of irregular shape and size. Atrophy appears in the late stages. Histologically we find a dense, subepidermal zone of homogenized collagen beneath which is an accumulation of lymphocytes. The histologic features resemble those of balanitis xerotica; however, keratotic plugging of follicles, dense parakeratosis, and edema or microvesiculation at the epidermo-dermal junction help to characterize lichen sclerosus.[16]

The similarity between certain forms of lichen sclerosus and *scleroderma* has frequently been emphasized. Indeed, some varieties of lichen sclerosus can hardly be differentiated from the form of scleroderma known as "white spot disease."[122, 321, 569] According to many authorities the two dermatoses are only different manifestations of the same disorder,[396] though others doubt this.[893] Like sclero-derma, lichen albus often affects the tongue.[395]

Lipocalcinogranulomatosis

Syn., hygromatosis lipocalcinogranulomatosa progrediens.

This is presumably a disease closely related to the lipo-fibro-calcareous myopathy. The first case described under this name was that of an 11-year-old girl in whom several, up to "goose-egg-sized," tumors developed around the scapulas, shoulder, elbow, and hip joints, bilaterally in symmetrical distribution. Biopsy revealed that the foci consisted of necrotic fat tissue which developed a "lipophagic granuloma," and upon disintegration the fatty material underwent calcification. The disease had begun nine years earlier and followed an undulating course with many remissions. The granulomas appear to develop mainly from the adipose tissue of the joint capsules and contain numerous pseudoxanthoma cells as well as calcium-ingesting foreign-body giant cells[916] (Fig. 281).

Several additional cases of lipocalcinogranulomatosis have since been described.[914, 917, 918] In one of these the formation of foci was limited to the tongue. In another, hypertrophy and ossification of a parathyroid was combined with pancreatic fat necrosis. The skeletal muscle fibers may likewise contain both fat and calcium. The frequent association of calcification in muscles and in the adjacent bursae has been interpreted as "an expression of hitherto unknown canalicular connections between joint capsules, tendons, tendon sheaths and muscles." The disease may be accompanied by osteitis fibrosa, hypercalcemia, hypercholesterolemia, and renal disease.[919]

In a patient with multiple para-articular foci (containing calcium, fat, and pseudoxanthoma cells) there was acute pancreatitis with pancreatic adiponecrosis, osteitis fibrosa, hypercalcemia (19.9 mg. %), pronounced parathyroid hyperplasia with adenoma formation, and finally fatal nephrocalcinosis. In addition this patient exhibited calcific deposits in: the parathyroids, anterior pituitary, a corpus albicans of the ovary, the mammary gland, and the reticuloendothelial cells of the spleen and liver.[918] Thus, here lipocalcinogranulomatosis was associated with a series of organ changes that can be reproduced experimentally by calciphylaxis. (Cf. "Lipo-Fibro-Calcareous Myopathy.")

Lipo-Fibro-Calcareous Myopathy

This is a chronic disease, often with long periods of remissions, characterized by the induration of skeletal muscle tissue and its gradual substitution by fatty, fibrous, and calcareous masses. In view of the usually symmetrical development of these lesions and their frequent association with mental disease, the malady was considered to be of nervous or "toxic" origin.[634, 635, 636, 637, 760]

Under the heading "polyfibromatoses," the lipo-fibro-calcareous myopathy has

been placed in one class with keloids, keloid-like scleroderma, Dupuytren's contracture, etc., as a "particular hyperplastic type of reactivity of the connective
tissue to any kind of external stimulus."[931]

It has frequently been observed that multiple, spontaneous fat necroses with
subsequent calcification and the formation of a fibrous, giant-cell-containing
granuloma can occur, especially in certain predisposed areas, such as the pannicu-

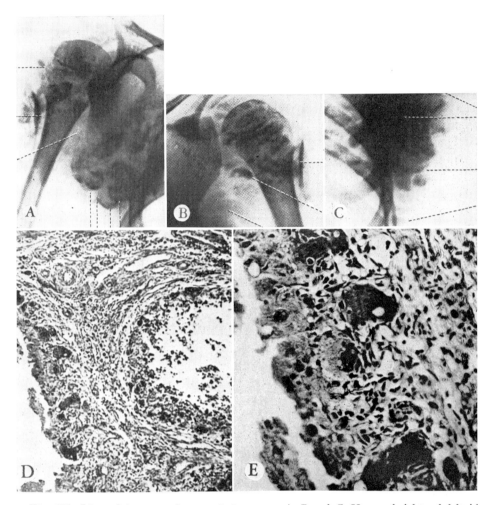

Fig. 281. Lipocalcinogranulomatosis in man. *A*, *B* and *C:* X-ray of right subdeltoid
bursa and retroscapular tumor with cloudy, shield-shaped and sickle-shaped shadows (dotted
lines). *D:* Histologic aspect of surgically removed portions of lipocalcinogranuloma. The cavity
on the left still contains remnants of calcium. The cavity on the right is lined by necrotic lipid-
containing material as well as calcium- and fat-containing macrophages. *E:* Higher magnification of a portion of D. Here, the fatty vacuoles in the giant cells are clearly visible.
(After Teutschlaender,[916] courtesy Fisher Verlag, Stuttgart.)

lus adiposus of the extremities, the periarticular fat, and the finger tips. This has been described as "lipocalcinogranulomatosis," but adjacent striated muscles are also affected.[253, 790, 915, 916, 919] The latter condition is obviously related to, if not identical with, the lipo-fibro-calcareous myopathy. (Cf. "Lipocalcinogranulomatosis.")

Lupus Erythematosus (Discoid and Disseminated)

There is still considerable controversy as to the relationship between the discoid and systemic forms of lupus erythematosus, but it is quite probable that the two are related and many dermatologists consider the former to be a localized, cutaneous variant of the latter.

Discoid lupus erythematosus (*syn.*, lupus sebaceous, lupus superficialis, ulerythema centrifugum, lupus erythematodes).—This is a usually chronic, but occasionally acute, disease of the skin characterized by red, well-circumscribed, scaly patches of various sizes and configurations which cause atrophy and superficial scar formation. The acute form is often fatal. The chronic form causes follicular plugging and occurs in the exposed areas (face, scalp, hands) (Fig. 282).

In one patient with severe discoid lupus erythematosus the "butterfly lesion" was excised and replaced by full-thickness skin grafts taken from postauricular

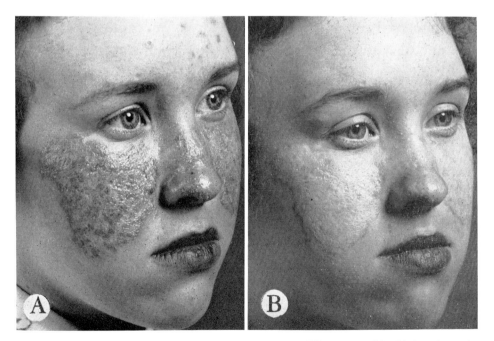

Fig. 282. Chronic discoid lupus erythematosus. Fifteen-year-old girl in whom the lesion was present for 13 years. *A:* Before treatment. *B:* Response to Camoquin.®
[After Winkelmann,[985] courtesy C. V. Mosby Co. (J. Chron. Dis.).]

sites. The disease evolved both in the grafts and in the donor sites, although it subsequently responded well to triamcinolone treatment.[681]

Disseminated lupus erythematosus (*syn.*, exanthematous or systemic lupus erythematosus, S.L.E.).—Although this disease may be fulminating and rapidly fatal, it usually runs a chronic undulating course characterized by variable periods of activity interspersed with remissions. It is distinguished clinically by fever, muscle and joint pains, anemia, leukopenia, and a skin eruption similar to that of discoid lupus erythematosus. It is accompanied by anomalies in the serum protein constitution, the most significant of which is the appearance of a factor responsible for the formation of the characteristic and diagnostically important "LE phenomenon." The most typical structural changes are: fibrinoid degeneration in the connective tissue, alteration of nuclear material that forms the "hematoxylin bodies," and less regularly the occurrence of epithelioid cell granulomas, which tend to enclose masses of fibrinoid and nuclear material (Fig. 283).

The relationship between systemic lupus erythematosus and ***rheumatoid arthritis*** is a matter of debate, but the two conditions are frequently associated.[518, 881, 971]

As previously stated, the combination of systemic lupus erythematosus and ***scleroderma*** is so common that the two diseases have been suspected to be merely different expressions of the same fundamental morbid change.[71, 224 416, 518, 729, 892, 907, 908, 971] In one woman who suffered from progressive scleroderma for fifteen years, eventually a typical systemic lupus erythematosus with a positive LE test developed.[679] LE cells can likewise occur in typical scleroderma.[942] The pulmonary lesions of systemic lupus erythematosus are also quite similar to those of scleroderma (Fig. 284).

Soft-tissue calcification is not as common in systemic lupus erythematosus as it is in scleroderma or dermatomyositis, but it may occur;[224, 518, 524, 971] the calcium deposits in systemic lupus erythematosus, like those in scleroderma, proved on X-ray diffraction to assume the apatite pattern.[224] It has been claimed, furthermore, that typical systemic lupus erythematosus may gradually develop into scleroderma with cutaneous calcinosis.[415] In one patient with extensive calcinosis in the soft tissues of the forearm and pelvis the clinical picture initially resembled that of lupus erythematosus disseminatus, but in later stages that of dermatomyositis or scleroderma.[363] These facts clearly suggest some relationship between the diseases.

In rare cases systemic lupus erythematosus may cause an ***encephalopathy*** owing to involvement of the cerebral blood vessels.[242]

The etiology of systemic lupus erythematosus is unknown, but the disease has long been considered to depend on some ***hypersensitivity reaction;*** one causative antigen may be related to the action of ***actinic rays*** on the sensitized body, since the patients are usually very sensitive to light.[341]

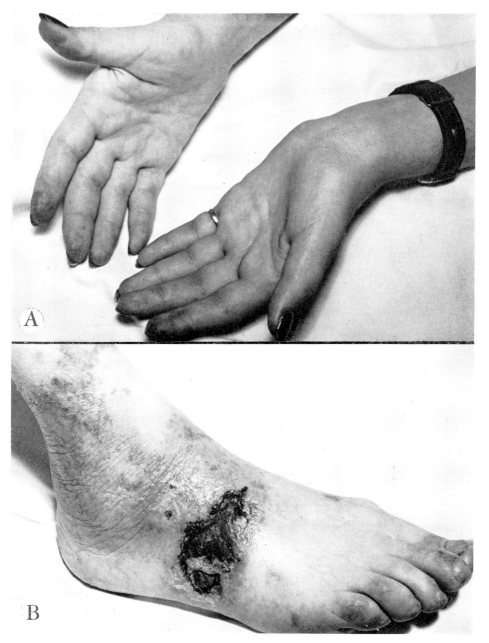

Fig. 283. Lupus erythematosus disseminatus. *A:* Petechial erythema about the finger tips. *B:* Reticulated pattern of petechial livedo and infarctive ulceration presumably due to the angiitis which accompanies this diease. The ulcer is superficial and has jagged edges.

[After Winkelmann,[985] courtesy C. V. Mosby Co. (J. Chron. Dis.).]

On the other hand, systemic lupus erythematosus—like dermatomyositis, scleroderma, and periarteritis nodosa—has been regarded as a typical disease of adaptation. It was "suggested that it is true of these *'stress dermatoses,'* as Osler, in 1900, said of the diseases of the 'erythema group,' that (1) 'similarity of lesions may result from a variety of causes,' and (2) 'unity of cause may be associated with a variety of lesions.' It is further suggested that many of these dermatoses, which have been attributed to either allergic reactions or emotional tensions, or both, may with profit be regarded as being variants of the stress response of Selye. Whether the wide variations in the response are due (1) to qualitative variations in the effect of the stressor agent, or (2) effects of the actual or apparent etiologic agent independent of its stressor effect, or (3) latent innate tendencies or

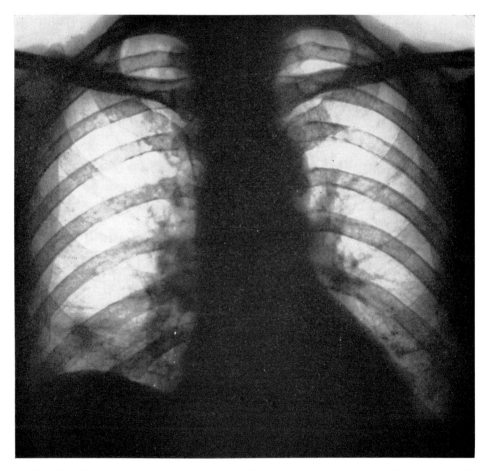

Fig. 284. Pulmonary changes in systemic lupus erythematosus. Changes near the base predominate on right side.

(After Hegglin,[434] courtesy Ztschr. f. Rheumaforschg.)

individual predilections of the patient, or any two, or all three, or other as yet unknown factors, remains to be elucidated."[35]

For unknown reasons systemic lupus erythematosus often responds very well to treatment with various ***antimalarial compounds***[985] and allegedly sometimes even to ***vitamin-E*** treatment.[159]

Mastocytomas and Urticaria Pigmentosa

Mastocyte tumors occur spontaneously in the dog[107, 425, 566] and mouse,[54, 260, 359] but they are uncommon in other species[752, 775] and extremely rare in man.[108, 127, 452] In one patient a mastocytoma was associated with hepatomegaly, splenomegaly, and diffuse focal accumulations of enormous numbers of mastocytes in the skeleton, lymph nodes, kidney, and ovary. There was also osteoporosis, presumed to result from the "lytic effects of the mast cell accumulations."[108] However, widespread sclerosis and fibrosis of the bones is quite common not only in patients suffering from mastocytomas but also in cases of urticaria pigmentosa.[777]

The focal accumulations of mastocytes in ***urticaria pigmentosa*** have likewise been looked upon as a kind of mast-cell tumor, especially since sometimes the disease is associated with a systemic mastocytosis[39, 367, 724, 745, 778, 872] (Fig. 285).

These spontaneous mastocyte proliferations are mentioned here because calciphylactic "dermatomyositis" depends largely upon mastocyte degranulation.

Milia and Epidermal Inclusion Cysts

In the skin epidermal, epidermoid, sebaceous, and dermoid cysts can occur. The term "epidermal" cysts refers to lesions within the epidermis (as seen in pemphigus), while "epidermoid" indicates cysts lined by epidermis. Epidermoid cysts may be congenital or due to traumatic displacement of epidermis into the subcutis. Very small, pinhead-sized, and often multiple lesions of this type are called "milia." They presumably result from obstruction of cutaneous gland ducts. Both epidermoid cysts and milia have a certain tendency to undergo calcification and sometimes even ossification. This is especially common in milia resulting from displacement of urinary tract epithelium and in sebaceous cysts.[16, 781]

Milk-Alkali Syndrome of Burnett et al.

Syn., milk-drinker's syndrome, Burnett's syndrome.

This condition was first reported under the descriptive heading "Hypercalcemia without hypercalciuria or hypophosphatemia, calcinosis and renal insufficiency— A syndrome following prolonged intake of milk and alkali." Its additional characteristics are normal serum alkaline phosphatase, marked renal insufficiency with uremia, mild alkalosis, generalized calcinosis, and ocular lesions reminiscent of band keratitis. Except for the ocular and renal lesions the condition markedly improves upon the withdrawal of excess milk, alkali, and calcium from the diet. The following sequence of events is thought to be responsible for this syndrome: "ex-

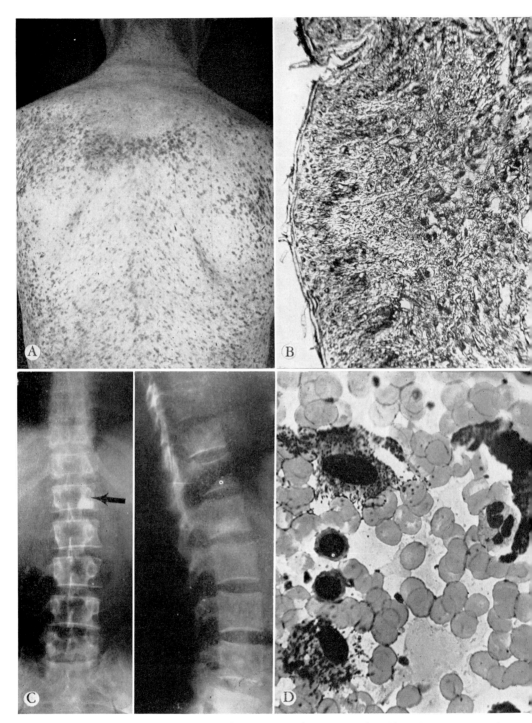

Fig. 285. Urticaria pigmentosa (mastocytosis). *A:* Extensive skin lesions on the back. *B:* Skin biopsy showing multitude of mast cells in corium. *C:* (Left) Antero-posterior X-ray of dorso-lumbar spine showing coarse and dense vertical trabeculae and condensing islets in vertebral bodies (arrow). *C:* (Right) Lateral roentgenogram of dorso-lumbar spine showing essentially similar changes. *D:* Bone-marrow aspirate showing mastocytes with coarse granules in cytoplasm (oil immersion).

[After Poppel *et al.*,[724] courtesy Yearbook Publishing Inc. (Am. J. Radiol.).]

cessive intakes of milk (a foodstuff high in calcium and phosphorus) and alkalis; kidney damage; tendency to fixation in urinary calcium excretion; hypercalcemia; tendency to supersaturation in respect to calcium phosphate; and calcinosis."[161]

Although the milk-alkali syndrome is now recognized as a specific morbid entity, "in some cases hyperparathyroidism or sarcoidosis may be present and these should always be suspected. In other cases evidence may be found of potassium depletion, hypomagnesemia or some other electrolyte disturbance."[902]

The *calcinosis* may manifest itself by the formation of multiple subcutaneous calcified nodules,[161] massive calcinosis with huge, but often reversible, periarticular calcium deposits,[461, 645, 735] or calcification of arteries and even of the penis.[645]

The ocular changes were described as "white, chalk-like plaques in the sclera of each eye,"[645] hazy, granular, subepithelial deposits running concentrically with the limbus, or small glasslike particles in the conjunctivas of the palpebral fissure which upon biopsy were shown to contain an amorphous material, presumably calcium salts.[161, 206, 954] The most typical ocular change is a perilimbal, calcium infiltration of the cornea, a "band keratitis"[735] (Fig. 286).

The *bones* often show signs of proliferation, especially in the periosteal and cancellous regions.[161]

There may be multiple, papular, pruritic *skin lesions,*[735] but their possible association with evanescent cutaneous calcinosis has not been examined, although in some cases of this syndrome generalized pruritus is associated with subcutaneous calcified nodules.[161]

The *parathyroids* may show secondary hyperplasia[161] or even adenoma formation[461] in the presence of little or no hypercalcemia (despite nephrocalcinosis).

In one patient who had long been kept on a milk-alkali diet there developed hypercalcemia, diffuse calcinosis (especially around the joints), calcification of the sclera, a peptic ulcer, and a parathyroid adenoma. Removal of the adenoma resulted in rapid recovery. It was emphasized that "because of the frequent occurrence of peptic ulcer in primary hyperparathyroidism, differentiation between this disease and the milk-alkali syndrome may be difficult, once renal insufficiency, presumably secondary to hypercalcemia, has advanced to the point of phosphorus retention." In such cases the parathyroid adenoma may be either primary or the result of the milk-alkali regimen[685] (Fig. 287).

A particularly striking feature of the milk-alkali syndrome is the extraordinary *variability of its manifestations* and their relative independence of the blood calcium. It has been pointed out, for example, that: (1) Hypercalcemia may continue for many months after cessation of a large calcium intake. (2) Moderate impairment in renal function with nephrocalcinosis may be the only abnormality present when the patient comes under observation. (3) Clinical recognition is possible even when—as often happens—many of the characteristic criteria are absent.[735]

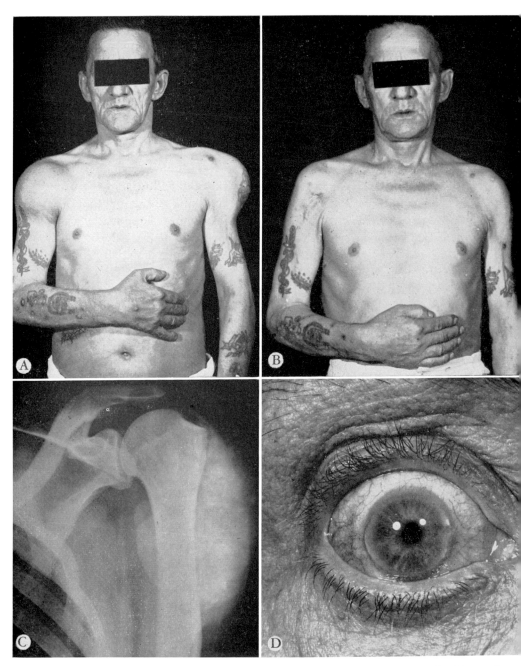

Fig. 286. Milk-alkali syndrome. *A* and *C:* Soft-tissue swelling about both shoulders and papular skin lesions. *B:* The heavy calcium deposit about the humerus disappeared completely during the 23 months following cessation of milk and alkali ingestion. *D:* Paralimbal corneal infiltration (band keratopathy) of calcium and hyperemia of sclera.

(After Randall *et al.*,[735] courtesy Arch. Int. Med.)

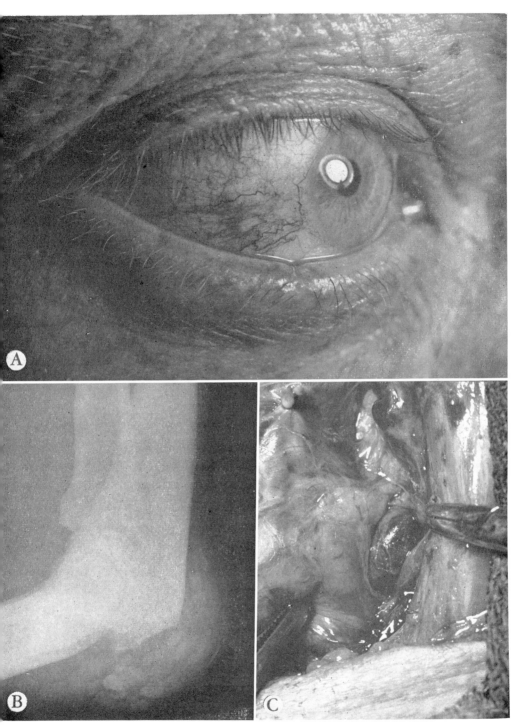

Fig. 287. Burnett's syndrome due to primary hyperparathyroidism. *A:* Conjunctival suffusion with scleral and limbal calcification. *B:* Calcification around elbow joint. *C:* Parathyroid adenoma exposed during operation.

(After Nielsen,[885] courtesy The Mason Clinic.)

Myositis Fibrosa

Syn., interstitial or nodular polymyositis.

It has been amply demonstrated that rheumatoid arthritis, rheumatic fever, scleroderma, and disseminated lupus erythematosus are all accompanied by small fibrous or granulomatous nodules in the striated musculature.[518, 535] The muscle fibers thus affected show hyalinization or vacuolization with the formation of macrophages. Occasionally the nodules are difficult to distinguish from the lymphorrhages of myasthenia gravis,[168] and allegedly quite similar foci can be found in "healthy" persons and in patients who die from tumors, cirrhosis of the liver, or coronary arteriosclerosis.[201] Such nodules may be responsible for what is commonly known as "muscular rheumatism"; they could be related to dermatomyositis. (Cf. p. 353.)

Myositis Ossificans (Circumscribed and Progressive)

This disease is characterized by bone formation in muscles. It occurs in two forms: one circumscribed and self-limited, the other progressive.[518, 781]

Circumscribed (traumatic) myositis ossificans.—This lesion results from *traumatic injuries* usually in the muscles of the thigh and brachialis anticus.[102, 114] If induced by repeated trauma to the thigh muscles of horsemen, it is called "Rider's bone."[65] When it appears following trauma to the elbow joint it is allegedly almost always the result of inappropriate treatment.[115] It may occur within spontaneous *hematomas*[622] or even at the site of intramuscular injection of blood.[283] Sometimes it is apparently preceded by *cartilaginous metaplasia* of the connective tissue between the muscle bundles,[381] but contrary to earlier views it is now not thought to depend upon the displacement of periosteum. In any event, this localized form does not appear to be fundamentally related to the systemic disease.[91, 114]

Myositis ossificans can be attended by *nervous complications*,[531] and it occurs with particular frequency in paraplegics,[655] particularly after poliomyelitis.[227]

Allegedly, *sarcomatous* transformation has occasionally been observed, but in these cases it is difficult to exclude the possibility that the lesion was sarcomatous from the beginning.[781]

Here, as in many experimental calciphylactic syndromes, "challenge" by topical trauma is undeniably present, but we do not know what stimulus acts as a sensitizing agent; some such systemic factor must be at play, since normally trauma does not induce bone formation.

Myositis ossificans circumscripta can also be *produced experimentally* by trauma in the dog,[374] and occasionally calcification of individual muscle fibers occurs in mice at sites where topical myositis has been produced by the intramuscular injection of neurotropic viruses.[774]

Progressive myositis ossificans (*syn.*, polymyositis ossificans).—This is presumably an entirely different disease entity. It depends upon a dominant ***hereditary*** trait,[648] is frequently congenital, and is associated with various malformations. The ossification does not occur in muscle tissues proper, but in the ligaments and fasciae in and around muscles. In general, ossification spreads along the fibrous septa and tendons, commencing at the bone[438, 619, 671, 763] (Figs. 288, 289, 290).

Like the localized form the progressive, generalized variety often follows some ***injury*** (e.g., fall, cold, infection). It usually progresses in spells with chills and

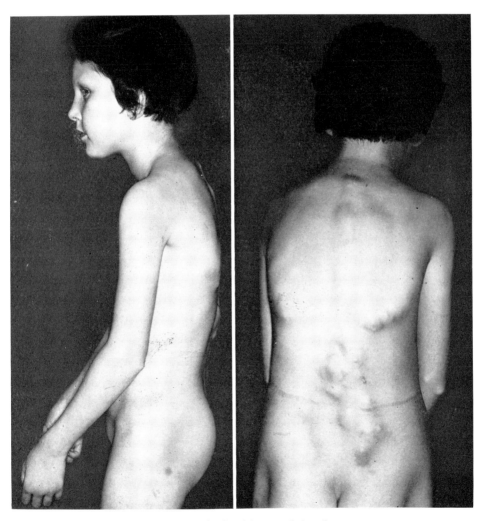

Fig. 288. Myositis ossificans. Kyphosis with several dorsal exostoses. (After Kirchhof and Klingmüller,[531] courtesy Springer-Verlag, Berlin.)

fever, accompanied by swelling and tenderness of the newly formed lesions.[64] (Cf. also "Topical Tissue Injury.")

Myositis ossificans progressiva may occur in combination with ***scleroderma-like*** skin lesions[390, 391] or acute fever with generalized ***cutaneous rashes.***[874]

According to a careful evaluation of the entire world literature there are intimate relations between ***calcinosis universalis*** (interstitialis) and myositis ossificans: both represent essentially connective-tissue diseases often associated with rheumatic or rheumatoid lesions in other organs.[524]

In myositis ossificans progressiva there is a considerable rise in the ***calcium avidity*** of tissues, as shown by an increased calcium retention following administration of a standard dose;[411] sometimes there is also pronounced hypercalcemia.[264]

Like many experimental calciphylactic syndromes myositis ossificans progressiva tends to ***spread in the cranio-caudal direction.*** Frequently the sub-

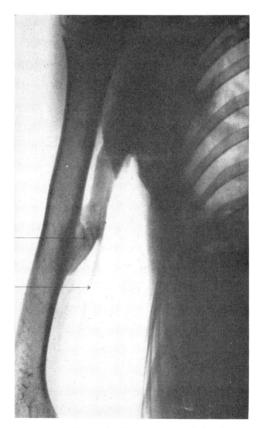

Fig. 289. Myositis ossificans. Bony bridges connect skeletal parts (upper arrow) or end freely in musculature (lower arrow).

(After Kirchhof and Klingmüller,[531] courtesy Springer-Verlag, Berlin.)

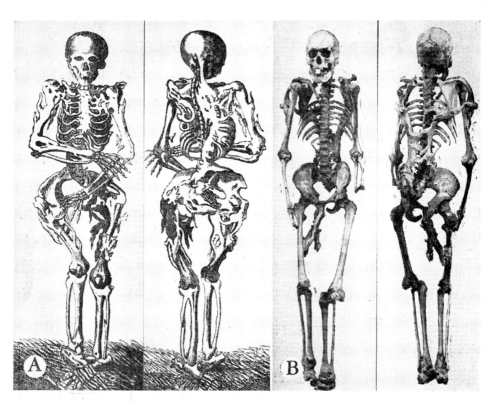

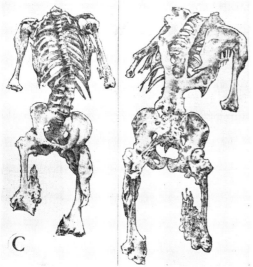

Fig. 290. Myositis ossificans. Skeletons of three particularly severe cases of myositis ossificans progressiva.

(After Stonham,[899a] courtesy Lancet.)

cutaneous muscles of the nape of the neck are the first to show radiologically detectable calcification and ossification.[183, 449, 555]

Myositis ossificans progressiva may be associated with ***osteogenic sarcoma or myxoliposarcoma*** formation.[702]

Necrobiosis Lipoidica Diabeticorum

Syn., dermatitis atrophicans maculosa lipoidea diabetica, necrobiosis lipoidica seu diabetica.

These are sharply outlined, oval or irregularly shaped, sclerotic plaques, yellow in the center and violaceous at the periphery. They usually occur in women on the forearms, palms, soles, neck, and face.

Allegedly, the incidence of diabetes is only 25 per cent.[886] The lesion has often been confused with, or seen in combination with, morphea.[149]

Histologically the collagen is found to be swollen, homogeneous, and slightly basophilic. The elastic tissue in the foci is largely destroyed. There are perivascular infiltrates of histiocytes, lymphocytes, fibroblasts, and plasma cells, with occasional foreign-body giant cells. The blood vessels in the dermis may become obliterated. "The inflammatory cells at times surround islands of epithelioid cells and sarcoidosis is mimicked."[781]

In one diabetic woman with calcium deposits at the fingertips intense local calcification developed also at the site of insulin injections. The case is cited to show that both systemic predisposition and local eliciting factors are involved in the causation of this change.[790]

Neurofibromatosis

Syn., von Recklinghausen's disease, fibroma molluscum, multiple neurofibromatosis.

In this disease neurofibromatous nodules develop throughout the subcutaneous tissue, along the nerves, and in many visceral organs. The cutaneous nodules may be pedunculated and many of them are not manifestly attached to nerves. There may be cutaneous pigmentation ("café au lait" patches) as well as a variety of tumors, such as neurilemmomas, meningiomas, optic nerve tumors, chromaffin tumors, angiomas, nevi, and lipomas.[474]

In this disease there is no particular tendency toward calcinosis in association with the fibrosis, but the frequent occurrence of pigmentation and malignancy suggests a possible relationship to the scleroderma-dermatomyositis group of diseases. Neurofibromatosis can be attended by osteitis fibrosa.[324, 810]

Osler-Rendu-Weber's Syndrome

Syn., hereditary hemorrhagic telangiectasis.

This disease is transmitted as a simple dominant characteristic. It leads to extreme dilatation of capillaries and arteries in the extremities, trunk, and mucous membranes. The lesions can be nodular or spider-shaped and frequently cause hemorrhage. Within the cutaneous nodules there may occur massive deposition of amyloid or calcium salts.

Allegedly, there is an increased number of arteriovenous shunts and glomera at the acral regions and vascular derangements in these may be partly responsible for calcification. In the shunts there is often diapedesis of erythrocytes and accumulation of PAS positive, often metachromatically staining material, which may attract calcium from the circulating blood[393] (Figs. 291–294).

Osler-Rendu-Weber's disease can also occur in combination with frank cutaneous calcinosis and transient hypercalcemia[228] or scleroderma.[653]

Osteitis Deformans

Syn., Paget's disease, leontiasis ossea.

This is an acquired disorder of unknown etiology with destruction and neoformation of bone in which the removed osseous tissue is replaced by excessive amounts of soft, poorly mineralized osteoid tissue. It may be localized to one bone or polyostotic, but even in the latter case the entire skeletal system is rarely affected. Therefore, it is probable that this condition is not entirely due to a systemic metabolic derangement.

Despite their bulk the affected soft bones become characteristically deformed by the stress of weight-bearing; this results in kyphosis, scoliosis, and lordosis with deformation of the tibias and femurs. In the course of bone reconstruction, the original Haversian lamellar pattern is destroyed and replaced by random foci of newly formed osseous tissue. Usually, narrow cement lines can be seen between the original and newly formed lamellar systems; these create a pathognomic "mosaic" pattern. There is also pronounced subperiosteal new-bone formation, which makes the bones broad and irregular. The marrow spaces between the cancellous spicules are filled with loose, fibrous connective tissue.[754]

Although *trauma* as such is not particularly important, the stress of weight-bearing obviously plays a decisive role in the creation of the deformities.[781]

The osseous changes may be accompanied by severe general calcification of *arteries*,[65] or marked arteriosclerosis in the vessels adjacent to the Pagetic bone.[289]

The serum *calcium* and *phosphorus* are normal, but *alkaline phosphatase* may be extremely high in the polyostotic form. "If *nephrocalcinosis* complicates the picture, chronic pyelonephritis and secondary hyperparathyroidism with its accompanying blood findings may be seen."[781]

Osteogenesis Imperfecta

Syn., osteopsathyrosis, Lobstein's syndrome.

This is a familiar disorder characterized by fragility of the bones, blue sclerae, laxity of ligaments, osteoporosis, and frequently precocious arcus senilis, unusual fineness of the hair and defects in the dental enamel.

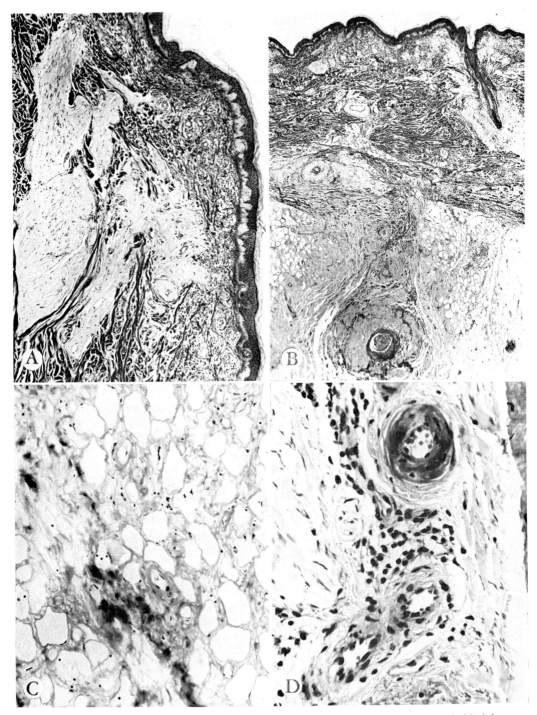

Fig. 291. Osler-Rendu-Weber's syndrome with cutaneous amyloidosis. *A:* Nodular amyloid deposit in derma and cutaneous papillae. (van Gieson, ×64.) *B:* Fine streaks of amyloid in papillary body and thick bands around vessels and hair follicles. (van Gieson, ×22.) *C:* Amyloidosis and consequent thickening of interstices between fat cells in subcutis. (Congo red, ×125.) *D:* Amyloid deposition in one arteriole while others remained unaffected. (Congo red, ×310.)

[After Gottron and Korting,[393] courtesy Springer-Verlag, Berlin (Arch. klin. u. exper. Dermat.).]

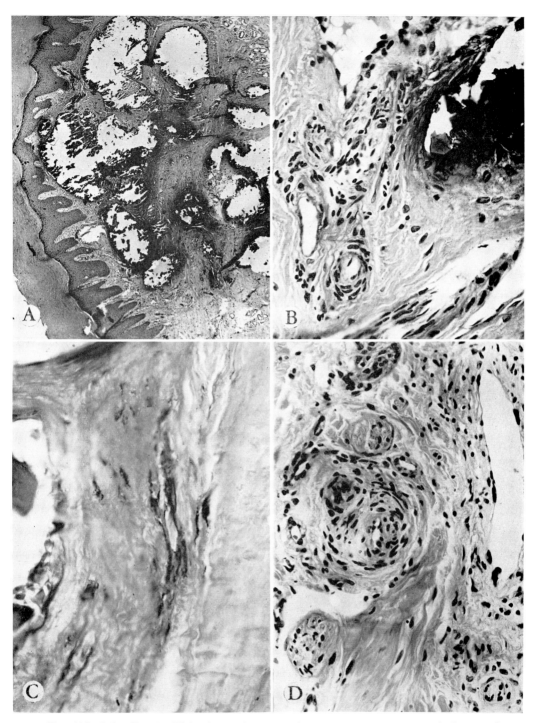

Fig. 292. Osler-Rendu-Weber's syndrome with cutaneous calcinosis. *A:* Lumps of calcium deposition in cutis. (Hematoxylin-eosin, ×23.) *B:* Higher magnification of a portion of A, showing dilatation of some vessels, while others have narrow lumen and thick wall, in the vicinity of calcareous deposit. *C:* PAS-positive granular structures in the vicinity of a calcium deposit. *D:* Dilatation of capillaries around a glomus in which vessel walls are very cellular and many nuclei unusually large. (Hematoxylin-eosin, ×360.)

[After Gottron and Korting,[393] courtesy Springer-Verlag, Berlin (Arch. klin. u. exper. Dermat.).]

Usually two forms are distinguished: ***Osteogenesis imperfecta congenita*** is hereditary and transmitted by a dominant gene; the infant is frequently stillborn or dies shortly after birth, with multiple spontaneous bone fractures. ***Osteogenesis imperfecta tarda*** develops during late childhood or adolescence; "It seems probable that imperfections in the quality and quantity of intercellular matrix of certain mesenchymal tissues are the essential defect."[22]

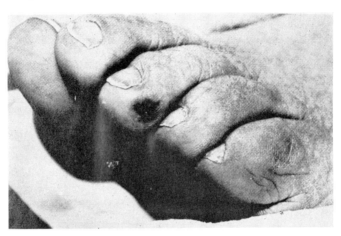

Fig. 293. Osler-Rendu-Weber's syndrome with flat angioma-like formations on toes. Punctate calcium deposits within the foci.

[After Gottron and Korting,[393] courtesy Springer-Verlag, Berlin (Arch. klin. u. exper. Dermat.).]

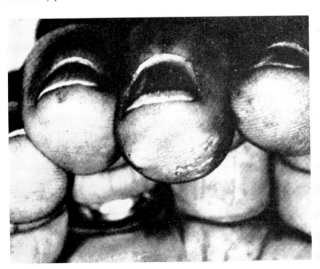

Fig. 294. Osler-Rendu-Weber's syndrome with calcinosis of the finger tips.

[After Gottron and Korting,[393] courtesy Springer-Verlag, Berlin (Arch. klin. u. exper. Dermat.).]

The disease is mentioned here mainly because a very similar condition can be reproduced in rats by the excessive administration of vitamin-D compounds to their mothers during pregnancy or lactation.[806, 811] There is no reason to believe that vitamin-D overdosage plays any part in the pathogenesis of spontaneous osteogenesis imperfecta in man, but the fundamental biochemical defects—produced by hereditary stigmatization in children and by vitamin-D compounds in rats—may be related.

Osteopetrosis

Syn., marble-bone disease, Albers-Schönberg's disease.

This is allegedly a hereditary disorder transmitted as a simple, recessive characteristic. Grossly the affected bones become very dense and hard. The normally spongy parts become as solid as the bone shafts and the marrow cavities are also gradually replaced by dense bone. The excessive proliferation of osseous tissue tends to compress nerves and vessels, eventually resulting in miliary bone necroses.[781, 992]

Rather similar osteopetrosis may be induced by intoxication with lead, phosphorus, fluorine, or beryllium as well as by chronic treatment with parathyroid hormone or vitamin-D compounds, and in certain animal species by estrogens.[812] It is uncertain, therefore, whether all cases described as "marble-bone disease" are due to the same fundamental morbid process. An excessive parathyroid hormone secretion should be suspected in those comparatively rare cases that are accompanied by soft-tissue calcification and renal disease.[198, 810]

Osteoporosis

Osteoporosis occurs in the course of various quite unrelated diseases and does not represent a specific morbid entity. It frequently accompanies dermatomyositis, particularly in patients with widespread calcareous deposits in the soft tissues. "This demineralization possibly may be explained by the muscular weakness and inactivity of the extremities."[694]

However, in our animals with calciphylactic dermatomyositis the bone absorption took the form of a generalized, acute osteitis fibrosa which could not be duplicated by mere inactivity. Demineralization of the bones may be an essential part of the pathogenic process in calcinoscleroses; apparently, here the "calcium hunger" of the tissues cannot be satisfied by the dietary intake, and hence the skeletal stores are mobilized.

Osteosis Cutis

The formation of single or multiple bony plates in the skin has been described as osteosis cutis,[928] but it is highly probable that—at least in many cases—this condition merely represents one variant of cutaneous calcinosis (cf. p. 329). It will be recalled that in calciphylaxis cutaneous calcinosis almost always progresses to preosseous tissue induction, yet virtually never continues to true bone formation.

Osteosis cutis may occur as an isolated lesion in the absence of systemic disease,[80] but it has also been seen in calcified sclerodermatous plaques.[723]

Panniculitis

Syn., relapsing, febrile, nodular, nonsuppurating panniculitis; Parkes-Weber-Christian's disease.

This syndrome is characterized by bluish, erythematous skin patches overlying firm subcutaneous nodules and plaques on the extremities and trunk. In the affected regions the subcutaneous fat is infiltrated by foamy histiocytes, lymphocytes, plasma cells, and fibrous tissue. There may be liquefaction-necrosis and in rare instances calcification.[16, 781]

In cutaneous calcinosis calcification also occurs preferentially in adipose tissue,[118] and in certain forms of dermatomyositis the subcutaneous fat shows lesions indistinguishable from ordinary panniculitis.[957]

Pemphigus

Pemphigus is an acute or chronic, bullous or vesicular, usually fatal skin disease. The bullae may affect any part of the body as well as the oral and vaginal mucosae. Four types are distinguished: pemphigus vulgaris, vegetans, foliaceus, and erythematosus. The disease is not known to produce calcification. It is mentioned only because, like the calciphylactic reactions, pemphigus is frequently accompanied by tissue eosinophilia, collagen degeneration, and liquefaction-necrosis at the epidermo-dermal junction. One form of it, pemphigus erythematosus, may be difficult to differentiate from lupus erythematosus.

Pemphigus often responds very favorably to treatment with anti-inflammatory corticoids.[781] Because of this feature and the frequently striking dependence of exacerbations upon emotional disturbances, pemphigus has been classified as a **stress disease.**[143]

Periarteritis Nodosa

Syn., polyarteritis, panarteritis nodosa, disseminated necrotizing periarteritis.

This is an inflammatory disease of the arteries affecting all coats and not, as the name "periarteritis" suggests, only the adventitia. The arteries tend to assume a nodular appearance because of the segmental development of the lesions. The clinical course is usually chronic with associated gastroenteric symptoms and peripheral neuropathy.[33, 994] Eosinophilia occurs occasionally, and hypertension in most cases.[543] In addition to this basic type it is customary to distinguish: hypersensitivity angiitis, allergic granulomatous angiitis, and temporal or giant-cell arteritis; but presumably the underlying process of all these variants is essentially the same. Even the so-called "rheumatic arteritis" and the arteritis that frequently occurs in combination with rheumatoid arthritis, erythema nodosum, erythema induratum, disseminated lupus erythematosus, and scleroderma probably belong to the same family.[781]

In connection with our principal topic the association of periarteritis nodosa with *scleroderma* is of special interest.[547, 592] The pulmonary lesions of periarteritis nodosa are likewise reminiscent of those seen in scleroderma (Fig. 295). In one case scleroderma with periarteritis nodosa was associated with myositis, arthritis, osteoporosis, and degenerative and inflammatory changes in the peripheral nerves and spinal cord. Two of the parathyroids "were markedly enlarged and exhibited an impressive picture of chronic, interstitial parathyroiditis (parathyroid cirrhosis) with intensive connective-tissue and blood-vessel proliferation, as well as infiltration with lymphocytes and plasma cells."[547] It will be recalled that parathyroid hormone given in combination with Fe-OS can cause periarteritis of the hepatic artery, while certain chromium and iron salts can produce parathyroid sclerosis as a healing stage of calciphylaxis in suitably sensitized rats.

Since periarteritis nodosa is often accentuated by emotional disturbances and may respond well to anti-inflammatory hormone treatment, it has been classified as a *stress disease*.[143] The fact that overdosage with mineralocorticoids can produce periarteritis nodosa in animals has also been interpreted in this sense.[813]

Poikiloderma Vasculare Atrophicans

Syn., poikiloderma of Jacobi, poikilodermatitis, dermatitis atrophicans reticularis.

This dermatosis is characterized by pigmentation, telangiectases, and usually atrophy. It may occur as a separate entity, but it is more commonly secondary to other skin diseases, such as scleroderma, dermatomyositis, and lupus erythematosus.[781]

Intermediate forms between poikiloderma and dermatomyositis or scleroderma have been designated as "poikilodermatomyositis" or "sclerodermatomyositis," respectively. Both forms may be associated with calcinosis.[277]

In connection with the concept of calciphylaxis it is especially interesting that in certain cases of "poikilodermatitis" *mucinous degeneration* of the collagen occurs with subsequent calcification.[383] *Calcification* is also common in the so-called "scleropoikiloderma."[222, 485, 507] The sometimes particularly pronounced generalized calcinosis of poikilodermatomyositis tends to be accompanied by hypercalcemia and has been ascribed to hyperparathyroidism.[158, 716]

In one case of "poikilodermatomyositis" abundant *iron* deposition was observed within the affected muscles.[186]

Peyronie's disease, cf. "Scleroderma."

Progeria

Syn., Hutchinson-Gilford syndrome.

This so-called "premature senility" shows signs of both infantilism and senility. It tends to become manifest a few months after birth and is characterized by cessation of growth, a large skull, birdlike features, atrophic and frequently wrinkled

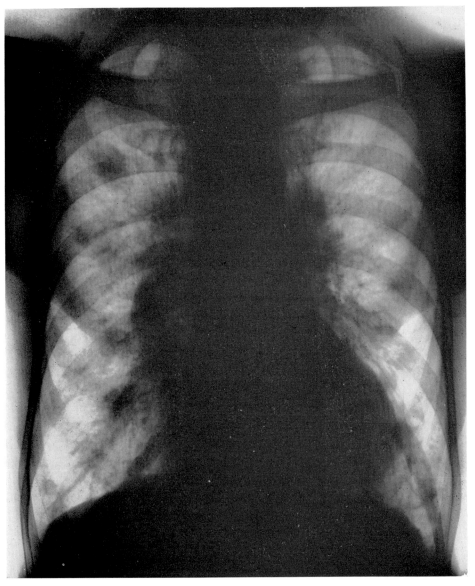

Fig. 295. Pulmonary changes in periarteritis nodosa. Nodular lesions and vascular type of fibrosis.

(After Hegglin,[434] courtesy Ztschr. f. Rheumaforschg.)

skin, and usually severe mental defects. The patients rarely survive beyond the second decade, and, terminally, severe arteriosclerosis develops, frequently with calcification and myocardial infarction.[217, 239, 781]

Pseudohypoparathyroidism

Syn., Seabright-Bantam syndrome.

The manifestations of this condition resemble those of true hypoparathyroidism, but they cannot be corrected by the administration of parathyroid hormone. Apparently, here the tissues are unable to respond normally to the hormone without there being any failure of hormone production. The disease has been called the "Seabright-Bantam syndrome" because the Seabright-Bantam rooster fails to develop male characteristics owing to end-organ insensitivity to testosterone.

In pseudohypoparathyroidism, cataracts as well as intracerebral and cutaneous calcification are even more common than in true hypoparathyroidism. The disease is often also associated with short stature, stocky build, a rounded face, and short metacarpal bones.[11, 690, 758]

Pseudoxanthoma Elasticum

This is an uncommon, familial disease with particularly prominent ocular manifestations. It is characterized by marked degeneration and thickening of fragmented and partially calcium-incrustated elastic fibers. The elastic elements of the heart and blood vessels throughout the body may be simultaneously involved. The skin lesions are often symmetric. The affected skin is relaxed, hangs in folds, and is often covered by numerous yellowish soft papules.[16, 781]

Various xanthomatous foci may undergo calcification, but this is particularly true in certain cases of pseudoxanthoma elasticum.[16] The latter may even be associated with generalized calcinosis, arteriosclerosis, and Paget's disease, presumably because the fundamental affection of the elastic tissue predisposes to abnormal calcification.[873]

Psoriasis

This is a chronic dermatosis of unknown origin, characterized by multiple reddish-brown, sharply demarcated, dry papules and plaques covered by a thin layer of silvery scales. The lesions are usually symmetrically distributed on the extensor surfaces of the extremities, especially the elbows and knees, as well as on the chest, but can also involve the scalp, back, and occasionally the entire body surface. There may be a widespread erythroderma with exfoliative dermatitis, sometimes associated with rheumatoid arthritis. Curiously, the exfoliative, erythrodermatous lesions can be provoked by ACTH.[781] Even gentle removal of the scales produces typical, slightly bleeding surface patches (Auspitz' sign).

The pathognomonic histologic features are: (1) parakeratosis, (2) acanthosis with thinning of the suprapapillary epidermis, (3) elongation of the rete pegs and dermal papillae, (4) occasional epidermal "Munro microabscesses" with poly-morphonuclear neutrophils, (5) edema and some clubbing (widening of the upper portion) of the "test-tube-like" dermal papillae, and (6) dilated, straight papillary capillaries, which are probably responsible for Auspitz' sign.[754]

Allegedly, *scleroderma* can occasionally develop on the basis of psoriasis,[537] and there also appears to be some relationship between psoriasis, impetigo herpetifor-mis, and hypoparathyroidism. Hypoparathyroidism with hypocalcemia has re-peatedly been noted in impetigo herpetiformis, and in one patient first diagnosed to have impetigo herpetiformis typical psoriasis developed as the blood calcium decreased.[243] Several dermatologists who consider psoriasis closely related to im-petigo herpetiformis claimed that both conditions can be improved by treatment with parathyroid hormone or DHT.[544, 591]

Raynaud's Syndrome

This condition is characterized by constriction of the small arteries or arterioles of the extremities resulting in pallor, cyanosis, and occasionally even symmetrical gangrene of the limbs. Nothing is known about the early histologic changes but obstructive vascular disease may be found when necrosis of the fingers oc-curs.[16, 596, 781, 971] The term "Raynaud's disease" has been used by some to indicate that this is a special morbid entity, but there is no proof to support this view; many types of interference with the peripheral circulation may result in this phe-nomenon. It is quite proper, therefore, to speak of Raynaud's phenomenon even when the syndrome results from thromboangiitis obliterans or other vascular dis-eases.

The frequent association of Raynaud's syndrome with *scleroderma*—espe-cially sclerodactyly—has already been mentioned (cf. "Scleroderma"). Raynaud's syndrome may be accompanied by multiple subcutaneous *calcareous nodules* in the fingers even in the absence of scleroderma,[196, 700] but the blood calcium is usually not elevated;[505] indeed, the phenomenon may appear as a complication of *hypoparathyroid tetany.*[504] For example, a positive Chvostek's sign has been observed in a case of Raynaud's disease with calcareous scleroderma.[362]

X-irradiation of the pituitary region allegedly exerts a favorable effect upon Raynaud's syndrome,[638] but this claim requires confirmation.

On theoretic grounds Raynaud's syndrome has been interpreted as a "disease of adaptation" due to *stress,*[742] but there is little objective evidence to support this view.

Reiter's Syndrome

Syn., oculo-urethro-synovial syndrome of Fiessinger-Leroy-Reiter.

This disease is found almost exclusively in young adult males and is character-ized by migratory arthritis, urethritis, conjunctivitis, and sometimes kerato-derma.[16] It is generally considered to be an infectious disease, possibly due to a virus.[314] In some cases pleuropneumonia-like organisms of the "L" strain have been isolated,[565] but frequently an etiologic factor cannot be identified. The disease is self-limited, resolving spontaneously after about two to four weeks.[960]

Severe forms of Reiter's syndrome may be associated with pronounced hyperkeratosis (especially of the feet and hands), mono- or polyarthritis of the rheumatoid type, and extreme muscular atrophy.[711]

No connection has as yet been found between Reiter's syndrome and what we call the calcinoscleroses; the syndrome is mentioned only because of the articular and ocular lesions which, especially when combined with keratoderma, have some resemblance to certain experimental calciphylactic responses.

Renal Disease

It is well known that renal tissue is particularly susceptible to calcification following local, traumatic, or chemical injuries of various kinds. Diverse forms of **nephrocalcinosis** and **urinary calculi** may be ascribed to this property.

It has been noted, furthermore, that patients with unilateral renal calculi often develop recurrences on the other side. In such cases needle biopsy revealed bilateral alterations of the renal stroma. "These data tend to substantiate the hypothesis . . . that most kidney stones represent renal collagen disease—that is, a disease of the tubule connective tissue matrix or mucoprotein."[51]

Renal insufficiency also enhances **systemic calcinosis** not merely as a result of a direct effect upon calcium and phosphorus excretion but also indirectly through the stimulation of the parathyroids[821, 823] (Fig. 276).

Chronic renal disease frequently produces compensatory hyperplasia of the parathyroids with generalized calcinosis.[722] This glandular hyperfunction is an adaptive phenomenon designed to readjust the deranged calcium and phosphorus metabolism; hence, the resulting calcinosis is a typical example of a "disease of adaptation."[807, 821, 823, 938]

In connection with our problem it is of special interest that certain forms of renal insufficiency can induce a systemic predisposition both for calciphylaxis in experimental animals and for calcinosis (particularly of the heart) in man.[823] Cutaneous calcinosis is exceptional but may likewise occur in patients with severe renal insufficiency.[16] In a case of hypertensive nephritis there was extensive calcium deposition in the alveolar walls of the lung and in a thrombus of the right auricular appendage.[65] Calcinosis of the heart, liver, and spleen was seen in two patients with chronic Bright's disease in association with advanced pulmonary tuberculosis.[600a]

In one patient chronic nephritis resulted in generalized calcinosis affecting the lung, kidney, stomach, and entire arterial system. In addition "about the larger joints of the upper extremities and about the feet were many fluctuant tumor masses of various size, and distributed along the course of many of the peripheral arteries were innumerable bead-like nodules which could be felt, while x-ray plates showed extensive calcification of the peripheral arteries and large irregular deposits about the joints." The contents of the fluctuating periarticular masses contained 30 per cent calcium phosphate. At autopsy the patient proved to have right hydronephrosis, severe interstitial nephritis, calcium deposits in the wall of the left auricle, and two enlarged, presumably adenomatous parathyroids. The bones showed extensive osteitis fibrosa.[464] Massive calcinosis of several joints has also been observed in a patient with polycystic kidneys.[160]

In one patient chronic nephrosclerosis was associated with a parathyroid adenoma and generalized calcinosis affecting mainly the heart, cardiovascular system, and lungs. Several calcified plaques developed in the subcutaneous tissue of the legs and over the scapulas. At the same time there was a striking pigmentation of the skin (allegedly present in 50 per cent of patients developing calcinosis after renal disease). Parathyroidectomy caused regression of the cutaneous calcinosis.[279]

In a two-year-old girl with eventually fatal chronic nephritis there developed pronounced parathyroid hyperplasia, severe generalized osteitis fibrosa with multiple calcium deposits in the heart, and Mönckeberg sclerosis of the arteries.[785]

In a patient with salt-losing nephritis severe generalized calcinosis developed during the terminal stage of the disease. Death was due to uremia. A high-alkali diet, given to the patient for therapeutic purposes, may have contributed to the development of the calcinosis.[382] Osteomalacia with "pseudofractures" is allegedly characteristic of renal tubular insufficiency[68] (Fig. 296).

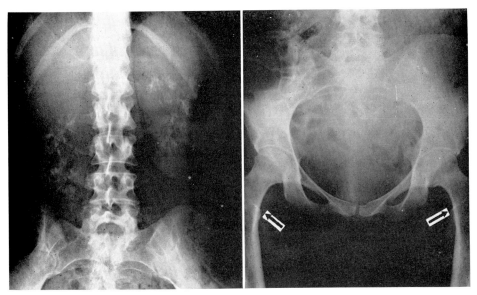

Fig. 296. Nephrocalcinosis with osteomalacia. *Left:* Nephrocalcinosis. *Right:* Associated osteomalacia and pseudofractures (arrows) characteristic of renal tubular insufficiency. (After Bartholomew *et al.*,[68] courtesy Postgrad. Med.)

Even calcinosis of the entire cardiovascular system can occur in association with chronic glomerulonephritis and skeletal demineralization. In one such case calcinosis was considered to result from renal hyperparathyroidism, although at autopsy no parathyroid tissue could be found (there was a basophilic pituitary adenoma and a greatly enlarged pineal gland).[147]

In surveying a group of patients with renal disease, it was found that "the common sites of calcification in this series were the subcutaneous tissues, heart and arteries, and to a lesser extent the lungs." Nephrocalcinosis was common, but in the case of a primary renal disease this is not necessarily an indication of systemic calcinosis. Blood-chemical studies on a large number of patients with diverse renal lesions led to the conclusion that "metastatic calcification seems to occur only in cases showing oversaturation of the serum in respect to both calcium and phosphate."[443]

Rheumatoid Arthritis

Syn., atrophic arthritis, chronic infectious arthritis, proliferative arthritis.

This is a chronic disease which affects many joints and produces systemic effects such as debility and loss of weight. The specific lesion is a proliferation of granulation tissue in synovial and periarticular tissues over the joint surfaces and in subchondral spaces. There is pain, limitation of motion, deformity, and sometimes bony ankylosis.[397]

Some relationship between *calcinosis* and "rheumatism" has long been suspected. According to one view, tissue calcification is only one manifestation of rheumatoid arthritis,[682] while another theory holds that rheumatoid disease merely determines the localization of the calcinosis.[524]

Occasionally rheumatoid arthritis is associated with typical *scleroderma*[121, 259] or "pseudoscleroderma."[481] The same is true of juvenile rheumatoid arthritis or Still's disease. In one such case Still's disease (diagnosed by Sir Frederic Still) occurred in combination with calcinosis circumscripta (mainly of the hands), mild sclerodactyly, and Raynaud's syndrome; indeed, "cases of juvenile rheumatoid arthritis attended by mild sclerodactylia are not extremely rare," though calcinosis is infrequent.[299] Still's disease may also be associated with *ocular lesions* such as uveitis and band-shaped keratitis.[424]

In rheumatoid arthritis the *blood calcium* may be high, and if so, partial parathyroidectomy allegedly can produce a significant improvement.[621]

The cause of the normocytic, hypochromic anemia characteristic of rheumatoid arthritis remains unknown. *Iron* is normally absorbed from the gut,[769] but in a series of 61 cases stainable iron was absent from the bone marrow in 19 patients.[749] It was thought that there might be an increased tissue avidity for iron comparable to that postulated as the cause of the anemia of infection.[182] The plasma clearance of intravenously injected Fe-OS is accelerated in patients with rheumatoid arthritis,[769] a fact which was attributed to an overactivity of the RES. The histochemically demonstrable iron concentration in the liver, spleen, lungs, lymph nodes, and adrenals remains within normal limits in rheumatoid arthritis. There is hyperplasia of the RES with significant enlargement of the spleen, but allegedly these changes cannot account for the rapid decline in plasma iron after Fe-OS injection. However, "on the basis of this splenic enlargement, it is tentatively suggested that the spleen may contain approximately twice as much iron in this disease as is normally the case."[366]

One patient with rheumatoid arthritis and an unusually large number of subcutaneous nodules had a ***positive LE test;*** there was also rheumatoid lung disease characterized by diffuse nonspecific fibrosis and typical nodules in the lungs.[755]

In view of the frequent aggravation of rheumatoid arthritis by stressful emotional disturbances and because the disease is highly susceptible to treatment with antiphlogistic hormones, it has been classified as a ***"stress disease."***[143]

Rheumatic Fever

Syn., Bouillaud's disease.

This is an acute or chronic inflammatory process, often initiated by a preceding Group-A hemolytic streptococcus infection. It is most common among children and tends to recur after remissions. The inflammation is disseminated in the connective tissues of many organs and may manifest itself as myocarditis, valvulitis arthritis, serositis, subcutaneous nodules (which show hyaline necrosis sometimes with calcification), or rashes. There are also generalized nonspecific manifestations, such as fever and increased erythrocyte sedimentation rate.[16, 397]

Calcinosis universalis may allegedly follow attacks of rheumatic fever,[682] but this is extremely rare. In a boy of 15 rheumatic fever was followed by extensive ***calcification in the shoulder joint*** and the skin of the arm. Histologically, calcium deposition was most pronounced around elastic fibers.[675]

Exceptionally, rheumatic fever with carditis may be associated with ***dermatomyositis.***[522, 536]

Rheumatoid Spondylitis

Syn., Bekhterev's syndrome, arthritis of Marie-Strümpell, rhizomelic spondylitis, spondylitis ossificans ligamentosa, ankylosing spondylitis, adolescent or juvenile spondylitis, spondylarthritis ankylopoietica, spondylitis deformans, atrophic spondylitis. (The term "rheumatoid spondylitis" was adopted by the American Rheumatism Association.)

This is a rheumatoid arthritis which may be limited to the spine or also affect the shoulders and hips. The most important lesions occur in the sacroiliac, posterior intervertebral (apophyseal), and costovertebral joints.

The early changes are inflammatory and resemble rheumatoid arthritis as manifested in other joints. There is synovitis, chondritis and juxta-articular osteitis, but the first lesions appear to be invariably in the synovial membranes and consist of lymphocytic and plasma cell infiltrations. The late changes, with pronounced calcification and ossification under the spinal ligaments, result in the characteristic "bamboo spine." Unlike in hypertrophic osteoarthritis of the spine, exostoses are relatively uncommon and calcification as well as ossification occurs mostly in the periphery of the intervertebral discs.[22, 119]

Romberg's Disease

This is a progressive facial hemiatrophy due to an atrophic, sclerodermatous process involving the skin, subcutaneous tissues and bone, along the distribution of the fifth cranial nerve. It usually appears in the second decade of life.[16]

The frequency of facial hemiatrophy in scleroderma has already been mentioned, but it is questionable whether in addition there exists a specific syndrome such as is implied by the term "Romberg's disease."

Rothmund's Disease

Syn., Rothmund-Thomson syndrome, Thomson's disease.

This is a poikiloderma with conspicuous telangiectasia, often preceded by a transitory erythema. It develops between the third and sixth months of age and affects predominantly the face, extremities, and buttocks. The teeth are usually normal but there may be microdontia, hypogenitalism, small stature, small hands and feet, epidermal atrophy, and irregular clumping of the elastic tissue. The disease is inherited as a recessive characteristic and tends to become stationary after two or three years. It is often accompanied by marked photosensitivity[761] and cataract formation.[343]

Rothmund's disease has frequently been confused with *Werner's syndrome;* some investigators consider it to be merely a variant of the latter,[16] but others strongly oppose this view.[209, 761, 920]

In any event, the disease appears to be closely related to the other calcinoscleroses in that it may be accompanied by soft-tissue *calcification* as well as by signs of *dermatomyositis.*[539, 779]

Sarcoidosis

Syn., Boeck's sarcoid, Besnier-Boeck-Schaumann's disease, lupus pernio of Besnier, benign lymphogranulomatosis of Schaumann.

Sarcoidosis is a chronic disease, frequently interrupted by remissions, which affects young adults predominantly but not exclusively. Its granulomatous lesions resemble tubercles but show little or no central necrosis. Lymph nodes, bones (especially the acral regions), and skin are sites of predilection. There may be iridocyclitis and uveoparotid fever.

In about half the cases of sarcoidosis the characteristic foreign-body-type giant cells in the granulomas contain either oval, doubly contoured, laminated and often calcified **"Schaumann bodies,"** or star-shaped, spiculated **"asteroid bodies."** In involuting lesions the nodules are surrounded by proliferating fibrous tissue.[781] The calcareous deposits in sarcoid granulomas, which now bear his name, were described by Schaumann in 1917.[782] But much before that, Metchnikoff[651] saw these formations as intra- or extracellular calcific deposits surrounding tubercle bacilli. Schaumann bodies can be produced particularly well in hamsters infected with photochromogenic and other Mycobacteria.[255, 347] An investigation of these by electron microscopy and selected area electron diffraction revealed them to be composed of an apatite similar to that of bone, probably hydroxyapatite. They also contain iron, which appears to be attached to the shell of the apatite crystal. At the beginning of calcium deposition the microorganisms appear to be viable, as judged by morphologic criteria; but later, as the Schaumann bodies develop, the bacteria disintegrate.[737] The simultaneous presence of calcium and iron in Schaumann bodies has previously been noted, using Perls's and von Kóssa's methods.[303, 651, 885, 963]

Even when calcium is present, the granulomas of sarcoidosis are only remotely reminiscent of those seen in experimental calciphylaxis or in the classical collagen diseases of man. Yet, there are many observations which suggest that even if the causative pathogen of sarcoidosis should turn out to be a microbe or allergen, it may still act through some mechanism related to calciphylaxis.

Massive soft-tissue calcification is rare in sarcoidosis, yet it may occur, e.g., in the form of nephrocalcinosis[678] or calcinosis of the ear cartilage.[74]

Different investigators estimated that marked **hypercalcemia** occurs in 20 to 100 per cent of the patients with sarcoidosis;[420, 937] simultaneously there is a rise in blood phosphatase.[420] These changes have been ascribed to the skeletal granulomas, but severe hypercalcemia—though conducive to nephrocalcinosis—may occur in sarcoidosis even when the skeleton is not involved.[246] Furthermore, in some patients with sarcoidosis there is **hypocalcemia;**[576, 995] this could be ascribed to remissions in an associated hyperparathyroidism but not to osteolytic granulomatous lesions themselves. The occasional occurrence of diffuse **osteoporosis**[506, 707] is also independent of osseous sarcoidosis.

It has been thought that sarcoidosis may be a special form of **hyperparathyroidism,**[707] but in the few patients in whom the parathyroids were examined they showed no obvious abnormalities.[442] Besides—unlike in hyperparathyroidism—in sarcoidosis the blood phosphorus and the calcium tolerance are allegedly normal, while the blood protein content is high.[420] A modification of the hyperparathyroidism theory postulates that parathyroid function is only periodically increased as a compensatory reaction during the course of sarcoidosis.

In sarcoid granulomas there are numerous **mastocytes**[783, 913] and the concentration of hyaluronic-acid-containing **mucoproteins** is said to be directly proportional to the number of mastocytes in connective tissue. It has been argued, therefore, that in patients with sarcoidosis the mucoprotein content of the bone marrow should be high. Of course, mucoproteins bind much more calcium than do serum proteins;[632, 762] "the hypothesis concerning the mucoproteins' role in the disturbance of the calcium balance in sarcoidosis is thus presumably intimately associated with the character of this disease as a general disturbance of the entire RES and it appears that similar phenomena are not unusual in other mesenchymal diseases." Allegedly, hypercalcemia, hypophosphatemia, and a great increase in alkaline phosphatase may also occur in rheumatic fever.[707] Furthermore, the skeletal lesions of urticaria pigmentosa, which were thought to resemble those of sarcoidosis, are likewise associated with dense accumulations of mastocytes.[109, 743, 776, 991]

It is unlikely that hypercalcemia is a secondary consequence of **hyperproteinemia,** since the blood calcium may be high even in patients whose blood-protein level is normal.[609, 646] Besides, the rise in blood calcium is often accompanied by hypercalciuria and concerns mainly the ionized, not the protein-bound, fraction.[13]

Currently the most popular hypothesis ascribes the hypercalcemia of sarcoidosis to an ***increased intestinal absorption of calcium*** accompanied by excessive calcium discharge from the skeleton.[246, 442]

The similarity of this metabolic derangement to **hypervitaminosis D** and the great vitamin-D sensitivity of patients with sarcoidosis[420, 567] gradually led to the assumption that sarcoidosis may be due to an intoxication with vitamin D or similar compounds. This kind of hypervitaminosis could result from an increased absorption, a decreased detoxification, or even an endogenous production of vitamin-D derivatives.[567] On the other hand, it may simply reflect an increased sensitivity to these compounds.[87]

In a patient with sarcoidosis, nephrocalcinosis, and renal failure, treatment with prednisone corrected the hypercalcemia and simultaneously improved kidney function.[678] Cortisone can also induce lasting remissions in the clinical picture of sarcoidosis;[572] however, these may be associated with tetanic convulsions.[663] All these facts have been cited in support of the vitamin-D theory because in certain respects cortisone and vitamin D are antagonists.[20] Be this as it may, the hypercalcemia and hypercalciuria of both sarcoidosis and hypervitaminosis D are favorably influenced by glucocorticoids, which augment the fecal excretion and diminish the intestinal absorption of calcium.[20, 87, 251, 256, 351, 442, 887]

Sometimes, despite normal serum calcium levels, hypercalciuria and typical symptoms of the "hypercalcemia syndrome" may be observed in patients with sarcoid ascribed to a hypersensitivity to vitamin D. Here, hypercalcemia may develop while the manifestations of sarcoidosis are suppressed by glucocorticoids.[472] In any event factors other than vitamin D must also be operative, since the manifestations of sarcoidosis are not identical with those of hypervitaminosis D.

In connection with the interpretation of the calcinoscleroses as a group of inter-related diseases it is also noteworthy that sarcoidosis may occur in association with **subcutaneous steatonecrosis,**[480] **scleroderma,**[780] **erythema nodosum,** and less frequently **erythema multiforme.**[976]

Ocular lesions are common in sarcoidosis, particularly chorioretinitis, iridocy-clitis and granulomatous changes in the conjunctiva,[472] band keratitis, and sub-conjunctival calcium deposits.[233, 954]

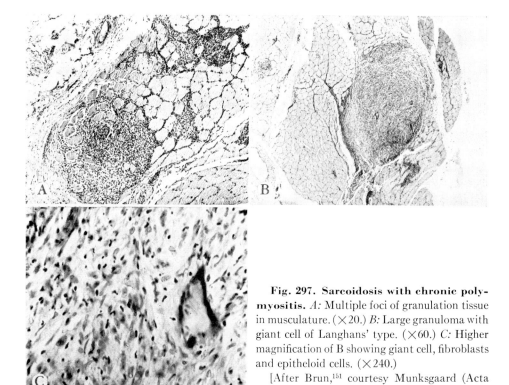

Fig. 297. Sarcoidosis with chronic poly-myositis. *A:* Multiple foci of granulation tissue in musculature. ($\times 20$.) *B:* Large granuloma with giant cell of Langhans' type. ($\times 60$.) *C:* Higher magnification of B showing giant cell, fibroblasts and epitheloid cells. ($\times 240$.)

[After Brun,[151] courtesy Munksgaard (Acta Psychiat. et Neurol. Scand.).]

The skeletal musculature is also frequently involved in sarcoidosis. Indeed, cer-tain cases present as chronic **polymyositis** without obvious lesions elsewhere[151] (Fig. 297). Occasionally, sarcoidosis with typical calcified Schaumann bodies and Langhans' giant cells is virtually limited to the striated musculature. "It is sug-gested that sarcoidosis may develop in muscles affected by a pre-existing disorder of muscle" without inducing the usual clinical manifestations of sarcoidosis.[234] **Polyarthritis** is likewise a frequent presenting symptom.[976]

EDTA therapy is said to be often very useful in sarcoidosis even when there are no obvious calcium deposits.[989]

Scleredema Adultorum Buschke

Syn., edematous scleroderma of Hardy, Buschke-Ollendorff syndrome, sclerofascia of Blaschko.

This disease resembles acute scleroderma but authorities do not agree in their view about the relationship between the two conditions. Scleredema adultorum usually develops after an infection (e.g., scarlet fever or influenza) as an acute non-pitting erythematous induration which begins at the neck and spreads rapidly to the face and down the back and chest. There is no itching or burning. The dermatosis generally clears within several months without leaving sequelae, although there may be recurrences. The essential change is a pronounced thickening of the cutis, with homogenization and diffuse swelling of the collagen bundles. The histochemical basis for the swelling is not clear.[16]

In connection with its possible relationship to calciphylaxis it is interesting that in scleredema adultorum there may be marked blood *eosinophilia*,[905] so that the disease has been considered to be an allergic response to the evocative microorganism.[530] Furthermore, both eosinophils[726] and *mastocytes*[349, 350, 773] are particularly abundant in the cutaneous lesions.

The frequent intercellular accumulations of *metachromatic material* are considered to represent hyaluronic acid derived from these mastocytes.[133] Thyroid hormone treatment often produces beneficial results, allegedly by diminishing the accumulation of hyaluronic acid in the affected regions.[133] Furthermore, a mucinous, metachromatically staining substance is often seen between the proliferating fibroblasts and collagen fibers.[349, 350] Indeed one of the characteristic features of this disease is the heavy infiltration of the fasciae, which may be due to a kind of lymphatic stasis and which led early investigators to designate the condition as "sclerofascia of Blaschko."[165]

In a case of scleredema (diagnosed by Buschke) one of the most prominent derangements was a generalized muscle disease accompanied by pronounced *hypercalcemia* (16.1 mg. %) with hypokaliemia. The original suspicion of dermatomyositis was abandoned because the muscles showed no sign of necrosis, waxy degeneration or inflammation but were merely infiltrated by an amorphous mass which pushed the fibers apart. The fasciae were similarly affected.[166]

On the whole, scleredema adultorum was considered to be more reminiscent of *myxedema* than of *scleroderma*[349] but, like scleroderma, it may affect the tongue[306, 344] and in many cases the differential diagnosis is virtually impossible.[1] Painfulness of the lips is another characteristic manifestation of scleredema.[451]

Also like scleroderma and various forms of hypercalcemia, scleredema adultorum may be associated with a variety of *ocular changes* including trophic corneal disturbances with superficial punctate keratitis.[135] Inflammatory changes in the cutaneous *nerves* have likewise been described.[456]

One of the most striking characteristics of scleredema adultorum is its frequent eruption immediately after a period of acute **stress.** For example, cases have been known to occur following influenza,[56, 164, 306, 455] nephritis,[590] bronchial catarrh, epidemic parotitis, herpes, scarlet fever, encephalitis, impetigo, pyoderma of the arms, tonsillitis, and mastitis,[306, 773] as well as at a site of trauma.[509] For this reason and because of the beneficial effect of antiphlogistic corticoids, scleredema was also considered to be a "stress dermatosis."[135] Yet in almost all instances the eliciting episode, though nonspecific, was an infection, which suggests some degree of specificity.

Sclerema Neonatorum

Syn., sclerema, sclerema adiposum, subcutaneous fat necrosis, adiponecrosis subcutanea neonatorum, cytosteatonecrosis of the subcutaneous tissue of the newborn, lipophagic granuloma.

This disease is characterized by fat-tissue necroses, becoming manifest two to twenty days after birth as deep subcutaneous indurations and disappearing completely within four months. It represents one form of panniculitis.[16]

While some authors claim that sclerema occurs predominantly in well-nourished, large infants,[397] others maintain that it is a disease of marantic, dehydrated babies.[135, 167] In any event, sclerema is usually elicited by some local or systemic injury such as trauma, infection, and cold.[466]

Opinion is divided as to the relationship between sclerema and true **scleroderma** of the newborn.[402, 540, 599] However, in cases definitely diagnosed as sclerema, **nephrocalcinosis**[167] or **calcification of necrotic fat tissue** in the subcutaneous lesions themselves[249, 322] have been noted. Sometimes the affected fat tissue undergoes calcification with giant-cell formation[325] virtually indistinguishable from the lesions seen in various experimental calciphylactic syndromes.

The occasional association of sclerema neonatorum with polymyositis even raised the question of a possible relationship between sclerema and **dermatomyositis.**[254]

The sclerematous subcutis contains unusually large amounts of **cholesterol, calcium,** and **phosphorus** as well as **glycerides** of a high melting point;[187] not infrequently there is **hypocalcemia.**[466] However, in another study, chemical analysis of subcutaneous fat and fat-free skin of eight sclerema and four control babies exhibited no difference either in the characteristics of the fat or in the calcium or phosphorus contents of the fat-free tissue. "These findings lend no support to the hypothesis that sclerema neonatorum is caused by a chemical change of the subcutaneous tissue."[188]

Scleroderma

Syn., scleriasis, dermatosclerosis, progressive systemic sclerosis. (Cf. also "Scleredema Adultorum Buschke.")

Generalities.—Scleroderma is characterized by induration of the skin in localized patches or diffuse areas, associated with atrophy of the epidermis and sometimes pigmentation, vasomotor disturbances and calcinosis. It is customary to distinguish:

1. ***Circumscribed scleroderma.*** This may take the form of:
   A. *Plaques* often surrounded by a lilac ring.
   B. *Stripes*, also known as "sclérodermie en coup de sabre."
   C. Small *droplets* designated as morphea guttata, or "white spot disease."
   D. *Ring-shaped* scleroderma ("sclérodermie anulaire"), which tends to encircle a toe, finger, or limb, resulting in edema of the peripheral part and sometimes spontaneous amputations.
   E. *Acrosclerosis and sclerodactyly*, which affect primarily the extremities, are transitional forms between circumscribed and systemic scleroderma, since they tend to be associated with lesions at other sites. (Cf. "Acrosclerosis.")
   F. *Peyronie's disease* is a form of scleroderma localized on the penis. It was considered to be "a collagenosis that should be included among the diseases of adaptation."[266]

2. ***Systemic scleroderma or systemic sclerosis.*** This is usually subdivided according to the speed of its progression into:
   A. *Primarily acute and generalized scleroderma.* This usually starts with an edematous infiltration of the face, which gradually becomes indurated and involves the entire head spreading to the thorax until the patient is enveloped in a veritable carapace. It is frequently accompanied by telangiectases, trophic disturbances, brownish pigmented patches and eventually cachexia conducive to death (Figs. 298, 299).
   B. *Chronic scleroderma.* This often begins with Raynaud's syndrome and acrosclerosis, but may gradually spread to the entire body.

Many dermatologists believe that the Thibierge-Weissenbach syndrome (characterized by calcinosis), the scleredema of Buschke (also known as edematous scleroderma of Hardy) and sclerema neonatorum are merely modifications of systemic scleroderma.[99] However, this interpretation is not generally accepted[203] and hence we discuss these conditions separately in this text.

The literature on scleroderma has been summarized in several detailed ***reviews.***[71, 475, 718, 892, 935, 971]

Characteristics.—**Histologically** the initial stages are characterized by swelling of the collagen fibers with interstitial edema and often perivascular lymphocytic infiltration. During later stages the collagen forms thick bands which usually run parallel to the epidermis and may spread into the underlying aponeuroses. The

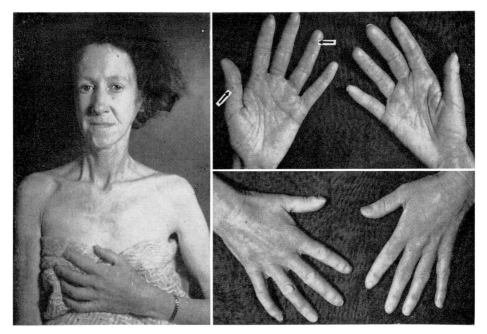

Fig. 298. Generalized scleroderma. Pinched appearance of mouth and absence of natural creases on forehead. Skin of neck is tight and there are anomalies of pigmentation with telangiectatic spots on face. On hands skin is "hidebound" and thickened. Both index fingers, right thumb and fifth right finger show characteristic tapering. Telangiectatic spots on fourth left finger and left thumb (arrows).

(After Goetz,[384] courtesy Clinical Proceedings.)

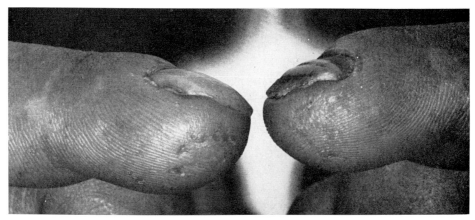

Fig. 299. Trophic disturbances in generalized scleroderma. "Rat-bite defects" in fingers presumed to result from peripheral arteritis.

(After Hegglin,[434] courtesy Ztschr. f. Rheumaforschg.)

vessels become scarce and often edematous, with proliferation of the intima and sometimes obliterating arteriolitis. The cutaneous appendages (hair, cutaneous glands and muscles) undergo atrophy or vanish completely, and degenerative changes appear in the nerves of the skin. There is atrophy of the epidermis and the papillae disappear.[99]

The *electron microscopic appearance* of the collagen fibrils may remain normal; hence, it was concluded that scleroderma does not primarily affect the structure of the fibrils, although it increases their number.[49, 323] However, in one case of nodular scleroderma, electron microscopic investigation allegedly showed "incipient degeneration of collagen fibrils."[871]

Sometimes there develops a "nodular *elastica* proliferation" in the papillary stratum.[553] A considerable accumulation of *metachromatic mucoid substances* may produce a condition designated as *"scleromyxedema."*[392, 520, 545] A somewhat similar lesion (often described as *"myxomatosis cutis papulosa,"* or "lichen myxedematosus") tends to form reddish-yellow or yellowish-white shiny nodules, 1 or 2 mm. in diameter, usually around hair follicles. One such case in an elderly diabetic was shown to be characterized histologically by the deposition of PAS-positive and mucicarmine-tingible substances around hair follicles and sweat glands.[542] The metachromatic imbibition of the skin is usually associated with intense local *mastocytosis*[684, 967] and sharp variations in *mucopolysaccharides*.[906, 930]

The histologically demonstrable *iron* content of the skin does not appear to be increased in scleroderma.[323]

The often very intense *calcinosis* of the skin may lead to massive indurating, or cystic and often exulcerating cutaneous lesions, which discharge milky or gritty calcified material, but if deep-seated, they may undergo ossification without exulceration.[923] The calcium-containing, closed cavities are allegedly lymphatic cysts[924] (Fig. 300). Subcutaneous calcareous concretions, especially in the vicinity of the joints and in the fingers, are quite common in scleroderma[250, 313, 468, 793] (Figs. 301, 302).

Calcinosis may also occur in the muscles and viscera affected by scleroderma and thereby create transitional forms more or less reminiscent of generalized calcinosis and dermatomyositis[71, 126, 339, 384, 518, 524, 617, 647, 734, 907, 908, 924, 971] (Fig. 303). In sclerodactyly the calcium deposits are said to be rich in magnesium and silica.[139]

On the basis of a literature survey it is estimated that in calcinosis circumscripta the incidence of scleroderma is about 40 per cent, while in calcinosis universalis it is about 32 per cent.[475]

Scleroderma may also be associated with calcareous subdeltoid bursitis[294] or with massive calcification in the liver and spleen.[423]

Among the visceral manifestations of systemic scleroderma the lesions in the **esophagus** are perhaps the most characteristic. They are grossly detectable in about 10 per cent of the patients and almost constant in acrosclerosis. Sometimes

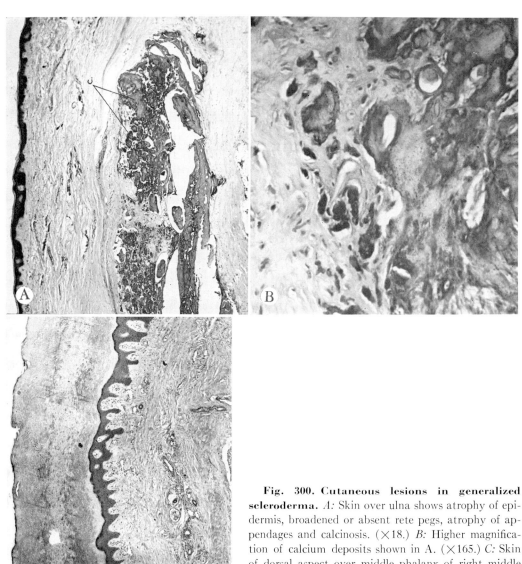

Fig. 300. Cutaneous lesions in generalized scleroderma. *A:* Skin over ulna shows atrophy of epidermis, broadened or absent rete pegs, atrophy of appendages and calcinosis. (×18.) *B:* Higher magnification of calcium deposits shown in A. (×165.) *C:* Skin of dorsal aspect over middle phalanx of right middle finger shows hyperkeratinization, dilated subpapillary venous plexus, atrophy of appendages and thickening of collagen bundles. (×22.)

(After Goetz,[384] courtesy Clinical Proceedings.)

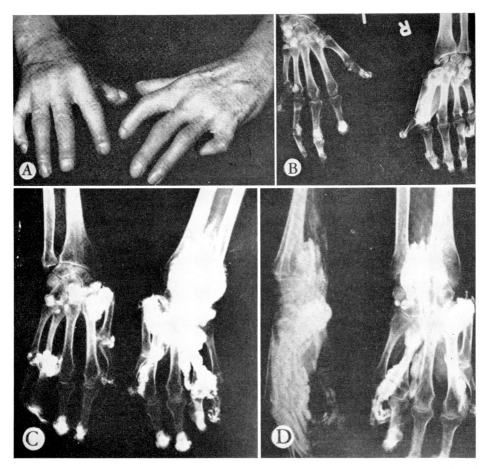

Fig. 301. Scleroderma with calcinosis. *A:* Marked flexion deformity with shortening of fingers. *B:* X-ray of A shows soft-tissue calcinosis and auto-amputation of a left terminal phalanx; calcinosis particularly severe at pressure point of left thumb. *C:* Extensive calcinosis in skin and subjacent tissues with involvement of flexor tendon sheaths, auto-amputation of terminal phalanges and subluxation of first metacarpals. *D:* Lateral view of C shows calcinosis of tendon sheaths.

(After Ingram, Jr.,[475] courtesy Am. J. Roentgenol.)

they cause no functional disability but often result in stenosis with severe difficulties in deglutition. The esophageal changes can be detected radiographically during life or as whitish mucosal patches at autopsy[71, 99, 267, 270, 340, 373, 384, 575, 657] (Figs. 304, 305, 306). There may also be lesions in other parts of the *gastrointestinal tract*,[84, 384, 575, 718] the *oral and nasal cavities* (buccal mucosa, tongue, and gingivae),[21, 58, 84, 453, 470, 550, 575, 650, 718, 805] or the *tonsils and fauces*.[550, 718] Among the *dental* changes[84, 575] thickening of the periodontal membrane[387, 552, 718, 890] is most characteristic.

Sometimes sclerodermatous patches may appear even in the *vaginal*[25, 291] or *rectal*[357] *mucosa* and in the *larynx* and *trachea*.[340, 470]

There may be diffuse sclerosis, sometimes with calcification of the *lungs*.[84, 340] This is demonstrable radiographically and has been described as "pulmosclerosis cystica" or "pulmosclerosis compacta" depending on whether there is cavitation[14, 120, 126, 197, 272, 373, 378, 431, 434, 618, 657, 718, 932, 961] (Figs. 307, 308, 309). The interstitial fibrosis is frequently associated with elastic-tissue proliferation and metaplasia of the alveolar epithelium. Allegedly "scleroderma is very rarely accom-

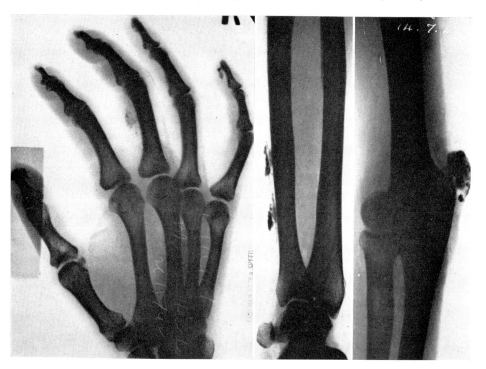

Fig. 302. Generalized scleroderma. *Left*: Absorption of tufts of terminal phalanges and deposits of calcium in subcutaneous tissue particularly in thumb, third and fifth fingers. *Middle*: Calcinosis along ulnar border. *Right*: Calcification in bursa of olecranon.
(After Goetz,[384] courtesy Clinical Proceedings.)

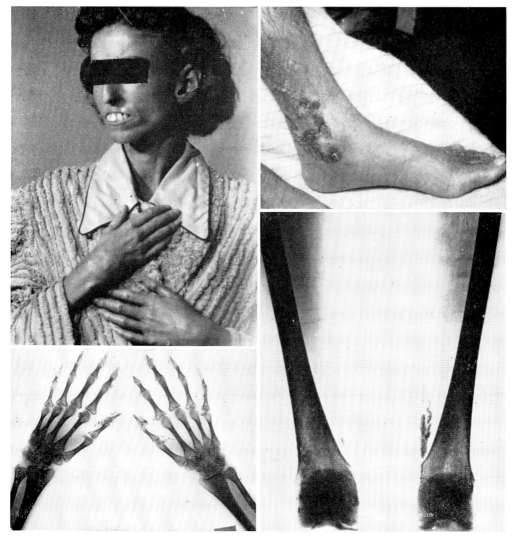

Fig. 303. Scleroderma with calcinosis. *A:* Hawklike facies (taut skin, tight mouth) and subcutaneous nodules on the hands. *B:* Ulceration on leg. *C:* X-rays of the hands show areas of calcification. *D:* Calcific deposits in lower third of both thighs.

(After Douglas and Randel,[274] courtesy New York State J. Med.)

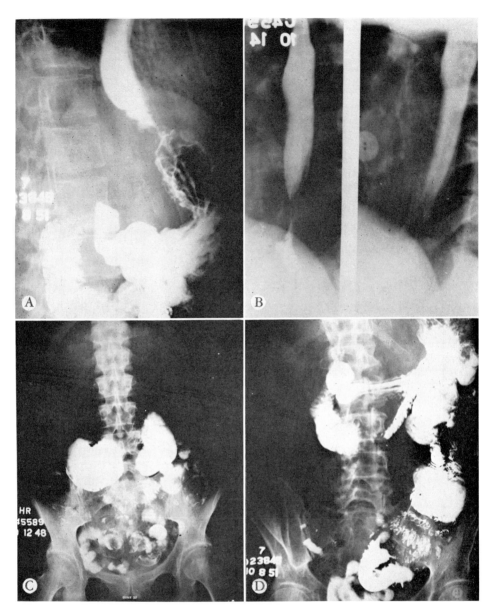

Fig. 304. Roentgen changes in systemic scleroderma. *A:* Dilated esophagus with relative narrowing in sphincter area. Stomach atonic; emptying time delayed. *B:* Fairly rigid and narrow esophageal segment. *C:* Dilatation of small bowel, ascribed to neuromuscular derangement. *D:* Narrowing throughout sphincter area. Stomach was atonic. Neuromuscular disturbance throughout small bowel.

[After Boyd *et al.*,[126] courtesy American Medical Association (Arch. Int. Med.).]

panied by a malignant tumor, but when this collagen disease involves the lung, the appearance of a carcinoma is not rare."[786]

Lesions in the **skeletal musculature** are common and strongly suggest a close relationship to dermatomyositis. There is muscle fibrosis and inflammation, sometimes with calcification and necrosis.[84, 287, 384, 575, 718] These lesions are accompanied by marked EMG-changes.[427]

Essentially similar changes have also been seen in the striated musculature of the **heart**;[61, 84, 99, 126, 384, 385, 575, 577, 657, 718, 961] they cause pronounced ECG-changes[309, 386, 394, 412, 620, 657] and can eventually lead to congestive heart failure and even death[14, 287] (Fig. 310).

Obstructive **vascular lesions** reminiscent of arteriosclerosis, periarteritis nodosa or Buerger's disease are uncommon, but their existence suggests that transitional forms between scleroderma and these diseases can occur[14, 553] (Fig. 311). In one case scleroderma was combined with obstruction of the **thoracic duct**.[439]

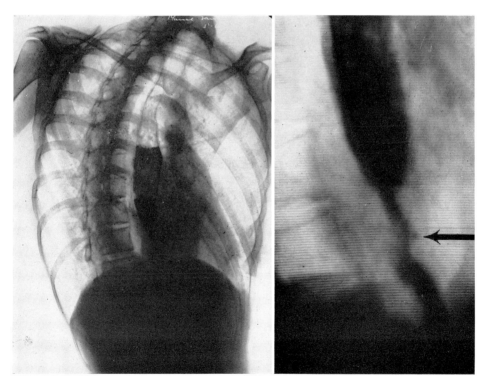

Fig. 305. Esophageal lesions in generalized scleroderma. *Left:* Narrowing of lower third of esophagus with moderate dilatation of middle third. High column of mucus overlies barium which is held up because of constriction. *Right:* Ulcer niche in narrowed portion of esophagus (arrow).

(After Goetz,[384] courtesy Clinical Proceedings.)

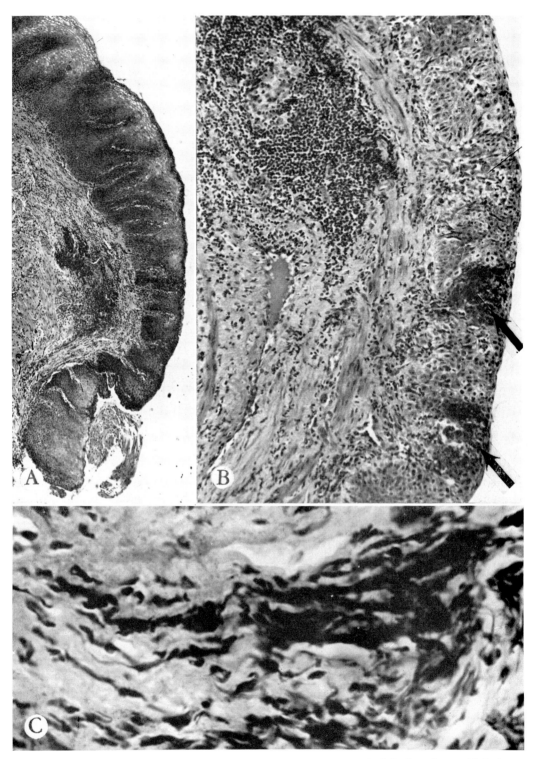

Fig. 306. Esophageal lesions in generalized scleroderma. *A:* Snip from lower third of
esophagus shows thickening of epithelium (leukoplakia) near top and calcification with round
cell infiltration in muscularis mucosae. (×55.) *B:* Snip of esophagus showing round cell infiltration of muscularis mucosae near top and hemorrhages in epithelial layer (arrows). (×150.)
C: Higher magnification of calcification in submucosa of same esophagus. (×640.)

(After Goetz,[384] courtesy Clinical Proceedings.)

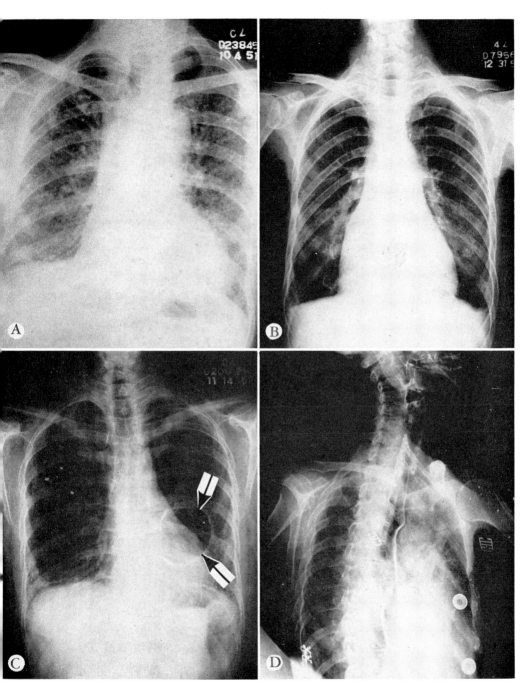

Fig. 307. Roentgen changes in systemic scleroderma. *A:* Focal fibrotic change through-out the lung fields. At autopsy, a year later, extensive pulmonary fibrosis was found. *B:* Heart, enlarged through both salients. *C:* Basilar fibrosis and large pneumonocele (retouched and marked by arrows) in left base. Shortly after this roentgenogram was taken patient developed a spontaneous pneumothorax. *D:* Thin-walled atonic esophagus. No peristaltic activity was present.

[After Boyd *et al.,*[126] courtesy the American Medical Association (Arch. Int. Med.).]

417

The ***kidney*** is frequently involved; it usually shows an essentially vascular lesion with thickening of the small and medium-sized arteries.[14, 99, 527, 562, 961, 718, 940] Some authors even speak of a special "scleroderma kidney," characterized by rapid destruction of renal tissue with acute or subacute focal and minor renal-cortical necroses. The larger interlobular arteries become dilated and develop a peculiar mucoid thickening similar to Wharton's jelly. The smaller arteries are affected by fibrinoid necrosis and eventually uremia may develop.[174, 419, 434, 667] Occasionally there is also thickening of the glomerular basement membrane accompanied by

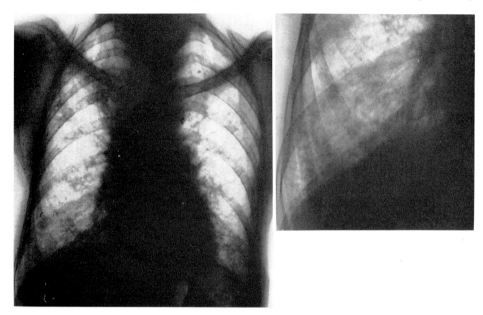

Fig. 308. Pulmonary changes in scleroderma. Typical "scleroderma lung" showing reticular and nodular shadows near base of both lungs. *Left:* General view. *Right:* Higher magnification of left base.
(After Hegglin,[434] courtesy Ztschr. f. Rheumaforschg.)

subendothelial hyaline deposits of the "wire loop" type, characteristic of lupus erythematosus disseminatus[304, 721] or even fatal nephrosclerosis[189] (Fig. 312).

A review of the literature shows that the ***liver*** is likewise often affected in scleroderma. There may be portal hypertension, abnormal liver function, hepatic fibrosis, focal necrosis, portal and biliary cirrhosis. Although it would have been difficult to prove that these lesions were not coincidental, it was thought that "in view of the protean nature of the disease and its propensity for involvement of the gastrointestinal tract, a causative relationship may exist."[935]

The ***osteoarticular*** lesions of scleroderma suggest a close relationship to the rheumatic group of diseases. In acrosclerosis, osteoporosis (sometimes associated with hyperostosis and severe joint lesions) occurs in the fingers and toes as a di-

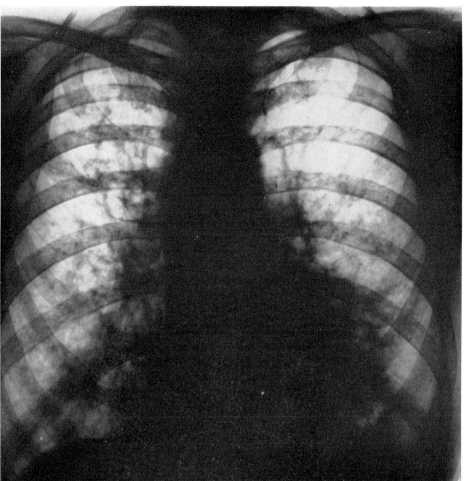

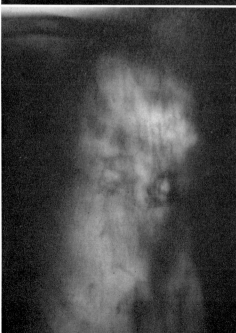

Fig. 309. Pulmonary changes in scleroderma. Typical honeycomb lung. *Top:* General view. *Bottom:* Tomogram clearly shows cavitation in right upper field.

(After Hegglin,[434] courtesy Ztschr. f. Rheumaforschg.)

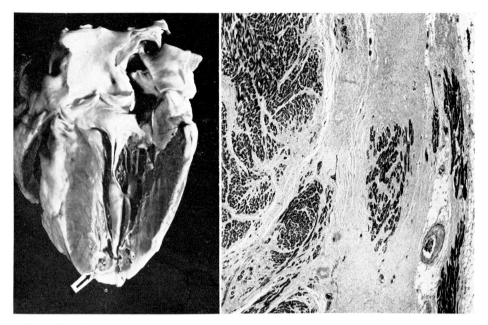

Fig. 310. Cardiac lesions in generalized scleroderma. *Left:* Small heart with marked hypertrophy of left and moderate hypertrophy of right ventricle. Cusps and openings of coronary arteries are healthy. Fibrosis of myocardium with calcified scar near apex (arrow). *Right:* Left ventricle halfway between apex and base. Cardiac muscle almost entirely replaced by dense connective tissue. Vessel is virtually normal.

(After Goetz,[384] courtesy Clinical Proceedings.)

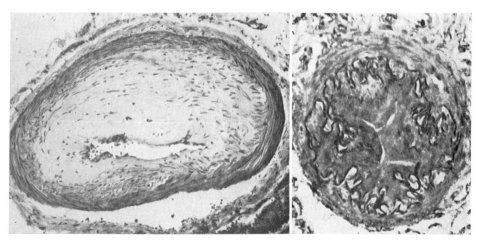

Fig. 311. Vascular lesions in generalized scleroderma. *Left*: Branch of inferior mesenteric artery showing sparsely nucleated, mucinous tissue. ($\times$80.) *Right:* Digital artery completely occluded by acellular fibrin-like material. Media shows degeneration and vacuolization. Internal elastic membrane is fragmented. ($\times$ 150.)

(After Goetz,[384] courtesy Clinical Proceedings.)

420

rect consequence of immobilization and invasion by the surrounding cutaneous lesions. However, rheumatoid arthritis also occurs quite often in the large joints that are far from any cutaneous lesions and sometimes osteoporosis is generalized[5, 84, 126, 373, 580, 647, 718] (Fig. 313). Conversely, in a significant number of the patients suffering from rheumatoid arthritis there are, allegedly, cutaneous lesions characteristic of scleroderma.[99] The combination of scleroderma with osteopoikilosis[97] is undoubtedly quite exceptional.

Among the **ocular lesions** of scleroderma bilateral cataracts are perhaps the most frequent.[269, 339, 575, 626, 718, 803, 968] This change is also characteristic of Werner's and Rothmund's syndromes, which are presumably related collagen diseases.

In rare instances there is constriction of the **ear ducts,** sometimes progressing to complete blockade.[99]

Great importance has been attached to lesions in the **nervous system** because they are assumed to play an etiologic role. Undoubtedly, scleroderma is often associated with more or less severe neurologic complications[176, 258, 531, 595, 693, 718] and sometimes the skin lesions show a striking, symmetrical, *metameric distribution,* which suggests some nervous component in their pathogenesis.[138, 212] Furthermore, scleroderma may develop *in the territory supplied by an injured nerve.*[417, 770] Scleroderma "en coup de sabre" or "en bandes," also known as *linear scleroderma*, often follows the course of nerves[60, 692, 766, 867] (Fig. 314). Hence, these lesions "are thought to be trophoneuroses, i.e., having segmental peripheral nerve distribution, and are associated with atrophy of the underlying tissue. The arrangement of lesions in certain localized areas suggests the involvement of the nervous system."[608] In a patient in whom linear scleroderma developed a few months after a severe nervous strain, the attendant ocular changes consisted of sectoral atrophy of the mesodermal layers of the iris on the side of the skin lesion. "The nature of the eye changes indicated their neurotrophic origin, suggesting a connection of scleroderma with the nervous system, which is especially distinct in linear scleroderma."[803] In another patient with linear scleroderma in whom the involved area corresponded roughly to the terminal distribution of the fifth nerve, the oral mucosa as well as the alveolar process itself, gradually became deformed as the lesion developed.[610]

The metameric distribution may also be due to *central ganglionic lesions.*[870] In thirteen patients with scleroderma the linear lesions lay in the long axis of spinal root zones and did not always follow the distribution of peripheral nerves. "The spacial distribution of lesions, the high incidence of demonstrable lesions of the spine in patients with linear scleroderma and the similarity of these lesions to trophic disturbances suggest that this disease originates from lesions in the nervous system."[770]

In some cases *epilepsy*[413] or at least convulsions[413] were noted, but their sclerodermatous nature could not be proven.

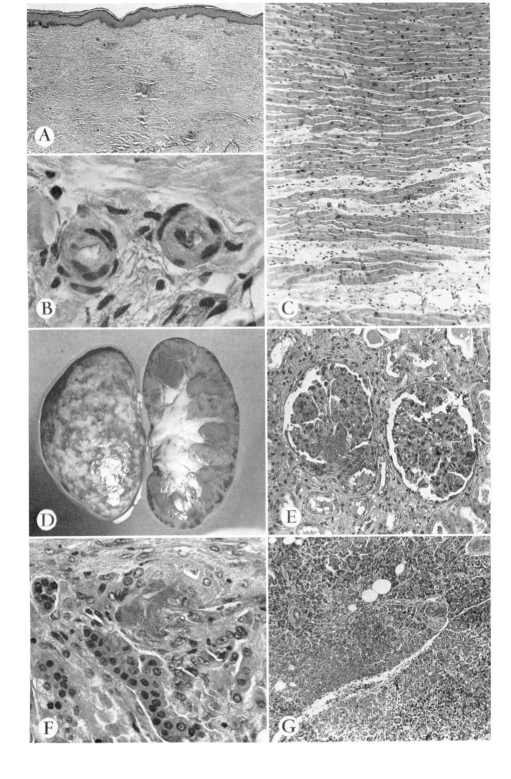

Scleroderma may also be combined with *brain lesions* caused by endarteritis obliterans[636] or other types of disseminated ischemic encephalopathy,[123] encephalitis[533] and related cerebral lesions[717] as well as with more diffuse changes throughout the central nervous system.[975] The disease has been known to develop after highly *traumatic emotional experiences*[71, 310, 326, 892] and it occurs comparatively frequently in *psychotic* patients.[738]

EEG-changes have likewise been reported,[701] particularly a "moderate degree of diffuse electrocortical activity"[84] and changes "suggestive of a decrease in the ionized calcium of the tissue fluids."[912] However, other investigators could detect no noteworthy EEG-changes and stated that no morphologic lesions in the sympathetic ganglia could be found to account for the radiologically demonstrable gastrointestinal disturbances.[100]

In sclerodermatous skin the *peripheral nerves* may undergo profound alterations.[225] A detailed study of two cases of scleroderma showed consistent lesions in the terminal reticulum of the cutaneous nerves as well as derangements in skin sensitivity and sweat secretion.[498] Allegedly, scleroderma with peripheral neuropathy[526] may result from the deposition of mucoid material in the connective sheaths of nerves. Severe morphologic lesions can also occur in the *sympathetic nervous system*,[696] particularly the sympathetic ganglia.[30, 232, 697, 732] The frequency of Raynaud's phenomenon in incipient scleroderma, as well as the occasional appearance of hypo- or hypersecretion of sweat with hypo- or hyperesthesia and morphologically detectable changes in the terminal reticulum of the vegetative nerve fibers[498] represent additional manifestations of derangements in the autonomic nervous system.

A nervous component in the pathogenesis of scleroderma is suggested by the frequency of an attendant *facial hemiatrophy;*[7, 17, 23, 99, 764] even when the latter is not very obvious, sensibility-chronaxia measurements suggest a definite nervous involvement.[75, 482] Sometimes there is *atrophy of half of the entire body.*[19, 37, 408, 641, 897]

Numerous cases of *"hemiscleroderma"* have been reported in which the skin was only unilaterally affected.[99]

Fig. 312. Systemic changes in scleroderma. *A:* Biopsy of skin showing atrophy of epidermis and thickened collagen of dermis extending below persistent sweat glands. *B:* Thickened arterioles in dermis. *C:* Loose acellular connective tissue between myocardial fibers in scleroderma. The degree of coronary arteriosclerosis was slight and this fibrosis did not have the density or perivascular distribution of the usual interstitial cardiac fibrosis. *D:* Capsular and cut surfaces of kidneys showing patchy hemorrhages in outer half of pale yellow cortex. *E:* Fibrinoid necrosis in afferent arterioles and within glomerular tufts in kidney. *F:* Fibrinoid necrosis in an arteriole of zona glomerulosa of adrenal. *G:* Focus of recent necrosis in pancreas.

(After Alexander *et al.,* [14] courtesy Am. J. Med.)

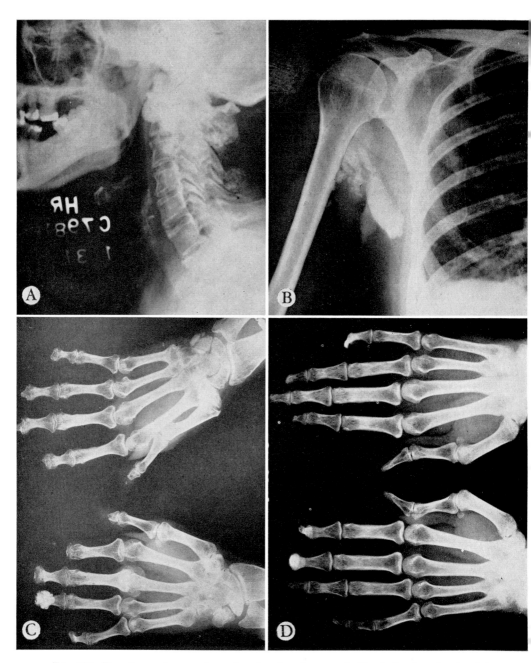

Fig. 313. Roentgen changes in systemic scleroderma. *A:* Cervical spine, showing intra-muscular and paravertebral ligament calcification. *B:* Calcium deposit intramuscularly about the shoulder. *C:* Acrosclerosis, sclerodactyly and narrowed interphalangeal joints. *D:* Acro-sclerosis and sclerodactyly.

[After Boyd *et al.*,[126] courtesy American Medical Association (Arch. Int. Med.).]

Allegedly, normal **skin transplanted** into a sclerodermatous area becomes affected, while sclerodermatous skin transplanted into a previously normal area heals. These findings were likewise cited in support of the trophoneurosis theory.[430] However, in one case sclerodermatous skin transplanted (within a tubular flap, according to Tagliacozzi) into a healthy area not only failed to show healing but also exhibited a spreading of the lesion.[213]

Among the endocrine disturbances associated with scleroderma, **parathyroid dysfunction** received the greatest attention. In scleroderma the *tissue calcium* content (not only of the skin but also of the muscle, heart, lung, kidney, and pancreas) is said to be far above normal. In addition there may be visible soft-tissue calcification, particularly nephrocalcinosis. Conversely, the bone calcium (rib) was usually subnormal. In view of these findings and of other data in the literature, scleroderma was considered to be a "dysparathyroidism."[556]

However, as a rule there is no *hypercalcemia* in scleroderma[384] even in the presence of multiple calcareous concretions[581]—despite the emphatic claim of some

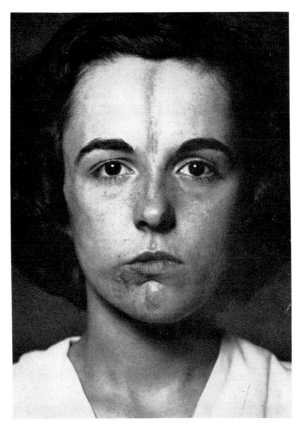

Fig. 314. Linear scleroderma. "Coup de sabre" lesion associated with facial hemiatrophy. [After Winkelmann,[985] courtesy C. V. Mosby Co. (J. Chron. Diseases).]

surgeons that the blood calcium is "usually high"[505, 582, 962]—and there is no significant change in calcium balance.[47]

In one case of calcareous scleroderma, the blood calcium did not rise unduly following treatment with calcium or parathyroid hormone. Hence, it was concluded that the defect in this disease is an unusual tendency to capture calcium in the affected skin rather than an exaggerated tendency to develop hypercalcemia. This may explain why the blood calcium levels are rarely elevated (and may be subnormal) in scleroderma despite the calcinosis.[714]

Structural lesions in the parathyroids have frequently been noted in scleroderma but their significance is difficult to assess; the glands may be enlarged to the point of tumor formation or so atrophic as to become impossible to find despite careful search at autopsy.[71, 384, 557, 582, 708, 718] The effect of ***parathyroidectomy*** has already been discussed (p. 10).

Scleroderma can be accompanied by ***Addison's disease,***[558, 736, 765] or at least intense pigmentation and muscular weakness; but the diagnosis of adrenal deficiency is difficult owing to the frequent association of scleroderma with non-Addisonian hyperpigmentation, vitiligo, and muscle fibrosis.[699, 869] Yet, even structural lesions in the ***adrenals*** have been repeatedly noted,[61, 229, 575, 718, 907] particularly sclerosis,[14] necrosis,[495] cortical tumors,[146, 708] and heavy lymphocytic infiltration.[436]

Scleroderma may also be associated with ***acromegaly***[178, 965] or ***pituitary hemorrhage and inflammation.***[768] Sometimes there is thyroid fibrosis,[437] ***hypo-*** or ***hyperthyroidism,***[869] but scleroderma is more commonly found in combination with Graves's disease.[4, 501, 551, 558, 665, 668, 699, 736, 750, 868] Still, in some respects scleroderma—especially the edematous variety—resembles myxedema and may be attended by very high blood-cholesterol values.[669] This "scleromyxedema" is considered to be merely a variant of diffuse scleroderma.[489] However, the statement that "histologically normal thyroids are not found in any case of progressive scleroderma"[278] may be questioned (Fig. 314a).

In one patient with scleroderma there was acinar atrophy and focal fibrinous necrosis of the ***pancreas,*** with acute necrosis of its small arteries. The patient also had esophageal lesions, nephrosclerosis, hypertension with signs of periarteritis nodosa, and three duodenal ulcers.[27] Interstitial fibrosis in the pancreas may also occur,[14, 718] and this is sometimes accompanied by enlargement of the Langerhans' islands.[18] In one case there were large masses of amorphous tissue between the parenchymal cells, but their nature has not been determined.[18]

"Scleroatrophic alterations" in the ***submaxillary glands*** of patients suffering from scleroderma or rheumatoid arthritis have been interpreted as particular localizations of diffuse collagen disease.[996]

We have already mentioned that scleroderma may be associated with various other morbid states, such as ***dermatomyositis,***[57, 71, 270] ***lupus erythematosus,***[57] *periarteritis nodosa,*[57] *psoriasis, ichthyosis, leukemia, Sjögren's syndrome, psychic and nervous diseases,* as well as a variety of *infections.*[71] As judged by a series of observations allegedly "rheumatic infection either precedes or accompanies the appearance of the scleroderma syndrome."[536] In a twelve-year-old girl scleroderma was attended by *ankylosing atrophic arthritis,*[31] and the disease is quite commonly combined with *rheumatoid arthritis,*[71] *keloids,*[77] and *blood eosinophilia.*[905] In exceptional cases, scleroderma is attended by cutaneous *tuberculosis,*[780, 867] *urticaria factitia,*[98] or *splenic lesions.*[718]

Sclerodermatous skin is usually free of amyloid, but cases of cutaneous *amyloidosis* may be diagnosed clinically as scleroderma because of the striking resemblance between the two diseases.[570]

Whether the incidence of *malignancy* is increased in scleroderma remains to be shown, but the disease can occur in conjunction with leukemia[62, 357, 557] or carcinoma of the lung,[269, 786] and, at least in one patient, there was massive sarcomatous transformation of the entire sclerodermatous skin area.[414]

Among the *biochemical changes* that characterize scleroderma, we have already mentioned alterations in calcium metabolism. In addition there may be marked hypercholesterolemia,[669] but usually the blood cholesterol, sugar, and phosphate levels are normal.[71, 384, 575] Determinations of other metabolites (N.P.N., proteins, vitamin A, vitamin C, potassium, sodium, chlorides, etc.) likewise failed to reveal any specific metabolic error that could be held responsible for this disease.[71, 575]

Factors influencing the course of scleroderma.—Among the potential eliciting factors *local trauma* is probably most important.[71, 258, 284, 305, 370, 384, 600, 892] *Fractures,* exposure to *cold* or *heat,* as well as mechanical *pressure* upon the skin, such as occurs particularly over tuberosities of the ischia,[142] or compression of the thighs exerted by elastic garters,[221] may induce local sclerodermatous lesions. Apparently, the most diverse types of injuries may be effective in this respect; for example, topical scleroderma has been noted following a severe *blow,*[368] *vaccination,*[370] exposure to *trichloroethylene*[744] or to *silver polish,* and handling of *ice.*[345] The disease is said to occur with particular frequency in *stonemasons.* One instance was observed in a *coppersmith;*[129] another, at the site of a *shrapnel* wound, may have been due to trauma or to a more specific metal effect.[788] "Scleroderma-like" lesions were seen to appear after subcutaneous *camphor* infiltration.[241]

Among habitual *betel-nut* (Areca catechu) chewers in Taiwan, buccal scleroderma is said to be quite common. For chewing, the nut is wrapped in Pipera leaf (Piper catechu) and a paste of crude calcium and spice powder (Pulvis cinnamoni) is placed upon it. About ten minutes after the nut is taken, the pupils contract and there is hypersalivation and a sensation of excitement.[903] This observation is mentioned because it suggests that local challenge may be the cause of

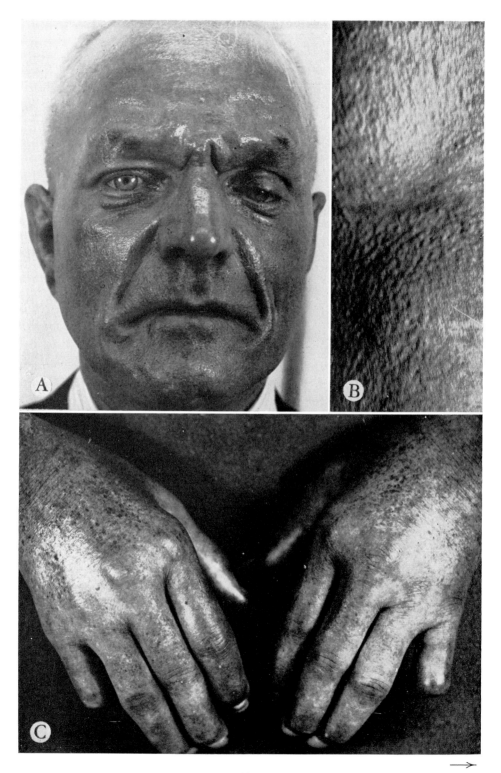

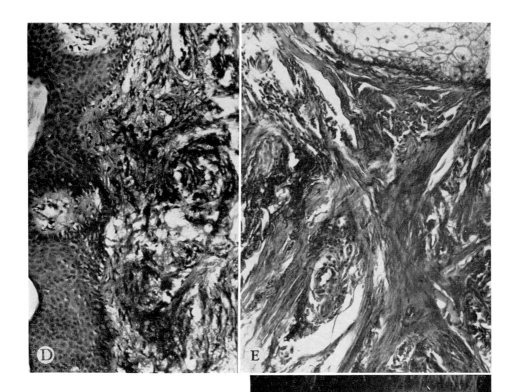

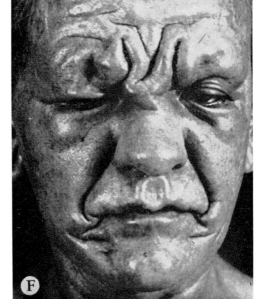

Fig. 314a. Scleromyxedema. 61-year-old man. *A:* Typical facial expression. *B:* Characteristic papules on the radial side of the right elbow. *C:* Sclerodactyly in scleromyxedema. *D:* Histologic aspect of one of the skin papules showing ample metachromatic material and mast cells underneath epidermis. *E:* Sclerotic skin from the left cheek. The thick collagen bundles stain slightly metachromatically (toluidene blue). *F:* Another case of scleromyxedema in a 57-year-old woman.

(After Jansen *et al.*,[489] courtesy Nederl. Tijdschr. voor Geneesk.)

429

oral scleroderma and because, in experimental calciphylaxis, the apparently responsible pathogens (like IPR and 5HT) sometimes possess a particularly pronounced effect upon the salivary glands. However, the true sclerodermatous nature of the betel-nut-induced changes remains to be proven.

In two cases a condition thought to be diffuse scleroderma developed after **solar irradiation,** perhaps owing to sensitization by **hematoporphyrin,** since large amounts of this compound were found in the urine.[549] Hematoporphyrinuria was also noted in another sclerodermatous patient.[403] Scleroderma has been seen to occur after **ultraviolet irradiation**[368] and, of course, patients with dermatomyositis, a closely related disease, are quite commonly photosensitive.

In discussing the lesions characteristic of scleroderma, we have already reviewed the evidence suggesting that **nervous** factors may contribute to the development of this disease.

In a **pregnant** woman a pre-existing scleroderma was greatly aggravated during gestation.[71]

Scleroderma may appear after a **pulmonary infarct**[706] (some authors speak of a "postinfarction sclerodactylia"), which allegedly developed in 21 per cent of a series of 178 consecutive cases of acute **myocardial infarction.**[499]

Indeed, scleroderma develops so often immediately after some psychic, physical, or infectious injury that it is regarded as a disease of adaptation elicited by **stress.**[310] Allegedly "there is a close relationship between the anatomo-pathologic alterations observed in scleroderma in the skin, the vessels, and the viscera (especially the heart and the kidney) and the analogous lesions described in the general adaptation syndrome."[70]

Among the therapeutic interventions **parathyroidectomy** received special attention, but the relevant literature has already been discussed in the section on the history of calciphylaxis (p. 10). It may be significant in connection with the probable etiologic role of calcification in the production of this disease that scleroderma—with or without manifest calcification—is favorably influenced by treatment with the calcium chelating agent sodium-EDTA.[202, 251, 463, 534, 607, 672, 680, 713, 728, 772, 883, 925, 983] In the course of this therapy the urinary calcium and copper elimination is increased two- to threefold and the zinc excretion ten- to thirtyfold; hence, it remains to be seen whether the therapeutic effect of EDTA is to be ascribed to the enforced loss of one or the other among these metals.[463] It will be recalled that both copper- and (to an even greater extent) zinc-salts can act as calciphylactic challengers.[479]

Since **DHT** mobilizes calcium from the skeleton, it was thought that it may also be of benefit in certain cases of scleroderma, especially those associated with calcinosis. Although animal experiments indicate that the bone calcium liberated by DHT actually tends to accumulate in the skin, beneficial results have allegedly been seen in a few sclerodermatous patients following this treatment.[467]

It has also been claimed that scleroderma is favorably influenced by **vitamin E,** but the published data are not very convincing.[48, 153, 159, 262, 377, 686] The same is true of the beneficial results allegedly obtained with **PABA.**[713, 992]

ACTH and **glucocorticoids** are rarely beneficial in scleroderma.[713]

The Sideroscleroses

Syn., iron-calcium incrustations, siderofibroses.

This morbid entity is not a disease, but merely a lesion characterized by iron and calcium incrustation conducive to local sclerosis. The so-called **"Gamna corpuscles"** are sharply delimited, minute, but usually macroscopically visible, indurated nodules most commonly found in the spleen, occasionally also in the liver, ovary, and other locations. Giant cells frequently develop in their vicinity.[179, 361, 515, 945] Most investigators agree that these fibrous nodules result from small hemorrhages in which the liberated iron somehow attracts calcium and stimulates fibrosis. It is highly probable that here we are dealing with a phenomenon very closely related to that of experimental calciphylaxis.

Sjögren's Syndrome

Syn., Sjögren's disease, dacryosialoadenopathia atrophicans.

This condition may be related to Mikulicz's disease[781] and is characterized by dryness of the mucous membranes owing to inadequate secretion of saliva and tears. The secretion of the stomach, sweat glands, and the glands of the respiratory tract may also be decreased. There is lymphocytic infiltration in the parotid and lacrimal glands, accompanied by parenchymal atrophy (a picture very similar to that of Mikulicz's disease); but sometimes the lesions are more reminiscent of uveoparotid fever (Heerfordt's syndrome) and sarcoidosis. There may also be necrotizing arteritis, subcutaneous rheumatoid nodules, and rheumatoid arthritis; hence, the condition is usually listed as a member of the collagen disease group.[781]

In relation to the concept of the calcinoscleroses, it is of interest that Sjögren's disease is sometimes associated with scleroderma and calcinosis[308, 421, 583, 875, 877] (Fig. 315).

"Stiff-Man Syndrome" and the "Stiffness Syndrome" of Guinea Pigs

Guinea pigs kept on pasteurized milk rations do not grow well and develop a syndrome characterized by wrist stiffness, muscular dystrophy, arteriosclerosis, calcium deposition in various soft tissues with pathologic lesions in bones and teeth, as well as deafness, eosinophilia, fever, and an increased sedimentation rate. The excess calcium is laid down in the diverse cartilages, renal tissue, stroma of striated muscles, gastrointestinal tract, blood vessels, and even in hair follicles.[554, 561, 715, 948, 949, 950, 951, 952] Stigmasterol (25 μg. daily) has a definite curative effect.[554]

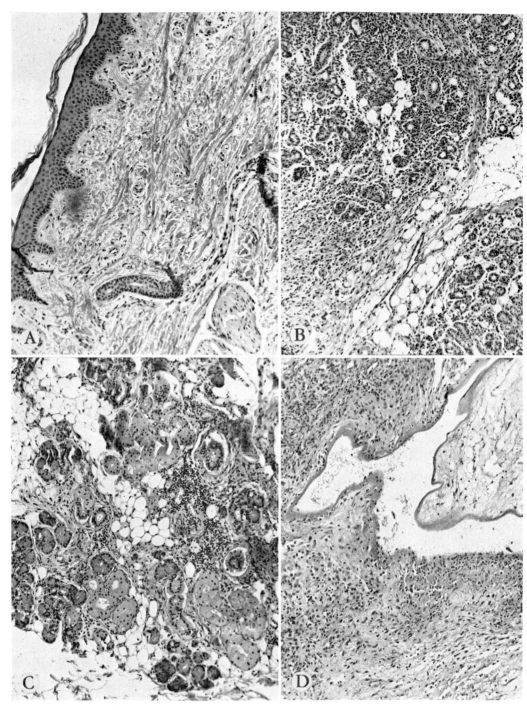

Fig. 315. Sjögren's syndrome associated with scleroderma. *A:* Skin biopsy with epidermal atrophy and dermal fibrosis characteristic of scleroderma. (Hematoxylin-eosin, ×110.) *B:* Parotid gland with mild atrophy of acini and moderate diffuse lymphocytic infiltration of stroma. (Hematoxylin-eosin, ×120.) *C:* Submaxillary gland with severe atrophy, stromal fibrosis and mild lymphocytic infiltration. Serous acini appear to be swollen with brightly eosinophilic cytoplasm. (Hematoxylin-eosin, ×85.) *D:* Sternoclavicular joint with fibrinoid synovitis comparable to rheumatoid arthritis. (Hematoxylin-eosin, ×85.)

[After Shearn[875] courtesy Am. College of Physicians (Ann. Int. Med.).]

This syndrome allegedly resembles calcinosis, dermatomyositis, and sclero-derma.[554, 561] However, there is no definite evidence of any fundamental relation-ship between this experimental condition and the "stiff-man syndrome" of human pathology except that the latter is believed by some to be a variant of dermatomyositis,[955] which is probably identical with the so-called "fibromyosi-tis."[698]

The characteristic features of the stiff-man syndrome are progressive rigidity of skeletal muscles with episodes of sustained cramps; particular predilection for neck and arm muscles; degenerative changes with collagen formation in the affected muscles and occasionally psychic derangements, atheromatosis, lowered serum phosphorus and glycosuria.[40, 422, 970]

Thrombotic Thrombocytopenic Purpura

Despite its descriptive name, the basic lesion in thrombotic thrombocytopenic purpura (TTP) is vascular rather than thrombotic. The affected blood vessels reveal subendothelial, segmental accumulations of hyaline material which pro-trude into the lumen and there may become covered by platelets. TTP is often accompanied by systemic lupus erythematosus, periarteritis nodosa, "wire loop" lesions in the kidney, or rheumatoid arthritis and has hence been regarded as a collagen disease.[86, 908]

The possible participation of derangements in calcium metabolism in the patho-genesis of this disease has not yet been examined.

Thromboangiitis obliterans (cf. "Buerger's Disease").

Topical Tissue Injury

It is a well-known fact that the most varied chemical and physical agents can produce calcification at the site of their application. This observation was at the basis of the concept that "dystrophic calcification" occurs wherever tissue is dam-aged and that this is a purely nonspecific phenomenon. As we have outlined else-where, this view is incorrect, since under usual circumstances most types of injuries do not result in calcification; in fact, calcium deposition occurs only if either the locally applied agent possesses certain specific calcifying properties or the or-ganism is generally sensitized by some systemic calcifier (e.g., parathyroid hor-mone) for this form of response. Nevertheless, calcification at sites of injury is so common that a detailed discussion of the relevant literature would be impractical. Suffice it to mention a few instructive examples.

Calcification and even ossification may occur in *scars* resulting from mechanical *trauma* or *burns*.[134, 265, 524] Apparently, topical injuries have a special tendency to cause calcification and sometimes even ossification if they produce necrosis and hemorrhage.[65, 155, 332] (Cf. "Myositis Ossificans.")

A particularly intense calcium deposition was produced in a young woman by topical injury to the knee, presumably because she was predisposed for calcinosis owing to a chronic hypercalcemia of unknown origin.[307] Cases of this type re-emphasize the important influence of systemic predisposing factors in the induction of topical calcification by nonspecific means.

Calcinosis of the ear-cartilage or ear-lobe may result from mechanical trauma but is most commonly due to *frostbite.*[268, 342, 759]

Cutaneous calcification was noted on the hands of a woman who for many years had to wash large quantities of *copper* kitchenware.[524, 751] (Cf. "Calcinosis Cutis.") Other types of chemical irritation, e.g., the injection of *calcium* or *bismuth* salts into the buttocks,[16] may also induce local calcinosis in man, as they do in experimental animals. It remains to be seen whether in all these cases the precipitation of calcium is due exclusively to the direct calcifying effect of the injected drugs or whether systemic predisposing factors also play a role.

Occasionally, calcareous tendinitis and tendovaginitis may occur following local *infections* in the hand and foot.[78] Certain *parasitic infestations* actually heal through "calcination" of the parasite. This is especially evident, for example, in *trichinosis,*[781] *Echinococcus* infestation[68] (Fig. 316) and in horses infected with *Sclerostomum bidentatum.*[265] Infection with *Toxoplasma gondii* also appears to create a special predisposition for calcification. In congenital toxoplasmosis (due to infection in utero or during the first few months of life) the characteristic lesions are hydrocephalus, necrotic granulomatous foci in the brain with focal calcium deposition, and bilateral chorioretinitis. There may also be multiple small focal necroses in the viscera, particularly the heart.[22] Toxoplasmosis in adults is less common, but in one case pronounced calcinosis developed acutely around both knee joints.[6] (For *Histoplasma* and *Coccidioides* infection cf. "Calcinosis of the Lung.")

It is, of course, well known that *tubercles* tend to heal with tissue calcification[781] and that calcium deposition is common in inflamed gallbladders[68] (Fig. 316), *varicose veins* (particularly hemorrhoids), *foreign-body granulomas, infarcts, diverse forms of tissue necrosis,* and particularly in *lithopedions.*[754, 781] Even topical injury due to an *insect bite* has on occasion caused local calcification with ossification in the skin,[265, 804] and the very exceptional nature of this occurrence again shows the importance of systemic predisposing factors.

An excellent review of traumatic tissue calcification in various organs, including the brain, heart valves, tendons, and muscles, brought out the fact that *virtually no organ is immune* against this type of response but in general the stroma rather than the parenchyma is subject to calcification.[265]

Tumors

Calcification in tumors.—Many kinds of neoplasms have a great tendency to undergo calcification.[192, 524, 676] This is especially evident in the cutaneous *"calcifying epithelioma" of Malherbe*[16, 781] and certain *basal cell carcinomas of*

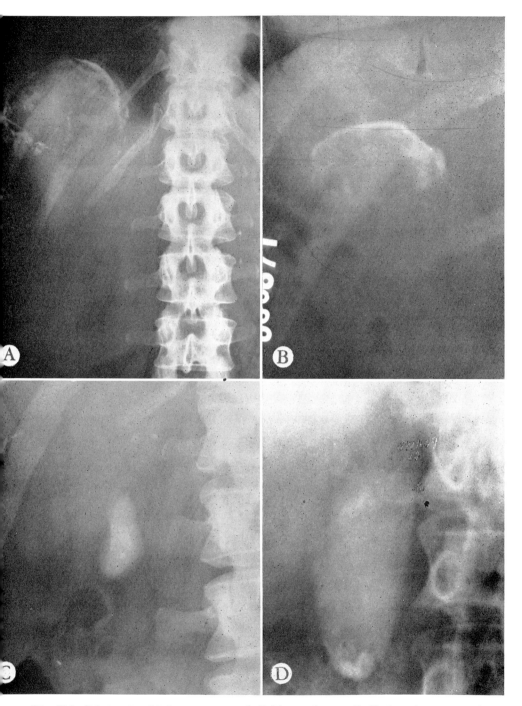

Fig. 316. Calcinosis of biliary system. *A:* Echinococcic cyst. *B:* Neglected empyema of gallbladder. Both present cystlike lesions with thick, irregularly calcified capsule in right upper abdominal quadrant, a frequent result of chronic inflammation. *C:* Chronic cholecystitis with "milk of calcium" bile simulates a dye-filled gallbladder although here no cholecystographic medium was used. *D:* Tuberculous psoas abscess mimics dye-filled gallbladder.

(After Bartholomew *et al.,*[68] courtesy Postgrad. Med.)

the skin, particularly the so-called "basosquamous" variety.[16] Calcifying tumors have also been described under such names as *fibroma petrificans, lipoma petrificum, chondroma ossificans, angioma ossificans, and carcinoma psammosum.*[265]

An extensive analysis of various *calcifying cutaneous epitheliomas* has led to the conclusion that in these "calcification represents an effort to stimulate solid scar-tissue formation. If the organism sometimes overshoots its aim, this results in intense calcium incrustation with inflammation and exulceration, so that scar formation occurs only in this round-about way. This phenomenon of over-compensation is far from unique (e.g., excessive granuloma formation or giant callus formation)."[265]

Massive calcification may also occur in a variety of other neoplasms, for example in *leiomyomas of the esophagus*[969] and *various adrenal tumors.*[280] Psammoma bodies are especially common in *meningiomas* and certain *prostatic tumors.*[781]

The bone formation characteristic of *dermoids* and *teratomas* need not be discussed here, since it is obviously unrelated to the calcinoses. It may be relevant to note, however, that calcification occurs frequently in *atheromatous cysts* of the skin[265, 497] as well as in papillary and follicular *carcinomas of the thyroid.*[72, 73]

Calcinosis induced by tumors.—Ever since Virchow first enunciated his concept of "metastatic calcification" it has been generally assumed that systemic calcinosis develops in patients with *destructive bone tumors* because the organism is flooded with calcium and phosphate. This process undoubtedly plays an important role whenever the skeleton is attacked by metastatic carcinomas, multiple myeloma, leukemia, etc. However, a study of calcinosis in leukemia suggests that skeletal mucopolysaccharides might also participate by providing the matrix in which subsequent calcium deposition can take place.[407]

It has also become evident that hypercalcemia sometimes conducive to calcinosis can develop even in patients with *malignant tumors that do not form bone metastases.*[26, 28, 216, 614, 615, 720, 899, 956] Furthermore, in some patients removal of the primary tumor was followed by reduction of the blood calcium level to normal. It was assumed that various malignant *tumors act through the production of parathyroid hormone-like substances.*[13, 216] However, if this were the case, parathyroidectomy should have no curative value. Yet it may be cited in favor of this concept that in rabbits transplantation of carcinoma XV-2 produces a state reminiscent of hyperparathyroidism and there is hypercalcemia, hypophosphatemia, nephrocalcinosis, and bone resorption by numerous giant cells.[978, 979]

It has also been postulated that *tumors may produce parathyrotrophic substances* which raise the blood calcium through the stimulation of parathyroid hormone secretion.[578, 899] According to yet another suggestion, the *tumors might produce a vitamin-D-like substance* which increases calcium absorption from the gastrointestinal tract, thus imitating the defect allegedly noted in sarcoido-sis.[20, 441, 442] The literature on the various mechanisms that may lead to hyper-calcemia in patients with neoplasia or sarcoidosis has been reviewed elsewhere.[29]

A systematic study on the cutaneous manifestations of malignant disease led to the conclusion that the most diverse malignant neoplasms induce a tendency for the development of "cachectic skin" (dry, inelastic, scaly, pale, and yellow), pruritus, bullous reactions resembling dermatitis herpetiformis or pemphigus, telangiectasis, and dermatomyositis. "Acanthosis nigricans, in which there is a hypertrophy and pigmentation of the skin, is in most cases associated with malig-nancy."[335] These findings are mentioned because of the frequency of skin lesions in calciphylaxis.

Urticaria

Syn., hives, nettle rash.

This dermatosis is characterized by the appearance of intensely itching wheals or welts with elevated, usually white centers and a surrounding area of erythema. The lesions appear in crops widely distributed over the body surface and tend to disappear in a few days without causing systemic manifestations. Urticaria is men-tioned here only because in exceptional instances it can apparently undergo rapid and massive calcification.[16] In this respect it resembles the calciphylactic der-matoses associated with mastocyte degranulation.

Villonodular Synovitis

Syn., pigmented villonodular synovitis.

This is an inflammation of the synovial membranes, usually encountered in young adult males and principally localized in the larger joints (knee, ankle, occa-sionally shoulder). Macroscopically, there is nodular thickening of the synovia with the production of long, slender, filamentous processes that project into the joint cavity. Since the condition is associated with much hemorrhage, the villi assume a deep brown or yellowish color. Histologically, the inflammation consists principally of intense histiocytic infiltration accompanied by the deposition of hemosiderin granules in the villi and proliferation of subepithelial connective tis-sue. In addition, there are many lipid-containing phagocytes and occasionally giant cells surrounded by considerable fibrosis; the resulting picture is not unlike that of the giant-cell tumors of tendons and bones.[754, 781] Allegedly, these lesions may become malignant;[977] but if such a transformation occurs, it must be rare.[598]

It is very probable that here iron pigment participates in the stimulation of fibrosis and giant-cell formation, but nothing is known about the possible role of secondary calcification.

Werner's Disease

Syn., Werner's syndrome, progeria of the adult. Although many investigators refer to this disease merely as "scleroderma with cataracts," this designation has been rejected because, allegedly, the cutaneous changes are not identical with those of scleroderma (nor, incidentally, with those of Rothmund's syndrome). Hence, it was proposed that Werner's syndrome be called "heredo-familial atrophic dermatosis with skin ulcers" and Rothmund's syndrome "heredo-familial atrophic dermatosis with telangiectases."[920]

This is a recessive or irregular dominant hereditary disease which is characterized by tense, adherent, mottle-pigmented skin, sclerodactyly and keratosis on pressure-points (sometimes with intractable leg ulcers). It is accompanied by precocious graying of the hair, often premature baldness, juvenile cataracts, osteoporosis, and often calcification in muscles, ligaments, and arteries (especially in the lower extremities), hypogonadism and diabetes.[16, 111, 127, 180, 343, 397, 410, 477, 695, 761, 920]

Sometimes intense fibrosis of the esophagus, skeletal musculature, and trachea, as well as arthritis, are prominent.[127] In one case there were multiple adenomas in the parathyroid, thyroid, and adrenal cortex;[695] in another patient hypercalcemia and hyperphosphaturia raised the question of a possible hyperparathyroidism.[298] The signs and symptoms of Werner's syndrome as well as an allegedly observed "disturbance of calcium metabolism point rather to a participation of the parathyroid than of any other ductless gland."[695]

Werner's syndrome may be associated with calcification of tendons, ligaments, and bursae as well as Mönckeberg's sclerosis of the arteries.[448] Sometimes soft-tissue calcification, especially in the cardiovascular system, osteoporosis, and osteoarthritis are prominent.[483, 796] In one case there was retinitis pigmentosa, hypertension, and uremia combined with a thyroid adenocarcinoma, and a survey of the literature "strengthens the impression that there is a relative increase in the incidence of neoplasia in these cases."[943]

VII
Speculations

In the previous chapters we limited ourselves to an almost purely descriptive account of the production and features of the manifold calciphylactic syndromes. In view of the novelty and complexity of this topic continuous excursions into speculative interpretation could readily have led to confusion between facts and opinions. However, now that most of the basic observations have been described and photographically illustrated, we may attempt an analysis of their pathogenesis and biologic significance.

The seven major problems that we propose to study are:

1. The mechanisms of **sensitization, challenge,** and **adjuvation.**

2. The phenomenon of **direct calcification** in the absence of calciphylactic sensitization.

3. Why a variable **critical period** must elapse between sensitization and challenge and a **latency period** between challenge and the manifestation of lesions.

4. The relationship between calciphylaxis, **stress,** and **hormones.**

5. The **local factors** responsible for the vastly different calciphylactic reactivity of various sites within the same organism.

6. The phenomena of local and systemic **resistance** to calciphylaxis.

7. The **biologic significance** of calciphylaxis in comparison with other presumably defensive pathophysiologic reactions, such as inflammation and the formation of immune bodies.

GENERALITIES

To begin with, it may be helpful to concretize our opinions about the actions of the principal components of a calciphylactic response by schematic drawings. These diagrams—like almost anything that we shall be able to say in this final chapter—are based largely on speculation and will undoubtedly have to be modified as we learn more. The excuse for such schematization and generalization at this time is its heuristic value; only a map of our incomplete data can show us the gaps where further work is required.

The activity of direct calcifiers and of agents conducive to calciphylaxis is schematically illustrated in Diagram I.

439

Diagram I

The Action of Calcifiers, Challengers and Adjuvants

1. Calcifiers

A. Direct (e.g., KMnO₄). Like challengers, act locally by attracting calcium, but unlike challengers, they do so even without sensitization.

B. Indirect (e.g., DHT). Act systemically by making calcium generally available through hypercalcemia. Yet they cannot induce calcification in any one selected target without local challenge.

2. Challengers

A. Direct. Can act both topically (e.g., FeCl₃ s.c.) and systemically (e.g., Fe-Dex i.v.), but cause calcification only in sensitized organism.

B. Indirect (e.g., mastocyte depletors). Act systemically through liberation of endogenous direct challengers.

3. Adjuvants

A. Pure (e.g., dextran). Have no challenging potency themselves but increase activity of local challenger.

B. Challenger-adjuvants (e.g., dextrin). Have slight challenging potency which can be greatly augmented by admixture of direct challengers.

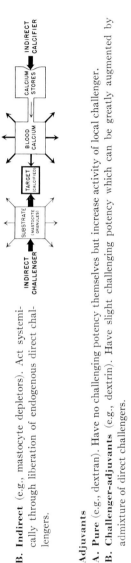

Calcifiers.—*Direct* calcifiers (e.g., $KMnO_4$) resemble challengers in that they attract calcium into the tissue area with which they come in contact;* As it were, they "pull" calcium from the blood into the tissues. However, unlike challengers, direct calcifiers can do this without sensitization even against a concentration gradient, since soon after the beginning of their action the calcium content becomes higher in the target area than in the blood.

Indirect calcifiers (e.g., DHT, parathyroid hormone) do not attract calcium to the site of their application; they liberate calcium from the stores (mainly the skeleton) into the blood. Thus they indirectly facilitate calcification throughout the body without necessarily producing calcium deposition at any one point. In other words, the indirect calcifier does not "pull" calcium into a target area but— through the production of hypercalcemia—"pushes" it especially to wherever local conditions (e.g., calciphylactic challenge) create a topical calcium avidity.

Challengers.—*Direct* challengers can be applied topically (e.g., $FeCl_3$ s.c.) or systemically (e.g., Fe-Dex i.v.). In either case they act directly upon the target to which they are applied or carried by the blood. They increase the calcifiability of this target without augmenting the calcium avidity of other tissues. Thus their action is direct in that it affects only targets with which they come into immediate contact, but there is ample evidence that the effect of these agents is not due to a direct chemical precipitation of calcium. Very probably, direct challengers produce a local accumulation of calcifiable substrate before calcification occurs.

The topical calcium avidity created by direct challengers—unlike that induced by direct calcifiers—is not sufficiently great to produce calcinosis except following sensitization by an indirect calcifier. Thus, for example, $FeCl_3$ s.c. or Fe-Dex i.v. causes no calcinosis by itself, but after sensitization with DHT or parathyroid hormone both induce calcification in the tissues in which they become lodged. Here, both the "pull" of topical calcium avidity and the "push" of hypercalcemia are required to produce a response.

Indirect challengers act merely by liberating endogenous direct challengers.

Adjuvants.—*Pure adjuvants* (e.g., dextran) have no challenging potency themselves but increase the activity of local challengers if they are mixed with them. Their mechanism of action is unknown, but they may facilitate the interaction between challengers and tissues.

Challenger adjuvants (e.g., dextrin)—as the name implies—can act both as challengers and as adjuvants. They possess only a slight challenging potency but this can be considerably enhanced by the admixture of direct challengers.

---

* For the sake of brevity the terms "calcium" and "calcification" will be used in this discussion to include also the phosphate, carbonate and various calcifiable materials that accompany calcium in the body.

DIRECT CALCIFICATION

Topical treatment with direct calcifiers (e.g., $KMnO_4$, $PbCl_2$, $CeCl_3$, $LaCl_3$) produces local calcification even without any sensitization by an indirect calcifier.[829a, 865] Hence, direct calcifiers may be viewed as challengers to which the body is constantly sensitive even under ordinary physiologic conditions. These compounds can presumably attract calcium to tissues even when the blood calcium levels are normal. We refer to this form of calcium attraction as "topogenic" because it depends merely upon local conditions; it differs thereby from the "systemogenic" calcification that depends primarily upon systemic factors which provide an excess of calcium. Such an excess may be provided, for example, through the liberation of calcium salts from the skeletal stores (e.g., hyperparathyroidism, destructive bone tumors) or through the inhibition of normal calcium excretion (e.g., diseases of the kidney or colon).

The earlier terms "dystrophic" and "metastatic" calcification were confusing. It is not any kind of tissue injury or "dystrophy," but a set of very specific changes elicited by direct calcifiers in the target that is responsible for the topogenic form. On the other hand, the systemogenic variety is not invariably the consequence of a calcium "metastasis" from the bones; it can also result from an excessive intake or an impeded excretion of calcium and phosphorus.

The first truly systematic studies on the effects of direct calcifiers were those of von Kóssa.[545a] In 1901, soon after he developed his calcium stain, von Kóssa observed that in rabbits subcutaneous injection of preparations of aloin, mercury, bismuth, phosphorus, lead, iodine, and copper can produce a "toxic calcinosis" with precipitation of calcium in certain internal organs, particularly the kidney and liver. The injection site itself frequently showed intense inflammation, but no mention was made of any local calcification. After carefully reviewing scattered earlier observations and comparing them with his own findings, von Kóssa[545a] came to the conclusion that these induced calcifications are not due to the redistribution of the pre-existing calcium stores because the bones showed no demonstrable decrease in their calcium content. He assumed that all these drugs act by poisoning the calcium excretory mechanism of the kidneys.*

Our recent findings on the production of topical calcification at the site of subcutaneous injection with $KMnO_4$ and various heavy metal salts definitely show that this type of calcification is not merely due to a diminution of calciuria but represents a direct topical effect upon connective tissue. These direct calcifiers do not act by precipitating calcium themselves, since they attract much more than an equivalent amount of calcium; this fact gives further support to the view that direct calcifiers act by transforming the injection site into a "calcium trap."

---

* In one experiment von Kóssa administered 20–30 μg. of manganese sulfate s.c. daily to seven rabbits. One of these showed occasional calcium deposits in the kidneys but, he concluded, since the remaining six "exhibited no trace of calcification, the above-mentioned finding must be considered to be coincidental," especially because even untreated rabbits often suffer from nephrocalcinosis.

SENSITIZATION

In calciphylaxis sensitization appears to depend upon treatment with an ***agent which promotes soft-tissue calcification in general.*** Such systemic or indirect calcifiers are: parathyroid hormone, vitamin D_2 or D_3, DHT, NaAST, or even certain surgical operations which stimulate endogenous parathyroid hormone production (e.g., total nephrectomy, gastric or esophageal fistulas). Yet, this form of sensitization is not due merely to the establishment of a high blood calcium or phosphate level, nor even to the whole set of biochemical changes that cause "nonspecific calcinosis" in the usual organs of predisposition.

For example, rats chronically treated with large amounts of DHT or parathyroid hormone eventually die with intense calcification of the cardiovascular system, kidney, and alimentary tract, yet they fail to respond with a calciphylactic reaction to either topical or systemic challenge. Bilateral nephrectomy—especially if combined with the oral administration of an excess of calcium acetate or Na_2HPO_4—produces intense calcification of the heart, but here again subcutaneous challenge with $FeCl_3$ rarely results in a large calciphylactic wheal and intravenous injection of Fe-Dex does not produce pancreatic calcification readily. Conversely, a single oral dose of DHT—too small to induce nonspecific cardiovascular or renal calcification—consistently sensitizes for these typical calciphylactic responses. Obviously, calciphylactic sensitization cannot be ascribed simply to the creation of a general tendency for calcium precipitation; it appears to depend upon a whole set of very specific biochemical changes. Some of the factors that modify susceptibility to this kind of reactivity have already been identified.

We saw, for example, that intense systemic stress (e.g., restraint), glucocorticoids (e.g., triamcinolone), mastocyte depletors (e.g., PMX), or hypophysectomy can induce a state of refractoriness during which normally potent doses of sensitizers (e.g., DHT or parathyroid hormone) and challengers (e.g., albumen) are ineffective. On the other hand, small doses of challengers can be activated by adjuvants (e.g., dextran). ***Presumably, certain inhibitory side effects of systemic calcifiers*** (e.g., the creation of stress, mastocyte depletion, an unfavorable hormonal response, or interference with adjuvation) may prevent calciphylactic sensitization even under conditions that lead to "nonspecific calcinosis" in predisposed organs.

This comparative independence of calciphylactic sensitivity from the blood calcium and phosphate levels was also noted in the experiments on the ***"critical period."*** In the course of chronic daily treatment with large doses of DHT, cutaneous challenge (e.g., epilation) during the first few days produced the expected calciphylactic wheals, while at a later time similar challenge became ineffective. Yet, the blood calcium and phosphate levels remained essentially the same during the entire period of observation, and the nonspecific (cardiovascular and renal) calcinosis characteristic of DHT intoxication actually became worse as calciphylactic sensitivity vanished.[491] Here, resistance to calciphylaxis may have been due to various factors: for example, the mere stress effect of DHT overdosage or the sequestration in previously calcified foci of essential materials, such as readily available stores of calcium, phosphate, and PAS-positive substances needed to bind calcium. (Cf. also "Critical Period," p. 454.)

The ***site of action of calciphylactic sensitizers*** is still unknown. These agents do not appear to cause calcium precipitation merely by virtue of their direct effects upon the target area. For example, subcutaneous injection of as much as 100 μg. of DHT or vitamin D_2 causes no local calcium deposition, although these amounts are far in excess of that which could conceivably reach the injection area after oral treatment with the usual doses.[830] Mixtures of DHT (100 μg.) and $FeCl_3$ (25 μg.) also failed to elicit topical calcification so that even the simultaneous presence in the target area of both sensitizer and challenger does not suffice.

These findings are somewhat unexpected, since earlier observers claimed to have obtained topical calcification at the site of treatment with parathyroid hormone or vitamin D.[130, 131] We therefore repeated our work with still larger doses of DHT (1 mg. or more/day) and parathyroid hormone (150 units ×2/day). Under these conditions topical calcification was occasionally produced by these indirect calcifiers. However, positive results were inconstant and occurred only in the presence of very intense nonspecific calcinosis in internal organs. In this event calciphylactic sensitivity is so high that virtually any topical injury produces local calcification. It may be assumed, therefore, that indirect calcifiers produce topical calcification only when given at dose levels sufficient to induce an extraordinary degree of systemic sensitization; of course then even the mere trauma of an injection or the irritation by the nonspecific local effects of the injected substances and their contaminants can act as challengers. This type of calcinosis evidently cannot be ascribed to a direct calcifying potency.

CHALLENGE

We have seen that calciphylactic challengers produce topical calcification only after sensitization by a systemic calcifier. It is convenient to distinguish—at least in principle—between ***direct and indirect calciphylactic challengers.*** The former appear to act themselves; the latter, only through the liberation from tissues of endogenous direct challengers (e.g., mastocyte granules).

When direct challengers are applied topically, for example to the subcutaneous tissue, they incrustate the collagen fibers and thereby prepare them for the binding of calcium. It is for this reason that calciphylactic challenge has been referred to as a kind of ***"vital mordanting."***[849] This type of binding is reminiscent of chelation and it may be significant in this connection that among all the metals tested, no monovalent cation has as yet been demonstrated to possess challenging potency.*

The underlying biochemical factors have not been clarified, but they may well be related to the physiologic process of calcium deposition in osteoid tissue. In newly formed embryonic bone the collagen fibers become strongly PAS positive when they begin to attract calcium and this PAS-positive material may act as a calcium trap.

As judged by the aspect of tissues challenged by microscopically visible substances (e.g., by iron salts), the calcium is first deposited around particles of the challenger. Then the latter disappear, so that one gains the impression of an *exchange reaction* in which the challenger is gradually replaced by calcium. However, the removal of the challenger is not indispensable for the process of calcification; certain challengers (e.g., ThO_2) form minute crystals which cannot easily be absorbed and yet cause local calcification. Furthermore, 1 or 2 μg. of iron can attract enough calcium to form a tissue depot 2 cm. in diameter and several mm. in thickness; here, there can be no question of a stoichiometric replacement of iron by calcium.

Beyond this point it is difficult to analyze the process of challenging, by purely morphologic means. Yet, it is perhaps significant that in following the histogenesis of calcification induced by PMX or Thorotrast® in the sensitized animal, calcium is seen first around the metachromatic mastocyte granules that were discharged on contact with these challengers. Then, as the granules lose their metachromasia, calcium gradually replaces them. Observations such as these suggest that in the final analysis *even so-called direct challengers may act indirectly* through the liberation or local accumulation of calcifiable materials (e.g., mastocyte granules, PAS-positive substances); if so, the latter would represent direct endogenous challengers. Indeed, even $FeCl_3$ and other salts which have no specific mastocyte discharging action may turn out to be indirect challengers which attract calcium not to themselves, but to some endogenous calcium mordant (e.g., PAS-positive material). Hence, in theory it is not possible to distinguish between directly and indirectly acting challengers with certainty, but the distinction is of practical value in that it separates compounds of different biologic properties.

Direct challengers can be applied *topically* to the target area (e.g., $FeCl_3$ s.c.) or *systemically* (e.g., Fe-Dex i.v.), but in either case their mechanism of action appears to be direct in that they must reach the target area to be efficacious. The manifold characteristics of the various calciphylactic syndromes are presumably due to the fact that diverse challengers possess specific affinities for different tissues.

---

* In the calciphylactic syndromes produced by NaH_2PO_4 or $NaClO_4$ the challenging potency appears to reside in the anions since other phosphates and perchlorates are also active while other sodium salts are not.[823] Besides, these salts are indirect challengers whose action is relayed through other compounds.

Our experiments suggest that in salts only the ***metallic components*** possess direct challenging potency. These active metals are usually, but not necessarily, cations; for example, both $SnCl_2$ and Na_2SnO_3 are approximately equally potent challengers.[479] On the other hand even non-metallic anions can exhibit indirect challenging potency (e.g., NaH_2PO_4, $NaClO_4$).

The direct challenging potency does not even depend entirely upon the atomic structure of the metal; it is largely determined by the other, in themselves inert, parts of the molecule that are the ***carriers*** of the active metal. For example, the calciphylactic syndromes produced (after sensitization with DHT) by Fe-Din and Thorotrast® are almost identical and quite different from those induced by Fe-Dex or Fe-OS. Obviously, Fe is the active ingredient in Fe-Din, Fe-Dex, and Fe-OS, since the carriers (dextrin, dextran, and sucrose) are ineffective by themselves, while iron acts as a challenger even when given in the form of various simple inorganic salts (e.g., $FeCl_2$, $FeCl_3$, $FeSO_4$). Similarly in Thorotrast® it is evidently the thorium that is effective and not the dextrin, which is merely added as a stabilizer. Many additional observations could be cited in support of this view. For example, the thyroid-parathyroid-carotid-body syndrome produced by $CrCl_3$ i.v. is virtually indistinguishable from that elicited by $FeCl_2$ i.v., but quite unlike that caused by $FeCl_3$ i.v. or Fe-OS i.v. Presumably, ***physical factors*** (such as the rate of absorption, spreading, entrance into phagocytes, precipitation on collagen and elastic fibers) play a decisive role in determining the challenging activity of metals.

It has been claimed that the ***valency of elements*** may also be important in this connection because in a small series of Sn-, Ti- and Fe-salts the low valent form of each element proved to be most active.[478] On the other hand, the previously mentioned fact that no monovalent cation possesses challenging potency has been established on a very large number of compounds. (Cf. Table 2, pp. 50–51.)

In analyzing the intimate mechanism of the calciphylactic challenge, ***iron*** salts are of special interest because they are readily available in the body under physiologic and pathologic conditions.

As early as 1904 it had been assumed[792] that iron salts could initially act as mordants for calcium in bone, though later, simultaneously with the deposition of calcium, the iron reaction decreases. Essentially similar observations published by others[292, 904] are also in agreement with the interpretation of calciphylactic challengers (such as iron) as vital mordants for calcium. In any event, the literature is replete with data showing a close, though not necessarily causal, relationship between iron and calcium deposition in the diverse forms of calcinosis that occur in man.[157, 175, 240, 265, 292, 379, 601, 614, 789, 792, 904]

Using EDTA as a decalcifying agent, it was possible to remove calcium from bones without affecting their iron content. It could be demonstrated with this technique that following a single i.v. injection of Fe-Dex considerable quantities of Prussian-blue-tingible iron are deposited in the hypertrophic cartilage cells of the epiphyseal plates, the newly forming trabeculae of the adjacent metaphysis, and the subperiosteal bone layer. The osteoblasts themselves likewise take up iron in growing young rats and these skeletal ferric deposits persist for many weeks.[709]

Histologically demonstrable iron also occurs in embryonic and rachitic bone but vanishes as calcification progresses.[792, 904] Prussian-blue-positive iron compounds appear in tissues even during the initial stages of the calcium deposition or bone formation that can be induced experimentally by surgical interventions.[850, 860]

It will be recalled that when iron salts are used as challengers in calciphylaxis, the Prussian-blue-positive material tends to disappear from the target area as the calcium enters; indeed, later even the calcific deposits vanish and only sclerosis remains. Hence, calciphylactic reactions could be at the root of certain connective-tissue diseases in which neither iron nor calcium is demonstrable by the time the lesions are fully developed. Besides, as we have seen, calcification is not uncommon in certain collagen diseases, such as scleroderma, dermatomyositis, and sarcoidosis, as well as in the various forms of cardiovascular sclerosis.[848]

Siderocalciphylactic sensitization depends not only upon treatment with a systemic calcifier but also upon the intravenous injection of soluble iron (e.g., Fe-Dex) simultaneously with another (topical or systemic) challenger. It has long been known that circulating iron particles tend to be phagocytosed and fixed by the histiocytes of inflammatory foci.[162, 435, 649] The same mechanism may be responsible for the sensitizing effect of intravenous Fe-Dex in siderocalciphylaxis. After sensitization with DHT subcutaneous injection of a pure adjuvant (e.g., dextran) or of distilled water causes no topical calcification. Yet, after sidero-calciphylactic sensitization (e.g., with DHT p.o. + Fe-Dex i.v.) such an injection is very effective in this respect, perhaps because it induces a mild local inflammation and attracts blood-borne iron to the treated site. The iron thus fixed may then be further activated by the adjuvant effect of the compound (e.g., dextran) that attracted it to the focus. Similarly, after siderocalciphylactic sensitization, various mast cell depletors (PMX, 48/80) produce not only large calciphylactic wheals at the site of injection but—if mast cell depletion is generalized—even dermatomyositis-like cutaneous and muscular inflammation.[842]

All the typical indirect challengers so far examined (PMX, 48/80, PVP, distilled water, glucocorticoids) are mastocyte depletors. Presumably they act by liberating ***mastocyte granules*** which subsequently attract calcium, especially in the presence of phosphate and *iron*. This process can readily be followed under the microscope. For example, in rats sensitized by DHT p.o. and 24–48 hours later given Fe-Dex i.v. and PMX s.c. (the latter soon after the PMX injection), the subcutaneous mastocytes are seen to discharge their granules. The free granules swell, lose their metachromasia, and are gradually incrusted with calcium salts; consequently they become larger and stain positively with the von Kóssa procedure. As these calcified granules migrate toward the elastic and collagen fibers they disintegrate and form a very fine dust. At the same time the fibers take up iron, swell and become homogeneous, while fine calcified or uncalcified mastocyte granules impregnate them. (Cf. Diagram II.)

Even parenteral injection of distilled water causes mastocyte depletion, but only in the cells with which it comes into direct contact.[312, 958] Degranulation of mast cells can also be obtained by physiologic saline, Tyrode solution, hyaluronidase, mechanical trauma[958] and various other procedures that induce *topical stress*. It is quite in accordance with expectations, therefore, that in rats sensitized by

Diagram II
Mechanism of Siderocalciphylaxis

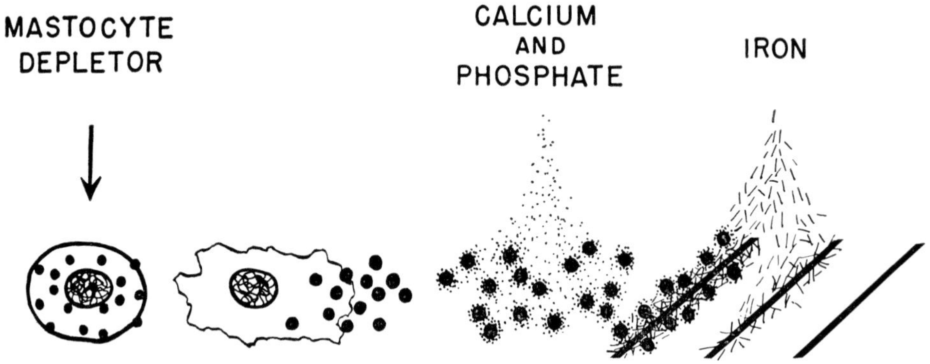

| MASTOCYTE DEPLETOR | CALCIUM AND PHOSPHATE | IRON |

DHT p.o. + Fe-Dex i.v., even subcutaneous injection of distilled water suffices to produce a topical calciphylactic wheal. However, systemic changes ("dermatomyositis") are not produced in this manner, presumably because water causes discharge of mastocyte granules only at the site of its application.[837a]

The histologic patterns of mucopolysaccharide secretion by mast cells in the course of *systemic stress* have been subjected to careful analysis. Apparently there are two forms of reaction to systemic stress: one characterized by swelling with discharge of granules and vacuole formation; the other, by shrinking with lysis of the granules. The reaction-form characterized by swelling, degranulation, and vacuolization is regarded as a consequence of glucocorticoid activity; in adrenalectomized rats stress (induced by formalin injections) elicits only shrinkage and lysis of mastocyte granules.[451a] Be this as it may, the potent protective effect of stress against the subsequent induction of calciphylaxis may well be related to mastocyte discharge, especially since mastocyte depletors are particularly efficacious prophylactic agents. Yet it remains to be shown whether stress acts through mastocyte depletion or whether mastocyte depletors owe their efficacy to the production of stress. The protective effect of glucocorticoid pretreatment may likewise be ascribed to mastocyte depletion, but here again final proof is still lacking.

In connection with the role of mastocytes in calcification another rarely cited observation is of great interest. In weanling rats placed on a *low-calcium diet* numerous mastocytes accumulate on the surface of, within, or under the endosteum when growth becomes arrested. There is no corresponding increase in the mastocyte population elsewhere in the body. Treatment with vitamin D restores the normal structure of the bones and leads to the disappearance of excess mastocytes, while injections of parathyroid hormone merely produce osteitis fibrosa without diminishing the mastocyte population in the bones. These observations raised the question whether mastocytes might not produce precursors of ground substance, alkaline phosphatase or other materials necessary for osteogenesis.[941] Mastocytes are normally plentiful in bone marrow and "they can be made to accumulate in the bones of rats by feeding a diet deficient in calcium and in vitamin D or by other conditions of stress."[643]

Certain observations suggest that "a function of the tissue mast cells in the normal rat is the rapid initiation of acute inflammation at the site of injury and that degranulation of these cells prior to infection somewhat delays the inflammatory response and therefore slightly diminishes host resistance." This view was based on the observation that in rats the experimental production of cutaneous mucormycosis causes—within minutes—a discharge of mastocytes at the site of infection, this being rapidly followed by *inflammation*. Conversely, in animals whose mast cells were depleted by pretreatment with 48/80 or by the induction of alloxan diabetes, inflammation was delayed and resistance correspondingly decreased.[879] However, the inflammatory potential and the resistance to infection were not very markedly diminished by mastocyte depletion; besides there is no definite proof that even this slight change was causally related to the degranulation of mast cells.

In view of the much discussed relationships between calciphylaxis and the *collagen diseases* a recent study entitled "Vasculitis, Mast Cells and the Collagen Diseases"—by Smyth and Gum[886a]—is of special interest. The authors point out that according to the literature mastocytes are particularly plentiful in the skin, ciliary body, synovial membranes, gastrointestinal tract, cardiovascular system, pleura, pericardium, and lung. "It is these tissues with the high mast cell content that are the sites of many of the changes one encounters in the connective tissue diseases." There is a good deal of evidence that mast cells can produce not only histamine and heparin but also hyaluronic acid and 5HT. Dermal fibrosis has been produced in rats by the repeated injection of 5HT,[617a] and allegedly "these changes simulate the proliferation of collagenous and fibrous tissues within the dermis seen in human scleroderma."[886a]

It has been shown, furthermore, that in normal individuals the injection of 5HT into and around the joints produces only transient swelling and erythema which disappears within 30 minutes, while in rheumatoid patients the response is greatly exaggerated and lasts two to eight hours. This exaggerated reactivity to the extra-vascular injection of 5HT can be blocked by the intravenous injection of 5HT antagonists.[786a, 786b]

There are good grounds for believing that hypersensitivity plays an important role in the development of systemic lupus erythematosus and perhaps rheumatoid arthritis. "The mast cells may be a link in the chain of immunological events which result in the vascular lesion of these and allied connective tissue diseases."[886a] Disruption and degranulation of mast cells has been observed in various species subjected to anaphylactic shock by albumen.[902a] The injection of homologous or heterologous antigens into previously sensitized mice likewise results in an explosive degranulation of mast cells.[181a]

At first sight it may seem paradoxical that many qualitatively different agents should produce many qualitatively different diseases through the intermediary of the same response, namely, mastocyte discharge. However, we have seen that in calciphylaxis mastocyte depletors can produce qualitatively distinct lesions depending upon the kind of challenger used; apparently here the response depends upon a synergism between mast-cell products whose action is not specific and challengers whose action is highly specific.

As a working hypothesis it may be assumed, therefore, that the same mastocyte depletor "A" may, through its effect upon the mastocytes, produce highly selective lesions in Target "A," "B," or "C," depending upon which target-specific challenger was used. This could be illustrated in the following manner·

$$
\text{Mastocyte depletor "A"} \longrightarrow \text{Mastocytes}
\begin{cases}
\text{Target "A"} \longleftarrow \text{Challenger "A"} \\
\text{Target "B"} \longleftarrow \text{Challenger "B"} \\
\text{Target "C"} \longleftarrow \text{Challenger "C"}
\end{cases}
$$

On the other hand, various mastocyte depletors may produce identical reactions in the same Target "A" if it alone has been made responsive by pretreatment with an appropriate Challenger "A," as illustrated below:

$$
\left.
\begin{array}{l}
\text{Mastocyte depletor "A"} \\
\text{Mastocyte depletor "B"} \\
\text{Mastocyte depletor "C"}
\end{array}
\right\}
\longrightarrow \text{Mastocytes} \longrightarrow \text{Target "A"} \longleftarrow \text{Challenger "A"}
$$

If this working hypothesis is correct, it would explain how the same pathogen, through the same mastocyte-depleting effect, could produce different lesions in different individuals, each subject responding with the particular target that has been rendered hypersensitive; on the other hand, in an individual with a given type of induced hypersensitivity various pathogens could affect the same target through their common mastocyte-depleting effect.

This hypothesis is also compatible with the observation that the same mastocyte depletor that elecits a lesion when administered after challenge can actually prevent this same change if given prior to challenge, since in the latter case the mastocyte granules are exhausted before they can produce any damage. The situation is somewhat comparable to that of a single-barrel gun whose trigger is pulled before it is aimed at the target and hence cannot be fired effectively after taking aim unless time is allowed for reloading.

It remains to be seen whether anything corresponding to calciphylactic challenge is involved in the production of collagen diseases, but should this be the case our hypothesis might be applicable to those clinical connective-tissue diseases that structurally resemble calciphylactic syndromes.

The cardinal role of mastocyte components in calciphylaxis (or even in siderocalciphylaxis) is still far from being definitely proven, but our interpretation would fit the known facts equally well if other stored endogenous challengers were involved.

There may be ***other organic endogenous challengers*** apart from the constituents of mastocyte granules. In this connection, mucopolysaccharides not originating in mastocytes, the compounds constituting the bone matrix, and elastic tissue deserve special attention.

Parathyroid hormone—presumably the most important endogenous sensitizer for calciphylaxis—raises not only the blood calcium but also the blood *mucopolysaccharide* level.[301, 337] It will be recalled that this hormone does not merely liberate calcium and phosphorus from bone but also sets free the organic matrix which normally attracts and binds the inorganic components of the skeleton. Indeed, there is a good deal of evidence in support of the view that parathyroid hormone regulates normal and abnormal calcification, including the development of nephrocalcinosis and nephrolithiasis; it appears to do so partly through its effect upon the ground substance, particularly the mucopolysaccharides and metachromatic substances in general.[52, 53, 301, 337, 563]

Parathyroid extract decreases bone matrix hexosamine both in intact and in parathyroidectomized rats, while formaldehyde inactivated extract fails to produce this change. "These data suggest that the dissolution of organic bone matrix and calcium mobilization are closely correlated effects of parathyroid hormone."[500] It is also interesting in this connection that large amounts of mucopolysaccharides and mucoproteins can be found in the renal tubules of experimental animals in which nephrocalcinosis is produced by an excess of parathyroid hormone, as well as in the urine of patients with urinary calculi.[125, 301] These effects upon the organic constituents of connective tissue may also play a part in physiologic and pathologic forms of endogenous calciphylactic sensitization by parathyroid hormone.

Yet, the view that the increase in serum mucopolysaccharides induced by parathyroid hormone results from dissolution of the bone matrix has recently been questioned. Allegedly "one can calculate, within reasonable limits, that the increase in serum calcium which would have to accompany that observed for serum mucopolysaccharides would have to be fantastically high." Various stressors raise the blood mucopolysaccharide level and the hypothesis was advanced "that extraneous material in parathyroid extract influences normal production and/or destruction of serum mucoproteins by the liver."[426] The nephrocalcinosis induced in the rat by NaH_2PO_4, vitamin D_2, or parathyroid extract is undoubtedly associated with an increase in the renal hexosamine content, but this rise is very slight in comparison with the great increase in renal calcium concentration.[460]

In any event, parathyroid hormone (like the vitamin-D compounds) must liberate organic matrix together with calcium and phosphate from the bones when it causes their absorption. We do not know whether the matrix constituent that normally binds calcium retains this capacity after dissolution, but if so it could well continue to act as a calcium binder when transposed into soft tissues.

In this discussion it was silently assumed that the challenger, directly or indirectly, adds some calcium binding material to tissue. This is not necessarily so. While dissolved and reconstituted collagen fibrils readily attract calcium salts in vitro, the native collagen-rich tissues of rat-tail tendon or calf-skin (which supplied the collagen used for in vitro investigations of calcium nucleation) fail to mineralize under conditions identical with those used in testing reconstituted collagen fibrils. From this it has been inferred that in vivo the ground substance may exert a regulatory effect upon nucleation; it may shield the reactive sites in the collagen fibril under ordinary conditions, but by rapid depolymerization release calcium, thereby promoting nucleation. For example, alkaline phosphatase might act not by supplying products that promote calcification, but by *destroying a substance inhibitory to crystallization.*[643, 680a] At present we have no evidence indicating whether calciphylactic challenge acts by the removal of an inhibitor or by the provision of a promotor of calcification.

Any general discussion of calciphylactic challenge must also envisage the possibility that similar phenomena may play a part even in the pathogenesis of lesions that depend upon the *attraction by topical challenge of materials other than calcium.*[848] For example, trauma to blood vessels can attract either calcium[820] or lipids with consequent atheroma formation,[974] depending upon the systemic sensitizer used; in either case the final outcome is sclerosis, sometimes with hyalinization of the challenged area. It is by no means inconceivable, therefore, that the concept of calciphylaxis may also be applicable to topical attraction by challenge of other organic or inorganic materials.

Finally, it should be remembered that *calciphylactic challengers can induce characteristic local changes by themselves,* although unlike the direct calcifiers they do not produce calcification without sensitization. We saw, for example, that intracutaneous and subcutaneous injection of $FeCl_3$ results not only in the local accumulation of iron-containing macrophages but also in a highly selective iron impregnation of all the collagen fibers in the surroundings. On slides stained with hematoxylin-eosin or PAS this change is associated with diffuse local basophila[830] (Fig. 6). There are other challengers which can elicit characteristic changes by themselves: Fe-OS produces cholangitis with dilatation of the bile ducts (Figs. 99, 100); Thorotrast®, non-calcifying ThO_2 deposits in phagocytes (Fig. 147); $ZnCl_2$, hepatic and splenic lesions, etc. All these actions of the challenger proper are greatly aggravated or qualitatively altered by previous sensitization, but they must be taken into account in evaluating the calciphylactic nature of a lesion. In some cases even what may appear to be an action of the challenger proper may actually depend upon sensitization by endogenous parathyroid hormone; hence, such effects must always be examined not only in intact but also in parathyroidectomized animals.

This survey of the extremely complex mechanisms involved in the actions of challengers clearly shows that in calciphylaxis we are not dealing merely with *nonspecific tissue damage* such as was held responsible for the "dystrophic" calcification. In fact—as we have repeatedly emphasized—strong irritants and corrosives that cause visible manifestations of nonspecific damage (e.g., inflammation and necrosis) are ineffective as calciphylactic challengers.

Adjuvation

Many substances can increase the effect of a direct challenger when mixed with the latter. Some of these sensitizers have no challenging potency by themselves and are, therefore, called *"pure adjuvants"*; others, the *"challenger adjuvants,"* have some challenging effect of their own but this can be greatly augmented by the admixture of direct challengers.[703, 848]

Nothing definite is known about the physicochemical mechanism of adjuvation, but among many compounds tested, gelatin and dextran proved to be the most active pure adjuvants.[703] These as well as many other potent compounds of this group are viscous materials and this physical property may be partly responsible for their effect. Whatever the mechanism, adjuvants might act upon the challenger, for example, by favorably influencing the rate of its decomposition and absorption, its spreading through tissues, or its adhesion to connective-tissue fibers. Substances which are very potent *adjuvants for antigens*—for example, the complete and incomplete adjuvant of Freund—are ineffective as calciphylactic adjuvants; apparently the two types of adjuvation do not depend upon the same physicochemical properties.

It is noteworthy that certain *adjuvants for hormones* that appear to act as absorption-retarding agents (e.g., corn oil and liquid paraffin) actually deprive challengers of their potency, while others (e.g., carboxymethylcellulose) are essentially inert in this respect, at least as judged from experiments in which $FeCl_3$ was used as the challenger.[829a]

The common feature of these vehicles for calciphylactic challengers, antigens and hormones is that they augment the effect of active ingredients suspended or dissolved in them. But there is no reason to believe that this activation is achieved by the same mechanism in all three cases.

Certain challengers (e.g., $CrCl_2$) are more active when given in adjuvant (e.g., dextran) solution than in water even when they are injected ***intravenously.***[837a] While this observation does not teach us much about the mechanism of adjuvation, it does show that adjuvants do not act merely by retaining the challengers at the site of application.

Up to now, the phenomenon of adjuvation has been used merely as a pharmacologic procedure of potentiation. It is possible, however, that there exist also **endogenous adjuvants.** In the previous pages, we have surveyed the evidence suggesting that certain endogenous organic compounds (e.g., mucopolysaccharides, constituents of bone matrix) may act as challengers, but it is also conceivable that they could act as adjuvants. This possibility deserves special attention with regard to endogenous polysaccharides or proteins and their split-products which are chemically related to dextran and gelatin.

THE CRITICAL PERIOD

In discussing the diverse forms of calciphylaxis, we have repeatedly had occasion to note that their development is decisively influenced by the time interval that elapses between treatment with the sensitizer and the challenger. This critical period can affect not only the intensity of the resulting syndrome but even its quality.

We have seen, for example (p. 118), that depending upon timing given doses of DHT and Fe-Dex may produce two fundamentally different calciphylactic syndromes or none at all. If challenge precedes sensitization by a day or two, it causes uterine but no pancreatic calcification, while if challenge follows sensitization, the pancreas undergoes calcification and the uterus does not. Finally, if challenge either precedes or follows sensitization by a week or more, no calciphylactic response is observed either in the uterus or in the pancreas.

The majority of the calciphylactic reactions are most easily obtained by challenge 24–48 hours after sensitization, but there are many exceptions: the DHT + Fe-OS syndrome (predominant calcification of the left auricular appendage and the bile ducts) is most intense and constant if the sensitizer and challenger are given simultaneously; DHT + 5HT causes muscle lesions most regularly in the case of challenge four to five days after sensitization.

It would be difficult to reconcile these facts with the assumption that the critical period is necessary only to allow time for the development of a hypercalcemia before the challenger is applied. Besides—as we said in our discussion of sensitization—during chronic daily treatment with DHT, conducive to a constant increase in blood calcium and phosphate, challenge by epilation is possible only at the beginning of treatment. Evidently the mere induction of a certain level of hypercalcemia or hyperphosphatemia does not suffice for calciphylactic sensitization; presumably a whole set of biochemical changes must coincide. The relative proportion of calcium, phosphorus, and endogenous adjuvants, the state of the mastocyte system, the intensity of stress produced by the evocative agents, the absorption and excretion of the pathogenic compounds, as well as the activity of the endocrine glands can all influence the resulting syndrome.[858]

THE LATENCY PERIOD

None of the calciphylactic syndromes develops immediately upon application of the challenger, but the latency period between this moment and the first appearance of detectable changes varies considerably; indeed, even in the same animal the lesions in different organs do not necessarily develop concurrently.

One of the most acute responses of this type is the calcification of discharged mastocyte granules in rats with the calciphylactic dermatomyositis syndrome induced by DHT + Fe-Dex + PMX. Here, redness and swelling of the skin with histologically demonstrable calcification of discharged mastocyte granules becomes evident within hours after the PMX injection and it is invariably obvious by the end of the first day. In rats challenged by intravenous $CrCl_3$ following DHT sensitization the thyroids, parathyroids, and carotid bodies undergo calcification within two to three days. Yet cutaneous lesions may not become evident until a week later, although no treatment is given after the challenge.

The latency period of calciphylaxis probably depends in part upon the time necessary to liberate enough calcium (or calcifiable matrix) from the skeleton for transposition into the challenged sites. However, other factors must account for the differences in the reaction time of various targets within the same animal.

LOCAL FACTORS

It is well known that the "inflammatory potential" of various parts of the body—that is the ability to respond with inflammation—is not the same. This is also true of what might be called the *"calciphylactic potential"* of tissues. For example, in the rat the paws are singularly insensitive to calciphylactic challenge; even if a challenger is injected directly into the paw of a sensitized animal, the adjacent skin of the extremity will respond much more readily than the paw itself. Similarly, many intravenously injected substances which accumulate in the RES (Fe-Dex, Thorotrast®) cause little or no splenic calcification, although the spleen takes up much larger quantities of these materials than other sites which do develop calciphylactic responses. Many additional examples of this kind have been cited in previous chapters, but the reasons for the difference in organ sensitivity are not clear. It is possible that an excessive accumulation of challenger may prevent a calciphylactic response as a consequence of overchallenge, but probably structural differences in the various targets are likewise of importance.

It has long been observed that *elastic fibers* possess a particular tendency to undergo calcification.[292, 512] Of course, now that we know that *mastocytes* play a role in calciphylaxis it is rather probable that the high calciphylactic potential of certain regions (e.g., the lips as well as the skin over the neck and back) finds its explanation, at least in part, in the plentiful availability of mastocyte granules. On the other hand, while the subcutaneous injection of PMX or 48/80 regularly produces intense topical calcinosis in siderocalciphylactically sensitized rats, intraperitoneal treatment with the same compounds is rarely effective although the peritoneum likewise contains many mastocytes.

Presumably, different targets do not possess merely a quantitatively but even a *qualitatively different calciphylactic potential.* Otherwise it would be difficult to explain why salivary glands respond especially well to local treatment with 5HT without being particularly hypersensitive to other topically applied challengers, while the skin, which responds readily with topical calciphylaxis to most inorganic challengers, does not respond to a local injection of 5HT.

Of course many other factors may influence regional sensitivity to calciphylaxis. It was found, for example, that in certain locations the *alkaline phosphatase* content of the skin is very high and that the concentration in this enzyme varies greatly in different species and in different skin regions within the same species.[784] In view of the probable relationship between alkaline phosphatase and calcification further studies on the role of this enzyme in determining the local calciphylactic potential would be desirable.

RESISTANCE

We have seen that resistance to calciphylaxis can be induced by various means (e.g., exposure to stress, treatment with mastocyte dischargers or glucocorticoids), but here we shall consider only the kind of resistance that is induced by calciphylaxis itself. It has repeatedly been observed that after a calciphylactic response is elicited, animals become insensitive to renewed treatment with the same evocative agents.

In some instances this acquired resistance is most probably due to exhaustion of the available stores of minerals and calcifiable matrix; this and possibly other metabolic consequences of calciphylaxis would undoubtedly also interfere with the normal development of a critical period. Severe systemic calciphylactic reactions may even induce temporary resistance as a result of their stressor action.

On the other hand, a merely local resistance to the induction of a topical calciphylactic response may be the consequence of local stress. It will be recalled that this mechanism has been considered as a possible explanation of "overchallenge." While it seems justified to incriminate local stress when a great variety of topically applied stimuli share the property of preventing calciphylactic challenge, this designation does not help us to appraise the underlying mechanism. Of course, local stress may cause a topical mastocyte discharge, inflammation, or damage to calcifiable collagen fibrils, but we have no experimental data to prove or disprove that any of these phenomena represents the decisive factor.

Although the possibility of immunological defense reactions against calciphylaxis cannot be ruled out a priori, there is no basis for assuming that antibody formation plays a role in any kind of acquired resistance against calciphylactic challenge. On the other hand—as we have seen—there is good reason to believe that a mastocyte discharge induced by an antigen-antibody interaction can protect against calciphylaxis.

It is interesting that virtually no resistance develops against calcinosis produced by direct calcifiers (e.g., subcutaneous injections of $KMnO_4$). This observation appears to suggest that in calciphylaxis the cause of resistance does not lie in the deposition of calcium itself, but rather in general metabolic changes attending sensitization and challenge.

STRESS AND HORMONES

Since stress is invariably associated with a strong endocrine response, it is convenient to discuss conjointly the effect exerted by stress and by hormones upon calciphylaxis.

In our description of the factors that influence calciphylaxis we have already enumerated the observations which led us to believe that stress and hormones can decisively influence calciphylactic reactivity. We have seen that hypophysectomy and treatment with large doses of glucocorticoids can inhibit various forms of calciphylaxis, while renal damage as well as certain interventions on the gastrointestinal tract (gastric or esophageal fistulas) exert an inverse sensitizing effect, presumably through the stimulation of parathyroid hormone secretion. We have also seen that various compounds liberated and made available during stress from endogenous sources (iron, mucopolysaccharides, mastocyte granules, thymocyte debris) can influence the course of calciphylaxis; these natural challengers are likewise subject to hormonal regulation. Before attempting to correlate all these data, let us mention a few additional pertinent facts from the earlier literature.

It has been amply demonstrated that corticoids can not only produce hyaline changes in the cardiovascular system, the kidney, and the connective tissue, but also exert an important influence upon the induction of metastatic calcification by vitamin D_2 in the rat.[817] It has also been shown that the toxic effects of DHT are increased by concurrent treatment with cortisol, ACTH, and thyroxine, while they are counteracted by STH and anabolic testosterone derivatives.[818] Allegedly, vitamin D_2 increases even the so-called "metacorticoid hypertension" in the rat.[404] In connection with such interactions between corticoids and indirect calcifiers (e.g., parathyroid hormone, vitamin-D compounds), it is perhaps significant that both groups of compounds act mainly on the cardiovascular system, the kidney, and the connective-tissue stroma, that is, target organs preferentially affected by the collagen diseases.

It has been found, furthermore, that cortisone antagonizes certain actions of parathyroid hormone (e.g., upon calcium and phosphate metabolism, the structure of bones, teeth, and kidneys). Allegedly this mutual antagonism may be due to opposing actions upon calcifiable substrate, since parathyroid extract was reported to enhance depolymerization, while cortisone allegedly increases polymerization of mucopolysaccharides.[563] Indeed, the calcification induced by parathyroid hormone may not be entirely due to its ability to raise serum calcium levels but also to its effect upon the calcifiability of connective tissue, which in turn is subject to regulation by corticoids.[53]

The fact that both exposure to stress and treatment with glucocorticoids can inhibit calciphylactic responses suggested that the prophylactic effect of stress may be mediated through the adrenals and merely reflect an increased glucocorticoid secretion. However, this is not the case, since in adrenalectomized animals maintained on threshold doses of glucocorticoids exposure to stress still succeeds in preventing calciphylaxis.[494] In rats receiving no substitution therapy or treated only with mineralocorticoids similar experiments cannot be performed owing to their low stress-resistance. Hence, we cannot exclude the possibility that the anticalciphylactic effect of stress in the adrenalectomized animal is due to a synergism resulting from a "conditioning" of the stress effect by the glucocorticoids that are given for life maintenance.

It would be premature to attempt the formulation of a theory designed to correlate all the manifold interactions between stress and hormones in connection with calciphylaxis. Yet, it may be of some assistance in guiding further research to draw a tentative picture of the pathways through which stress may affect the target of a calciphylactic response (Diagram III). This picture will necessarily be incomplete and largely hypothetical, but at least it is based on assumptions which are not incompatible with the facts known today.

Stress stimulates hypophyseal ACTH production, which in turn increases the glucocorticoid secretion of the adrenals, and glucocorticoids have been shown to inhibit certain calciphylactic reactions. Although preliminary observations suggest that thyrotrophic hormone (TTH) and somatotrophic hormone (STH) also influence calciphylactic responsiveness, their action has not yet been sufficiently documented to justify detailed discussion here. Besides, the influence of stress upon TTH and STH production is likewise much less clearly established than its effects upon ACTH secretion.

There is ample evidence to show that stress can damage renal function and that the kidney plays a decisive role in calcium and phosphate metabolism. Apparently, certain forms of renal failure stimulate compensatory parathyroid hormone secretion as a defensive (adaptive) reaction to the resulting derangement in mineral metabolism. Parathyroid hormone causes bone absorption with a discharge from the skeleton not only of minerals but also of calcifiable matrix. Thus, the target area can be sensitized for calciphylaxis through a pathway which reaches the end-organ by way of the kidney, parathyroids, bones, and the metabolic pool for minerals and calcifiable materials.

Finally, we have seen that such compounds as iron, mucopolysaccharides, mastocyte granules, and thymocyte debris which can be made available from endogenous sources during stress-induced catabolism also affect calciphylaxis. It will be noted that some of these potential actions of stress (e.g., glucocorticoid secretion) inhibit, while others (e.g., calcium, phosphate liberation) enhance, calciphylactic responsiveness; indeed, the result of some actions may be diametrically

Diagram III*

Participation of Hormones in Calciphylaxis

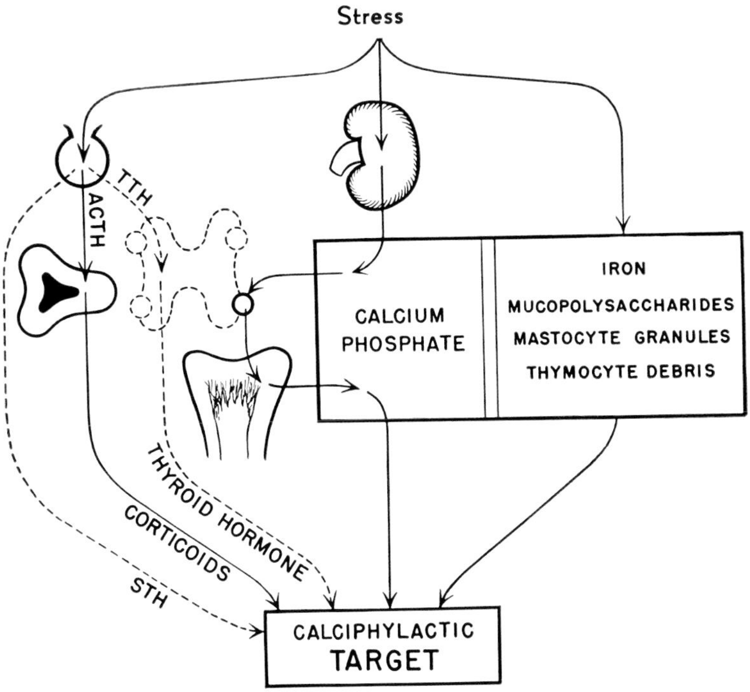

* For the sake of simplicity certain obvious metabolic interrelations have not been indicated in this sketch. For example, the liberation of some individually enumerated metabolites is undoubtedly affected by corticoids, and mucopolysaccharides can be provided under the influence of parathyroid hormone from bone. These compounds are listed separately in two boxes only because during stress their metabolism can also be affected through nonhormonal pathways and some of them are less strictly under renal control than are calcium and phosphate.

opposite, depending upon the time of their occurrence. For example, loss of calcium, phosphate, iron, mastocyte granules, etc., prior to sensitization may actually
diminish sensitivity to the same calciphylactic reactions which would be enhanced
if the discharge occurred after sensitization. This potential duality of effect may
explain the apparently paradoxical observations which showed that exposure to
stress or treatment with mastocyte dischargers did in fact sometimes inhibit and
at other times stimulate calciphylaxis, depending upon timing.

THE BIOLOGIC SIGNIFICANCE OF CALCIPHYLAXIS

Perhaps the most important fact brought out by research on calciphylaxis was
the demonstration that there exists an endogenously regulated biologic mechanism
through which the organism can induce calcium precipitation selectively at certain
sites and thereby initiate localized defensive inflammatory responses to injury.
Thus calciphylaxis is a fundamentally defensive (phylactic) response which can
sequestrate a pathogen and increase topical resistance to injury through granuloma formation and sclerosis. However, like many other basically defensive reactions
(e.g., serological immunity), calciphylaxis can also become the cause of morbid
lesions.

Probably the greatest handicap to our understanding of the real significance of
the calcinoses was the generally accepted view that calcium precipitation in tissues is merely a consequence of necrosis—a secondary and essentially passive
physicochemical phenomenon. It had long been known that damaged tissue, for
example a tubercle or a scar, can undergo calcification, but no great biologic importance was attached to observations of this kind because of the current view
epitomized by the dictum "Calcification is but one of the means the organism possesses to bury its dead."[332]

Certain recent observations came quite close to the essence of calciphylaxis; it
was found, for example, that an intramuscular injection of turpentine increases the
local tissue calcium concentration in the rat and that this increase is enhanced by
vitamin-D_2 treatment. But even this response was merely viewed as additional
proof supporting the view that "calcification is a consequence of necrosis."[398]

It may be opportune, therefore, in these final pages to survey some of the data
suggesting that in calciphylaxis the organism possesses a delicately regulated
mechanism through which it can actively stimulate inflammation and sclerosis in
selected target areas. We shall see that these changes, like any other inflammatory
process, can have defensive value, but under certain circumstances they can assume morbid proportions and become the essence of the resulting disease. We shall
see furthermore how, quite incidentally, research on calciphylaxis called attention
to the existence of a special stroma depot system (SDS) which, unlike the RES,
sequestrates potentially toxic material in the extracellular elements and sometimes in the fibroblasts of the stroma. A study of the SDS called attention to the

fact that despite the structural similarity of connective tissue throughout the body, different regions possess organ-specific stroma elements; the stroma of the various organs possesses affinities for different challengers and undergoes calcification under different circumstances. This stroma specificity appears to depend upon chemical interactions, between the connective tissue and the histologically distinct "noble elements" of the organs, which have hitherto not been amenable to experimental study.

The phylactic value of calciphylaxis.—Many facts suggest that under certain circumstances a calciphylactic reaction can have a **topical** phylactic, that is, defensive, value. This was demonstrated with particular clarity in experiments in which the granuloma-pouch technique was employed to determine the resistance of the skin to necrosis.

Rats (110 g. ♀) were given DHT (1 mg. p.o.) on the first day and 24 hours later a granuloma pouch was produced by the subcutaneous injection of 25 ml. air under the shaved dorsal skin. The controls received no calciphylactic challenger, while in the experimental animals yolk (10%, 5 ml.) was injected directly into the air sac immediately after its formation. As expected, in the controls the skin over the air pouch did not show any abnormal change while in the yolk-injected animals it underwent more or less pronounced calcification. On the seventh day the air was replaced by croton oil (10%, 0.5 ml. in olive oil) in the air sacs of both the control and the experimental animals. This resulted in the formation of large areas of necrosis in the controls but not in the rats in which the croton oil came to lie underneath a layer of calciphylactically challenged skin. This protection was noticeable not only in heavily calcified regions but often even at points which, despite challenge, failed to undergo macroscopically visible calcification (Plate XII, *F*).

It is known that local stress, induced by various topical irritants, can produce local nonspecific resistance to the induction of necrosis by the subsequent topical application of diverse tissue irritants. However, depending upon circumstances, inflamed foci may become either more or less than normally sensitive to damage[825] and it might have been expected that a heavily calcified area would become less resistant to an irritant such as croton oil. Yet our experiments clearly showed that calciphylaxis increases topical tissue resistance, not only to croton oil but also to a variety of other noxious agents.

An altogether different **systemic** protective effect is exerted by calciphylaxis upon organs removed from the area of challenge. We have seen, for example, that the extensive cutaneous calcification induced by subcutaneous infiltration with Fe-Dex or albumen can protect the rat against intoxication by otherwise fatal doses of orally administered DHT. The mechanism of this protection is not yet fully clarified, but it is reasonable to assume that here resistance is induced by the deviation of calcium, or calcifiable matrix, from more vital internal organs to the skin; consequently the cardiovascular system and the kidney are protected against an otherwise fatal calcinosis. We do not know whether, in clinical medicine, calciphylaxis can play any such defensive role by establishing foci which would compete with the primary vital targets of pathogens through the deviation of potentially toxic compounds into less vital areas. The fixation abscess is thought to act this way, but there is no reason to suppose that its effect is related to calciphylaxis.

In the rat, iron tends to localize in areas of chemically or bacterially induced inflammation. This iron is subsequently transformed into ferritin or hemosiderin. Since at the same time the resistance of the animals to bacteria is increased, it was concluded that iron can augment nonspecific resistance.[435] Iron and calcium often occur in association and iron compounds are particularly potent challengers; hence the possible relationship between this iron-induced and the calciphylactically elicited nonspecific resistance also deserves to be explored.

The concept of the stromal depot system (**SDS**).—We have seen that various parenterally administered challengers exhibit different affinities for the connective-tissue elements of diverse regions. For example, Fe-OS is preponderantly deposited in the connective tissue of the biliary ducts, the duodenum, and the left auricular appendage; Thorotrast® in the facial skin, the esophagus, and the joints; $CrCl_2$ in the stroma of the thyro-parathyroid system and the carotid body. This characteristic distribution pattern is observed even in animals which have not been sensitized for calciphylaxis or in which calciphylactic responsiveness has been inhibited (e.g., by PMX, stress, or glucocorticoids). We must therefore conclude that although many particulate compounds (including some challengers, such as yolk) are taken up by phagocytes of the RES, others are selectively deposited in the stroma of certain organs. Indeed some challengers are taken up both by the RES and the SDS; for example, Fe-Dex is stored in the splenic and hepatic phagocytes as well as in the stroma of the pancreas, kidney, and uterus. Histologically, there appears to be no essential difference between the connective tissue of the parathyroids, the pancreas, and the kidney, nor is there any striking structural feature that distinguishes the connective tissue of the facial skin from that of other cutaneous regions; yet they must be essentially different, as judged by their fundamentally dissimilar affinities for challengers.

These findings led us to accept the *principle of stroma specificity*. This concept assumes that different organs have specific stromal elements, presumably because of some close chemical interactions between the connective tissue and the typical components (epithelium, muscle, nerve) characteristic of each organ.

Under the name "pharmacothesaurismoses" Di Mattei[633] recently reviewed a number of probably related findings, some gathered from the literature, others made by himself. Apparently there are many observations which indicate that systemically administered drugs can be stored for long periods in the connective tissue of man. He defined "pharmacothesaurismosis" as "a disease characterized by the abnormal presence in tissues of an exogenous chemical substance, e.g., a drug, for an almost unlimited length of time, in the absence of symptoms of general intoxication but always accompanied by lesions at the site of the depot." The well-known preferential storage of certain metals (e.g., arsenic, lead, mercury) in the connective-tissue elements of the oral mucosa, the skin, and the skeleton—all sites preferentially affected by calciphylaxis—may also be relevant, but the possible induction of calcification by such drug deposits has not yet been examined.

Calciphylaxis and infectious diseases.—There may be some relationship between the fundamental reaction forms of the body to systemic infections and to systemic calciphylaxis. Most of the calciphylactic syndromes (like the systemic infections) develop in three stages:

1. The **stage of incubation** (stadium prodromorum) and premonitory signs, during which the target area shows signs of edema often with mild inflammation, but no calcification. If the target area is extensive, these local signs are associated with manifestations of general malaise.

2. The **height of the disease** (stadium acmes), at which time the lesions are fully developed and calcification is diffuse and maximal in extent. The initial edema subsides, but stroma infiltration by inflammatory cells, particularly eosinophils, continues and there is no sign of any demarcation between the affected areas and the adjacent tissues.

3. The **stage of healing** (stadium convalescentiae), a period of recovery during which the initially diffuse connective-tissue lesions are broken up into small cysts or tubercles whose center is occupied by necrotic calcified debris or epithelioid histiocytes and polynuclear giant cells not unlike those seen in tuberculosis or sarcoidosis. These foci are surrounded by capsules of connective tissue, lymphoid elements, and plasma cells. The nodules often suppurate and result in the formation of perforating abscesses.

In view of the frequent **localization** of the experimental calciphylactic lesions in the mediastinum near the hilus of the lungs, fauces, spleen, lymph nodes, joints, and other sites of predilection for the localization of microbes, the similarity to infectious diseases may be striking. These facts raise the question to what extent the localization of living pathogens at such sites might not be merely due to the passive attraction of germ into the stromal depot system rather than to any active migration into areas of predilection.

The virtually constant evolution of primarily diffuse calciphylactic lesions into strictly circumscribed, encapsulated, and often suppurating foci suggests furthermore that in clinical pathology miliary lesions, multiple microabscesses and tubercles need not necessarily result from the spreading of a central microbial seed, but may equally well be the consequence of a **concentric shrinking and subsequent sharp delimitation of originally diffuse stroma reactions** to chemical pathogens. This process of contraction and focus formation appears to be but one manifestation of the general phenomenon of wound-healing by contraction of the connective tissue in the injured area as we see it classically in the cicatrization of surface defects.

Relationships between calciphylaxis and the collagen diseases. The concept of the "calcinoscleroses."—The great similarity between many experimentally induced calciphylactic syndromes and certain collagen diseases has been sufficiently discussed in connection with our concept of the calcinoscleroses. By way of a synopsis let us merely re-emphasize here the following **points of resemblance:**

1. Predilection for localization of lesions in connective tissue, particularly that of the skin, cardiovascular system, and joints.

2. The structural characteristics of lesions, especially inflammation, sclerosis, hyalinization, and the deposition of PAS-positive and/or metachromatic material.

3. The common occurrence of more or less prominent calcinosis both in calciphylaxis and in many clinical collagen diseases, particularly calcinosis universalis, dermatomyositis, sarcoidosis, scleroderma, and arteriosclerosis.

4. Responsiveness to glucocorticoid therapy.

5. The prominent participation of mastocytes in the development of the lesions.

6. Dependence of the lesions upon a singular state of hypersensitivity which does not appear to result from the development of highly specific antigen-antibody interactions.

Naturally, we must ask ourselves what factors could correspond to calciphylactic sensitization and challenge in the causation of spontaneous collagen diseases.

As regards **sensitization,** the first possibility to consider is a special form of hyperparathyroidism, perhaps one resulting from unusual fluctuations in parathyroid hormone secretion. Activation of the parathyroids depends largely upon various endogenous and exogenous stimuli, particularly renal insufficiency, anomalies in the function of the gastrointestinal tract, and the diet. We have also had occasion to quote several observations which suggest that certain spontaneous diseases of man (e.g., sarcoidosis and the idiopathic hypercalcemia of infancy) may be due to a special form of hypervitaminosis D resulting from an excessive sensitivity to the vitamin rather than to exogenous vitamin-D intoxication. It is very problematic, however, whether any of these possible mechanisms of calciphylactic sensitization actually play a part in the pathogenesis of clinical collagen diseases.

We know even less about **challengers** which may precipitate maladies of this kind in man. Only few of the potent metallic calciphylactic challengers are likely to occur in the body in effective quantities. Among these, iron and possibly zinc or copper may play a role. This is particularly probable with regard to iron, since in man tissue deposits of this metal are often associated with calcium precipitates— e.g., in the hemochromatoses and sideroscleroses and also in any kind of osseous or extraskeletal calcium deposit. None of these metallic challengers has actually been proven to play a role in the common clinical collagen diseases, but it is interesting that metal chelators (particularly EDTA) appear to be efficacious in a variety of collagen diseases, such as scleroderma, dermatomyositis, and perhaps even lupus erythematosus.

We have mentioned that some investigators now consider **nephrocalcinosis** and even certain forms of **urinary calculi** to be special forms of collagen disease because here the calcifiable matrix appears to be derived from connective-tissue mucopolysaccharides. The latter may be suspected of acting as calciphylactic challengers, especially because the mucopolysaccharide-containing mastocyte granules possess a high challenging potency; furthermore, connective-tissue components possess a great calcium affinity in calciphylaxis. The question may even be raised of the possible participation of calciphylactic mechanisms in the production of **hepatic sclerosis, cholangitis,** and **biliary calculi,** since calciphylactic lesions occur with great frequency in the liver and the biliary tract.

Noncalcifying calciphylactic reactions.—It seems paradoxical to speak of a calciphylactic reaction in the case of lesions which show virtually no calcification; yet we have seen that various changes which are elicited by challengers only after pretreatment with a calcifier do not exhibit any appreciable degree of calcium precipitation. Thus, for example, 5HT produces a muscular dystrophy, and Fe-OS a periarteritis nodosa of the hepatic artery, only after pretreatment with some such calcifying agent as DHT or parathyroid hormone. Therefore, these reactions must be regarded as essentially calciphylactic even though they are not accompanied by calcinosis.

In considering the possible calciphylactic origin of clinical diseases, it will have to be kept in mind that the absence of histochemically demonstrable calcium does not necessarily exclude this mechanism of causation. It would seem particularly desirable to explore the possibility that some mechanism related to calciphylaxis may be involved in the development of those lesions in which topical stimuli produce changes only in the event of poorly understood types of hypersensitivity; for example, in the development of keloids, amyloidosis, hyalinosis, the Shwartzman-Sanarelli phenomenon, atheromatosis at points of local stress, and drug hypersensitivity. It is quite conceivable that challenge may result in the topical deposition of calcium, hyalin, amyloid, or other substances, depending upon the form of sensitizer used.

Calciphylaxis and neoplasia.—There are many reasons for suspecting some relationship between calciphylaxis and neoplasia. We have seen that squamous metaplasia of the tracheal epithelium occurs frequently in DHT-sensitized animals challenged by $CrCl_3$ i.v. (Fig. 60), while after the intracarotid injection of $CrCl_3$ the unilateral calcification of the tongue is accompanied by abnormal and often extremely deep epithelial ingrowths into the affected area. Here there is intense mitotic proliferation in the basal layer of the lingual epithelium, often with the formation of atypical cell proliferations which resemble precancerous lesions

(Fig. 35). It may not be pure coincidence, furthermore, that several of the most active calciphylactic challengers (e.g., Fe-Dex, Thorotrast®) are sufficiently intense carcinogens to have been withdrawn from clinical use in man.* It has long been suspected that stroma reactions play a decisive role in determining the invasive properties of epithelial growths and it is possible that calciphylaxis may so derange the equilibrium between the epithelium and connective tissue that the chance of malignant transformation is enhanced.

On the other hand, we have learned that in rats bearing the transplantable Walker tumor, DHT treatment followed by infiltration of the neoplasm with Fe-Dex may lead to a partial destruction of the growth with calcification of even the malignant cells themselves (Fig. 38). This observation suggests the possibility of selectively destroying tumor tissue by appropriate calciphylactic procedures.

Conversely, if crushed Walker tumor brei is injected as a direct challenger into the DHT-sensitized rat there usually develops a calcified cutaneous ring around the growing neoplasm, while the skin covering the tumor remains normal (Fig. 317). Here again, partial destruction of neoplastic cells was achieved, since calcified necrotic portions were invariably detectable in the centers of the transplants. However, the neoplastic tissue continued to proliferate, and up to now it has not been possible to achieve a complete destruction of transplantable tumors by these means.

Possible physiologic significance of calciphylaxis.—As a defensive reaction, calciphylaxis undoubtedly can play a homeostatic role in protecting tissues against injury. It is much more questionable whether calciphylaxis also participates in normal physiologic processes, such as ossification or the elimination of calcium through the skin. Preosseous tissue readily develops in calciphylactically challenged areas but this process rarely continues to true ***bone formation.*** Although the iron content of normal bone is comparatively high, we have no proof that any mechanism related to challenge by iron plays a part in physiologic osteogenesis.

Large masses of calcium are commonly seen in the process of extrusion together with the skin or through breaks in the skin of challenged areas (Fig. 318); occasionally we also observe minute intraepithelial granules of calcium or calcified scales in the experimental calciphylactic dermatoses. It remains to be seen, however, whether related processes are of any physiologic significance in the ***elimination of calcium*** or in the induction of physiologic or pathologic ***scale formation*** in cutaneous epithelia.

The complete shedding and subsequent renewal of the skin—obtained after DHT sensitization by extensive infiltration of the subcutis with a challenger (e.g., Fe-Dex or albumen)—is reminiscent of ***exuviation*** as we find it physiologically in lower animals, such as snakes or insects. However, we have no proof of any funda-

---

* They are now manufactured mainly for experimental purposes and veterinary medicine.

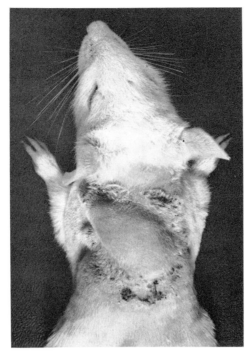

Fig. 317. Circinate cutaneous calcinosis produced by DHT around a Walker tumor transplant. Rat (100 g. ♀): DHT (1 mg. p.o.) 1st day + 0.2 ml. of crushed Walker tumor brei, s.c., 2d day; killed 6th day. The tumor is manifestly growing (although its center proved to be necrotic and calcified). There developed a ring of cutaneous calcinosis around the tumor, but the skin covering the neoplasm remained normal.

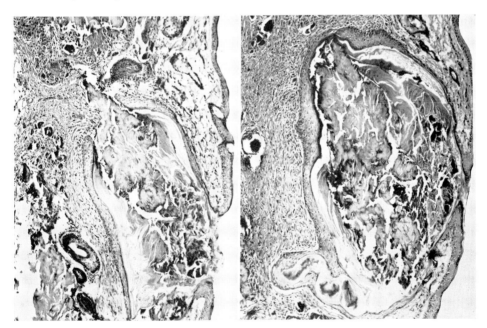

Fig. 318. Extrusion of calcified skin masses following treatment with DHT + Fe-Dex i.p. Rat (200 g. ♀): Fe-Dex (1 ml. = 50 mg. Fe, i.p.) 1st day + DHT (1.5 mg. p.o.) 2d day; killed 30th day. *Left:* Calcified skin is partially isolated from healthy dermis by an undergrowth of epithelium. *Right:* Calcified skin completely isolated by new epithelium. (PAS, ×70.)

mental connection between this experimental lesion and a physiologic cutaneous molt.

In view of its profound influence upon calcium metabolism the possible participation of calciphylaxis should be considered in relation to all physiologic phenomena that depend upon or affect the presence of calcium in tissues. It would serve no purpose to review all of these here. Let us mention only some recent experiments suggesting that even the ***humoral transmission of nervous impulses*** may be more fundamentally linked with calcium than with acetylcholine. These observations "show that the excitant action of acetylcholine on the adrenal medulla is dependent upon the presence of calcium and suggest that acetylcholine evokes adrenal medullary secretion by causing calcium ions to penetrate the adrenal medullary cells."[275] We have seen that several forms of calciphylaxis can produce histologically demonstrable degrees of calcinosis within the cytoplasm or even in and around the nucleus of cells; it would be of great interest to establish whether minor degrees of such changes in cell permeability to calcium could play a part in normal physiologic processes.

Calciphylaxis and stress.—There are many striking similarities between the body's response to stress and to calciphylaxis. In both instances, we are dealing with largely nonspecific adaptive mechanisms in which the connective tissue plays a prominent part. Among all the structural elements of the body, the connective tissue is most nonspecific with regard to its structure, its evolutional potentialities, and its function. The histologic appearance of connective tissue is essentially the same in organs whose other components are quite dissimilar. Connective tissue retains better than any other the capacity to develop from one type (e.g., loose connective tissue) into other forms (e.g., adipose, tendon, or bone tissue); this structural plasticity makes it eminently suitable to fulfil the functions of binding and supporting other elements and to fill out the space between them, acting as a spongelike repository for excess water and solids. In addition, through inflammation and cicatrization it helps adaptation to local injuries, while through some of its more specialized components (RES, lymphocytes, plasmocytes, mastocytes) it participates in many general nonspecific phenomena.

Thus defense against local and systemic stress depends largely upon the activity of connective tissue. In the course of our work on the general adaptation syndrome we have learned that this function is in turn regulated by the pituitary-adrenocortical axis. On the other hand, improper adaptation to stress—particularly a faulty hormonal response of the hypophysis or adrenal cortex—may result in "diseases of adaptation," most of which are connective-tissue diseases.

Recent work on calciphylaxis suggests that the parathyroids exert a very similar, essentially nonspecific, adaptative function through their action upon stromal elements by regulating their sensitivity to challengers. Both the pituitary-adrenocortical and the parathyroid hormones may therefore be regarded as essential ingredients of the humoral system, which through its effect upon connective tissue regulates nonspecific adaptability.

The close interactions between these two hormonal mechanisms are also evidenced by other observations. Depending upon circumstances, both topical and systemic stress can either elicit or prevent calciphylactic responses and such typical "stress hormones" as glucocorticoids can protect against changes induced be it by stress or by calciphylaxis.

One of the most puzzling problems raised by the lesions elicited either by stress or by calciphylaxis is their often exquisite specificity of structure, despite the comparative nonspecificity of their causation. This is apparently due to the fact that the diseases of adaptation, whether induced by stress or by calciphylaxis, are essentially pluricausal.[823] They depend both upon comparatively nonspecific humoral factors—such as pituitary, adrenocortical, or parathyroid hormones—and upon certain modifying or conditioning factors which add the elements of specificity.[813] With regard to the potential pathogenic effect of the parathyroids, we formulated this view some thirty years ago, as follows: "Diverse, still largely unidentified conditioning factors may be responsible for the fact that an increase in parathyroid hormone secretion produces one or the other disease under different circumstances."[810] This view now receives additional support from the study of calciphylaxis.

The principal aim of future investigations into the basic mechanism of this new biologic phenomenon will be to show to what extent a better understanding of it can be of help in the prevention and cure of disease.

Bibliography

1. ABRAMOWITZ, E. W. A case for diagnosis (Scleredema adultorum? Scleroderma?), Arch. Dermat. & Syph., **55**:705, 1947.

2. ACEVEDO, D. E., and AIQUEL, D. J. Resultados alejados de la paratiroidectomia en la esclerodermia, Arch. Soc. cir. hosp., Santiago (Chile), **3**:190, 1951.

3. ACEVEDO, D. E.; VELASCO, A. S.; and MUNNICH, G. Esclerodermia, Rev. Med. Chile, **73**:563, 1945.

4. ACUÑA, M.; PUGLISI, A.; and DEL CASTILLO, E. B. Hipertiroidismo caquectizante con esclerodermia, Arch. argent. pediat., **8**:980, 1937.

5. ADRIAN, C., and ROEDERER, J. Les arthropathies au cours de la sclérodermie, Ann. dermat. et syph., **1**:299, 341, 395, 1920.

6. AEFFNER, E.; SCHMIDTKE, L.; SEEBERGER, H. J.; and VOELKEL, A. Kasuistischer Beitrag zur akuten Erwachsenen-Toxoplasmose (Encephalitis, Myositis ossificans, symptomatische Psychose), Nervenarzt, **26**:161, 1955.

7. AFZELIUS, A. Sklerodermie mit Hemiatrophia facialis, Arch. Dermat. u. Syph., **106**:3, 1911.

8. AKANUMA, J. An autopsy case of generalized calcinosis, Tr. Jap. Path. Soc., **18**:429, 1928.

9. AKERREN, Y. Die differentialdiagnostische Deutung der Bluteosinophilie bei Polymyositis und gleichartigen Krankheitszuständen, Acta med. scandinav., **75**:34, 1931.

10. ALBERTINI, A. VON; DIETRICH, A.; FRAENKEL, E.; MEYENBURG, H. VON; PICK, L.; and SCHMIDT, M. B. Handbuch der speziellen pathologischen Anatomie und Histologie, Knochen, Muskeln, Sehnen, Sehnenscheiden, Schleimbeutel. Verlag Julius Springer, Berlin, vol. IX/I, 1929.

11. ALBRIGHT, F.; BURNETT, C. H.; SMITH, P. H.; and PARSON, W. Pseudo-hypoparathyroidism, an example of Seabright-Bantam syndrome, Endocrinology, **30**:922, 1942.

12. ALBRIGHT, F., and ELLSWORTH, R. Studies on the physiology of the parathyroid glands. I. Calcium and phosphorus studies on a case of idiopathic hypoparathyroidism, J. Clin. Invest., **7**:183, 1929.

13. ALBRIGHT, F., and REIFENSTEIN, E. C., JR. The Parathyroid Glands and Metabolic Bone Disease. Selected Studies. Baltimore: Williams & Wilkins Co., 1948.

14. ALEXANDER, H. L.; WEISS, R. S.; COOPER, Z. K.; GOLDMAN, M. L.; SMITH, J. R.; MENDELOFF, A. I.; ELLIOTT, G. V.; DAUGHADAY, W. H.; SCHROEDER, H. A.; GERMUTH, F. G.; SHAPLEIGH, J. B.; and GOLDMAN, A. Scleroderma with congestive heart failure, Am. J. Med., **14**:231, 1953.

15. ALLAN, W. Dermatomyositis or scleroderma? Report of a case, Arch. Dermat. & Syph., **19**:265, 1929.

16. ALLEN, A. C. The Skin: A Clinicopathologic Treatise. St. Louis: C. V. Mosby Co., 1954.

17. ALLINGTON, H. V. Localized atrophy of skin and subcutaneous tissue (Hemiatrophia faciei? Scleroderma?), Arch. Dermat. & Syph., 41:437, 1940.

18. ALQUIER, L., and TOUCHARD, P. Lésions des glandes vasculaires sanguines dans deux cas de sclérodermie généralisée, Arch. méd. expér. anat. path., 19:687, 1907.

19. ALVAREZ, G. Concideraciones patogenicas sobre hemiatrofias progresivas combinadas con esclerodermia, Arch. argent. pediat., 21:83, 1944.

20. ANDERSON, J.; DENT, C. E.; HARPER, C.; and PHILPOT, G. R. Effect of cortisone on calcium metabolism in sarcoidosis with hypercalcaemia. Possibly antagonistic actions of cortisone and vitamin D, Lancet, Oct. 9: 720, 1954.

21. ANDERSON, W. Sclérodermie de la peau et de la muqueuse buccale, Dermat. Soc. London (Ann. dermat. et syph.), 9:914, 1898.

22. ANDERSON, W. A. D. Pathology. St. Louis: C. V. Mosby Co., 3d ed., 1957.

23. ANDREWS. Scleroderma and facial hemiatrophy, Arch. Dermat. & Syph., 12:914, 1925.

24. ANNAMUNTHODO, H. Calcinosis, Am. J. Surg., 99:951, 1960.

25. ANONYMOUS. Scleroderma with vaginal lesions, Arch. Dermat. & Syph., 44:696, 1941.

26. ANONYMOUS. Case records of the Massachusetts General Hospital (Case 39061), New England J. Med., 248:248, 1953.

27. ANONYMOUS. Hypertension, oliguria, arthralgias, abnormal esophageal motility and glomerulonephritis, Am. J. Med., 31:471, 1961.

28. ANONYMOUS. Case records of the Massachusetts General Hospital (Case 43161), New England J. Med., 256:750, 1957.

29. ANONYMOUS. Hypercalcemia—Doubled causes and a dilemma, Ann. Int. Med., 54:1026, 1961.

30. AOYAGI. Veränderungen der sympathischen Ganglien bei diffuser Sklerodermie, Deutsche med. Wchnschr., 38:1120, 1912.

31. APERT, E.; BRAC; and ROUSSEAU. Sclérodermie avec arthropathies ankylosantes et atrophie musculaire chez une enfant de douze ans, Bull. Soc. franç. dermat. et syph., 19:244, 1908.

32. APPELMANS, R., and CARDOEN, C. Le syndrome "calcinose," Rev. belge path. et méd. expér., 21:37, 1951.

33. ARKIN, A. Clinical and pathological study of periarteritis nodosa. A report of five cases, one histologically healed, Am. J. Path., 6:401, 1930.

34. ARMALY, M. F. Ocular involvement in chondrodystrophia calcificans congenita punctata, A.M.A. Arch. Ophth., 57:491, 1957.

35. ARNOLD, H. L., JR. Stress dermatoses. Suggested integration of the allergic psychogenic dermatoses, A.M.A. Arch. Dermat. & Syph., 67:566, 1953.

36. ARNOLD, W. Epithelkörperchentumor mit allgemeiner Calcinose, Virchows Arch. path. Anat., 306:427, 1940.

37. ARTOM, M. Emiatrofia facciale progressiva, Arch. ital. dermat. sifil., 13:458, 1937.

38. ASAROVA, A. M. Hepp's pseudotrichinosis or dermatomyositis subacuta, Vrach. delo, **14**:1133, 1931.

39. ASBOE-HANSEN, G., and KAALUND-JØRGENSEN, O. Systemic mast-cell disease involving skin, liver, bone marrow, and blood associated with disseminated xanthomata, Acta haemat., **16**:273, 1956.

40. ASHER, R. A woman with the stiff-man syndrome, Brit. M.J., Feb. 1: 265, 1958.

41. ATKINSON, F. R. B., and WEBER, F. P. Cutaneous and subcutaneous calcinosis, Brit. J. Dermat., **50**:267, 1938.

42. ATLAS, D. H.; GABERMAN, P.; and EISENBERG, H. L. Syndrome of masked hyperparathyroidism (Case reports), Ann. Int. Med., **44**:1195, 1956.

43. ATSMON, A.; FRANK, M.; NATHAN, P.; and DE VRIES, A. Recurrent acute hyperparathyroidism with severe gastro-intestinal manifestations. Report of a case with recovery after removal of a parathyroid adenoma, Gastroenterology, **39**:83, 1960.

44. ATWATER, N. W.; BIBLE, R. H., JR.; BROWN, E. A.; BURTNER, R. R.; MIHINA, J. S.; NYSTED, L. N.; and SOLLMAN, P. B. Steroidal aldosterone antagonists, J. Org. Chem., **26**:3077, 1961.

45. AUDEOUD, H. Polymyosite et dermato-myosite, Rev. méd. Suisse Romande, **62**: 446, 1942.

46. AUKEN, G., and LOUW, A. To tilfaelde af dermatomyositis, Nord. med., **28**:2369, 1945.

47. BACHMAN, D. M. Metabolic balances of nitrogen and electrolytes in generalized scleroderma, Clin. Res., **8**:145, 1960.

48. BAGUENA, M. B., and CANDELA, R. B. Exito de la vitamina E en un caso de esclerodermia con dermatomiositis, Rev. clin. españ., **39**:41, 1950.

49. BAHR, G. F.; SCHUERMANN, H.; and GRECELIUS, G. Elektronenmikroskopische Untersuchungen bei progressiver Sklerodermie. Lupus erythematodes acutus (und Acrodermatitis chronica atrophicans), Hautarzt, **2**:513, 1951.

50. BAILEY, H. Cutaneous and subcutaneous calcinosis. Scleroderma (Right cheek?), Arch. Dermat. & Syph., **41**:1140, 1940.

50*a*. BAINBRIDGE, W. S. Lithopedion. Report of a case, with a review of the literature, Am. J. Obst., **65**:31, 1912.

51. BAKER, R., and CONNELLY, J. P. Bilateral and recurrent renal calculi. Evidence indicating renal collagen abnormality and results of salicylate therapy, J.A.M.A., **160**:1106, 1956.

52. BAKER, R.; REAVEN, G.; and SAWYER, J. Effect of toluidine blue on metastatic calcification, Proc. Soc. Exper. Biol. & Med., **83**:281, 1953.

53. BAKER, R.; REAVEN, G.; and SAWYER, J. Ground substance and calcification: The influence of dye binding on experimental nephrocalcinosis, J. Urol., **71**:511, 1954.

54. BALI, T., and FURTH, J. A transplantable splenic tumor rich in mast cells; observations on mast cells in varied neoplasms, Am. J. Path., **25**:605, 1949.

55. BALLIN, M. Parathyroidism, Ann. Surg., **96**:649, 1932.

56. BAMBERGER, E. Das Sklerödem und seine Beziehungen zu den Sklerodermien, Arch. Dermat. u. Syph., **168**:313, 1911.

57. BANKS, B. M. Is there a common denominator in scleroderma, dermatomyositis,

disseminated lupus erythematosus, the Libman-Sacks syndrome and polyarteritis nodosa? New England J. Med., 225:433, 1941.

58. BARBER, H. W. Circumscribed scleroderma of the buccal mucous membrane, Proc. Roy. Soc. Med., 37:73, 1944.

59. BARBILIAN, N., and REPCIUC, E. Ueber die heterotopische Verkalkung, Virchows Arch. path. Anat., 303:552, 1939.

60. BARKER, N. W. An unusual case of dermatomyositis, Proc. Staff. Meet., Mayo Clin., 5:169, 1930.

61. BARLOW, G. B. Scleroderma associated with adrenal neoplasm, Arch. Dermat. & Syph., 39:1021, 1939.

62. BARNARD, R. D., and APPEL, A. Scleroderma associated with malignant estrapenic leukoblastosis ("Leukemia"), Urol. & Cutan. Rev., 54:345, 1950.

63. BARON, A. Ueber eine neue Erkrankung der Wirbelsäule, Jahrb. f. Kinderh., 104: 357, 1924.

64. BARR, D. P. Myositis ossificans progressiva, J. Missouri M.A., 27:75, 1930.

65. BARR, D. P. Pathological calcification, J. Missouri M.A., 27:593, 1930.

66. BARR, D. P., and BULGER, H. A. The clinical syndrome of hyperparathyroidism, Am. J. M. Sc., 179:449, 1930.

67. BARTELS, E. C., and CATTELL, R. B. Calcinosis treated by parathyroidectomy, Ann. Int. Med., 17:859, 1942.

68. BARTHOLOMEW, L. G.; CAIN, J. C.; BULBULIAN, A. H.; and DAVIS, G. D. Misleading calcific shadows in the abdomen, Postgrad. Med., 30:51, 1961.

69. BASCH, G.; LEIBOVICI, R.; DURUPT, A.; and BASCH, M. Sclérodermie avec concrétions calcaires (syndrome de Thibierge-Weissenbach) associée à une atrophie cutanée. Parathyroïdectomie, Bull. mém. soc. méd. hôp. Paris, 50:516, 1934.

70. BASSI, G. Application de nouvelles méthodes et de nouveaux concepts à l'étude de la collagénopathie sclérodermique, Union méd. Canada, 79:623, 1950.

71. BASSI, G. La malattia sclerodermica. Bologna: Istituto Editoriale Medico, 1951.

72. BATSAKIS, J. G. Calcospherites and thyroid carcinoma, Univ. Michigan M. Bull., 22:530, 1956.

73. BATSAKIS, J. G.; NISHIYAMA, R. H.; and RICH, C. R. Microlithiasis (Calcospherites) and carcinoma of the thyroid gland, A.M.A. Arch. Path., 69:493, 1960.

74. BATSON, J. M. Calcification of the ear cartilage associated with the hypercalcemia of sarcoidosis. Report of a case, New England J. Med. 265:876, 1961.

75. BAUER, J. Progressive facial hemiatrophy, disseminated scleroderma and muscular cramps, Confinia neurol., 7:3, 1946.

76. BAUER, J. M., and FREYBERG, R. H. Vitamin D intoxication with metastatic calcification, J.A.M.A., 130:1208, 1946.

77. BECHET. Scleroderma and fibroma, Arch. Dermat. & Syph., 13:706, 1926.

78. BECK, C. Ueber Tendinitis und Tendovaginitis prolifera calcarea, Deutsche Ztschr. Chir., 58:328, 1901.

79. BECKER, G. Beiträge zur Orthologie und Pathologie der Plexus chorioidei und des Ependyms, Beitr. path. Anat. u. allg. Path., 103:457, 1939.

80. BECKER, S. W. Osteosis Cutis, Arch. Dermat. & Syph., 10:163, 1924.

81. BECKMANN, R., and MENNE, F. Ist die Dermatomyositis eine Vitaminmangel-krankheit? Betrachtungen über pathogenetische Beziehungen zur Dystrophia musculorum progressiva Erb, Monatschr. Kinderh., **100**:54, 1952.

82. BECKS, H.; COLLINS, D. A.; and AXELROD, H. E. The effects of a single massive dose of vitamin D₂ (D-Stoss therapy) on oral and other tissues of young dogs, Am. J. Orthodontics, **32**:452, 1946.

83. BECKS, H.; COLLINS, D. A.; and FREYTAG, R. M. Changes in oral structures of the dog persisting after chronic overdoses of vitamin D, Am. J. Orthodontics, **32**:463, 1946.

84. BEERMAN, H. The visceral manifestations of scleroderma. A review of the recent literature, Am. J. M. Sc., **216**:458, 1948.

85. BEESON. Acrodermatitis chronica atrophicans with scleroderma, Arch. Dermat. & Syph., **13**:690, 1926.

86. BEIGELMAN, P. M. Variants of the platelet thrombosis syndrome and their relation-ship to disseminated lupus, A.M.A. Arch. Path., **51**:213, 1951.

87. BELL, N. H.; GILL, J. R., JR.; and BARTTER, F. C. A demonstration of hypersensi-tivity to vitamin D in sarcoidosis, The Endocrine Soc. 43rd. Meet. June 22–24, New York, 1961. J. Clin. Endocrinol. & Metab., **21**:48, 1961.

88. BELL, W. BLAIR. On the part played by the calcium salts in the blood and tissues, with special reference to their influence in regard to the female genital functions; together with a description of a simple method of quantitative analysis, Brit. M.J., April 20: 920, 1907.

89. BENEDETTI, G., and CONTI, C. Sulla trasmissione sperimentale della dermatomio-site, Minerva med., **39**:146, 1948.

90. BENJAMOWITSCH, E., and MASCHKILLEISSON, L. N. Weitere Beiträge zur Frage über die Atrophie der Haut. III. Acrodermatitis chronica atrophicans und ihre Beziehung zur Sclerodermie, Acta dermat.-venereol., **14**:313, 1933.

91. BERGK, W. Ist die Myositis ossificans traumatica eine Behandlungsfolge? Chirurg, **11**:374, 1939.

92. BERKAY, F., and BUKE, H. Paratiroidektomi ve stellektomi kombinasyonu ile tedavi edilmis nadir bir skleroderma vak'asi, Türk. tib. cem. mec., **18**:284, 1952.

93. BERKELEY, W. N., and BEEBE, S. P. A contribution to the physiology and chem-istry of the parathyroid gland, J. Med. Res., **20**:149, 1909.

94. BERNHEIM, A. R., and GARLOCK, J. H. Parathyroidectomy for Raynaud's disease and scleroderma; a preliminary report, Ann. Surg., **101**:1012, 1935.

95. BERNHEIM, A. R., and GARLOCK, J. H. Parathyroidectomy for Raynaud's disease and scleroderma. Late results, Arch. Surg., **38**:543, 1939.

96. BERNSTEIN, E. T., and GOLDBERGER, L. A. Complete subsidence of scleroderma with dihydrotachysterol, J.A.M.A., **130**:570, 1946.

97. BERNUTH, F. VON. Über Sklerodermie, Osteopoikilie und Kalkgicht im Kindesalter, Ztschr. Kinderh., **54**:103, 1932.

98. BETTMANN. Ueber eine besondere Form der Urticaria factitia bei der Sclerodermie, Berl. klin. Wchnschr., **38**:365, 1901.

99. Beurey, J.; Jeandidier, P.; Mougeolle, J. M.; and Cherrier, F. La scléroder-mie, Gaz. méd. France, **65**:133, 1958.

100. Bevans, M. Pathology of scleroderma with special reference to the changes in the gastrointestinal tract, Am. J. Path., **21**:25, 1945.

101. Bevans, M., and Taylor, H. K. Lesions following the use of Ertron in rheumatoid arthritis, Am. J. Path., **23**:367, 1947.

102. Binnie, J. F. On myositis ossificans traumatica, Ann. Surg., **38**:423, 1903.

103. Black, B. M. Hyperparathyroidism, Am. Lectures in Endocrinol. Springfield: Charles C Thomas, 1953.

104. Blanckenburg, K. Klinische Betrachtungen über einen Fall von Calcinosis dis-seminata universalis, Münch. med. Wchnschr., **84**:249, 1937.

105. Blaschko, H., and Gumpert, M. Verkalkte Scrotalxanthome, Arch. Dermat. u. Syph., **146**:323, 1924.

106. Blom-Ides, C. Zur Klinik und Pathogenese der Dermatomyositis, Hautarzt, **3**: 211, 1952.

107. Bloom, F. Spontaneous solitary and multiple mast-cell tumors (mastocytoma) in dogs, Arch. Path., **33**:661, 1942.

108. Bloom, G.; Franzén, S.; and Sirén, M. Malignant systemic mast-cell disease (mastocytoma) in man, Acta med. scandinav., **168**:95, 1960.

109. Bluefarb, S. M., and Salk, M. R. Urticaria pigmentosa with bone lesions, gastro-intestinal symptoms and splenomegaly, A.M.A. Arch. Dermat., **70**:376, 1954.

110. Boas, E. P., and Scholz, T. Calcification in the pineal gland, Arch. Int. Med., **21**:66, 1918.

111. Boatwright, H.; Wheeler, C. E.; and Cawley, E. P. Case reports. Werner's syndrome, Arch. Int. Med., **90**:243, 1952.

112. Bogaert, L. van, and Eyckmans, R. Poikilodermatomyosites et réticuloses, Arch. belg. dermat. et syph., **2**:12, 1948.

113. Böger, A., and Gros, H. Die Behandlung der Dermatomyositis mit Penicillin, Deutsche med. Wchnschr., **74**:924, 1949.

114. Böhler, L. Entstehung, Verhütung und Behandlung der Myositis ossificans trau-matica, Chirurg, **8**:877, 1936.

115. Böhler, L. Die Ursachen der Myositis ossificans traumatica nach Ellbogenverren-kungen, Fortschr. Geb. Röntgenstrahlen, **53**:823, 1936.

116. Bohnstedt, R. M. Kasuistischer Beitrag zur Frage Impetigo herpetiformis und Tetanie, Arch. Dermat. u. Syph., **169**:357, 1933.

117. Bohse, T., and Benjaminsson, G. Dermatomyositis, Ugesk. laeger, **105**:1049, 1943.

118. Bolam, M. Calcinosis with report of a case of calcinosis universalis, Brit. J. Der-mat., **47**:340, 1935.

119. Boland, E. W. Spondylitis. *In* Arthritis and Allied Conditions, p. 621. Philadel-phia: Lea & Febiger, 6th ed., 1960.

120. Bonard, E. C. Le poumon dans la sclérodermie, Schweiz. med. Wchnschr., **88**:373, 1958.

121. Bongini, O. Sull'associazione artrite cronica primaria e sclerodermia, Settimana med., **36**:218, 1948.

122. BORDA, J. M., and DE ROA, A. O. Liquen escleroso y atrofico de tipo "white spot disease," Rev. argent. dermatosif., **26**:453, 1942.

123. BOURNE, F. M.; HOWELL, D. A.; and ROOT, H. S. Renal and cerebral scleroderma, Canad. M.A.J., **82**:881, 1960.

124. BOWIE, M. A. Dupuytren's Contracture. *In* Arthritis and Allied Conditions, p. 1228. Philadelphia: Lea & Febiger, 6th ed., 1960.

125. BOYCE, W. H.; GARVEY, F. K.; and NORFLEET, C. M. Ion-binding properties of electrophoretically homogeneous mucoproteins of urine in normal subjects and in patients with renal calculus disease, J. Urol., **72**:1019, 1954.

126. BOYD, J. A.; PATRICK, S. I.; and REEVES, R. J. Roentgen changes observed in generalized scleroderma. Report of sixty-three cases, Arch. Int. Med., **94**:248, 1954.

127. BOYD, M. W. J., and GRANT, A. P. Werner's syndrome (progeria of the adult). Further pathological and biochemical observations, Brit. M.J., Nov. 7: 920, 1959.

128. BOYLE, A. J.; CLARKE, N. E.; MOSHER, R. E.; and McCANN, D. S. Chelation therapy in circulatory and sclerosing diseases, Proc. Conf. on Biol. Aspects Metal-Binding, Sept. 6–9, Pennsylvania State Univ., 1960, Fed. Proc., **20**:243, 1961.

129. BRAMWELL, B. Diffuse sclerodermia: Its frequency; its occurrence in stone-masons; its treatment by fibrolysin-elevations of temperature due to fibrolysin injections, Edinburgh M.J., **12**:387, 1914.

130. BRAND, T. VON, and HOLTZ, F. Über die lokale Gewebsverkalkung nach subcutaner Zufuhr von bestrahltem Ergosterin, Hoppe Seyler's Ztschr. physiol. Chem., **195**: 241, 1931.

131. BRAND, T. VON, and NAUCK, E. G. Verkalkungsvorgänge in Gewebekulturen unter dem Einfluss von Nebenschilddrüsenhormon und von Vitamin D, Arch. Exper. Zellforsch., **14**:276, 1933.

132. BRAUER. Sklerodermie, Nordostdtsch. dermat. Ver., May 9, Danzig, 1929, Zentralbl. Haut- u. Geschlechtsk., **32**:319, 1930.

133. BRAUN-FALCO, O. Neueres zur Histopathologie des Scleroedema adultorum (Buschke), Dermat. Wchnschr., **125**:409, 1952.

134. BREDA, A. Concrezioni calcari e produzioni osteiformi nel connettivo sottocutaneo dell uomo, Gior. ital. mal. vener., **50**:244, 1915.

135. BREININ, G. M. Scleredema adultorum. Ocular manifestations, A.M.A. Arch. Ophth., **50**:155, 1953.

136. BRIGGS, J. N., and ILLINGWORTH, R. S. Calcinosis universalis treated with adrenocorticotrophic hormone and cortisone, Lancet, Oct. 25: 800, 1952.

137. BRINKMANN, E. Mastzellenreticulose (Gewebsbasophilom) mit histaminbedingtem Flush und Übergang in gewebsbasophile Leukämie, Schweiz. med. Wchnschr., **89**:1046, 1959.

138. BRISSAUD, E. Pathogénie du processus sclérodermique, Presse méd., **5**:285, 1897.

139. BROCK, J. Ueber calcinosis circumscripta (Kalkgicht) mit Sklerodaktylie im Kindesalter, Ztschr. Kinderh., **58**:751, 1936.

140. BROCK, W. G. Dermatomyositis and diffuse scleroderma. Differential diagnosis and reports of cases, Arch. Dermat. & Syph., **30**:227, 1934.

141. BROCQ, P.; FEYEL, P.; and SLUCZEWSKI, A. Trois cas de métaplasie osseuse du

chorion cytogène de l'endomêtre. Aperçus pathogéniques, Gynéc. et obst., **47**:613, 1948.

142. BRODY, J., and BELLIN, D. E. Calcinosis with scleroderma, Arch. Dermat. & Syph., **36**:85, 1937.

143. BRODY, S. Psychiatric observations in patients treated with cortisone and ACTH, Psychosom. Med., **14**:94, 1952.

144. BROGDON, B. G., and CROW, N. E. Chondrodystrophia calcificans congenita, Am. J. Roentgenol., **80**:443, 1958.

145. BRONSKY, D.; KUSHNER, D. S.; DUBIN, A.; and SNAPPER, I. Idiopathic hypoparathyroidism and pseudohypoparathyroidism. Case reports and review of the literature, Medicine, **37**:317, 1958.

146. BROOKS, H. Hypernephroma with long-standing symptoms of adrenal deficiency, with scleroderma and sclerodactylia, J. Cut. Dis., **32**:191, 1914.

147. BROWN, C. L., and GINSBURG, I. W. Osteoporosis associated with extensive metastatic calcification and chronic renal disease, Arch. Path., **30**:108, 1940.

148. BRUCE, G. M. Retinitis in dermatomyositis, Tr. Am. Ophth. Soc., **36**:282, 1938.

149. BRUCE-JONES, D. B. S. A case clinically resembling morphoea with a tuberculous background and indeterminate histology suggestive of necrobiosis lipoidica, Brit. J. Dermat., **49**:238, 1937.

150. BRÜCKEL, K. W.; PFEIFFER, E. F.; and KRÜCKE, W. Das dermatomyositische Syndrom, Hautarzt, **2**:148, 1951.

151. BRUN, A. Chronic polymyositis on the basis of sarcoidosis, Acta psychiat. et neurol. scandinav., **36**:515, 1961.

152. BRUNNER, M. J., and LOBRAICO, R. V., JR. Dermatomyositis as an index of malignant neoplasm. Report of a case and review of the literature, Ann. Int. Med., **34**:1269, 1951.

153. BRUNSTING, H. A., and EYSTER, W. H., JR. Localized scleroderma, Arch. Dermat. & Syph., **66**:632, 1952.

153*a*. BRUYN, G. W. On so-called neuromyositis. A critical review, Psychiat. Neurol. Neurochir., **64**:79, 1961.

154. BRYANT, J. H., and WHITE, W. H. A case of calcification of the arteries and obliterative endarteritis, associated with hydronephrosis in a child aged six months, Guy's Hosp. Rep., **55**:17, 1901.

155. BULLITT, J. B. Ossifying hematoma, California & West. Med., **27**:508, 1927.

156. BUNNELL, S. Surgery of the Hand. Philadelphia: J. P. Lippincott Co., 2d ed., 1949.

157. BUNTING, H. Histochemical analysis of pathological mineral deposits at various sites, A.M.A. Arch. Path., **52**:458, 1951.

158. BUREAU, Y. Un cas de poïkilodermatomyosite (maladie de Petges et Cléjat), Bull. Soc. franç. dermat. & syph., **45**:858, 1938.

159. BURGESS, J. F. Vitamin E (tocopherols) in the collagenoses, Lancet, Aug. 7: 215, 1948.

160. BURKHOLDER, T. M., and BRAUND, R. R. Massive calcinosis with chronic renal insufficiency due to polycystic kidneys: A case report, J. Urol., **57**:1001, 1947.

161. BURNETT, C. H.; COMMONS, R. R.; ALBRIGHT, F.; and HOWARD, J. E. Hypercal-

cemia without hypercalcuria or hypophosphatemia, calcinosis and renal insufficiency, New England J. Med., **240**:787, 1949.

162. BURROWS, H. Some Factors in the Localisation of Disease in the Body. London: Baillière, Tindall & Cox, 1932.

163. BURSTEIN, S. H., and RINGOLD, H. J. A steroidal mustard of the androstane series, J. Org. Chem., **26**:3084, 1961.

164. BUSCHKE, A. Discussion (scleroderma), Arch. Dermat. & Syph., **58–59**:286, 1901–2.

165. BUSCHKE, A. Ueber das Sklerodem und seine Beziehung zur Sklerodermie, Dermat. Wchnschr., **70**:17, 1920.

166. BUSCHKE, A., and OLLENDORFF, H. Skleroedema adultorum mit muskulärer Lokalisation, Med. Klin., **23**:1406, 1927.

167. BUTLER, A. M.; WILSON, J. L.; and FARBER, S. Dehydration and acidosis with calcification at renal tubules, J. Pediat., **8**:489, 1936.

168. BUZZARD, E. F. The clinical history and post-mortem examination of five cases of myasthenia gravis, Brain, **28**:438, 1905.

169. BYRON, C. S., and MICHALOVER, S. Calcinosis and scleroderma with parathyroidectomy, Ann. Int. Med., **18**:225, 1943.

170. CALDWELL, I. W. A dermatomyositic symptom-complex associated with malignant disease, Brit. J. Cancer, **9**:575, 1955.

171. CALDWELL, I. W., and AITCHISON, J. D. Pulmonary hypertension in dermatomyositis, Brit. Heart J., **18**:273, 1956.

172. CALONIUS, P. E. B., and JÄÄMERI, K. E. U. Mast cells in keloids, Ann. chir. et gynaec. Fenniae, **50**:9, 1961.

173. CALVERT, R. J.; NARDELL, S. G.; and RAEBURN, C. Angiopathies in acrosclerosis, Angiology, **6**:129, 1955.

174. CALVERT, R. J., and OWEN, T. K. True scleroderma kidney, Lancet, July 7: 19, 1956.

175. CAMERON, G. R. The staining of calcium, J. Path. & Bact., **33**:929, 1930.

176. CANTALOUBE, P., and CHABER, J. Sclérodermie avec signes tabétiques, Soc. neurol. Séance 5 fév. 1925. Rev. neurol., **1**:209, 1925.

177. CARCASSONNE, F. Un cas de sclérodermie traitée par la parathyroïdectomie, J. méd. Paris, **57**:367, 1937.

178. CARDARELLI, A. Acromegalia e sclerodermia, Studium, **17**:161, 1927.

179. CARERE-COMES, O. Ueber die Struktur und die Histogenese der Gamna-Höfe in der Milz. Zugleich ein Beitrag zur Kenntnis einer muskulären Milzcirrhose, Beitr. path. Anat. u. allg. Path., **101**:549, 1938.

180. CARLETON, A. Skin disease and cataract, Brit. J. Dermat., **55**:83, 1943.

181. CAROL, W. L. L., and VAN DER ZANDE, F. Adiponecrosis subcutanea neonatorum (sog. Sklerodermie), Acta Dermat.-venereol., **7**:180, 1926.

181*a*. CARTER, P. B.; HIGGINBOTHAM, R. D.; and DOUGHERTY, T. F. The local response of tissue mast cells to antigen in sensitized mice, J. Immunol., **79**:259, 1957.

182. CARTWRIGHT, G. E., and WINTROBE, M. M. Anemia of infection. Review, Advances Int. Med., **5**:165, 1952.

183. CASSAR, A., and DE BEAUJEU, A. J. Un nouveau cas de myosite ossifiante progressive, Arch. électric. méd., **38**:362, 1930.

184. CATCHPOLE, B. N.; JEPSON, R. P.; and KELLGREN, J. H. Peripheral vascular effect of cortisone in rheumatoid arthritis, scleroderma and other related conditions, Ann. Rheumat. Dis., **13**:302, 1954.

185. CAUGHEY, J. E., and RICHARDSON, W. Acrosclerosis with a report of a case treated with cortisone, New Zealand M.J., **51**:227, 1952.

186. CERUTTI, P. Considerazioni in tema di poichilodermatomiosite, Gior. ital. dermat. e sifil., **89**:631, 1948.

187. CHANNON, H. J., and HARRISON, G. A. The chemical nature of the subcutaneous fat in the normal and sclerematous infant, Biochem. J., **20**:84, 1926.

188. CHEN, T. T. A chemical study of sclerema neonatorum, Nat. M.J. China, **16**:360, 1930.

189. CHEVALIER, R. B., and PONTIUS, E. E. Scleroderma with death caused by acute renal failure, Am. J. Clin. Path., **31**:428, 1959.

190. CHIARI, O. M. Ueber die herdweise Verkalkung und Verknöcherung des subkutanen Fettgewebes. Fettgewebssteine. (Ein Beitrag zur Lehre der sog. Kryptolithiasis), Ztschr. Heilk., suppl. H., **28**:1, 1907.

191. CHILDREY, J. H. Ossification in the auricle: 7 cases, Laryngoscope, **48**:339, 1938.

192. CHILESOTTI, E. Les carcinomes calcifiés de la peau (épithéliomes calcifiés). Étude sur un carcinome de la peau, primitif, multiple, calcifié, Rev. méd. Suisse Romande, **24**:317, 389, 457, 513, 1904.

193. CHORAZAK, T.; KOCHANOWICZ, T.; and PIETRZYKOWSKA, A. Das Werner-Syndrom in der Gruppe der kongenitalen Hautatrophien mit einem Bericht über einen eigenen Fall, Hautarzt, **12**:116, 1961.

194. CHRISTENSEN, E., and REMVIG, O. Et tilfaelde af dermatomyositis kombineret med polyneuritis, Ugeskr. laeger, **107**:886, 1945.

195. CHRISTIANSON, H. B.; BRUNSTING, L. A.; and PERRY, H. O. Dermatomyositis: Unusual features, complications and treatment, A.M.A. Arch. Dermat., **74**:581, 1956.

195a. CHRISTIE, A., and PETERSON, J. C. Pulmonary calcification in negative reactors to tuberculin, Am. J. Publ. Health, **35**:1131, 1945.

196. CHRISTMAN, H. E. Calcareous concretions in Raynaud's disease, Am. J. Roentgenol., **30**:177, 1933.

197. CHURCH, R. E., and ELLIS, A. R. P. Cystic pulmonary fibrosis in generalised scleroderma. Report of two cases, Lancet, March 4: 392, 1950.

198. CLAIRMONT, P., and SCHINZ, H. R. Klinische, röntgenologische und pathologisch-anatomische Beobachtungen zur Marmorknochenerkrankung, Arch. klin. Chir., **132**:347, 1924.

199. CLARK, A. S. Scleroderma (of the edematous variety, followed by atrophy), Arch. Dermat. & Syph., **5**:669, 1922.

200. CLARKE, N. E.; CLARKE, C. N.; and MOSHER, R. E. The "in vivo" dissolution of metastatic calcium. An approach to atherosclerosis, Am. J. M. Sc., **229**:142, 1955.

201. CLAWSON, B. J.; NOBLE, J. F.; and LUFKIN, N. H. Nodular inflammatory and degenerative lesions in muscles from 450 autopsies, Am. J. Path., **23**:910, 1947.

202. COBURN, R. F., and SCHMID, F. R. Progressive systemic sclerosis, Quart. Bull., **34**:49, 1960.

203. COCKAYNE, E. A. Congenital and acquired sclerodermia in childhood, Brit. J. Child. Dis., **13**:225, 1916.

204. CODMAN, E. A. The Shoulder. *In* Rupture of the supraspinatus tendon and other lesions in or about the subacromial bursa. Boston: Thomas Todd, 1934.

205. COFFEY, R. J.; CANARY, J. J.; and DUMAIS, C. C. Hyperparathyroidism and chronic calcific pancreatitis, Am. Surgeon, **25**:310, 1959.

206. COGAN, D. G.; ALBRIGHT, F.; and BARTTER, F. C. Hypercalcemia and band keratopathy; report of nineteen cases, Arch. Ophth., **40**:624, 1948.

207. COHEN, R.; BURNIP, R.; and WAGNER, E. Calcification of the intervertebral disc in a child; report of a case, Ann. West. Med. & Surg., **3**:202, 1949.

208. COLAIZZO, G. Calcificazione asintomatica di tutto il lobo destro della tiroide, Inform. med., **9**:54, 1954.

209. COLE, H. N. Congenital cataracts in sisters with congenital ectodermal dysplasia, J.A.M.A., **130**:894, 1946.

210. COLLAZO, J. A.; RESA, R.; and FERNANDEZ CRUZ, A. Hypercalcämische und antitetanische Wirkung der Exstirpation der Carotisdrüsenzone, Klin. Wchnschr., **14**:748, 1935.

211. COMBES, F. C. Sclerodactylia following injury, Arch. Dermat. & Syph., **38**:976, 1938.

212. COMEL, M. Sclerodermia a focolai circoscritti multipli a simmetria metamerica speculare, Gior. ital. dermat. e sifil., **77**:5, 1936.

213. COMEL, M. Modificazioni delle alterazioni cutanee della vitiligo e della sclerodermia in zone di trapianto cutaneo, Dermatologica, **96**:366, 1948.

214. COMROE, B. I.; CHAMBERLIN, G. W.; and SUNDERMAN, F. W. Interstitial calcinosis. Report of a case and review of the literature, Am. J. Roentgenol., **41**:749, 1939.

215. CONNOR, T. B.; HOPKINS, T. R.; THOMAS, W. C., JR.; CAREY, R. A.; and HOWARD, J. E. The use of cortisone and ACTH in hypercalcemic states, The Endocrine Soc. 38th. Meet. June 7–9, Chicago Palmer House, 1956.

216. CONNOR, T. B.; THOMAS, W. C., JR.; and HOWARD, J. E. The etiology of hypercalcemia associated with lung carcinoma, Proc. 48th Annual Meet. Am. Soc. Clin. Invest., Atlantic City, April 30, 1956, J. Clin. Invest., **35**:697, 1956.

217. COOKE, J. V. The rate of growth in progeria with a report of two cases, J. Pediat., **42**:26, 1953.

218. COPE, O.; CULVER, P. J.; MIXTER, C. G., JR.; and NARDI, G. L. Pancreatitis, a diagnostic clue to hyperparathyroidism, Ann. Surg., **145**:857, 1957.

219. COPEMAN, W. S. C. Textbook of the Rheumatic Diseases. Edinburgh: E. & S. Livingstone, Ltd., 2d. ed., 1955.

220. CORDERO, A. A., and CURIA, L. Esclerodermatomiositis con calcinosis universal, Prensa méd. argent., **45**:582, 1958.

221. CORDIVIOLA, L. A., and QUEVEDO, C. C. Esclerodermia de origen traumatico, Rev. argent. dermat., **28**:92, 1944.

222. CORMIA, F. E. Poikiloderma-like dermatoses: Report of a case with unusual localization and atypical features, Brit. J. Dermat., **49**:13, 1937.

223. CORNBLEET, T. Scleroderma treated with viosterol, Arch. Dermat. & Syph., **40:** 491, 1939.

224. CORNBLEET, T.; REED, C. I.; and REED, B. P. X-Ray Diffraction studies in calcinosis, J. Invest. Dermat., **13:**171, 1949.

225. CORONINI, C.; KOVAC, W.; LASSMANN, G.; and NIEBAUER, G. Zum Sklerodermie-Problem, Acta neuroveg., **21:**231, 1960.

226. COSACESCO, A. Résultats de la parathyroïdectomie dans la sclérodermie, Lyon chir., **45:**229, 1950.

227. COSTELLO, F. V., and BROWN, A. Myositis ossificans complicating anterior poliomyelitis, J. Bone & Joint Surg., **33-B:**594, 1951.

228. COSTELLO. M. J. Cutaneous calcinosis, New York J. Med., **35:**1266, 1935.

229. COSTELLO, M. J. Scleroderma due possibly to adrenal neoplasm, Arch. Dermat. & Syph., **42:**969, 1940.

230. COTTEL, C. E. Dermatomyositis and malignant neoplasm, Am. J. M. Sc., **224:**160, 1952.

231. COVARRUBIAS, A. La paratiroidectomia en el tratamiento de la esclerodermia, Bol. trab. Acad. argent. cir., **27:**958, 1943.

232. CRAIG, W. MCK., and KERNOHAN, J. W. The surgical removal and histological studies of sympathetic ganglia in Raynaud's disease, thrombo-angiitis obliterans, chronic infectious arthritis and scleroderma, Surg. Gynec. & Obst., **56:**767, 1933.

233. CRICK, R. P.; HOYLE, C.; and SMELLIE, H. The eyes in sarcoidosis, Brit. J. Ophth., **45:**461, 1961.

234. CROMPTON, M. R., and MacDERMOT, V. Sarcoidosis associated with progressive muscular wasting and weakness, Brain, **84:**62, 1961.

235. CRUM, W. B., and TILL, H. J. Hyperparathyroidism with Wenckebach's phenomenon, Am. J. Cardiol., **6:**838, 1960.

236. CUNNINGHAM, W. P. Scleroderma inusitatum, New York M. J., **97:**489, 1913.

237. CURTIS, A. C.; BLAYLOCK, H. C.; and HARRELL, E. R., JR. Malignant lesions associated with dermatomyositis, J.A.M.A., **150:**844, 1952.

238. CURTIS, A. C.; HECKAMAN, J. H.; and WHEELER, A. H. Study of the autoimmune reaction in dermatomyositis, J.A.M.A., **178:**571, 1961.

239. CUSHING, H. Hyperactivation of the neurohypophysis as the pathological basis of eclampsia and other hypertensive states, Am. J. Path., **10:**145, 1934.

240. DAHL, L. K. The stages in calcification of the rat kidney after the administration of uranium nitrate, J. Exper. Med., **97:**681, 1953.

241. DAHLENBURG, A. Sklerodermieartige Infiltrate nach Kampferinjektionen, Dermat. Wchnsch., **110–111:**440, 1940.

242. DALY, D. Central nervous system in acute disseminate lupus erythematosus, J. Nerv. & Ment. Dis., **102:**461, 1945.

243. DANBOLT, N. Kasuistischer Beitrag zur Frage Psoriasis pustulosa-Impetigo herpetiformis, Acta dermat.-venereol., **18:**150, 1937.

244. DANISCH, F. Impetigo herpetiformis bei post-operativer Tetanie und parathyreoipriver Kachexie. Ein Beitrag zur Kenntnis des Verhaltens der inkretorischen Organe und des sympathischen Nervensystems bei Epithelkörpercheninsuffizienz, Frankf. Ztschr. Path., **38:**290, 1929.

245. Danowski, T. S. Electrolyte and endocrine studies in muscular dystrophy, Am. J. Phys. Med., **34**:281, 1955.

246. Davidson, C. N.; Dennis, J. M.; McNinch, E. R.; Willson, J. K. V.; and Brown, W. H. Nephrocalcinosis associated with sarcoidosis, Radiology, **62**:203, 1954.

247. Davis, A. E. Relationship of disturbed pancreatic function to haemosiderosis, Lancet, Sept. 30: 749, 1961.

248. Davis, A. H., and Warren, S. Calcification of the skin in diabetes mellitus, Arch. Path., **16**:852, 1933.

249. Davis, E., and Brain, R. T. Sclerema neonatorum, Brit. J. Dermat., **59**:312, 1947.

250. Davis, H. Case of Raynaud's disease associated with calcareous degeneration, Proc. Roy. Soc. Med., (Dermat. Sect.) **5**:99, 1912.

251. Davis, H., and Moe, P. J. Favorable response of calcinosis universalis to edathamil disodium, Pediatrics, **24**:780, 1959.

252. Davison, C. Dermatomyositis: A clinicopathologic study; report of a case with complete necropsy, Arch. Dermat. & Syph., **19**:255, 1929.

253. Degrell, I., and Sinkó, O. Ein Fall von Lipocalcinogranulomatosis, Zentralbl. Chir., **86**:1326, 1961.

254. Demel, V. C. Di un caso di sclerema dei neonati a forma polimiositica, Arch. ital. dermat. e sifil., **4**:81, 1928.

255. Dennis, E. W.; Goble, F. C.; Berberian, D. A.; and Frelih, E. J. Experimental tuberculosis of the Syrian hamster (Cricetus auratus), Ann. New York Acad. Sc., **52**:646, 1949.

256. Dent, C. E.; Flynn, F. V.; and Nabarro, J. D. N. Hypercalcaemia and impairment of renal function in generalized sarcoidosis, Brit. M. J., Oct. 10: 808, 1953.

257. Depalma, A. F. Surgery of the Shoulder. Philadelphia: J. B. Lippincott Co., 1950.

258. Dercum, F. X. Scleroderma, J. Nerv. & Ment. Dis., **21**:431, 1896.

259. Dercum, F. X. On scleroderma and chronic rheumatoid arthritis, J. Nerv. & Ment. Dis., **25**:703, 1898.

260. Deringer, M. K., and Dunn, T. B. Mast-cell neoplasia in mice, J. Nat. Cancer Inst., **7**:289, 1947.

260a. Dieudonné, J.-M., and Selye, H. Unpublished.

261. Diss, and Woringer, F. Les fausses sclérodermies du nourrisson, Bull. Soc. franç. dermat. et syph., **36**:960, 1929.

262. Dobrev, D. Our experience in the complex treatment of scleroderma with penicillin, vitamin E and placental extract, Sbornik trudove Naucizsled kozno-venerol. Inst. M.N.Z.S.G., **6**:17, 1960.

263. Dobriner, E. Collection of urine. *In* Conference on metabolic aspects of convalescence including bone and wound healing. 10th Meet., New York, June 15, 16: Ed. C. Reifenstein, Jr., 1945.

264. Dobrzaniecki, M. W. Sur un cas de myosite ossifiante progressive, Bull. mém. Soc. anat. chir., **61**:1333, 1935.

265. Doessekker, K. Beitrag zur Kenntnis der Kalkablagerungen, mit spezieller Berücksichtigung der sog. verkalkten Epitheliome der Haut, Arch. Dermat. u. Syph., **129**:260, 1921.

266. Domenech, A. L. Forma localizada de colagenosis, Rev. confed. med. panamer., 4:99, 1957.

267. Donoghue, F. E. Esophageal involvement in diffuse scleroderma, Proc. Staff Meet. Mayo Clin., 34:75, 1959.

268. Dörfell. Kalkeinlagerungen im Gewebe nach Frostschäden, Zentralbl. Haut-u. Geschlechtsk., 25:62, 1928.

269. Dörken, H. Beobachtungen bei progressiver Sklerodermie. (Ösophagusveränderungen–Katarakt—Tod an Karzinom), Radiol. clin., 24:156, 1955.

270. Dornhorst, A. C.; Pierce, J. W.; and Whimster, I. W. The oesophageal lesion in scleroderma, Lancet, April 3: 698, 1954.

271. Dost, F. H. Die Behandlung einer kindlichen genuinen Polymyositis (Dermatomyositis) mit Penicillin, Arch. Kinderh., 140:183, 1950.

272. Dostrovsky, A. Progressive scleroderma of the skin with cystic sclerodermal changes of the lungs, Arch. Dermat. & Syph., 55:1, 1947.

273. Dostrovsky, A., and Sagher, F. Dermatomyositis and malignant tumour, Brit. J. Dermat., 58:52, 1946.

274. Douglas, A. H., and Randel, W. H., Jr. A case of scleroderma and calcinosis circumscripta, New York, J. Med., 53:87, 1953.

275. Douglas, W. W., and Rubin, R. P. The role of calcium in the secretory response of the adrenal medulla to acetylcholine, J. Physiol., 159:40, 1961.

276. Dowling, G. B. Generalized sclerodermia, Brit. J. Dermat., 52:242, 1940.

277. Dowling, G. B. Scleroderma and dermatomyositis, Brit. J. Dermat., 67:275, 1955.

278. Dowling, G. B., and Griffiths, W. J. Dermatomyositis and progressive scleroderma, Lancet, June 24: 1424, 1939.

279. Dreskin, E. A., and Fox, T. A. Adult renal osteitis fibrosa with metastatic calcification and hyperplasia of one parathyroid gland. Report of a case, A.M.A. Arch. Int. Med., 86:533, 1950.

280. Drucker, W. D.; Longo, F. W.; and Christy, N. P. Calcification in a benign, non-functioning tumor of the adrenal, J.A.M.A., 177:577, 1961.

281. Ducasse, R. R. Calcification of the skin with unusual findings, Arch. Dermat. & Syph., 7:373, 1923.

282. Duffy, D. G., and Bardsley, A. Diffuse scleroderma with report of a case showing multiple lesions, M.J. Australia, June 16: 864, 1951.

283. Duken, J. Myositis ossificans circumscripta als Folge intramuskulärer Injektion von Blut bei Kindern, Ztschr. Kinderh., 52:528, 1931–32.

284. Duperrat, B., Guilaine, and Laugier. Sclérodermie post-traumatique locorégionale, Bull. Soc. franç. dermat. et syph., 66:692, 1959.

285. Durham, R. H. Scleroderma and calcinosis, Arch. Int. Med., 42:467, 1928.

286. Dux, K., and Czarnomska, A. Influence of oestrogens on alkaline phosphatase activity in autotransplants of vaginal epithelium, Folia biol., 8:283, 1960.

287. East, T., and Oram, S. The heart in scleroderma, Brit. Heart J., 9:167, 1947.

288. Eban, R. Idiopathic hypercalcaemia of infancy, Clin. Radiol., 12:31, 1961.

289. Edholm, O. G.; Howarth, S.; and McMichael, J. Heart failure and bone blood flow in osteitis deformans, Clin. Sc., 5:249, 1945.

290. EDSTRÖM, G. Osteopoikilie und Sklerodermie bei einem Fall von Polyarthritis rheumatica chronica, Acta chir. scandinav., **87**:117, 1942.

291. EHRENBERG, G. Beteiligung des Urogenitalapparates bei einem Fall von Sklerodermie, Berl. klin. Wchnschr., **48**:1382, 1911.

292. EHRLICH, S. Eisen- und Kalkimprägnation in menschlichen Geweben, insbesondere den elastischen Fasern, Zentralbl. allg. Path. u. path. Anat., **17**:177, 1906.

293. ELLER, J. J. Scleroderma; sclerodactylia (acrosclerosis?), Arch. Dermat. u. Syph., **37**:1076, 1938.

294. ELLER, J. J. Scleroderma over the right pectoralis muscle, associated with calcification of the right subdeltoid bursa, Arch. Dermat. & Syph., **92**:688, 1940.

295. ELLIS, J. T. Degeneration and regeneration in the muscles of cortisone-treated rabbits, Am. J. Phys. Med., **34**:240, 1955.

296. ELLIS, J. T., and BARR, D. P. Metastasizing carcinoma of the parathyroid gland with osteitis fibrosa cystica and extensive calcinosis, Am. J. Path., **27**:383, 1951.

297. ELLIS, M. M., and EYSTER, W. H. Some effects of insulin and glucokinin on maize seedlings, Science, **58**:541, 1923.

298. ELLISON, D. J., and PUGH, D. W. Werner's syndrome, Brit. M.J., July 23: 237, 1955.

299. ELLMAN, P., and PARKES WEBER, F. A case of juvenile rheumatoid arthritis with sclerodactylia and calcinosis, Ann. Rheumat. Dis., **7**:231, 1948.

300. EMERSON, K., JR.; WALSH, F. B.; and HOWARD, J. E. Idiopathic hypoparathyroidism; a report of 2 cases, Ann. Int. Med., **14**:1256, 1941.

301. ENGEL, M. B. Mobilization of mucoprotein by parathyroid extract, A.M.A. Arch. Path., **53**:339, 1952.

302. ENGFELDT, B., and GENTELE, H. On impetigo herpetiformis and its connection with parathyroprival tetany, Acta dermat.-venereol., **30**:50, 1950.

303. ENGLE, R. L., JR. The association of iron-containing crystals with Schaumann bodies in the giant cells of granulomas of sarcoid type, Am. J. Path., **27**:1023, 1951.

304. ENTICKNAP, J. B. The kidney of scleroderma, Lancet, Feb. 9: 316, 1952.

305. EPSTEIN, E. Idiopathic calcinosis cutis, Arch. Dermat. & Syph., **34**:367, 1936.

306. EPSTEIN, N. N. Scleredema adultorum (Buschke), J.A.M.A., **99**:820, 1932.

307. ERB, K. Zur Klinik und Ätiologie der Kalkgicht, Deutsche Ztschr. Chir., **230**:316, 1931.

308. ERCOLI, G., and LEPRI, G. Dacryosialoadenopathia atrophicans and sclerodermia, Ophthalmologica, **124**:129, 1952.

309. ESCUDERO, J., and McDEVITT, E. The electrocardiogram in scleroderma: Analysis of 60 cases and review of the literature. Am. Heart J., **56**:846, 1958.

310. FALCK, I. Die Beteiligung der inneren Organe bei der Sklerodermie, Ztschr. ges. inn. Med., **10**:1037, 1955.

311. FATHERREE, T. J., and HURST, C. Thromboangiitis obliterans and acrosclerosis. Case report, Northwest. Med., **40**:200, 1941.

312. FAWCETT, DON W. An experimental study of mast-cell degranulation and regeneration, Anat. Rec., **121**:29, 1955.

313. FEARNSIDES, E. G. Sclerodermia with subcutaneous calcareous concretions, Proc. Roy. Soc. Med. (Neurol. Sect.), **9**:73, 1916.

314. FELIX, H.; PRIEUR, F.; LABROUSSE, C.; MAS, J. P.; and LESCURE, J. Le syndrome oculo-urétro-synovial de Fiessinger-Leroy-Reiter. A propos de 80 observations vues au stade précoce, Semaine hôp. Paris, **37**:1691, 1961.

315. FERRIMAN, D. G. Hypoparathyroidism complicated by impetigo herpetiformis, Proc. Roy. Soc. Med., **46**:305, 1953.

316. FEUER, S. G., and FLIEGEL, O. Acute soft tissue calcinosis, Arch. Phys. Med. & Rehabilit., **42**:492, 1961.

317. FIEDLER, E. Ueber einen Fall von chronischer Polymyositis mit hochgradiger Eosinophilie und periodisch wiederkehrenden fieberhaften Exazerbationen, München. med. Wchnschr., **78**:1176, 1931.

318. FINDLAY, G. H.; PRICE, E. A.; and RENSBURG, C. R. J. VAN. Dermatomyositis with vesicular and bullous lesions, South African M.J., **25**:60, 1951.

319. FINDŎ, B., and MEITNER, E. R. Beitrag zur Frage der diffusen interstitiellen Lungenfibrose (Hamman-Rich-Syndrom), Ztschr. Aerztl. Forbild., **55**:784, 1961.

320. FINK, W. J., and FINFROCK, J. D. Fatal hyperparathyroid crisis associated with pancreatitis, Am. Surgeon, **27**:424, 1961.

321. FISCHER, W. Über eine dem Lichen sclerosus (Hallopeau) angenäherte Form der zirkumskripten Sklerodermie, Arch. Dermat. u. Syph., **110**:159, 1911.

322. FISCHL, R. Sur quelques affections du premier âge s'accompagnant d'induration cutanée, Rev. franç. pédiat., **7**:401, 1931.

323. FISHER, E. R., and RODNAN, G. P. Pathologic observations concerning the cutaneous lesion of progressive systemic sclerosis: An electron microscopic histochemical and immunohistochemical study, Arthritis & Rheumat., **3**:536, 1960.

324. FLIEGEL, O. Knochenveränderungen bei Neurofibromatose, Deutsche Ztschr. Chir., **193**:359, 1925.

325. FLORY, C. M. Fat necrosis of the newborn. Report of a case with necrosis of the subcutaneous and visceral fat, Arch. Path., **45**:278, 1948.

326. FOCK, H. Ein Fall von Kalkablagerungen unter der Haut oder sog. Kalkgicht, Acta med. scandinav., **65**:169, 1926–27.

327. FOLLET, M., and SACQUEPEE, M. A propos du procès-verbal Syndrome de Raynaud-Tétanie-Sclérodermie, Bull. Soc. méd. hôp. Paris, **19**:585, 1902.

328. FOLK, M. R. Band keratopathy associated with renal disease, Am. J. Ophth., **39**: 878, 1955.

329. FONTAINE, R. Les opérations endocrino-sympathiques peuvent-elles arrêter l'échéance fatale des formes suraiguës, généralisées de la sclérodermie? Ann. endocrinol., **5**:8, 1944.

330. FONTAINE, R., and ANDRADA, J. G. Reflexiones sobre la enfermedad de Raynaud y su tratamiento quirurgico, Prensa méd. argent., **45**:3269, 1958.

331. FONTAINE, R., and BRANZEU, P. L'ostéogénèse dans les artérites oblitérantes. Contribution à l'étude des ossifications hétérotopiques, Ann. anat. path., **16**:813, 1939.

332. FONTAINE, R.; MANDEL, P.; WITZ, J.; and OSTERTAG, Y. Contribution à l'étude clinique et biochimique des calcifications tissulaires et des ossifications hétérotopiques, Rev. orthop., **36**:3, 1950.

333. FONTAINE, R., and PILLA, P. Réflexions à propos de 39 interventions sur le thymus et les parathyroïdes, Ann. endocrinol., **7**:71, 1946.

334. FORMAN, L. Dermatomyositis in a patient with a past history of carcinoma of the ovaries. Proc. Roy. Soc. Med., **44**:880, 1951.

335. FORMAN, L. The skin manifestations of malignant disease with special reference to vascular changes and dermatomyositis, Brit. M.J., Oct. 25: 911, 1952.

336. FORSTER, E., and LEVY, F. Kyste sébacé de la joue calcifié avec ossification vraie, Rev. chir., **57**:788, 1938.

337. FOURMAN, J. Nephrocalcinosis in the rat: Effect of injecting chondroitin sulphate, Brit. J. Exper. Path., **41**:536, 1960.

338. FOX, H. Diffuse scleroderma, Arch. Dermat. & Syph., **2**:265, 1920.

339. FOX, H. Scleroderma with ulcers and calcareous deposits, Arch. Dermat. & Syph., **21**:153, 1930.

340. FOX, H. Generalized, progressive scleroderma associated with changes in the lungs, the larynx and the esophagus, Arch. Dermat. & Syph., **55**:269, 1947.

341. FOX, R. A. Disseminated lupus erythematosus—an allergic disease? A.M.A. Arch. Path., **36**:311, 1943.

342. FRAENKEL, E. Ueber Verkalkung und Verknöcherung der Ohrenmuschel, Fortschr. Geb. Röntgenstrahlen, **27**:253, 1919–21.

343. FRANCESCHETTI, A., and MAEDER, G. Cataracte et affections cutanées du type poikilodermie (syndrome de Rothmund) et du type sclérodermie (syndrome de Werner), Schweiz. med. Wchnschr., **79**:657, 1949.

344. FRANK, L. J. Scleredema adultorum (Buschke). Report of case involving the tongue, Arch. Dermat. & Syph., **36**:1052, 1937.

345. FRANK, L. J. A case for diagnosis (generalized progressive scleroderma?), Arch. Dermat. & Syph., **49**:210, 1944.

346. FREEMAN, S.; RHOADS, P. S.; and YEAGER, L. B. Toxic manifestations associated with prolonged Ertron ingestion, J.A.M.A., **130**:197, 1946.

347. FRENKEL, J. K. Hormonal effects on a sarcoid-like response with Schaumann bodies and amyloid in golden hamsters infected with photochromogenic mycobacteria, Am. J. Path., **34**:586, 1958.

348. FREUDENTHAL, W. Generalized scleroderma and dermatomyositis. A histological comparison, Brit. J. Dermat., **52**:289, 1940.

349. FREUND, H. Ueber Sklerödem (Buschke). Unter besonderer Berücksichtigung der Histologie, Arch. Dermat. u. Syph., **161**:92, 1930.

350. FREUND, H. Histologische Befunde bei Sklerödem (Buschke) (Demonstration), Zentralbl. Haut- u. Geschlechtsk., **33**:303, 1930.

351. FREYBERG, R. H., and GRANT, R. L. Calcium and phosphorus metabolism in a verified case of pituitary basophilism, Arch. Int. Med., **58**:213, 1936.

352. FRIEDEN, E. H.; STONE, N. R.; and LAYMAN, N. W. Nonsteroid ovarian hormones. III. The properties of relaxin preparations purified by counter-current distribution, J. Biol. Chem., **235**:2267, 1960.

353. FRIEDLÄNDER, J. Untersuchungen des Gesamtmineralwechsels bei Calcinosis universalis, Deutsches Arch. klin. Med., **166**:107, 1930.

354. FRIEDMANN, M. Ein Fall von Impetigo herpetiformis, Arch. Dermat. u. Syph., **165**:457, 1932.

355. FROBOESE, C. Ein neuer Fall von multiplem Myelom (Erythroblastom) mit Kalk-metastasen in Lungen, Nieren und der Uterusschleimhaut, Virchows Arch. path. Anat., **222**:291, 1916.

356. FROST, J. W.; SUNDERMAN, F. W.; and LEOPOLD, I. S. Prolonged hypercalcemia and metastatic calcification of the sclera following the use of vitamin D in the treatment of rheumatoid arthritis, Am. J. M. Sc., **214**:639, 1947.

357. FUKUDA, T.; KUSUNOKI, T.; and KUWABARA, S. Sclérodermie généralisée avec leu-cémie, traitée par parathyro¨dectomie, amélioration, Sang, **12**:445, 1938.

358. FURCOLOW, M. L. Tuberculin negative, histoplasmin positive, disseminated pulmonary calcification, Postgrad. Med., **8**:15, 1950.

359. FURTH, J.; HAGEN, P.; and HIRSCH, E. I. Transplantable mastocytoma in the mouse containing histamine, heparin, 5-hydroxytryptamine, Proc. Soc. Exper. Biol. & Med., **95**:824, 1957.

360. GALBRAITH, D. Collagen disease, M.J. Australia, Dec. 29: 964, 1956.

361. GAMNA, C. Un nuovo argomento per la discussione sulla natura delle lesioni sclero-siderotiche delle splenomegalie croniche, Minerva med., **9**:591, 1929.

362. GARCIN, R.; BERTRAND, I.; LAUDAT, M.; and CACHIN, C. Concrétions calcaires sous-cutanées des doigts associées à un syndrome de Raynaud avec sclérodactylie. Telangiectasies disséminées, Bull. mém. Soc. méd. hôp. Paris, **2**:1036, 1931.

363. GARDIKAS, C., and HADJIOANNOU, J. A case of extensive interstitial calcinosis, Brit. M.J., Nov. 4: 1196, 1961.

364. GARDINER, M. R. Metastatic calcification associated with white muscle disease in lambs, J. Am. Vet. M. A., **138**:553, 1961.

365. GÄRDLUND, W. Studien über Kraurosis vulvae unter besonderer Berücksichtigung ihrer Pathogenese und Aetiologie, Arch. Gynäk., **105**:317, 1916.

366. GARDNER, D. L., and ROY, L. M. H. Tissue iron and the reticuloendothelial system in rheumatoid arthritis, Ann. Rheumat. Dis., **20**:258, 1961.

367. GARDNER, L. I., and TICE, A. A. Histamine and related compounds in urticaria pigmentosa: Analyses of tissues having mast-cell infiltration, Pediatrics, **21**:805, 1958.

368. GARFIELD. Scleroderma, Arch. Dermat. & Syph., **14**:343, 1926.

369. GARLOCK, J. H. Parathyroidectomy for Raynaud's disease and scleroderma, Surg. Clin. North America, **16**:771, 1936.

370. GARRAHAN, J. P., and BORDA, J. M. Esclerodermia en la infancia. A proposito de tres observaciones, Bol. Acad. nac. med. Buenos Aires, **1**:37, 1945.

371. GARRAHAN, J. P.; LASCANO GONZÁLEZ, J. C.; GAMBIRASSI, A.; and MAGALHAES, A. Sobre el granuloma eosinofilo y la enfermedad de Hand-Schuller-Christian, Bol. Acad. nac. med. Buenos Aires, **1**:13, 1945.

372. GAVILANES, C. R., and PLEGUEZUELO, M. M. Patologia constitucional en gran canaria (III). Consideraciones etiopatogenicas y de tratamiento sobre un caso de dermatomiositis con calcinosis, Rev. clin. españ., **33**:177, 1949.

373. GEBAUER, A., and HALTER, K. Röntgenologische und endoskopische Studien bei progressiver Sklerodermie, Arch. Dermat. u. Syph., **186**:283, 1946–48.

374. GELBKE, H., and HERZOG, W. Beitrag zur experimentellen heterotopen Knochenbildung in der Muskulatur beim Hund, Zentralbl. allg. Path. u. path. Anat., **87**: 167, 1951.

375. GENNES, L. DE; MOREAU, L.; BRICAIRE, H.; and TOURNEUR, R. A propos d'un cas de sclérodermie avec lésions rénales, Bull. mém. Soc. méd. hôp. Paris, **73**:829, 1957.

376. GENTELE, H.; LODIN, A.; and ODQVIST-NIORDSON, A. M. Impetigo herpetiformis in conjunction with parathyroprival tetany, Acta dermat.-venereol., **37**:387, 1957.

377. GERLOCZY, F. Pathological role of d, 1α-tocopherol in premature newborn, Experientia, **5**:252, 1949.

378. GETZOWA, S. Cystic and compact pulmonary sclerosis in progressive scleroderma, Arch. Path., **40**:99, 1945.

379. GIERKE, E. VON. Ueber den Eisengehalt verkalkter Gewebe unter normalen und pathologischen Bedingungen, Arch. path. Anat. u. Physiol., **167**:318, 1902.

380. GILBERT, A., and POLLET, L. Présentation de malade. Un nouveau cas de concrétions phosphatées calcaires sous-cutanées, Bull. mém. Soc. méd. hôp. Paris, **49**: 957, 1925.

381. GIRAUD, P.; BERNARD, R.; LAVAL, P.; and SANSOT, M. Considérations sur la pathogénie de la myosite ossifiante. A propos d'un cas avec examen anatomique de tous les organes, Semaine hôp. Paris, **23**:617, 1947.

382. GJØRUP, S. Metastatic calcification in a patient with salt-losing nephritis, Danish Med. Bull., **3**:82, 1956.

383. GLÜCK, A. Dermatitis atrophicans reticularis (Poikilodermia atrophicans vascularis Jacobi) mit mucinöser Degeneration der kollagenen Fasern, Arch. Dermat. u. Syph., **118**:113, 1913.

384. GOETZ, R. H. The pathology of progressive systemic sclerosis (generalised scleroderma), Clin. Proc., **4**:337, 1945.

385. GOETZ, R. H. The heart in generalised scleroderma. Progressive systemic sclerosis, Angiology, **2**:555, 1951.

386. GOLDMAN, I. R.; YOUNG, J. M.; and KNOX, F. H. Myocardial involvement in generalized scleroderma, Dis. Chest, **25**:94, 1954.

387. GONDOS, B. Roentgen manifestations in progressive systemic sclerosis (diffuse scleroderma), Am. J. Roentgenol., **84**:235, 1960.

388. GOODMAN, H. A case of scleroderma diffusa in a girl nine years of age, J. Cut. Dis., **36**:210, 1918.

389. GORDON, H. Diffuse scleroderma with case report and autopsy findings, Ann. Int. Med., **2**:1309, 1928–29.

390. GOTO, S. Pathologisch- anatomische und klinische Studien über die sogenannte Myositis ossificans progressiva multiplex. (Hyperplasia fascialis ossificans progressiva), Arch. klin. Chir., **100**:730, 1912–13.

391. GOTO, S. Zur Kenntnis der sogenannten Myositis ossificans, Arch. klin. Chir., **187**: 781, 1937.

392. Gottron, H. A. Skleromyxödem. (Eine eigenartige Erscheinungsform von Myxo-thesaurodermie), Arch. Dermat. u. Syph., **199**:71, 1954.

393. Gottron, H. A., and Korting, G. W. Ueber Ablagerung körpereigener Stoffe (Amyloidosis, Calcinosis) bei Morbus Osler, Arch. klin. u. exper. Dermat., **207**: 177, 1958.

394. Gottsegen, G., and Romoda, T. Zur Kenntnis der Sklerodermischen Herzerkrankung, Ztschr. ges. inn. Med., **11**:134, 1956.

395. Gougerot, H. Encore un cas de coexistence d'une sclérodermie en plaque ou lichen porcelainé et de lichen lingual, Bull. Soc. franç. dermat. et syph., **47**:302, 1940.

396. Gougerot, H. Bord des sclérodermies (en plaques ou en gouttes) et du lichen albus: la licheno-sclérodermie, Bull. Soc. franç. dermat. et syph., **47**:303, 1940.

397. Gould, Adiponecrosis neonatorum, Blakiston's New Gould Medical Dictionary, p. 29, 2d ed., 1956.

398. Gounelle, H., and Rouquette, J.-P. Retentissement de la réaction inflammatoire et nécrotique sur le métabolisme calcique et la teneur tissulaire en calcium, Soc. biol. Séance 25 fév. 1961. Compt. rend. Soc. biol., **155**:304, 1961.

399. Graciansky, P. de. Deux formes de la dermatomyosite, Semaine hôp. Paris, **25**: 1406, 1949.

400. Grant, R. A.; Hathorn, M.; and Gillman, T. The inhibitory effect of 2:4-dini-trophenol on metastatic tissue calcification induced by calciferol, Biochem. J., **81**: 352, 1961.

401. Grasso, S., and Selye, H. Calciphylaxis in relation to the humoral production of occlusive coronary lesions with infarction, J. Path. & Bact. (in press).

402. Gray, A. M. H. On the identity of adiponecrosis subcutanea neonatorum with sclerema neonatorum, Brit. J. Dermat., **45**:498, 1933.

403. Greco, N. V., and Capurro, J. Esclerodermia y epidermolisis ampollosa distrofica con hematoporfirinuria, Rev. Asoc. med. argent., **53**:60, 1939.

404. Green, D. M.; Saunders, F. J.; Wahlgren, N.; and Craig, R. L. Self-sustaining, post-DCA hypertensive cardiovascular disease, Am. J. Physiol., **170**:94, 1952.

405. Grenaud, M., and Lescœur, L. Contribution à l'étude d'un cas de concrétions calcaires sous-cutanées chez une fillette, Monde méd., **42**:114, 1932.

406. Gretton-Watson, E. P. Dermatomyositis: Report of an acute case with commentary, Brit. J. Dermat., **49**:272, 1937.

407. Grosse, H. Über zwei Fälle von Kalkmetastase bei Leukämie, Zentralbl. allg. Path. u. path. Anat., **100**:187, 1959.

408. Grütz, O. Sclerodermia guttata follicularis mit halbseitiger Gesichts- und Körpera-trophie und endokrinen Krankheitssymptomen, Dermat. Ztschr., **53**:227, 1928.

409. Grzybowski, M. Zur Kenntnis der Dermatomyositis, Arch. Dermat. u. Syph., **174**:541, 1936.

410. Guerricchio, A. Sopra un caso di degenerazione genitosclerodermica (contributo clinico allo studio delle sindromi pluriglandolari), Policlinico (sez. prat.), **30**:970, 1923.

411. Gugliucci, A. Sondaggio del sistema neurovegetativo e ricambio del calcio in un caso di polimiosite ossificante progressiva, Morgagni, **77**:1243, 1935.

412. GUSEVA, N. G. Cardiac lesions in systemic scleroderma (Russian text), Terap. arkh., **32**:30, 1960.

413. GUSS, J. H. Scleroderma with unusual central nervous system manifestations, Virginia M. Monthly, **74**:454, 1947.

414. HAENSCH, R. Sarkombildung bei einer Sclerodermia progressiva, Hautarzt, **2**:129, 1951.

415. HAINAUT, J.; MUSIN, L.; and DRUEZ, G. Syndrome de Thibierge-Weissenbach dans un cas de lupus érythémateux, Acta clin. belg., **14**:608, 1959.

416. HALLOPEAU and TRASTOUR. Sur un lupus érythémateux développé dans le cours d'une sclérodermie avec asphyxie locale des extrémités et gangrène des phalanges chez une tuberculeuse, Ann. dermat. et syph., **1**:634, 1900.

417. HALTER, K. Hautveränderungen unter dem Bilde der progressiven Sklerodermie, entstanden im Gefolge peripherer Nervenverletzungen, Dermat. Wchnschr., **109**:1139, 1939.

418. HAMMAN, L., and RICH, A. R. Acute diffuse interstitial fibrosis of the lungs, Bull. Johns Hopkins Hosp., **74**:177, 1944.

419. HANNIGAN, C. A.; HANNIGAN, M. H.; and SCOTT, E. L. Scleroderma of the kidneys, Am. J. Med., **20**:793, 1956.

419a. HARBITZ, F. Extensive calcification of the lungs as a distinct disease, Arch. Int. Med., **21**:139, 1918.

420. HARRELL, G. T., and FISHER, S. Blood chemical changes in Boeck's sarcoid with particular reference to protein, calcium and phosphatase values, J. Clin. Invest., **18**:687, 1939.

421. HARRINGTON, A. B., and DEWAR, H. A. A case of Sjögren's disease with scleroderma, Brit. M.J., June 9: 1302, 1951.

422. HARVEY, A. M., and SHULMAN, L. E. Dermatomyositis. *In* Arthritis and Allied Conditions, p. 776. 6th ed. Philadelphia: Lea & Febiger. 1960.

423. HARVIER, P., and BONDUELLE, M. Sclérodermie progressive avec calcification hépato-splénique, Presse méd., **55**:369, 1947.

424. HATHERLEY, E. Uveitis and band-shaped keratitis in a case of Still's disease, Proc. Roy. Soc. Med., **44**:978, 1951.

425. HAUSER, H. Hautwucherungen mit basophil granulierten Zellen beim Hund, Experientia, **4**:197, 1948.

426. HAUSMANN, E. A revaluation of the effect of parathyroid hormone on mucopolysaccharide metabolism, Endocrinology, **68**:722, 1961.

427. HAUSMANOWA-PETRUSEWICZ, I., and KOZMINSKA, A. Electromyographic findings in scleroderma, Arch. neurol., **4**:281, 1961.

428. HAVARD, C. W. H. Hyperparathyroidism, Proc. Roy. Soc. Med., **52**:1049, 1959.

429. HAVERBACK, B. J.; DYCE, B.; BUNDY, H.; and EDMONDSON, H. A. Trypsin, trypsinogen and trypsin inhibitor in human pancreatic juice, Am. J. Med., **29**:424, 1960.

430. HAXTHAUSEN, H. Studies on the pathogenesis of morphea, vitiligo and acrodermatitis atrophicans by means of transplantation experiments, Acta dermat.-venereol., **27**:352, 1947.

431. HAYMAN, L. D., and HUNT, R. E. Pulmonary fibrosis in generalized scleroderma. Report of a case and review of the literature, Dis. Chest, **21**:691, 1952.

432. HECHT, M. S. Dermatomyositis in childhood, J. Pediat., **17**:791, 1940.

433. HECKSCHER, H. To tilfaelde af akut myositis. Dermatomyositis. Dermatomyositis haemorrhagica, Ugesk. laeger, **87**:147, 1925.

434. HEGGLIN, R. Die viszeralen Erscheinungen der Kollagenosen, Ztschr. Rheumaforsch, **20**:99, 1961.

435. HEILMEYER, L., and WÖHLER, F. Die Speicherung von Eisen im Entzundungsgebiet. Ergebnisse tierexperimenteller Untersuchungen, Deutsche med. Wchnschr., **86**:1581, 1961.

436. HEINE, J. Ueber ein eigenartiges Krankheitsbild von diffuser Sklerosis der Haut und innerer Organe, Virchows Arch. path. Anat., **262**:351, 1926.

437. HEKTOEN, L. Diffuse scleroderma associated with chronic fibrous changes in the thyroid and great diminution in the amount of thyroidin: Increase in the chromophile cells and of the colloid in the hypophysis, J.A.M.A., **28**:1240, 1897.

438. HELFERICH, H. Ein Fall von sogenannter Myositis ossificans progressiva, Aertzl. Intelligenz.-bl., **26**:485, 1879.

439. HELLER, A. Ein Fall von Sklerodermie als Beitrag zur Pathologie des Lymphgefässsystems, Deutsches Arch. klin. Med., **10**:141, 1872.

440. HENDRIKSSON, C. Acute hyperparathyroidism and acute pancreatitis, Acta path. microbiol. scandinav., **50**:42, 1960.

441. HENNEMAN, P. H.; CARROLL, E. L.; and DEMPSEY, E. F. The mechanism responsible for hypercalcuria in sarcoid, J. Clin. Invest., **33**:941, 1954.

442. HENNEMAN, P. H.; DEMPSEY, E. F.; CARROLL, E. L.; and ALBRIGHT, F. The cause of hypercalcuria in sarcoid and its treatment with cortisone and sodium phytate, J. Clin. Invest., **35**:1229, 1956.

443. HERBERT, F. K.; MILLER, H. G.; and RICHARDSON, G. O. Chronic renal disease, secondary parathyroid hyperplasia, decalcification of bone and metastatic calcification, J. Path. & Bact., **53**:161, 1941.

444. HERMETO, S., JR. Tratamento da esclerodermia pela paratireoidectomia. Rev. Assoc. paulista med., **15**:281, 1939.

445. HERMETO, S., JR. Os processos de reabsorpçao osseasignificaçao e consequencias cirurgicas, Rev. Assoc. paulista med., **16**:143, 1940.

446. HERMETO, S., JR. Hiperqueratose ictiosica generalizada. Paratireoidectomia, Sao Paulo med., **1**:325, 1945.

447. HERMETO, S., JR. Esclerodermia generalizada. Paratireoidectomia, Sao Paulo med., **1**:439, 1945.

448. HERSTONE, S. T., and BOWER, J. Werner's syndrome, Am. J. Roentgenol., **51**:639, 1944.

449. HERWIG, W. Beitrag zum Krankheitsbild der Myositis ossificans progressiva, Ztschr. Orthop., **88**:238, 1956.

450. HERXHEIMER, K., and SCHMIDT, W. Comments on the article, "A comparative study of acrodermatitis chronica atrophicans and diffuse scleroderma with associated morphoea atrophica" by F. P. Kanoky and R. L. Sutton, J. Cut. Dis., **29**:257, 1911.

451. HIGH, R. H. Calcifications in the spleen. Occurrence in histoplasmin and tuberculin reactors, Public Health Rep., **61**:1782, 1946.

451*a*. HILL, M., and POSPÍŠIL, M. The patterns of mucopolysaccharide secretion in mast cells in the course of stress, Acta histochem., **10**:109, 1960.

452. HISSARD, R.; MONCOURIER, L.; and JACQUET, J. Une nouvelle affection hémato-dermique, la mastocytose, Compt. rend. Acad. sc., **231**:253, 1950.

453. HOFBAUER, W. Sclerodermia diffusa, Sklerodaktylie mit Raynaud-artigen Erscheinungen und Schleimhautveränderungen, Wien. Dermat. Gesellsch. 25. Jan., 1940, Dermat. Wchnschr., **110–111**:800, 1940.

454. HOFF, F. Klinische und experimentelle Beiträge zur Frage des Kalkhaushaltes, Verhandl. Deutsch. Gesellsch. inn. Med., **46**:441, 1934.

455. HOFFMANN, E. Ueber Skleroedema (Skleremia) adultorum nach Grippe mit Veränderungen an den cutanen Nerven, Arch. Dermat. u. Syph., **145**:310, 1924.

456. HOFFMANN, E. Ueber Skleroedema (Skleremia) adultorum nach Grippe mit Gewebsveränderungen an den cutanen Nerven, Klin. Wchnschr. **2**:963, 1923.

457. HOFFMANN, E. Das Krankheitsbild des Skleroedema (Skleremia) adultorum (Buschke) (Ein neuer Fall nach Grippe), Med. Klin., **23**:392, 1927.

458. HOFMANN, H., and WHITE, P. D. Verkalkungen in Herzwandaneurysmen nach Myokardinfarkten, München. med. Wchnschr., **103**:1453, 1961.

459. HØJGAARD, K. Ikke- esterificerede fede syrer i plasma hos diabetikere og adiposi-taspatienter, Ugesk. laeger, **121**:875, 1959.

460. HOLDSWORTH, M. J., and HODGKINSON, A. The hexosamine content of the kidney in experimental renal calcification, Brit. J. Exper. Path., **42**:331, 1961.

461. HOLTEN, C., and LUNDBAEK, K. Renal insufficiency and severe calcinosis due to excessive alkali-intake, Acta med. scandinav., **151**:177, 1955.

462. HORWITZ, T. Dupuytren's contracture. Consideration of anatomy of fibrous structures of hand in relation to this condition with interpretation of histology, Arch. Surg., **44**:687, 1942.

463. HÖSLI, P. Die Behandlung der Sklerodermie mit dem di-Natriumsalz der Aethylen-Diamin-Tetraessigsäure; ein Beitrag zur Toxikologie der Versenate, 2. Mitteilung, Arzneimittel-Forsch., **10**:177, 1960.

463*a*. HOWARD, J. E. Clinical and laboratory research concerning mechanisms of formation and control of calculous disease by the kidney, J. Urol., **72**:999, 1954.

464. HUBBARD, R. S., and WENTWORTH, J. A. A case of metastatic calcification associated with chronic nephritis and hyperplasia of the parathyroids, Proc. Soc. Exper. Biol. & Med., **18**:307, 1921.

465. HUEBSCHMANN, P. Zur Histologie der Kalkmetastase, Zentralbl. allg. Path. u. path. Anat., **19**:737, 1908.

466. HUGHES, W. E., and HAMMOND, M. L. Sclerema neonatorum, J. Pediat., **32**:676, 1948.

467. HUMMEL, B. Erfahrungen über den Heilfaktor AT 10 bei der Sklerodermie, München. med. Wchnschr., **86**:96, 1939.

468. HUNTER, W. K. Sclerodermia with subcutaneous calcareous deposits, Glasgow M.J., **79**:241, 1913.

469. Hyde, L., and Hyde, B. Toxicity of large doses of vitamin D (Ertron), Ann. Int. Med., **27**:617, 1947.

470. Ihrke, R. E. The collagen diseases. Differential diagnosis with special reference to the eye, ear, nose and throat, Eye, Ear, Nose and Throat Monthly, **31**:295, 1952.

471. Ikle, C. Zur Histologie und Pathogenese der Dupuytrenschen Kontraktur, Deutsche Ztschr. Chir., **212**:106, 1928.

472. Illig, R., and Fanconi, G. Ueber einen Fall von Sarcoidosis im Kindesalter mit ungewöhnlichen Haut- und Augenveränderungen sowie einer Calcium-stoffwechsel-störung, Helvet. paediat. acta., **16**:211, 1961.

473. Inclan, A. Tumoral calcinosis, J.A.M.A., **121**:490, 1943.

474. Inglis, K. The nature of neurofibromatosis and related lesions, with special reference to certain lesions of bones illustrating the influence of intrinsic factors in disease when development of the body is abnormal, J. Path. & Bact., **62**:519, 1950.

475. Ingram, M. D., Jr. Calcinosis in scleroderma, Am. J. Roentgenol., **68**:918, 1952.

476. Irby, E. C., and Freed, C. C., Jr. Postphlebitic subcutaneous calcinosis. A case report and review of the literature, Virginia M. Monthly, **87**:563, 1960.

477. Irwin, G. W., and Ward, P. B. Werner's syndrome with a report of two cases, Am. J. Med., **15**:266, 1953.

478. Ishii, T. Influence of valency of chemical elements in producing cutaneous calcinosis in dihydrotachysterol-pretreated rats, Exper. Med. & Surg. (in press).

479. Ishii, T.; Jean, P.; and Selye, H. Role of chemical elements in eliciting experimental cutaneous calcinosis following pretreatment with dihydrotachysterol, Tohoku J. Exper. Med., **74**:235, 1961.

480. Izarn, P.; Emberger, J.-M.; and Pourquier, H. Sarcoïdose avec cytostéatoné-crose sous-cutanée, Tr. Soc. sc. méd. et biol., Séance 18 déc. Montpellier., Montpellier méd., **58**:4, 1960.

481. Jablonska, S., and Bubnow, B. Lésions pseudo-sclérodermiques dans le rhumatisme, Ann. dermat. et syph., **87**:241, 1960.

482. Jablonska, S.; Lukasiak, B.; and Bubnow, B. Zusammenhang zwischen der Hemiatrophia faciei progressiva und der Sklerodermie, Hautarzt, **9**:9, 1958.

483. Jacobson, H. G.; Rifkin, H.; and Zucker-Franklin, D. Werner's Syndrome: A clinical-roentgen-entity, Radiology, **74**:373, 1960.

484. Jadassohn, J. Ueber "Kalkmetastasen" in der Haut, Arch. Dermat. u. Syph., **100**:317, 1910.

485. Jaffe, K. Zwei Fälle von Sklero-Poikilodermie, Arch. Dermat. u. Syph., **159**:257, 1929–30.

486. Jager, B. V., and Grossman, L. A. Dermatomyositis, Arch. Int. Med., **73**:271, 1944.

487. Janker, R. Die verästelten Knochenbildungen in der Lunge, Fortschr. Geb. Roentgenstrahlen, **53**:840, 1936.

488. Janker, R. Knotige Knochenbildungen der Lungen, Fortschr. Geb. Roentgenstrahlen, **53**:260, 1936.

489. Jansen, L. H.; Reyers, J. G. C.; and van Baak, J. Scleromyxoedema, Nederl. tijdschr. geneesk., **105**:407, 1961.

490. JARVIS, J. L.; JENKINS, D.; SOSMAN, M. C.; and THORN, G. W. Roentgenologic observations in Addison's disease: Review of 120 cases, Radiology, **62**:16, 1954.

491. JEAN, P. Calcinose cutanée expérimentale. Thesis, Université de Montréal, Montréal, Canada, 1961.

492. JEAN, P., and SELYE, H. Cutaneous calcinosis as elicited by dihydrotachysterol, Proc. 2d. Canad. Conf. Res. Rheumat. Dis. Oct. 28–29, Toronto, p. 203, 1960.

493. JEAN, P., and SELYE, H. Prevention by stress of a cutaneous calcinosis elicited by dihydrotachysterol, 45th. Annual Meet. Fed. Am. Soc. Exper. Biol., Atlantic City, New Jersey, April 10–15, 1961, Fed. Proc., **20**:194, 1961.

494. JEAN, P., and SELYE, H. Prevention by stress of a cutaneous calcinosis in adrenalectomized rats, IVth. Internat. Congr. Allergol., New York City, Oct. 15–20, 1961.

495. JEDLICKA, V. Sklerodermie und innere Sekretion, Ceska Dermat., **8**:57, 1927.

496. JESSNER, M., and LOEWENSTAMM, A. Bericht über 66 Fälle von Acrodermatitis chronica atrophicans, Dermat. Wchnschr., **79**:1169, 1924.

497. JOANNOVICS, G. Ein Fall von verkalktem und verknochertem Atherom, Zentralbl. allg. Path. u. path. Anat., **12**:883, 1901.

498. JOHN, F. Sklerodermie und vegetatives Terminalreticulum, Arch. Dermat. u. Syph., **188**:374, 1949–50.

499. JOHNSON, A. C. Disabling changes in the hands resembling sclerodactylia following myocardial infarction, Ann. Int. Med., **19**:433, 1943.

500. JOHNSTON, C. C., JR.; DEISS, W. P., JR.; and HOLMES, L. B. Effect of parathyroid extract on bone matrix hexosamine, Endocrinology, **68**:484, 1961.

501. JONDS, V. Association d'un goître basedowifié avec un syndrome parkinsonien et avec sclérodermie, Rev. neurol, **1**:750, 1932.

502. JOSEPHSON, B. M., and ORIATTI, M. D. Chondrodystrophia calcificans congenita. Report of a case and review of the literature, Pediatrics, **28**:425, 1961.

503. JUNG, A. Les syndromes parathyroïdiens (en particulier recherches sur la lithiase rénale, la sclérodermie et discussion de l'hyperparathyroïdie suraiguë, aiguë et chronique), Rev. chir. Paris, **56**:305, 1937.

504. JUNG, A. Du traitement chirurgical de la tétanie, Ann. endocrinol., **8**:286, 1947.

505. JUNG, A., and HAKKI, A. C. Études sur la calcémie. Cent dosages du calcium sérique dans divers états pathologiques: Affections osseuses et ostéo-articulaires, sclérodermie, rétraction de l'aponévrose palmaire, chéloïdes et autres, Rev. chir. Paris, **51**:537, 1932.

506. JUSTIN-BESANÇON, L.; LAMOTTE-BARRILLON, S.; LAMOTTE, M.; GRIVAUX, M.; and ROUX, C. Sarcoïdose, localisations osseuses, troubles du métabolisme phosphocalcique, Semaine hôp. Paris, **36**:745, 1960.

507. KANEE, B. Scleropoikiloderma with calcinosis cutis, Raynaud-like syndrome and atrophoderma, Arch. Dermat. & Syph., **50**:254, 1944.

508. KAPPAS, A.; MILHORAT, A. T.; RHOADS, C. P.; and GALLAGHER, T. F. A study of adrenocortical and testicular physiology in dystrophia myotonica. A preliminary report, Am. J. Phys. Med., **34**:303, 1955.

509. KAPPESSER, W. Skleroedema adultorum Buschke nach Trauma, Hautarzt, **7**:221, 1956.

510. KARANI, S. B. Polydermatomyositis haemorrhagica, Proc. Roy. Soc. Med., **44**:921, 1951.

511. KARELITZ, S., and WELT, S. K. Dermatomyositis, Am. J. Dis. Child, **43**:1134, 1932.

512. KATASE, A. Experimentelle Verkalkung am gesunden Tiere, Beitr. path. Anat. u. allg. Path., **57**:516, 1914.

513. KATTHAGEN, A. Das Krankheitsbild der Calcinosis und einer erstmalig beobachteten besonderen Verlaufsform, der Calcinosis segmentalis congenita, Ztschr. Orth., **78**:543, 1949.

514. KAUFMAN, P.; BECK, R. D.; and WISEMAN, R. D. Vitamin D ("Ertron") therapy in arthritis. Treatment followed by massive, metastatic calcification, renal damage and death, J.A.M.A., **134**:688, 1947.

515. KAUFMANN, E., and STAEMMLER, M. Lehrbuch der speziellen pathologischen Anatomie. Berlin: Walter de Gruyter & Co., **1**:1. Hälfte, 1955.

516. KEHL, K. C. Dupuytren's contracture as sequel to coronary artery disease and myocardial infarction, Ann. Int. Med., **19**:213, 1943.

517. KEIL, H. Dermatomyositis and systemic lupus erythematosus. I. A clinical report of "transitional" cases with a consideration of lead as a possible etiologic factor, Arch. Int. Med., **66**:109, 1940.

518. KEIL, H. Dermatomyositis and systemic lupus erythematosus. II. A comparative study of the essential clinicopathologic features, Arch. Int. Med., **66**:339, 1940.

519. KEIL, H. The manifestations in the skin and mucous membranes in dermatomyositis, with special reference to the differential diagnosis from systemic lupus erythematosus, Ann. Int. Med., **16**:828, 1942.

520. KEINING, E., and BRAUN-FALCO, O. Zur Klinik und Pathogenese des Skleromyxoedems, Acta dermat.-venereol., **36**:37, 1956.

521. KELLER, R. Zur Dermatomyositis im Kindesalter, Ztschr. Kinderh., **58**:551, 1936–37.

522. KELLOGG, F., and CUNHA, F. Dermatomyositis. Report of case associated with rheumatic heart disease, California & West. Med., **50**:337, 1939.

523. KENNEDY, R. L. J., Calcinosis: Presentation of a case, Proc. Staff Meet. Mayo Clin., **7**:329, 1932.

524. KERL, W. Beiträge zur Kenntnis der Verkalkungen der Haut, Arch. Dermat. u. Syph., **126**:172, 1919.

525. KETRON, L. W., and ELLIS, F. A. Kraurosis vulvae (leucoplacia) and scleroderma circumscripta. A comparative histological study, Surg. Gynec. & Obst., **61**:635, 1935.

526. KIBLER, R. F., and ROSE, F. C. Peripheral neuropathy in the "collagen diseases," Brit. M.J., June 11: 1781, 1960.

527. KIČIĆ, M.; MIĆIĆ, R.; and BRANKOVAN, K. Sklerodermska nefropatija, Vojnosanit. pregled., **14**:289, 1957.

528. KILBURN, P. Calcinosis (A review with reports of four cases), Postgrad. M. J., **33**:555, 1957.

529. KINNEY, T. D., and MAHER, M. M. Dermatomyositis. A study of five cases, Am. J. Path., **16**:561, 1940.

530. KIRCHER, W. Sklerödem (Buschke) bei einem Kleinkinde, Arch. Kinderh., **141**: 148, 1951.

531. KIRCHHOF, J. K. J., and KLINGMULLER, G. Bewegungsstörungen, Reflexverhalten, elektrische Befunde bei sklerodermischen und myositischen Prozessen, Nervenarzt, **31**:162, 1960.

532. KIRSCH, R. Vererbbare Verknöcherung der Ohrmuschel, Ztschr. Laryngol. Rhinol. Otol., **32**:729, 1953.

533. KISSEL, P.; ARNOULD, G.; and BASSOT, J. Sclérodermie d'origine nerveuse, encéphalitique, Bull. mém. Soc. méd. hôp. Paris, **66**:1490, 1950.

534. KLEIN, R., and HARRIS, S. B. Treatment of scleroderma, sclerodactylia and calcinosis by chelation (EDTA), Am. J. Med., **19**:798, 1955.

535. KLEMPERER, P. The pathogenesis of lupus erythematosus and allied conditions, Ann. Int. Med., **28**:1, 1948.

536. KLINGMAN, W. O. Dermatoneuromyositis resulting in scleroderma, Arch. Neurol. & Psychiat., **24**:1187, 1930.

537. KLOTZ. Sclérodactylie, New York Dermat. Soc. 28 fév. 1899, Ann. dermat. et syph., **1**:547, 1900.

538. KLOTZ, O. Studies upon calcareous degeneration. 1. The process of pathological calcification, J. Exper. Med., **7**:633, 1905.

539. KNAP, J. A case of Rothmund's disease, Acta dermat.-venereol., **25**:302, 1945.

540. KNESCHKE, W. Sklerodermie im Säuglingsalter, Arch. Dermat. u. Syph., **146**:105, 1924.

541. KNORR, G. Über einen Fall von Verkalkung, Verknöcherung und Knochenmarksbildung in beiden Nebennieren, Beitr. path. Anat. u. allg. Path., **110**:441, 1949.

542. KNOTH, W., and EHLERS, G. Myxomatosis cutis papulosa (lichen myxoedematosus), Ztschr. Haut- u. Geschlechtskr., **30**:21, 1961.

543. KNOWLES, H. C., JR.; ZEEK, P. M.; and BLANKENHORN, M. A. Studies on necrotizing angiitis. IV. Periarteritis nodosa and hypersensitivity angiitis, A.M.A. Arch. Int. Med., **92**:789, 1953.

544. KOCH, F. Zur Frage der Identität von Impetigo herpetiformis, Psoriasis pustulosa und Psoriasis vulgaris, Hautarzt, **3**:165, 1952.

545. KONRAD, J., and WINKLER, A. Skleromyxödem (Arndt-Gottron), Arch. klin. u. exper. Dermat., **202**:254, 1956.

545*a*. KÓSSA, J. VON. Ueber die im Organismus künstlich erzeugbaren Verkalkungen, Beitr. path. Anat. u. allg. Path., **29**:163, 1901.

546. KOVACS, L. Dermatomyositis or rheumatism? Rheumatism, **17**:86, 1961.

547. KRAUS, E. J. Zur Pathogenese der diffusen Sklerodermie. Zugleich ein Beitrag zur Pathologie der Epithelkörperchen, Virchows Arch. path. Anat., **253**:710, 1924.

548. KRAUSE, P., and TRAPPE, M. Über die Calcinosis interstitialis (progressiva et regressiva) ein neues Krankheitsbild, Fortschr. Geb. Roentgenstrahlen, **14**:165, 1909–10.

549. KREIBICH, C. Sklerodermieartige Lichtdermatose, Arch. Dermat. u. Syph., **144**: 454, 1923.

550. KREN, O. Ueber Sklerodermie der Zunge und der Mundschleimhaut, Arch. Dermat. u. Syph., **95**:163, 1909.

551. KRIEGER, H. Ein Fall von Sklerodermie nach vorausgegangenem Morbus Base-dowii, München. med. Wchnschr., **50**:1772, 1903.

552. KROGH, H. W. Dental manifestation of scleroderma, J. Oral Surg., **8**:242, 1950.

553. KROMPECHER, S. Teleangiostenose, die morphologische Grundlage der "juvenilen" oder "spontanen" Gangränen (Endarteriitis obliterans, arteriitis obliterans, Thromboangiitis obliterans), Arteriosclerosis renum und scleroderma, Beitr. path. Anat. u. allg. Path., **85**:647, 1930.

554. KRUEGER, H. The Wulzen calcium dystrophy syndrome in guinea-pigs, Am. J. Phys. Med., **34**:185, 1955.

555. KUBLER, E. Neue Gesichtspunkte bei der Beurteilung der Verlaufsformen der Myositis ossificans progressiva, Fortschr. Geb. Röntgenstrahlen, **81**:354, 1954.

556. KUSUNOKI, T. Kalkstoffwechsel bei Sklerodermie, Dermat. Wchnschr., **108**:627, 1939.

557. KUSUNOKI, T., and KUWABARA, S. Über einen Fall von Sclerodermia diffusa, mit Leukämie kompliziert und durch Parathyreoidektomie gebessert, Arch. Dermat. u. Syph., **176**:256, 1937.

558. LAIGNEL-LAVASTINE, M. The internal secretions and the nervous system, J. Nerv. & Mental Dis., **48**:67, 1918.

559. LANE. Scleroderma (or keloids?), Arch. Dermat. & Syph., **9**:494, 1924.

560. LANGERON, L. Les interventions sur les glandes parathyroïdes. Quelques documents personnels, J. méd. sept. 25: 125, 1933.

561. LANSBURY, J.; SMITH, L. W.; WULZEN, R.; and WAGTENDONK, W. J. VAN. Relation of the "anti-stiffness factor" to collagen disease and calcinosis, Ann. Rheumat. Dis., **9**:97, 1950.

562. LARCAN, A.; RAUBER, G.; and STREIFF, F. Un nouveau cas de sclérodermie généra-lisée à manifestations rénales prépondérantes, Soc. Néphrol. Séance 16 nov. 1959. J. urol., **66**:176, 1960.

563. LARON, Z.; MUHLETHALER, J. P.; and KLEIN, R. The interrelationship between cortisone and parathyroid extract in rats, A.M.A. Arch. Path., **65**:125, 1958.

564. LARSEN, R. D., and POSCH, J. L. Dupuytren's contracture with special reference to pathology, J. Bone & Joint Surg., **40A**:773, 1958.

565. LARSON, E., and ZOECKLER, S. J. ACTH in Reiter's syndrome, four cases with re-view of the literature, Am. J. Med., **14**:307, 1953.

566. LARSSON, B. Statistical analyses of cutaneous tumours in dogs, with special refer-ence to mastocytoma, Nord. Vet. Med., **8**:130, 1956.

567. LARSSON, L. G.; LILJESTRAND, A.; and WAHLUND, H. Treatment of sarcoidosis with calciferol, Acta med. scandinav., **143**:280, 1952.

568. LAUBMANN. Hochgradigen Kalkmetastasierung bei Epithelkörperchentumor, Ver-handl. Deutsch. Path. Gesellsch., **27**:229, 1934.

569. LAUGIER, M. P. White spot disease, J. méd. Lyon, **39**:1083, 1958.

570. LEACH, W. B.; VASSAR, P. S.; and CULLING, C. F. A. Primary systemic amyloidosis presenting as scleroderma, Canad. M.A.J., **83**:263, 1960.

571. LEARNER, N., and BROWN, C. L. Ectodermal disorders in chronic hypoparathyroid-ism, J. Clin. Endocrinol., **3**:261, 1943.

572. LEBACQ, E., and GOSSART, J. Sarcoïdose gastrique avec hypercalcémie. Efficacité du traitement corticoïde, Bull. Soc. méd. hôp. Paris, **76**:706, 1960.

573. LEBON, J.; MANCEAUX; FABREGOULE; and GEORGES. Un cas de sclérodermie avec gros troubles de l'ossification. Rôle des parathyroïdes, Bull. mém. Soc. méd. hôp. Paris, **53**:921, 1937.

574. LECHELLE, P.; BARUK, H.; and DOUADY, D. Association de sclérodermie et de maladie de Dupuytren chez un spécifique, Bull. mém. Soc. méd. hôp. Paris, **51**:622, 1927.

575. LEINWAND, I.; DURYEE, A. W.; and RICHTER, M. N. Scleroderma (based on a study of over 150 cases), Ann. Int. Med., **41**:1003, 1954.

576. LEITNER, S. J. Der Morbus Besnier-Boeck-Schaumann. Chronische epitheloidzellige Reticuloendotheliose oder Granulomatose, Basle: Benno Schwabe & Co., 1949.

577. LELONG, M.; CANLORBE, P.; BERKMAN, M.; VASSAL, J.; and BOSQUET, A. Localisation cardiaque au cours d'une sclérodermie subaiguë œdémateuse, Arch. franç. pédiat., **17**:490, 1960.

578. LEMON, H. M., and KOTOB, N. Hypercitricemia and parathyroid function in advanced cancer, Cancer, **14**:934, 1961.

579. LEONARD, S. L. Effect of hormones on muscle glycogenolysis in hypophysectomized animals, Am. J. Phys. Med., **34**:297, 1955.

580. LEONTJEWA, L. A. Ueber Veränderungen der Knochen und Gelenke bei Sklerodermie, Arch. klin. Chir., **128**:293, 1924.

581. LEREBOULLET, P., and LELONG, M. Concrétions calcaires multiples de la peau avec sclérodermie localisée chez la mère et la fille., Soc. pédiat. Paris, Séance 18 fév. 1930, Bull. Soc. pédiat. Paris, **28**:53, 1930.

582. LERICHE, R., and Jung, A. Résultats de trois opérations parathyroïdiennes dans la sclérodermie, Bull. Soc. franç. dermat. et syph., **38**:1265, 1931.

583. LERICHE, R. Traitement chirurgical du syndrome de Sjögren (œil sec et bouche sèche), résultat au bout de vingt-huit mois d'une double section du nerf vertébral; nature de la maladie, Presse méd., **55**:77, 1947.

584. LERICHE, R. De la chirurgie physiologique, Bull. Acad. méd., **131**:724, 1947.

585. LERICHE, R., and JUNG, A. Essai de traitement de la sclérodermie par la parathyroïdectomie, Bull. mém. Soc. nat. chir., **57**:609, 1931.

586. LERICHE, R., and JUNG, A. Recherche sur la nature de la sclérodermie; les traductions tissulaires de l'hyperparathyroïdisme dans la sclérodermie, ostéolyse, surcharge calcifique de la peau, signification des chiffres indiquant la teneur en calcium du sérum et des urines, Presse méd., **43**:1361, 1935.

587. LERICHE, R., and JUNG, A. Résultats éloignés de diverses opérations parathyroïdiennes dans trois cas de sclérodermie, Rev. chir. Paris, No. **1**:77, 1935.

588. LERICHE, R.; JUNG, A.; and DEBAKEY, M. The surgical treatment of scleroderma. Rationale of sympathectomy and parathyroidectomy, based upon experimental investigations and a clinical study of 26 personal cases, Surgery, **1**:6, 1937.

589. LERICHE, R.; JUNG, A.; and SUREYYA, C. La peau dans l'hyperparathyroïdisme expérimental. Étude de la sclérodermie expérimentale, Presse méd., **43**:777, 1935.

590. LESNE, E.; DREYFUS-SEE, G.; and LAUNAY, C. Scléroédème généralisé consécutif à une néphrite subaiguë chez un enfant de 4 ans, Soc. pédiat. Paris, Séance 19 nov. 1929, Bull. Soc. pédiat. Paris, **27**:518, 1929.

591. LESZCZYNSKI, R. VON. Zur Anwendung von Parathyrioidea (G. Richter) und des Präparates A.T.10 bei der Behandlung der Impetigo herpetiformis und der Psoriasis vulgaris pustulosa, Dermat. Wchnschr., **106**:634, 1938.

592. LEVINE, B. Scleroderma, Arch. Dermat. & Syph., **41**:148, 1940.

593. LEVINE, B. A case for diagnosis (macular atrophy? Nonsyphilitic white spot disease? Anetoderma erythematodes of Jadassohn?) Arch. Dermat. & Syph., **41**:147, 1940.

594. LEWIN. Diskussion (Sklerodermie), Zentralbl. Gynäk., **18**:311, 1894.

595. LEWIN, G., and HELLER, J. Die Sclerodermie. Eine monographische Studie. Berlin: A. Hirschwald, 1895.

596. LEWIS, T. The pathological changes in the arteries supplying the fingers in warm-handed people and in cases of so-called Raynaud's disease, Clin. Sc., **3**:287, 1937–38.

597. LEWY, R. B. Dermatomyositis and scleroderma. Unusual causes of dysphagia, A.M.A. Arch. Otolaryngol., **52**:31, 1950.

598. LICHTENSTEIN, L. Tumors of synovial joints, bursae and tendon sheaths, Cancer, **8**:816, 1955.

599. LIEBERTHAL, D. Sclerema neonatorum and scleroderma. J. Cut. Dis., **36**:29, 1918

600. LIEBERTHAL, D. Scleroderma, Chicago Dermat. Soc. Meet. Nov. 25, 1925, Arch. Dermat. & Syph., **13**:692, 1926.

601. LIESEGANG, R. E. Über Kalkablagerungen der Haut, Arch. Dermat. u. Syph., **139**:73, 1922.

602. LIGHTWOOD, R. A case of dwarfism and calcinosis associated with widespread arterial degeneration, Arch. Dis. Childhood, **7**:193, 1932.

603. LILIENTHAL, L. Fall von Sklerodermie, Dermat. Ztschr., **16**:157, 1909.

604. LIPMAN, M. P., and TOBER, J. N. Peripheral manifestations of visceral carcinoma, Gastroenterology, **16**:188, 1950.

605. LITTLER, T. R. Acrosclerosis, Brit. M.J., Nov. 3: 1088, 1951.

606. LIVINGSTONE, D. J., and WALKER, J. Z. Calcinosis universalis, Glasgow **M.J.**, **30**:438, 1949.

607. LONDON, B., and BERK, J. E. Tri-sodium monohydrogen ethylenediamine tetra-acetate (tri-sodium EDTA) in the treatment of calcinosis associated with scleroderma, Bull. Sinai Hosp., **5**:39, 1957.

608. LONGACRE, J. J., and WAGNER, E. A. The surgical management of disabling contractures due to linear scleroderma, Plastic and Reconstruct. Surg., **9**:367, 1952.

609. LONGCOPE, W. T., and FREIMAN, D. G. A study of sarcoidosis based on a combined investigation of 160 cases including 30 autopsies from the Johns Hopkins Hospital and Massachusetts General Hospital, Medicine, **31**:1, 1952.

610. LOOBY, J. P., and BURKET, L. W. Scleroderma of the face with involvement of the alveolar process, Am. J. Orthodontics, **28**:493, 1942.

611. LORENZ, H. Die Muskelerkrankungen. Wien: Alfred Hölder, 1898.

612. LORENZ, H. Ueber Herzerscheinungen bei der acuten Polymyositis und deren Bedeutung für die Diagnostik der letzteren, Berl. klin. Wchnschr., **43**:727, 1906.

613. LÖWENBACH. Zur Kenntnis der Hautverkalkung, Arch. Dermat. u. Syph., **72**:450, 1904.

614. LUBARSCH, O., and PLENGE, K. Die krankhaften Ablagerungen und Speicherungen. *In* Handbuch der speziellen pathologischen Anatomie und Histologie. Berlin: Springer-Verlag, **3**:607, 1931.

615. LUCAS, P. F. Acute hypercalcaemia from carcinomatosis without bone metastasis, Brit. M.J., April 30: 1330, 1960.

616. LUGT, L. V. D. Dermatomyositis, Acta dermat.-venereol., **32**:27, 1952.

617. LUTZ, J. F. Calcinosis universalis, Ann. Int. Med., **14**:1270, 1941.

617a. MACDONALD, R. A.; ROBBINS, S. L.; and MALLORY, G. K. Dermal fibrosis following subcutaneous injections of serotonin creatinine sulphate, Proc. Soc. Exper. Biol. & Med., **97**:334, 1958.

618. MAHRER, P. R.; EVANS, J. A.; and STEINBERG, I. Scleroderma: Relation of pulmonary changes to esophageal disease, Ann. Int. Med., **40**:92, 1954.

619. MAIR, W. F. Myositis ossificans progressiva, Edinburgh M.J., **39**:13, 69, 1932.

620. MALAMUD, T., and MONASTIRSKY, N. La esclerodermia generalizada del adulto, probable enfermedad sistémica, Prensa méd. argent., **33**:868, 1946.

621. MALLET-GUY, P., and GUIGOU, P. Documents pour servir aux indications de la parathyroïdectomie (en particulier dans les rhumatismes chroniques), J. méd. Lyon, **31**:991, 1950.

622. MANDL, F. Beitrag zur Frage der Myositis ossificans traumatica, Zentralbl. Chir., **63**:2314, 1936.

623. MANDL, F. Established and presumed hyperparathyroidism in various diseases and its treatment, Progr. Med., **1**:1, 1948.

624. MANKOVSKII, B. N. The clinical and pathogenic aspects of dermatomyositis (Russian text), Zhur. Nevropat. i Psikhiat., **61**:543, 1961.

625. MARCHAND. Calcinosis universalis, München. med. Wchnschr: **57**:103, 1910.

626. MARCHIONINI, A., and LUX, L. Juvenile Katarakt bei Sklero-Poikilodermie, Arch. Dermat. u. Syph., **176**:309, 1937.

627. MARKOFF, N. Dermatomyositis, Helvet. med. acta, **18**:383, 1951.

628. MARQUEZY, R. A., and BONNETTE, J. Dermatomyosite infectieuse subaiguë, Semaine hôp. Paris, **24**:1923, 1948.

629. MARTIN, E. Knochenbildung in der Ohrmuschel und ihre Entstehungsursachen, Arch. Ohren. Nasen u. Kehlkopfh., **160**:23, 1951.

630. MASHBURN, J. D.; DAWSON, D. F.; and YOUNG, J. M. Pulmonary calcifications and histoplasmosis. Am. Rev. Resp. Dis., **85**:208, 1961.

631. MASUGI, M., and YÄ-SHU. Die diffuse Sklerodermie und ihre Gefässveränderung, Virchows Arch. path. Anat., **302**:39, 1938.

632. MATHER, G.; DAWSON, J.; and HOYLE, C. Liver biopsy in sarcoidosis, Quart. J. Med., **24**:331, 1955.

633. MATTEI, P. DI. Les pharmacothésaurismoses, Actual. pharmacol., **13**:189, 1960.

634. MATTIOLI-FOGGIA, C. Segni neurologici e psichiei nella sindrome denominata "miopatia lipo-fibro-calcarea," Acta neurol., **6**:734, 1950.

635. MATTIOLI-FOGGIA, C. La miopatia lipo-fibro-calcarea, Boll. Accad. med. Pistoiese Filippo Pacini, 1:9, 1952.

636. MATTIOLI-FOGGIA, C. Per la patogenesi nervosa di nodi lipo-fibro-calcarei, Boll. Accad. med. June 11: 139, 1958.

637. MATTIOLI-FOGGIA, C. Correlazioni radiologiche-electtromiografiche nella miopatia lipo-fibro-calcarea, Riv. patol. nerv. e ment., 80:965, 1959.

638. MAY, E.; HUET, J. A.; and BLOCH-MICHEL, H. Maladie de Raynaud traitée sans succès par la sympathéctomie et la stellectomie et très améliorée par la radiothérapie de la région hypophysaire, Bull mém. Soc. méd. hôp. Paris, 54:831, 1938.

639. McALPINE, D. A case of polymyositis with eosinophilia, Brit. J. Dermat., 48:238, 1936.

640. McCOMBS, R. P., and MacMAHON, H. E. Dermatomyositis associated with metastasizing bronchogenic carcinoma. A clinico-pathological conference, M. Clin. North. America, 31:1148, 1947.

641. McCRACKIN, H. Scleroderma. Report of a case with sclerodactylia and hemiatrophy, J. Pediat., 9:173, 1936.

642. McGARRAHAN, J. C. Dermatomyositis. Report of case, J.A.M.A., 102:680, 1934.

643. McLEAN, F. C., and URIST, M. R. Bone. An Introduction to the Physiology of Skeletal Tissue. Chicago: University of Chicago Press, 2d. ed., 1961.

644. McLEAN, G., and LEBO, L. Multiple calcinosis associated with hypervitaminosis D. Report of a case. South. M.J., 41:389, 1948.

645. McQUEEN, E. G. "Milk poisoning" and "Calcium gout," Lancet, July 12: 67, 1952.

646. McSWINEY, R. R., and MILLS, I. H. Hypercalcaemia due to sarcoidosis. Treatment with cortisone, Lancet, Oct. 27: 862, 1956.

647. MEDVEI, V. C. Extensive interstitial calcinosis with osteoporosis and scleroderma-dermatomyositis, Lancet, Dec. 1: 708, 1945.

648. MEHLHOP, C. Die sog. Myositis ossificans progressiva und ihre Therapie, Strahlentherapie, 96:428, 1955.

649. MENKIN, V. Dynamics of Inflammation. An Inquiry into the Mechanism of Infectious Processes. New York: Macmillan Co., 2d ed., 1950.

650. MENZEL, K. M. Ueber Veränderungen an der äusseren Nase, an deren Schleimhaut und im Rachen bei Sklerodermia diffusa, Monatschr. Ohrenh., 70:1409, 1936.

651. METCHNIKOFF, E. Lectures on the Comparative Pathology of Inflammation, Delivered at the Pasteur Institute in 1891. London: Kegan, Paul, Trench, Trübner & Co., 1893.

652. MICHON, P.; LARCAN, A.; and VERT, P. Aspects trompeurs d'une dermatomyosite, Bull. Soc. franç. dermat. et syph., 66:347, 1959.

653. MILBRADT, W. Atypische diffuse Sklerodermie mit Oslerschem Syndrom und Leberstörung, Dermat. Wchnschr., 99:973, 1934.

654. MILHORAT, A. T.; WEBER, F. C.; and TOSCANI, V. Metabolic studies in dermatomyositis with a note on the effect of wheat germ, Proc. Soc. Exper. Biol. & Med., 43:470, 1940.

655. MILLER, L. F., and O'NEILL, C. J. Myositis ossificans in paraplegics, J. Bone & Joint Surg., 31A:283, 1949.

656. MILLER, R. D.; FOWLER, W. S.; and HELMHOLZ, F. H., JR. Scleroderma of the lungs, Proc. Staff Meet. Mayo Clin., **34**:66, 1959.

657. MILLER, R. D.; KEATING, F. R.; and WINKELMANN, R. K. Progressive systemic sclerosis. Acrosclerosis with extensive visceral involvement, Proc. Staff Meet. Mayo Clin., **34**:58, 1959.

658. MILNE, J. Primary hyperparathyroidism, New England J. Med., **251**:393, 1954.

659. MILONE, F. P., and COPELAND, M. M. Calcific tendinitis of the shoulder joint. Presentation of 136 cases treated by irradiation, Am. J. Roentgenol., **85**:901, 1961.

660. MINDER, W. H. Besondere Befunde bei der Parathyreotoxikose, Schweiz. med. Wchnschr., **87**:667, 1957.

660a. MINTZ, D. H.; CANARY, J. J.; CARREON, G.; and KYLE, L. H. Hyperuricemia in hyperparathyroidism, New England J. Med., **265**:112, 1961.

661. MIXTER, G.; HINTON, J. W.; and PFEFFER, R. B. Pancreatitis in association with hyperparathyroidism, New York J. Med., **58**:3470, 1958.

662. MÖBIUS, W. Klinik der Myome, München. med. Wchnschr., **103**:73, 133, 1961.

663. MOEHLIG, R. C., and STEINBACH, A. L. Cortisone interference with calcium therapy in hypoparathyroidism, J.A.M.A., **154**:42, 1954.

664. MOFFAT, D. B. Demonstration of alkaline phosphatase and periodic acid-Schiff positive material in the same section, Stain Technol., **33**:225, 1958.

665. MÖLLER. Diffuse symmetrische Sklerodermie und Morbus Basedowi, Monatsch. prakt. Dermat., **37**:271, 1903.

666. MÓNUS, Z.; SZÜTS, I.; and PÓHR, E. Viszerale Veränderungen bei Skleroderma, Zentralbl. allg. Path. u. path. Anat., **94**:345, 1956.

667. MOORE, H. C., and SHEEHAN, H. L. The kidney of scleroderma, Lancet, Jan. 12: 68, 1952.

668. MORAWIECKA, J. Un caso de enfermedad de Basedow asociado a esclerodermitis y a osteomalacia, Rev. latinoamer. hormonol. y organotherap., **1**:1, 1928.

669. MOSCHCOWITZ, E. Effect of edema and integumentary infiltrations on basal metabolism, electrocardiogram and blood cholesterol, Arch. Int. Med., **67**:828, 1941.

670. MOSELEY, H. F. Shoulder Lesions. New York: Paul B. Hoeber, Inc., 2d ed., 1953.

671. MUENCHMEYER. Über Myositis ossificans progressiva, Ztschr. ration. Med., **34**:9, 1869.

672. MULLER, S. A.; BRUNSTING, L. A.; and WINKELMANN, R. K. The treatment of scleroderma with the new chelating agent, Edathamil, A.M.A. Arch. Dermat., **80**: 187, 1959.

673. MULLIGAN, R. M. Metastatic calcification associated with hypervitaminosis D and haliphagia, Am. J. Path., **22**:1293, 1946.

674. MUNSTER, L. A dermato-muco-polymyositisröl, Gyógyászat, **67**:717, 1927.

675. MUNTEAN, E. Die Calcinosis interstitialis im Röntgenbild und ihre Abgrenzung gegenüber anderen pathologischen Verkalkungen des peripheren Bindegewebes, Roentgenpraxis, **14**:210, 1942.

676. MURAKAMI, K. Zur Kenntnis der verkalkten Epitheliome der Haut, Arch. Dermat. u. Syph., **109**:51, 1911.

677. MURRAY-WILL, E. Scleroderma and syphilis, Brit. J. Dermat., **39**:201, 1927.

678. NAGLE, R. Hypercalcemia and nephrocalcinosis in sarcoidosis, J. Mount Sinai Hosp., **28**:268, 1961.

679. NAGY, E., and BALOGH, E. Zur Frage der Assoziation der progressiven Sklerodermie und des systematischen Erythematodes, Ztschr. Haut- u. Geschlechtskr., **30**:306, 1961.

679*a*. NATHANSON, L., and LOSNER, S. Ossification of auricles of external ears associated with acromegaly., Radiology, **48**:66, 1947.

680. NEJEDLY, O., and PIPER, H. G. Therapie der Sklerodermie mit Chelatbildnern, Hautarzt, **11**:378, 1960.

680*a*. NEUMAN, W. F., and NEUMAN, M. W. The Chemical Dynamics of Bone Mineral. Chicago: University of Chicago Press, 1958.

681. NEUMAN, Z.; SHULMAN, J.; and BEN-HUR, N. Successful skin grafting in discoid lupus erythematosus: Recurrence checked by triamcinolone ointment (Ledercort), Ann. Surg., **154**:142, 1961.

682. NEUWIRTH, M. Ueber einen Fall von Tendinofasciitis calcarea rheumatica, Mitt. Grenzgeb. Med. u. Chir., **16**:82, 1906.

683. NICHOLS, F. L.; HOLDSWORTH, D. E.; and REINFRANK, R. F. Familial hypocalcemia, latent tetany and calcification of the basal ganglia, report of a kindred, Am. J. Med., **30**:518, 1961.

684. NIEBAUER, G. Zur feingeweblichen Untersuchung der Sklerodermie, Acta neuro-veg., **21**:271, 1960.

685. NIELSEN, R. L. The milk-alkali syndrome due to primary hyperparathyroidism, Bull. Mason Clin., **14**:154, 1961.

686. NIKOLOWSKI, W. Vitamin E and skin diseases, Med. Klin., **55**:415, 1960.

687. NISBET, D. I., and RENWICK, C. C. Congenital myopathy in lambs, J. Comp. Path., **71**:177, 1961.

688. NORSA, G. Retrazione della aponevrosi palmare e sclerodermia, Gazz. osp., **55**:1285, 1934.

689. NUTT, A. B. Late fundus changes in a case of dermatomyositis, Proc. Roy. Soc. Med., **44**:979, 1951.

690. OBERST, B. B., and TOMPKINS, C. A. Pseudohypoparathyroidism, report of a case in a sixteen-month-old girl, A.M.A. Am. J. Dis. Child., **90**:205, 1955.

691. OCHSNER, A., and DEBAKEY, M. Surgical considerations, New Orleans M. & Surg. J., **92**:24, 1939.

692. O'DONOVAN, W. J. Facial morphoea, Brit. J. Dermat., **27**:377, 1915.

693. OFSTAD, E. Scleroderma (progressive systemic sclerosis), a case involving polyneuritis and swelling of the lymph nodes, Acta rheumat. scandinav., **6**:65, 1960.

694. O'LEARY, P. A., and WAISMAN, M. Dermatomyositis, Arch. Dermat. & Syph., **41**:1001, 1940.

695. OPPENHEIMER, B. S., and KUGEL, V. H. Werner's syndrome: a heredo-familial disorder with scleroderma, bilateral juvenile cataract, precocious graying of the hair and endocrine stigmatization, Tr. A. Am. Phys., **49**:358, 1934.

696. ORMEA, F. Sistema nervoso cerebro-spinale e sistema nervoso vegetativo nella patogenesi della sclerodermia diffusa, Acta neuroveg., **2**:386, 1951.

697. ORMEA, F. Zur Pathogenese der diffusen Sklerodermie, Hautarzt, **3**:301, 1952.

698. ORNSTEEN, A. M. Chronic generalized fibromyositis, Ann. Surg., **101**:237, 1935.

699. OSLER, W. On diffuse scleroderma with special reference to diagnosis and to the use of thyroid gland extract, J. Cut. & Genito-Urin. Dis., **16**:49, 127, 1898.

700. OSTROWSKI, S. Zur Pathologie und Klinik der Kalzinosis, Zentralbl. Chir., **86**:882, 1961.

701. PACELLA, B. L., and BARRERA, S. E. Electroencephalography: Its applications in neurology and psychiatry, Psychiat. Quart., **15**:407, 1941.

702. PACK, G. T., and BRAUND, R. R. The development of sarcoma in myositis ossificans, J.A.M.A., **119**:776, 1942.

703. PADMANABHAN, N., and SELYE, H. Systemic non-specific resistance, Basimetry (in press).

704. PADMANABHAN, N.; WALSH, J. T.; and SELYE, H. Induction of resistance against calciphylaxis, Dermatologica (in press).

705. PAGGI, B. Contributo clinico alla conoscenza dei rapporti tra sclerodermia e metabolismo del calcio, Policlinico (sez chir.), **41**:371, 1934.

706. PALEARI, A. Contributo alla conoscenza della sclerodermia (Studio clinico ed anatomopatologico considerazioni eziopatogenetiche), Gior. ital. dermat. e sifil., **80**:1073, 1939.

707. PALVA, T. Intravenous calcium infusion test in cases of sarcoidosis with normal or slightly elevated serum calcium, Acta tuberc. scandinav., **36**:152, 1958.

708. PARHON, C. I.; MARINESCO-BALOIU, D.; and TOMORUG, E. Étude anatomopathologique d'un cas de sclérodermie généralisée, Bull. mém. Soc. Roumaine endocrinol., **5**:368, 1939.

709. PAST, W. L. The histologic demonstration of iron in osseous tissue, Am. J. Path., **39**:443, 1961.

710. PAUTRIER, L. M., and WORINGER, F. L'anatomie pathologique des chéloïdes, Ann. dermat. et syph., **2**:1145, 1931.

711. PERNOD, J., and MEMIN, Y. Le syndrome de Fiessinger-Leroy-Reiter en Algérie (A propos de 122 cas), Semaine hôp. Paris, **37**:2291, 1961.

712. PERRAS, E. La calcinose sous-cutanée généralisée, Union méd. Canada, **81**:941, 1952.

713. PERRY, H. O. Recent treatment programs for generalized scleroderma, Arch. Dermat., **83**:300, 1961.

714. PERUTZ, A. Zur Frage der Kalzinosis bei Sklerodermie, Dermat. Wchnschr., **94**:189, 1932.

715. PETERING, H. G.; STUBBERFIELD, L.; and DELOR, R. A. Studies on the guinea pig factor of Wulzen and van Wagtendonk, Arch. Biochem., **17–18**:487, 1948.

716. PETGES, G., and PETGES, A. Poikilodermie. *In* Nouvelle Pratique Dermatologique. Paris: Masson & Cie, **6**:114, 1936.

717. PETRÁČEK, E., and PITHA, V. Unilaterálni sklerodermie s příznaky poruchy centrálni šedi mozkové, Česká dermat., **17**:251, 1937.

718. PFISTER, R., and NÄGELE, E. Die progressive Sklerodermie, Ergebn. inn. Med. u. Kinderh., **7**:244, 1956.

719. PINELLI, P. Boll. Soc. med. chir. Pavia, **5**:3, 1946.

720. PLIMPTON, C. H., and GELLHORN, A. Hypercalcemia in malignant diseases without evidence of bone destruction, Am. J. Med., **21**:750, 1956.

721. POLLACK, A. D. Visceral and vascular lesions in scleroderma, Arch. Path., **29**:859, 1940.

722. POLLACK, H., and SIEGAL, S. Parathyroid hyperplasia and calcinosis associated with renal disease, J. Mount Sinai Hosp., **2**:270, 1936.

723. POLLITZER, S. Ossification in a case of scleroderma, J. Cut. Dis., **36**:271, 1918.

724. POPPEL, M. H.; GRUBER, W. F.; SILBER, R.; HOLDER, A. K.; and CHRISTMAN, R. O. The roentgen manifestations of urticaria pigmentosa (mastocytosis) Am. J. Roentgenol., **82**:239, 1959.

725. POZO, H. P. DEL; GAJARDO, R. L.; WAISSBLUTH, H. R.; and OSSANDON, M. Dermatomiositis-calcinosis, Rev. Chilena pediat., **30**:318, 1959.

726. PREININGER, T. Skleroedema Buschke, Zentralbl. Haut- u. Geschlechtsk., **52**:484, 1935–36.

727. PRESLEY, S. J., and PAUL, J. T. Idiopathic hypoparathyroidism, Illinois M.J., **118**:298, 1960.

728. PRICE, J. M.; BROWN, R. R.; RUKAVINA, J. G.; MENDELSON, C.; and JOHNSON, S. A. M. Scleroderma (acrosclerosis) II. Tryptophan metabolism before and during treatment by chelation (EDTA), J. Invest. Dermat., **29**:289, 1957.

729. PRINGLE, J. J. Discussion: Raynaud's disease and sclerodermia of the face, Brit. J. Dermat., **6**:339, 1894.

730. PUDDU, V. Un caso di sclerodermia con calcificazioni operato di paratiroidectomia, Policlinico (sez prat.), **41**:1802, 1934.

731. PUTSCHAR, W. Über Vigantolschädigung der Niere bei einem Kinde, Ztschr. Kinderh., **48**:269, 1929.

732. RAKE, G. On the pathology and pathogenesis of scleroderma, Bull. Johns Hopkins Hosp., **48**:212, 1931.

733. RAMSDELL, E. G. Calcinosis universalis, West. J. Surg., **43**:624, 1935.

734. RAMSDELL, E. G. Parathyroidectomy for the calcinosis syndrome. Report of one end result and three additional cases, Tr. Am. Assoc. Study of Goiter, **16**:183, 1939.

735. RANDALL, R. E., JR.; STRAUSS, M. B.; and MCNEELY, W. F. The milk-alkali syndrome, Arch. Int. Med., **107**:163, 1961.

736. RASCH, C. Sklerodermie mit Affektion der Mundschleimhaut und Basedow-Addison-Symptomen. Bemerkungen über die Aetiologie der Krankheit, Dermat. Ztschr., **19**:244, 1912.

737. RASMUSSEN, P., and CAULFIELD, J. B. The ultrastructure of Schaumann bodies in the golden hamster, Lab. Invest., **9**:330, 1960.

738. READ, C. F. Diffuse scleroderma with concurrent psychosis, J. Nerv. & Ment. Dis., **56**:313, 1922.

739. REED, C. I.; STRUCK, H. C.; and STECK, I. E. Vitamin D Chemistry, Physiology, Pharmacology, Pathology, Experimental and Clinical Investigations. Chicago: University of Chicago Press, 1939.

740. REICH. Histologische Untersuchungen bei diffuser (progressiver) Sklerodermie, cir-

cumscripter Sklerodermie und sklerodermieähnlichen Veränderungen der Acrodermatitis chronica atrophicans, Arch. Dermat. u. Syph., **191**:505, 1950.

741. REICH, N. E., and REINHART, J. B. Dermatomyositis associated with hypertrichosis, Arch. Dermat. & Syph., **57**:725, 1948.

742. REICHERT, F. L. Revised concepts of the treatment of Raynaud's syndrome and thromboangiitis obliterans (Buerger's disease), Am. J. Surg., **91**:41, 1956.

743. REILLY, E. B.; SHINTANI, J.; and GOODMAN, J. Systemic mast-cell disease with urticaria pigmentosa, A.M.A. Arch. Dermat., **71**:561, 1955.

744. REINL, W. Sklerodermie durch Trichloräthylen-Einwirkung? Zentralbl. Arbeitsmed. Arbeitsschutz, **7**:58, 1957.

745. REMY, D. Die Mastocytose, Deutsche med. Wchnschr., **82**:719, 1957.

746. RENAUD, S. Superiority of alcoholic over aqueous fixation in the histochemical detection of calcium, Stain Technol., **34**:267, 1959.

747. RESA, R.; CRUZ, A. F.; and COLLAZO, J. A. Extirpacion de la zona del corpusculo carotideo. I. Communicacion. Consideraciones generales y resultados postoperatorios. II. Communicacion. La calcemia, An. med. int., **3**:675, 1934.

748. RESA, R.; CRUZ, A. F.; and COLLAZO, J. A. Extirpacion de la zona del corpusculo carotideo. III. Communicacion. Correlacion entre las paratiroides y el corpusculo carotideo en la regulacion del calcio, An. med. int., **4**:243, 1935.

749. RICHMOND, J.; GARDNER, D. L.; ROY, L. M. H.; and DUTHIE, J. J. R. Nature of anaemia in rheumatoid arthritis. III. Changes in the bone marrow and their relation to other features of the disease, Ann. Rheumat. Dis., **15**:217, 1956.

750. RICHTER, W. Pseudosklerodermie im Verlauf der Akrodermatitis chronica atrophicans in ihrer Stellung zur Sklerodermie, Arch. Dermat. u. Syph., **175**:123, 1937.

751. RIEHL. Ein Fall von Verkalkung der Haut (Kalksteine), München. med. Wchnschr., **49**:164, 1902.

752. RILEY, J. F. The Mast Cells. Edinburgh: E. & S. Livingstone Ltd., 1959.

753. RINALDI, S. Il contenuto in calcio del cristallino nello stato paratireoprivo sperimentale, Ann. Ottal. e clin. ocul., **65**:667, 1937.

754. ROBBINS, S. L. Textbook of Pathology with Clinical Applications. Philadelphia: W. B. Saunders Co., 1957.

755. ROBERTSON, J. L., and BRINKMAN, G. L. Nodular rheumatoid lung disease, Am. J. Med., **31**:483, 1961.

756. ROBINSON, S. S. Scleroderma and sclerodactylia associated with intermittent claudication, Arch. Dermat. & Syph., **36**:1054, 1937.

757. ROCH, M.; RUTISHAUSER, E.; and SALOZ, C. La polymyosite œdémateuse, J. Suisse méd., **76**:1035, 1946.

758. ROCHE, M. A case of pseudo-pseudohypoparathyroidism, J. Clin. Endocrinol., **15**:964, 1955.

759. ROLLIN. Lues III am Penis und Scrotum. Calcinose des linken Ohrläppchens nach Erfrierung, Zentralbl. Haut- u. Geschlechtsk., **27**:340, 1928.

760. RONCHETTI, G. La miopatia lipo-fibro-calcarea, Boll. soc. med. chir., Modena, **59**:878, 1959.

761. Rook, A.; Davis, R.; and Stevanovic, D. Poikiloderma congenitale Rothmund-Thomson syndrome, Acta dermat.-venereol., **39**:392, 1959.

762. Ropes, M. W.; Robertson, W. v. B.; Rossmeisl, E. C.; Peabody, R. B.; and Bauer, W. Synovial fluid mucin, Acta med. scandinav. suppl. 196: 700, 1947.

763. Rosenstirn, J. A contribution to the study of myositis ossificans progressiva, Ann. Surg., **68**:485, 1918.

764. Rosenthal, O. Ueber einen Fall von partieller Sklerodermie, mit Uebergang in halbseitige Gesichtsatrophie, combiniert mit Alopecia areata, Berl. klin. Wchnschr., **26**:755, 1889.

765. Rossbach, J. M. Addison'sche Krankheit und Sklerodermie, Arch. path. Anat., **50**:566, 1870.

766. Rothman, S., and Henningsen, A. B. Linear scleroderma following the course of nerves with muscular atrophy, Arch. Dermat. & Syph., **50**:59, 1944.

767. Rottenberg, E. N.; Slocumb, C. H.; and Edwards, J. E. Cardiac and renal manifestations in progressive systemic scleroderma, Proc. Staff Meet. Mayo Clin., **34**:77, 1959.

768. Roux, J. Sclérodermie et corps pituitaire, Rev. neurol., **10**:721, 1902.

769. Roy, L. M. H.; Alexander, W. R. M.; Richmond, J.; Gardner, D. L.; and Duthie, J. J. R. Nature of anaemia in rheumatoid arthritis. I. Metabolism of iron, Ann. Rheumat. Dis., **14**:63, 1955.

770. Rubin, L. Linear scleroderma. Association with abnormalities of the spine and nervous system, Arch. Dermat. & Syph., **58**:1, 1948.

771. Rudolph, C. C. Calcinosis universalis and dermatomyositis, J. Pediat., **4**:342, 1934.

772. Rukavina, J. G.; Mendelson, C.; Price, J. M.; Brown, R. R.; and Johnson, S. A. M. Scleroderma (Acrosclerosis). I. Treatment of three cases of the non-calcific variety by chelation (EDTA), J. Invest. Dermat., **29**:273, 1957.

773. Rummert, O. Ein Beitrag zur Kenntnis des Scleroedema adultorum, Dermat. Wchnschr., **89**:1563, 1929.

774. Rustigian, R., and Pappenheimer, A. M. Myositis in mice, following intramuscular injection of viruses of the mouse, encephalomyelitis group and of certain other neurotropic viruses, J. Exper. Med., **89**:69, 1949.

775. Sabrazes, J., and Lafon, C. Granulome de la lèvre à mastzellen et à eosinophiles chez un cheval, Folia haemat., **6**:3, 1908.

776. Sagher, F.; Cohen, C.; and Schorr, S. Concomitant bone changes in urticaria pigmentosa, J. Invest. Dermat., **18**:425, 1952.

777. Sagher, F., and Even-Paz, Z. The mast cells and mastocytosis with special reference to bone changes, South African M.J., **35**:470, 1961.

778. Sagher, F., and Schorr, S. Bone lesions in urticaria pigmentosa, report of central registry on skeletal X-ray survey. Preliminary and short report, J. Invest. Dermat., **26**:431, 1956.

779. Sannicandro, G. Sindrome di Rothmund con calcificazioni cutanee e sclerodermia progressiva. Loro rapporti con le lesioni delle paratiroidi, Arch. ital. dermat. e sifil., **11**:88, 1935.

780. SANNICANDRO, G. Sarkoide und sklerodermartige Tuberkulose mit symmetrischen Streifen an den Beinen, verbunden mit progressiver Sklerodermie, Arch. Dermat. u. Syph., **175**:623, 1937.

781. SAPHIR, O. A Text on Systemic Pathology. New York: Grune & Stratton, **1**:1958, **2**:1959.

782. SCHAUMANN, J. Études bactériologiques sur le lupus pernio et les sarcoïdes cutanées, p. 24. Stockholm: P. A. Norstedt & Söner, 1917.

783. SCHAUMANN, J. Notes on the histology of the medullary and osseous lesions in benign lymphogranuloma and especially on their relationship to the radiographic picture, Acta radiol., **7**:358, 1926.

784. SCHEEN, S. R., JR., and WINKELMANN, R. K. Alkaline phosphatase in skin of certain animals, Arch. Dermat., **83**:439, 1961.

785. SCHELLACK, D. Ueber Epithelkörperchenvergrösserung und Osteodystrophia fibrosa generalisata bei chronischer Niereninsuffiziens, Beitr. path. Anat. u. allg. Path., **103**:479, 1939.

786. SCHENKEL, J. P. Le poumon sclérodermique. Étude anatomo-clinique de cinq cas, Ann. anat. path., **5**:32, 1960.

786a. SCHERBEL, A. L. The effect of Marsilid in patients having rheumatoid arthritis. The theoretical causal role of certain amine oxidases, J. Clin. & Exper. Psychopath., **19**:118, 1958.

786b. SCHERBEL, A. L., and HARRISON, J. W. Response to serotonin and its antagonists in patients with rheumatoid arthritis and related diseases, Angiology, **10**:29, 1959.

787. SCHERRER, F. W. Calcification and ossification of external ears, Ann. Otol. Rhinol. & Laryngol., **41**:867, 1932.

788. SCHIRREN, C. Beitrag zur Frage Sklerodermie und Trauma, Hautarzt, **5**:258, 1954.

789. SCHLEGEL, A. Kalkmetastase und Kalkgicht. Inaugural-Dissertation Georg-August Universität, Göttingen, 1938.

790. SCHLIACK, V., and LISEWSKI, G. Calcinosis interstitialis localisata bei einer Diabetikerin, Klin. Wchnschr., **37**:629, 1959.

791. SCHMIDT–LA BAUME, F. Die Bedeutung des A.T.10 für die Dermatologie als Substitutionstherapie bei Hypocalcinosen, Med. Klin., **33**:1590, 1937.

792. SCHMORL. Ueber feine Knochenstrukturen und über den Eisengehalt des Knochengewebes unter pathologischen Verhältnissen, Verhandl. deutsche path. Gesellsch., **8**:144, 1904.

793. SCHOLEFIELD, R. E., and WEBER, F. P. A case of sclerodactylia with subcutaneous calcareous concretions, Brit. J. Dermat., **23**:276, 1911.

794. SCHOLZ, T. Diffuse interstitial calcinosis, report of a case with a review of the literature, Radiology, **22**:54, 1934.

795. SCHÖNHEIMER, R. Zur Chemie der gesunden und der atherosklerotischen Aorta, Hoppe-Seyler's Ztschr. physiol. Chem., **177**:143, 1928.

796. SCHOTT, J., and DANN, S. Werner's syndrome. A report of two cases, New England J. Med., **240**:641, 1949.

797. SCHREIBER, M. M., and TILLEY, J. C. Cutis laxa, Arch. Dermat., **84**:266, 1961.

798. SCHULTZE, W. Sklerodermie, Tagung Vereinigung Sudwest Deutscher Dermat. 21–22 Mai, Giessen 1938. Dermat. Wchnschr., **108**:82, 1939.

799. SCHULTZE, W. H. Verkalkung, Ergebn. allg. Path. u. path. Anat., **14**:706, 1910.

800. SCHULZE, F. Skelettveränderungen als Ursache von Verkalkungen, Mitt. Grenzgeb. Med. u. Chir., **36**:243, 1923.

801. SCHWARZ, J.; SILVERMAN, F. N.; ADRIANO, S. M.; STRAUB, M.; and LEVINE, S. The relation of splenic calcification to histoplasmosis, New England J. Med., **252**: 887, 1955.

802. SEGAL, E. L.; STARR, G. F.; and WEED, L. A. Study of surgically excised pulmonary granulomas, J.A.M.A., **170**:515, 1959.

803. SEGAL, P.; JABLONSKA, S.; and MRZYGLOD, S. Ocular changes in linear scleroderma, Am. J. Ophth., **51**:807, 1961.

804. SEHRT, E. Ueber Knochenbildung in der Haut, Virchows Arch. path. Anat., **200**: 395, 1910.

805. SELLEI, J. Sklerodermie und Schleimhaut, Arch. Dermat. u. Syph., **170**:464, 1934.

806. SELYE, H. Morphologische Studie über die Veränderungen nach Verfütterung von bestrahltem Ergosterin (Vigantol) bei der weissen Ratt, Krankheitsforschung, **7**:289, 1929.

807. SELYE, H. Zur Kenntnis der Kalkgicht (M. B. Schmidt) an Hand eines selbstbeobachteten Falles, Med. Klin., **25**:379, 1929.

808. SELYE, H. Action of parathyroid hormone on the epiphyseal junction of the young rat, Arch. Path., **14**:60, 1932.

809. SELYE, H. A condition simulating human scleroderma in rats injected with parathyroid hormone, J.A.M.A., **99**:108, 1932.

810. SELYE, H. Die Sklerodermie und ihre Entstehungsweise, Virchows Arch. path. Anat., **286**:91, 1932.

811. SELYE, H. Knochenveränderungen bei den Jungen Vigantolbehandelter Tiere, Verein deutscher Arzte in Prag, 26 Okt., 1928, Med. Klin., **25**:167, 1929.

812. SELYE, H. Textbook of Endocrinology. Montreal: Acta Inc. Med. Publ., 1947.

813. SELYE, H. Stress, Montreal: Acta Inc. Med. Publ., 1950.

814. SELYE, H. First Annual Report on Stress. Montreal: Acta Inc. Med. Publ., 1951.

815. SELYE, H. Influence of inoculation site upon the course of the anaphylactoid reaction to dextran, J. Allergy, **25**:97, 1954.

816. SELYE, H. The Stress of Life. New York: McGraw-Hill Book Co., Inc., 1956.

817. SELYE, H. Rolle der Nebennierenrinde bei der Entstehung verschiedenartiger Blutgefässveränderungen, München. med. Wchnschr., **98**:1015, 1956.

818. SELYE, H. Effect of various hormones upon the syndrome of dihydrotachysterol (AT-10) intoxication, Acta endocrinol., **25**:83, 1957.

819. SELYE, H. Experimental production of cutaneous calcinosis and sclerosis with dihydrotachysterol (AT-10), J. Invest. Dermat., **29**:9, 1957.

820. SELYE, H. Über den Einfluss lokaler Faktoren bei der Entstehung von Nierensteinen und Gewebsverkalkungen, Ztschr. Urol., **50**:440, 1957.

820a. SELYE, H. Humoral "conditioning" for the production of a suppurative, acute myocarditis by the oral administration of sodium phosphate, Am. Heart J., **55**:1, 1958.

820*b*. SELYE, H. Prevention by MgCl₂ and KCl of the vascular hypersensitivity induced by pretreatment with dihydrotachysterol (DHT), Internat. Arch. Allergy, **12**:145, 1958.

821. SELYE, H. The Chemical Prevention of Cardiac Necroses. New York: Ronald Press Co., 1958.

821*a*. SELYE, H. Quoted from The Chemical Prevention of Cardiac Necroses, reference 342 (unpublished). New York: Ronald Press Co., 1958.

822. SELYE, H. Wechselwirkungen zwischen Stress, Elektrolyten und Steroiden beim entstehen verschiedener Kardiopathien und Myopathien, Endokrinologie, **38**:195, 1959.

823. SELYE, H. The Pluricausal Cardiopathies. Springfield: Charles C Thomas, 1961.

824. SELYE, H. Calciphylaxis and the concept of "vital mordanting," Persp. Biol. & Med., **5**:233, 1962.

825. SELYE, H. Nonspecific resistance, Ergebn. allg. Path. u. path. Anat., **41**:208, 1961.

826. SELYE, H. Stress and renal function in relation to the hyalinizing and calcifying lesions of connective tissue, Ramon Guiteras Lecture, Am. Urol. Assoc., Los Angeles, May 24, 1961. J. Urol., **86**:687, 1961.

827. SELYE, H. Kalziphylaxie, Allergie und Asthma, **7**:241, 1961.

828. SELYE, H. Erzeugung von Osteitis fibrosa durch Calciphylaxie, Beitr. path. Anat. u. allg. Path., **125**:189, 1961.

829. SELYE, H. The development of the calciphylaxis concept, Prof. Houssay Jubilee Issue, Persp. Biol. & Med. (in press).

829*a*. SELYE, H. Unpublished.

830. SELYE, H.; SISTER ADRIAN MARIE; and JEAN, P. Systemic and topical factors involved in the production of experimental cutaneous calcinosis, J. Invest. Dermat., **37**:7, 1961.

831. SELYE, H., and BAJUSZ, E. A stress kutatás újabb eredményei es a stress-elmélet szerepe a modern kórtani munkában. I. Mi a stress? Orv. Hetilap, **101**:1, 1960.

831*a*. SELYE, H., and BAJUSZ, E. The prevention of experimental myopathies by various chlorides, J. Nutrition, **72**:37, 1960.

831*b*. SELYE, H., and CANTIN, M. Unpublished.

832. SELYE, H.; CANTIN, M.; and GENTILE, G. Effect of various electrolytes upon thallium intoxication, Chemotherapia (in press).

833. SELYE, H.; CANTIN, M.; and JEAN, P. Verhütung der experimentellen Calcinosis cutis durch Aminoazetonitril (AAN), Arch. klin. exper. Dermat., **212**:1, 1960.

834. SELYE, H.; CANTIN, M.; and VEILLEUX, R. Abnormal growth and sclerosis of the salivary glands induced by chronic treatment with isoproterenol, Growth, **25**:243, 1961.

835. SELYE, H., and DIEUDONNÉ, J.-M. Calcification of the parathyroids induced by calciphylaxis, Experientia, **17**:496, 1961.

836. SELYE, H., and DIEUDONNÉ, J.-M. Production of calciphylactic lesions in the chorioid plexus, Zhur. Nevropat. i Psikhiat., No. 12, 1961.

837. SELYE, H., and DIEUDONNÉ, J.-M. Changes in the carotid body induced by calciphylaxis, Biochim. e biol. sper. (in press).

837*a*. SELYE, H., and DIEUDONNÉ, J.-M. Unpublished.

837*b*. SELYE, H.; DIEUDONNÉ, J.-M.; and GABBIANI, G. The critical period in calciphylaxis, 46th Ann. Meet. Fed. Am. Soc. Exper. Biol., Atlantic City, April 14–19,
1962. Fed. Proc. (in press).

837*c*. SELYE, H.; DIEUDONNÉ, J.-M.; and TUCHWEBER, B. Siderocalciphylactic sensitization to distilled water, J.A.M.A. (in press).

838. SELYE, H.; DIEUDONNÉ, J.-M.; and VEILLEUX, R. Calciphylactic muscular dystrophy induced by DHT plus 5HT, Proc. Soc. Exper. Biol. & Med. (in press).

838*a*. SELYE, H.; DIEUDONNÉ, J.-M.; and VEILLEUX, R. Siderocalciphylactic sensitization to mastocyte dischargers, Am. J. Physiol. (in press).

838*b*. SELYE, H.; GABBIANI, G.; and DIEUDONNÉ, J.-M. Unpublished.

839. SELYE, H., and GENTILE, G. Erzeugung calciphylaktischer Speicheldrüsenverän-
derungen durch Serotonin. Naturwissenschaften, **48**:671, 1961.

840. SELYE, H., and GENTILE, G. Osteitis fibrosa induced by calciphylaxis in the absence of the parathyroids. Acta endocrinol. (in press).

841. SELYE, H., and GENTILE, G. Unpublished.

842. SELYE, H.; GENTILE, G.; and DIEUDONNÉ, J.-M. Effect of adjuvants upon cutaneous calciphylaxis induced by topical or systemic challenge, Internat. Arch.
Allergy (in press).

843. SELYE, H.; GENTILE, G.; and JEAN, P. An experimental model of dermatomyositis
induced by calciphylaxis, Canad. M.A.J., **85**:770, 1961.

844. SELYE, H.; GENTILE, G.; and PRIORESCHI, P. Cutaneous molt induced by calciphylaxis in the rat, Science, **134**:1876, 1961.

845. SELYE, H.; GENTILE, G.; and VEILLEUX, R. Production of calciphylactic, facial,
oesophageal, and mediastinal lesions by combined treatment with dihydrotachysterol and thorium dioxide, Brit. M.J. Nov. 4: 1194, 1961.

846. SELYE, H.; GENTILE, G.; and VEILLEUX, R. An experimental model of calcareous
subdeltoid bursitis induced by calciphylaxis, Arthritis & Rheumat. (in press).

847. SELYE, H., and GRASSO, S. Chemical production of myocardial necroses with vascular occlusions, Brit. J. Exper. Path., **42**:564, 1961.

848. SELYE, H.; GRASSO, S.; and DIEUDONNÉ, J.-M. On the role of adjuvants in calciphylaxis, Rev. Allergy & Appl. Immunol., **15**:461, 1961.

849. SELYE, H.; GRASSO, S.; and GENTILE, G. Various types of calcinosis induced by
egg albumen or yolk following sensitization with dihydrotachysterol (DHT),
Proc. Soc. Exper. Biol. & Med., **107**:600, 1961.

850. SELYE, H.; GRASSO, S.; and GENTILE, G. Cardiac ossification induced by a surgical
intervention, Eksper. khir., No. 6, p. 22, 1961.

851. SELYE, H.; GRASSO, S.; and GENTILE, G. Selective production of uterine or pancreatic lesions by the same calciphylactic system, Arch. Path. (in press).

852. SELYE, H.; GRASSO, S.; and PADMANABHAN, N. Topical injury as a means of producing calcification at predetermined points with dihydrotachysterol (DHT), Proc.
Zool. Soc. Calcutta, **13**:1, 1960.

853. SELYE, H., and HORAVA, A. Second Annual Report on Stress. Montreal: Acta Inc.
Med. Publ., 1952.

854. SELYE, H., and HORAVA, A. Third Annual Report on Stress. Montreal: Acta Inc. Med. Publ., 1953.

855. SELYE, H., and HEUSER, G. Fourth Annual Report on Stress. Montreal: Acta Inc. Med. Publ., 1954.

856. SELYE, H., and HEUSER, G. Fifth Annual Report on Stress. Montreal: Acta Inc. Med. Publ., 1955–56.

857. SELYE, H., and JEAN, P. Prevention of calciphylaxis by hypophysectomy, Endocrinology, **69**:986, 1961.

858. SELYE, H.; JEAN, P.; and VEILLEUX, R. Role of local trauma in production of cutaneous calcinosis by dihydrotachysterol, Proc. Soc. Exper. Biol. & Med., **104**:409, 1960.

859. SELYE, H.; JEAN, P.; and VEILLEUX, R. Sensitization by thallium to dihydrotachysterol overdosage, Proc. Soc. Exper. Biol. & Med., **106**:408, 1961.

860. SELYE, H.; LEMIRE, Y.; and BAJUSZ, E. Induction of bone, cartilage and hemopoietic tissue by subcutaneously implanted tissue diaphragms, W. Roux' Arch. Entwicklungsm., **151**:572, 1960.

861. SELYE, H., and NIELSEN, K. Action of desoxycorticosterone on non-protein nitrogen content of blood during experimental uremia, Proc. Soc. Exper. Biol. & Med., **46**: 541, 1941.

861*a*. SELYE, H., and NIELSEN, K. Factors influencing skeletal changes induced by aminoacetonitrile. Effect of Alizarin and Kernechtrot, A.M.A. Arch. Path., **64**:333, 1957.

862. SELYE, H., and NIELSEN, K. Histogenesis of experimental cutaneous calcinosis, Acta Morphol. Acad. Sc. Hungar., **10**:327, 1961.

863. SELYE, H., and PADMANABHAN, N. Selective calcification of the thymus induced by calciphylaxis, J. Endocrinol. (in press).

863*a*. SELYE, H., and PADMANABHAN, N. Unpublished.

864. SELYE, H.; PADMANABHAN, N.; and STREBEL, R. The histogenesis of connective tissue calcification induced by $KMnO_4$ and other "direct calcifiers," Prof. Syllaba Jubilee Volume (in press).

865. SELYE, H.; PADMANABHAN, N.; and WALSH, J. T. Schutzwirkung der Hypophysektomie gegenüber der sogenannten "dystrophischen Gewebsverkalkung," Virchows Arch. path. Anat. (in press).

865*a*. SELYE, H., and RENAUD, S. Prévention par le chlorure de potassium d'une myocardite purulente expérimentale, Presse Méd., **66**:99, 1958.

865*b*. SELYE, H.; STREBEL, R.; and DIEUDONNÉ, J.-M. Unpublished.

865*c*. SELYE, H.; STREBEL, R.; and VAŠKŮ, J. Unpublished.

865*d*. SELYE, H.; VAŠKŮ, J.; and GABBIANI, G. Experimental production of cholangitis and pancreatitis by ferric oxide saccharate (Fe-OS), Am. J. Gastroenterol. (in press).

866. SELYE, H.; VEILLEUX, R.; and CANTIN, M. Excessive stimulation of salivary gland growth by isoproterenol, Science, **133**:44, 1961.

866*a*. SELYE, H., and VEILLEUX, R. Unpublished.

867. SEQUEIRA, J. H. Two cases of fronto-nasal morphoea with remarks, Brit. J. Dermat., **23**:40, 1911.

868. SEQUEIRA, J. H. Sclerodermia with Graves's disease, Proc. Roy. Soc. Med. (Dermat. Sect.), **9**:66, 1916.

869. SEQUEIRA, J. H. Four cases of sclerodermia associated with disease of the thyroid gland, Brit. J. Dermat., **28**:31, 1916.

870. SEQUEIRA, J. H. Case of sclerodermia (sclerodactyly type) with adrenal insufficiency, Brit. J. Dermat., **34**:124, 1922.

871. SEVILLE, R. H. Progressive symmetrical sclerodermia with sclerodermatous nodules, Proc. Roy. Soc. Med., **44**:573, 1951.

872. SEZARY, A.; LEVY-COBLENTZ, G.; and CHAUVILLON, P. Dermographisme et mastocytose, Bull. Soc. franç. dermat. et syph., **43**:359, 1936.

873. SHAFFER, B.; COPELAN, H. W.; and BEERMAN, H. Pseudoxanthoma elasticum. A cutaneous manifestation of a systemic disease; report of a case of Paget's disease and a case of calcinosis with arteriosclerosis as manifestations of this syndrome, A.M.A. Arch. Dermat., **76**:622, 1957.

874. SHARMA, G. C.; JHALA, G. S.; and MEHTA, P. C. Myositis ossificans progressiva, Indian J. Surg., **23**:33, 1961.

875. SHEARN, M. A. Sjögren's syndrome in association with scleroderma, Ann. Int. Med., **52**:1352, 1960.

876. SHELDON, J. H. Haemochromatosis. London: Oxford University Press, 1935.

877. SHELDON, J. H. Sjögren's syndrome associated with pigmentation and sclerodermia of legs, Proc. Roy. Soc. Med. (Dermat. Sect.), **32**:255, 1939.

878. SHELDON, J. H.; YOUNG, F.; and DYKE, S. C. Acute dermatomyositis associated with reticulo-endotheliosis, Lancet, Jan. 14: 82, 1939.

879. SHELDON, W. H., and BAUER, H. Tissue mast cells and acute inflammation in experimental cutaneous mucormycosis of normal, 48/80-treated, and diabetic rats, J. Exper. Med., **112**:1069, 1960.

880. SHELLING, D. H.; ASHER, D. E.; and JACKSON, D. A. Calcium and phosphorus studies. VII. The effects of variations in dosage of parathormone and of calcium and phosphorus in the diet on the concentrations of calcium and inorganic phosphorus in the serum and on the histology and chemical composition of the bones of rats, Bull. Johns Hopkins Hosp., **53**:348, 1933.

881. SHULMAN, L. E., and HARVEY, A. M. Systemic lupus erythematosus. *In* Arthritis and Allied Conditions, p. 737. Philadelphia: Lea & Febiger, 1960.

882. SILVA, F.; PONDE, A. DE A.; and LICHTENBERG, F. Poikilodermatomyositis with calcinosis cutis, A.M.A. Arch. Dermat. & Syph., **68**:588, 1953.

883. SILVESTRINI, F., and MINETTI, L. Osservazioni sul trattamento della sclerodermia generalizzata, Rass. fisiopat. clin. e terap., **33**:343, 1961.

884. SIMPSON, J. R. Dermatomyositis, Proc. Roy. Soc. Med., **46**:288, 1953.

885. SKAVLEM, J. H., and RITTERHOFF, R. J. Coexistent pulmonary asbestosis and sarcoidosis, Am. J. Path., **22**:493, 1946.

886. SMITH, J. G., JR. Necrobiosis lipoidica: A disease of changing concepts, A.M.A. Arch. Dermat. & Syph., **74**:280, 1956.

886a. SMYTH, C. J., and GUM, O. B. Vasculitis, mast cells and the collagen diseases, Arthritis & Rheumat., **4**:1, 1961.

887. SOFFER, L. J. Symposium on endocrine and metabolic disorders. ACTH and cortisone. Physiologic and clinical considerations, M. Clin. North America, **36**:791, 1952.

888. SONTAG, L. W., and ALLEN, J. E. Lung calcifications and histoplasmin-tuberculin skin sensitivity, J. Pediat., **30**:657, 1947.

889. SPAHR, A., and BRENN, H. Die Calcinosis interstitialis bei Dermatomyositis, Helvet. paediat. acta, **12**:48, 1957.

890. STAFNE, E. C., and AUSTIN, L. T. A characteristic dental finding in acrosclerosis and diffuse scleroderma, Am. J. Orthodontics, **30**:25, 1944.

891. STARKE, O. Beitrag zur Kenntnis der Calcinosis universalis, Zentralbl. allg. Path. u. Anat., **86**:268, 1950.

892. ŠŤÁVA, M. Z. Dermosklerosy a jejich vztahy k tzv kolagenosam, Praha: Statni Zdravotnicke Nakladatelstvi, 1961.

893. STEIGLEDER, G. K., and RAAB, W. P. Lichen sclerosus et atrophicus, Arch. Dermat., **84**:219, 1961.

894. STEINBERG, H., and WALDRON, B. R. Idiopathic hypoparathyroidism. An analysis of fifty-two cases including the report of a new case, Medicine, **31**:133, 1952.

895. STEINBROCKER, O. The shoulder-hand syndrome, associated painful homolateral disability of the shoulder and hand with swelling and atrophy of the hand, Am. J. Med., **3**:402, 1947.

896. STEINBROCKER, O. The painful shoulder. *In* Arthritis and Allied Conditions, p. 1181. Philadelphia: Lea & Febiger, 6th ed., 1960.

897. STEVEN, J. L. Case of scleroderma with pronounced hemiatrophy of the face, body and extremities, death from ovarian tumour; account of the post-mortem examination: A sequel, Glasgow M.J., **50**:401, 1898.

898. STEVENSON, J.; MACGREGOR, A. M.; and CONNELLY, P. Calcification of the adrenal glands in young children. A report of three cases with a review of the literature, Arch. Dis. Childhood, **36**:316, 1961.

899. STONE, G. E.; WATERHOUSE, C.; and TERRY, R. Hypercalcemia of malignant disease: case report and a proposed mechanism of etiology, Ann. Int. Med., **54**:977, 1961.

899a. STONHAM, C. Myositis ossificans, Lancet, Dec. 31: 1485, 1892.

900. STOPP, H. Kasuistischer Beitrag zur Chondrodystrophia calcificans congenita, Ztschr. aerztl. Fortbild., **51**:196, 1957.

901. STRAUB, M., and SCHWARZ, J. Healed primary complex in histoplasmosis, Am. J. Clin. Path., **25**:727, 1955.

902. DE STRIHOU, C. VAN Y., and CROSNIER, J. Sur les accidents rénaux avec alcalose et hypercalcémie survenant chez des sujets gastralgiques (Syndrome de Burnett), Rev. franç. études clin. et biol., **6**:779, 1961.

902a. STUART, E. G. Mast cell responses to anaphylaxis. 65th Ann. Session, Am. Assoc. Anatomists, Providence, Rhode Island, March 19–21, Anat. Rec., **112**:394, 1952.

903. SU, I. P. Idiopathic scleroderma of the mouth, report of three cases, Arch. Otolaryngol., **59**:330, 1954.

904. SUMITA, M. Zur Frage der Eisenreaktion kalkhaltiger Gewebe, insbesondere des Knochens, Virchows Arch. path. Anat., **200**:220, 1910.

905. Szép, E. Das Blutbild der Sklerodermagruppe, Ungarische dermat. Gesellsch. 3–4 Okt. 1941, Dermat. Wchnschr., **115**:763, 1942.

906. Szodoray, L., and Tuza, C. Über die Histochemie der Sklerodermie, Hautarzt, **11**:63, 1960.

907. Talbott, J. H.; Gall, E. A.; Consolazio, W. V.; and Coombs, F. S. Dermatomyositis with scleroderma, calcinosis and renal endarteritis associated with focal cortical necrosis. Report of a case in which the condition simulated Addison's disease, with comment on metabolic and pathologic studies, Arch. Int. Med., **63**:476, 1939.

908. Talbott, J. H., and Ferrandis, R. M. Collagen Diseases. New York: Grune & Stratton, 1956.

909. Talbott, J. H.; Koepf, G. F.; Culver, G. J.; and Terplan, K. Dermatomyositis, disseminated calcinosis and metaplastic ossification, clinical studies over a period of 7 years in a female with rheumatoid arthritis, Arthritis & Rheumat., **2**:499, 1959.

910. Tanret, P. Sclérodermie, syndrome parathyroïde et leucémie à monocytes, Semaine hôp. Paris, **22**:1477, 1946.

911. Tate, B. C., and Trumper, H. B. Calcinosis cutis, Brit. J. Dermat., **45**:413, 1933.

912. Taylor, R. M., and Pacella, B. L. The electroencephalogram in scleroderma, J. Nerv. & Ment. Dis., **109**:42, 1949.

913. Teilum, G. Gleerups Forlag, Lund, Medicinska Framsteg, **2**:186, 1952 (after T. Palva, Acta tubercul. scandinav., **36**:152, 1958).

914. Teutschlaender, O. Ueber progressive Lipogranulomatose der Muskulatur; zugleich ein Beitrag zur Pathogenese der Myopathia osteoplastica progressiva, Klin. Wchnschr., **14**:451, 1935.

915. Teutschlaender, O. Lipocalcinogranulomatose und Calcinose, Zentralbl. allg. Path. u. path. Anat., **67**:387, 1937.

916. Teutschlaender, O. Die symmetrisch fortschreitende Lipocalcinogranulomatose (Hygromatosis lipocalcinogranulomatosa progrediens) und andere Schleimbeutelveränderungen (sog. "Bursitis calcarea and Lipoma arborescens"), Beitr. path. Anat. u. allg. Path., **103**:499, 1939.

917. Teutschlaender, O. Ueber eigenartige Sphärokristalle bei fortschreitender Lipocalcinogranulomatose (Calcinosis lipogranulomatosa progrediens) und anderen Verkalkungen, Zentralbl. allg. Path. u. path. Anat., **76**:369, 1941.

918. Teutschlaender, O. Epithelkörperchen und Knochenveränderungen bei Fortschreitender Lipocalcinogranulomatose (Calcinosis lipogranulomatosa progrediens), Klin. Wchnschr., **20**:714, 1941.

919. Teutschlaender, O. Die Lipoido-calcinosis oder Lipoidkalkgicht (Lipocalcinogranulomatose), Beitr. path. Anat. u. allg. Path., **110**:402, 1949.

920. Thannhauser, S. J. Werner's syndrome (progeria of the adult) and Rothmund's syndrome: two types of closely related heredofamilial atrophic dermatoses with juvenile cataracts and endocrine features. A critical study, with five new cases, Ann. Int. Med., **23**:559, 1945.

921. Thatcher, L. Hypervitaminosis D, Lancet, Jan. 4: 20, 1936.

922. Thibault, P. La micro-lithiase alvéolaire pulmonaire ou maladie de Puhr, Presse méd., **69**:2148, 1961.

923. THIBIERGE, G., and WEISSENBACH, R. J. Une forme de concrétions calcaires sous-cutanées en relation avec la sclérodermie, Bull. mém. Soc. méd. hôp. Paris, **30**:10, 1910.

924. THIBIERGE, G., and WEISSENBACH, R. J. Concrétions calcaires sous-cutanées et sclérodermie, Ann. dermat. et syph., **2**:129, 1911.

925. THIERS, H.; COLOMB, D.; and FAYOLLE, J. La chélation par l'E.D.T.A. (acide éthylène diamine tétracétique) en rhumatologie: thérapeutique d'assouplissement et de détoxication, Lyon méd., **202**:339, 1959.

926. THOMAS, C.; CORDIER, J.; and DUPREZ, A. Manifestations ophtalmoscopiques des dermatomyosites, Bull. Soc. franç. dermat. et syph., **66**:349, 1959.

927. THURSFIELD, H. Sclerodermia with myositis fibrosa. Discussion, Proc. Roy. Soc. Med. (Sect. Study Dis. Children), **5**:7, 1911–12.

928. TIJDENS, E. F., and RUITER, M. Über osteosis kutis, Acta dermat.-venereol., **29**:140, 1949.

929. TILP, A. Demonstration eines Falles von ausgebreiteter Kalzinosis, Verhandl. Deutsche path. Gesellsch., **14**:277, 1910.

930. TIRSCHEK, H.; WODNIANSKY, P.; AUERSWALD, W.; and DOLESCHEL, W. Das Verhalten des säuren Mukoproteins im Blutserum bei zirkumskripter und diffuser Sklerodermie, Dermat. Wchnschr., **140**:840, 1959.

931. TORCHI, M. Sulla cosiddetta miopatia lipo-fibro-calcarea. Osservazioni patogenetiche (nota preventiva), Riv. anat. patol. e oncol., **15**:63, 1959.

932. TRANQUADA, R. E.; SIMMONS, D. H.; and MILLER, J. H. Pulmonary fibrosis in scleroderma. Report of a case with pulmonary function studies to evaluate corticosteroid and relaxin therapy, A.M.A. Arch. Int. Med., **105**:607, 1960.

933. TRAPANI, I. L.; LEIN, A.; and CAMPBELL, D. H. Passive antibody decay in thyroidectomized rabbits, Nature, **183**:982, 1959.

934. TSCHISTOWITSCH, T., and KOLESSNIKOFF, H. Multiples diffuses Myelom (Myelomatosis ossium) mit reichlichen Kalkmetastasen in die Lungen und andere Organe, Virchows Arch. path. Anat., **197**:112, 1909.

935. TUFFANELLI, D. L., and WINKELMANN, R. K. Systemic scleroderma. A clinical study of 727 cases, Arch. Dermat., **84**:359, 1961.

936. TUMULTY, P. A., and HOWARD, J. E. Irradiated ergosterol poisoning. Report of two cases, J.A.M.A., **119**:233, 1942.

937. TURIAF, J., and BRUN, J. La sarcoïdose endothoracique de Besnier-Boeck-Schaumann. Localisations médiastino-pulmonaires et bronchiques. Atteintes cardiaques, Paris, Expansion scient. franç., 1955.

938. UEHLINGER, E. Nieren, Skelet und Kalziumstoffwechsel, Wien. klin. Wchnschr., **61**:417, 1949.

939. UMBER, F. Ueber Kalkgicht, Berl. klin. Wchnschr., **58**:909, 1921.

940. URAI, L.; MUNKACSI, I.; and SZINAY, G. New data on the pathology of true scleroderma kidney, Brit. M.J., March 11: 713, 1961.

941. URIST, M. R., and McLEAN, F. C. Accumulation of mast cells in endosteum of bones of calcium deficient rats, A.M.A. Arch. Path., **63**:239, 1957.

942. VACHTENHEIM, J., and ŠMÍD, V. Diffuse Sklerodermie und L.E.-Zellen, München. med. Wchnschr., **103**:1474, 1961.

943. VALERO, A., and GELLEI, B. Retinitis pigmentosa, hypertension and uraemia in Werner's syndrome. Report of a case with necropsy findings, Brit. M.J., July 30: 351, 1960.

944. VAŠKŮ, J.; PADMANABHAN, N.; and SELYE, H. Kalcifylaxe v zánětovém vaku, Vnitrni lekar. (in press).

945. VECCHI, B. DE, and PATRASSI, G. Ueber die Splenopathien mit Kalkeiseninkrustationen (Mizen mit Gamnaschen Höfen), Virchows Arch. path. Anat., **279**:553, 1930.

946. VERSE, M. Ueber Calcinosis universalis, Beitr. path. Anat. u. allg. Path., **53**:212, 1912.

947. VRIES, S. DE. Retinopathy in dermatomyositis, A.M.A. Arch. Ophth., **46**:432, 1951.

948. WAGTENDONK, W. J. VAN. A dietary factor essential for guinea pigs. III. Changes in the distribution of acid soluble phosphorus in the liver and kidneys during deficiency, J. Biol. Chem., **155**:337, 1944.

949. WAGTENDONK, W. J. VAN, and FREED, A. M. A dietary factor essential for guinea pigs. XI. Diffusible and non-diffusible plasma calcium during the deficiency of the antistiffness factor, J. Biol. Chem., **167**:225, 1947.

950. WAGTENDONK, W. J. VAN.; FREED, A. M.; and BALLOU, C. E. A dietary factor essential for guinea pigs. V. Phosphorus and calcium content of the blood and muscle during deficiency, Arch. Biochem., **5–6**:329, 1944–45.

951. WAGTENDONK, W. J. VAN; SCHOCKEN, V.; and WULZEN, R. A dietary factor essential for guinea pigs. II. A comparative study of the creatine excretion of animals on a diet deficient in this factor and in vitamin E, Arch. Biochem., **3–4**:305, 1943–44.

952. WAGTENDONK, W. J. VAN, and ZILL, L. P. A dietary factor essential for guinea pigs. VII. Changes in the distribution of the plasma protein during the deficiency, J. Biol. Chem., **159**:247, 1945.

953. WAINGER, C. K., and LEVER, W. F. Dermatomyositis. Report of three cases with post-mortem observations, Arch. Dermat. & Syph., **59**:196, 1949.

954. WALSH, F. B., and HOWARD, J. E. Conjunctival and corneal lesions in hypercalcemia, J. Clin. Endocrinol., **7**:644, 1947.

955. WALTON, J. N., and ADAMS, R. D. Polymyositis. Edinburgh: E. & S. Livingstone Ltd., 1958.

956. WARWICK, O. H.; YENDT, E. R.; and OLIN, J. S. The clinical features of hypercalcemia associated with malignant disease, Canad. M.A.J., **85**:719, 1961.

957. WEBER, F. P., and GRAY, A. M. H. Chronic relapsing polydermatomyositis with predominant involvement of the subcutaneous fat (panniculitis), Brit. J. Dermat., **36**:544, 1924.

958. WEGELIUS, O., and ASBOE-HANSEN, G. Mast cells and tissue water. Studies on living connective tissue in the hamster cheek pouch, Exper. Cell Res., **11**:437, 1956.

959. WEILL, J., and MAIRE, R. Rétraction de l'aponévrose palmaire et sclérodermie, Paris méd., **24**:263, 1934.

960. WEINBERGER, H. J., and BAUER, W. Diagnosis and treatment of Reiter's syndrome, M. Clin. North America, **39**:587, 1955.

961. WEISS, S.; STEAD, E. A., JR.; WARREN, J. V.; and BAILEY, O. T. Scleroderma heart disease with a consideration of certain other visceral manifestations of scleroderma, Arch. Int. Med., **71**:749, 1943.

962. WEISSENBACH, R. J.; GATELLIER, J.; and DURUPT, A. Sclérodermie progressive et parathyroïdectomie, Bull. Soc. franç. dermat. et syph., **40**:1439, 1933.

963. WELLER, C. V. Tonsillar tubercles containing intracellular concretions simulating foreign body pseudotubercles, Ann. Oto. Rhino. & Laryngol., **31**:110, 1922.

964. WELLS, H. G., and HOLLEY, S. W. Metastatic calcification in osteitis deformans (Paget's disease of bone), Arch. Path., **34**:435, 1942.

965. WERNIE, L. Sklerodermie und Akromegalie, Monat. Dermat., **47**:414, 1908.

966. WEST, W. T., and MASON, K. E. Degeneration and regeneration in experimental muscular dystrophy, Am. J. Phys. Med., **34**:223, 1955.

967. WESTBERG, F. Ein Fall von mit weissen Flecken einhergehender, bisher nicht bekannter Dermatose, Monat. prakt. Dermat., **33**:355, 1901.

968. WETTLER, H. Über einen Fall von Wernerschem Syndrom, Ophthalmologica, **124**: 279, 1952.

969. WEYLMAN, W. T., and SIMON, H. Mediastinal calcification, J.A.M.A., **177**:502, 1961.

970. WHALEN, R. E.; COMBS, J. J., JR.; and DEISS, W. P., JR. "Stiff-man" syndrome, Am. J. Med., **27**:679, 1959.

971. WHEELER, C. E.; CURTIS, A. C.; CAWLEY, E. P.; GREKIN, R. H.; and ZHEUTLIN, B. Soft tissue calcification with special reference to its occurrence in the "Collagen-Diseases," Ann. Int. Med., **36**:1050, 1952.

972. WICHMANN, B. E. The mast cell count during the process of wound healing. An experimental investigation on rats, Acta path. microbiol. scandinav., suppl. 108, p. 1, 1955.

972*a*. WICHMANN, W. Ein Fall von Kalkablagerungen unter der Haut. (Kalk-Gicht), Inaugural Dissertation, Friedrich-Wilhelms Univ., Berlin, 1910.

973. WILDER, W. T.; FRAME, B.; and HAUBRICH, W. S. Peptic ulcer disease in hyperparathyroidism: An analysis of fifty-two cases, Abstr. Scient. Papers, 42d Ann. Session Am. Coll. Phys., May 8–12, Miami Beach, 1961, Ann. Int. Med., **54**:1047, 1961.

974. WILLIAMS, A. W. Relation of atheroma to local trauma, J. Path. & Bact., **81**:419, 1961.

975. WILLIAMS, C. M. A case of diffuse scleroderma presenting unusual features, Arch. Dermat. & Syph., **9**:187, 1924.

976. WILLIAMS, M. J. Sarcoidosis presenting with polyarthritis, Ann. Rheumat. Dis., **20**:138, 1961.

977. WILLIS, R. A. Pathology of Tumors. London: Butterworth & Co. Ltd., 2d. ed., 1953.

978. WILSON, J. R.; MERRICK, H.; and WOODWARD, E. R. Hypercalcemia simulating hyperparathyroidism induced by XV-2 carcinoma in rabbits, Program 53d Ann. Meet. Am. Soc. Clin. Invest., May 1, Atlantic City, p. 72, 1961.

979. WILSON, J. R.; MERRICK, H.; and WOODWARD, E. R. Hypercalcemia simulating

hyperparathyroidism induced by XV-2 carcinoma of rabbit, Ann. Surg., **154**:485, 1961.

980. WILSON, R. A case of dermatomyositis, Bull. Vancouver, M.A., **24**:273, 1948.

981. WILSON, G. Calcinosis circumscripta, J.A.M.A., **104**:391, 1935.

982. WIND, L. T. DE. Hypervitaminosis D with osteosclerosis, Arch. Dis. Childhood, **36**:373, 1961.

983. WINDER, P. R., and CURTIS, A. C. Edathamil in the treatment of scleroderma and calcinosis cutis, A.M.A. Arch. Dermat., **82**:732, 1960.

984. WINKELMANN, R. K. Treatment of systemic scleroderma, Proc. Staff Meet. Mayo Clin., **34**:55, 1959.

985. WINKELMANN, R. K. Diagnosis and treatment of lupus erythematosus, dermatomyositis and scleroderma with emphasis on cutaneous findings, J. Chron. Dis., **13**:401, 1961.

986. WOLMAN, M.; STERK, V. V.; GATT, S.; and FRENKEL, M. Primary familial xanthomatosis with involvement and calcification of the adrenals. Report of two more cases in siblings of a previously described infant, Pediatrics, **28**:742, 1961.

987. YAMAMOTO, M. Ueber die Stabilisierung des Vitamins C durch Adrenalin, Hoppe-Seyler's Ztschr. physiol. Chem., **243**:266, 1936.

987a. YOUNG, J. M.; BILLS, R. J.; and ULRICH, E. Discrete splenic calcification in necropsy-material, Am. J. Path., **33**:189, 1957.

988. YOUNG, M. O., and HALPERT, B. Parathyroid adenoma with generalized metastatic calcification, Arch. Path., **44**:628, 1947.

989. ZABEL, H. Zur Behandlung der Sarcoidosis mit Na_2-EDTA, Arch. klin. u. exper. Dermat., **213**:535, 1961.

990. ZAGARESE, F. Come deve essere impostato il problema dell'osteosi paratiroidea e delle altre sindromi attribuite all'iperparatiroidismo, Ann. med. nav. e colon., **40**:277, 1934.

991. ZAK, F. G.; COVEY, J. A.; and SNODGRASS, J. J. Osseous lesions in urticaria pigmentosa, New England J. Med., **256**:56, 1957.

992. ZARAFONETIS, C. J. D. Para-aminobenzoic acid in the treatment of scleroderma and other disorders associated with excessive fibrosis, Disc. Conf. Oct. 1, 1954, J. Michigan M. Sc., **53**:782, 1954.

993. ZAWISCH-OSSENITZ, C. Marble bone disease; study of osteogenesis, Arch. Path., **43**:55, 1947.

994. ZEEK, P. M. Periarteritis nodosa, a critical review, Am. J. Clin. Path., **22**:777, 1952.

995. ZELLWEGER, H. Ueber einen Fall von Speicheldrüsen-Boeck. Beitrag zur endokrinen Funktion der Speicheldrüsen, Helvet. paediat. acta, **1**:485, 1946.

996. ZIBORDI, F. Considerazioni sulla scialografia sottomascellare nell'artrite reumatoide e nella sclerodermia, Ann. Laringol., **59**:437, 1960.

997. ZITNAN, D., and SITAJ, S. Chondrocalcinosis polyarticularis (familiaris) rentgenologicky a klinicky rozbor, Ceskoslov. rentgenol., **14**:27, 1960.

997a. ZVAIFLER, N. J.; REEFE, W. E.; and BLACK, R. L. Articular manifestations in primary hyperparathyroidism. Ann. Meet. Am. Rheum. Assoc., Hollywood-by-the-Sea, Fla., June 9–11, 1960. Arthritis & Rheumat., **3**:471, 1960.

Index

To facilitate the use of this index, boldface numerals (e.g., **17**) refer to principal discussions of a subject, and those in normal font (e.g., 17), to all other parts of the text.

Greek letters (e.g., α, β, γ, o, Δ), numbers which form parts of indexed words, short connecting words (e.g., *the, of, for, from, to, as*), and brackets are neglected in determining the alphabetical positions of entries.

When a "target organ" A is influenced by a stimulus B, this is indicated by an arrow pointing from B to A thus: $A \leftarrow B$, instead of the usual cumbersome entry: "A, effect of B upon." Conversely, the effect of A upon B is indicated by the entry: $B \leftarrow A$, while a general discussion of the interrelations between A and B is indexed thus: $A \rightleftarrows B$. If two stimuli B and C act upon the same target organ A, this is indexed: $A \rightarrow B \leftarrow C$. If either B or C acts alone, we write: $A \leftarrow B$, C as well as $B \rightarrow A$ and $C \rightarrow A$.

It is, of course, impossible to index highly complex interactions under each stimulus or target involved (and under all synonyms), but entries have been so selected that it will be rarely necessary to search for a specific item under more than two possible headings.

All generalities and multiple actions involving many tissues are listed under the heading "Calciphylaxis." It is necessary to confront the individual organs to see which agents affect them.

AAN (aminoacetonitrile), 52; *cf. also* Lathyrogenic compounds
anticalciphylactic potency of, 284
$\rightarrow$ calciphylaxis $\leftarrow$ DHT + plucking, 284
Abdominal wall $\leftarrow$ albumen i.p. + DHT, *Fig. 43*
Acetic acid, 52
Acetylsalicylic acid, 52
Acrodermatitis chronica atrophicans, 320
Acromegaly $\rightleftarrows$ scleroderma, 426
Acrosclerosis, 321, *Figs. 255, 256*
ACTH
$\rightarrow$ calciphylaxis $\leftarrow$ DHT + Fe-Dex i.v. + PMX s.c., 278
$\rightarrow$ dermatomyositis, 354, *Fig. 272*
$\rightarrow$ scleroderma, 431
Actinic rays, 374
Acute soft-tissue calcinosis, 327
Addison's disease $\rightleftarrows$ scleroderma, 426
Adenomyositis; *cf.* Dermatomyositis
Adiponecrosis neonatorum, 321
Adiponecrosis subcutanea neonatorum; *cf.* Sclerema neonatorum
Adipose tissue
$\leftarrow$ albumen i.p. + DHT, *Figs. 47, 52*
$\leftarrow$ albumen, Fe-Dex, Thorotrast® + DHT, 64
$\leftarrow$ DHT + Fe-Dex i.p., 5, *Fig. 82*

$\leftarrow$ DHT + Fe-Dex i.p., i.v., 255
$\leftarrow$ DHT + 5HT i.p., s.c., 151
Adjuvant (topical activator of challenger), **5**, 441
action of, 440
for antigens, 453
classification of, 25
direct, indirect effect of, 62
pure, 453
route of administration, 23
in topical calciphylaxis, 55
Adjuvants of challengers, definition of, **13**
Adjuvants of indirect calcifiers, definition of, **13**
Adjuvation, 453
localizing, 57
Adolescent spondylitis; *cf.* Rheumatoid spondylitis
Adrenal hormones; *cf.* Glucocorticoids
Adrenal tumors, calcification in, 436
Adrenalectomy
$\rightarrow$ calciphylaxis, 278
$\leftarrow$ DHT + triamcinolone + FeCl$_3$, plucking, 278
Adrenaline, 49
Adrenals
calcinosis of, 327
$\leftarrow$ CrCl$_3$ i.v. + parathyroid hormone s.c., 213, *Fig. 172*

521

Adrenals—*Continued*
  ← DHT + FeCl₂ i.v., 112
  ← DHT + FeCl₃, 82
  ← DHT + Fe-Din i.v., 136
  ← DHT + Fe-OS i.v., *Fig. 98*
  ← DHT + Pb-acetate i.v., 170, *Figs. 127, 127a*
  ← DHT + Thorotrast® i.v., 184
  ← DHT + yolk i.v., 198
  ← Fe-OS i.v. + NaAST i.p., *Fig. 196*
  ← Fe-OS i.v. + parathyroid hormone s.c., 215, *Fig. 181*
  ← KMnO₄ intra-iliac, 305
  ← scleroderma, 426
AgCH₃·COO, 28, 50
Age
  → calciphylaxis, 20, 289
  ← DHT + FeCl₃ s.c., plucking, 289
  ← DHT + Fe-Dex i.p., i.v., Thorotrast® i.v., 291
  ← KMnO₄ s.c., 303, *Fig. 242*
AgNO₃, 28, 50
  as direct calcifier, 311
Ag₂SO₄, 28
Albers-Schönberg's disease; *cf.* Osteopetrosis
Albumen, **13,** 53
  local challenging effect of, 58
  → calciphylaxis ← CrCl₂ + DHT, 62
  → calciphylaxis ← DHT + FeCl₃, Fe-Dex, 59
Albumen i.p.
  → calciphylaxis ← DHT, 87, 255, *Figs. 43–54*
  ← DHT + PMX s.c., 285
  ← DHT + restraint, 265, *Figs. 214, 215*
  → calcium in muscle ← DHT, 75
Albumen i.p., i.v.
  → calciphylaxis ← DHT, *Fig. 41*
  ← DHT + PMX s.c., 290
Albumen i.v. → calciphylaxis ← DHT, 86, *Figs. 39, 40, 42*
Albumen s.c.
  → calciphylaxis ← DHT, 242, *Figs. 198, 202, 205, 206*
  ← DHT (in cat, dog, hamster, monkey, mouse), 292
  ← DHT + FeCl₃ s.c. + PMX s.c., 287
  ← DHT + Fe-Dex s.c., 254
  ← DHT + Fe-Dex s.c. + PMX s.c., 285
  ← DHT + hypophysectomy + plucking, 276, *Fig. 225*
  ← DHT + parathyroidectomy, 246
  ← DHT + restraint + Thorotrast® s.c., 263
  ← NaAST, *Fig. 15*
  → lacrimal gland, 78
  → salivary gland, 78
AlCl₃, 27, 50
  as direct calcifier, 311
Alcohol-formol fixation, 33

Alizarin red, 35, 53
Alizarin red s.c. → calciphylaxis ← DHT, *Fig. 5*
Alkaline phosphatase, 35
  of the skin, 456
AlK(SO₄)₂, 27, 50
AlK(SO₄)₂ i.p., i.v. → calciphylaxis ← DHT, 97
Allantoic fluid (rat), 49
Allergic reactions, 12
  ⇌ calciphylaxis, 6
Allyl alcohol, 52
Allyl amine, 52
Allyl isothiocyanate, 52
AlNH₄(SO₄)₂, 27, 50
AlNH₄(SO₄)₂ i.p., i.v. → calciphylaxis ← DHT, 97
Al(NO₃)₃, 27, 50
Aloe (black, yellow), 52
Aloin, 52
Aluminum, as challenger, 4
Aluminum ammonium sulfate, 27
Aluminum chloride, 27
Aluminum nitrate, 27
Aluminum potassium sulfate, 27
Alveolar microlithiasis, 334
Aminoacetonitrile; *cf.* AAN
Ammonium sulfate, 27
Amyloidosis (cutaneous), in scleroderma, 427
Anetoderma erythematodes, 321
Angioma ossificans, 436
Angiomyositis; *cf.* Dermatomyositis
Animals; *cf.* Species
Ankylosing atrophic arthritis, with scleroderma, 427
Ankylosing spondylitis; *cf.* Rheumatoid spondylitis
"Annular scleroderma," calciphylactic, *Fig. 91*
Anterior pituitary, lyophilized, 49
Antigens, adjuvants for, 453
Antimalarial compounds → lupus erythematosus, 377
Aorta; *cf. also* Heart
  ← albumen i.v. + DHT, 86
  ← DHT + trauma, 82
Apresoline®, 52
Arabic gum, 51
Arbitrary four-grade scale, 31
"Arborizing type" of cutaneous calcinosis, *Figs. 13, 14*
Arteries ← CrCl₃ intracarotid + DHT, *Fig. 24*
Arteriosclerosis, 325

Arthritis of Marie-Strumpell; *cf*. Rheumatoid spondylitis

Asteroid bodies, 402

Astrofer®; *cf*. Fe-Din

Atheromatous cysts, calcification in, 436

Atrophic spondylitis; *cf*. Rheumatoid spondylitis

Atrophy, in scleroderma, 423

Atypical calciphylactic scleroderma, 145

Auricle ← DHT + Fe-OS i.v. + PMX s.c., 287, 291

Auriculo-biliary calciphylaxis, 138, 215, 230, 236, *Figs. 95–98, 176–81, 196*

Auriculo-cutaneous calciphylaxis, 86

Aurothioglucose, 50

Aurothiomalate, sodium, 50

BaCl₂, 27, 50

Barium chloride, 27

Basophilic degeneration, 36

Bekhterev's syndrome; *cf*. Rheumatoid spondylitis

Besnier-Boeck-Schaumann's disease; *cf*. Sarcoidosis

BiCl₃, 50

Bilateral nephrectomy; *cf*. Nephrectomy

Bile (ox), 49

Bile duct
    ← DHT + FeCl₂ i.v., 255
    ← DHT + Fe-OS i.v., 1, 5, 12, 256
    ← DHT + Fe-OS i.v. + PMX s.c., 287
    ← Fe-OS i.v. + parathyroid hormone s.c., 215, *Fig. 179*

Biliary system
    calcinosis of, *Fig. 316*
    ← Fe-OS i.v., *Fig. 99*

Bismuth → calcium in tissue, 434

Bismuth chloride, 27

Body constituents and tissue extracts, cutaneous calciphylactic challenging effect of, 49

Boeck's sarcoid; *cf*. Sarcoidosis

Bone
    ← DHT + Fe-Dex i.v. + PMX s.c., 128
    ← KMnO₄ intra-iliac, 305, *Figs. 246, 247*
    ← KMnO₄ s.c., *Figs. 248–50*
    ← scleroderma, 418

Bone, lamellated, 38

Bone diseases, in general, 325

Bone-formation
    ← albumen s.c. + DHT, 242, *Figs. 198, 202*
    ← albumen, Fe-Dex s.c. + DHT + parathyroidectomy, 246
    ← DHT + FeCl₃ s.c., *Fig. 9*
    ← DHT + Fe-Dex s.c., 242, *Figs. 199–203*
    ← DHT + yolk i.v., 246, *Fig. 204*

Bone-marrow extract, 49

Bouillaud's disease; *cf*. Rheumatic fever

Bradykinin, 52

Brain
    ← CrCl₃ intracarotid + DHT, *Fig. 25*
    ← scleroderma, 423

Brain extract, 49

British gum (dextrin), 51

Bromelain; *cf*. Bromelin

Bromelin, 53

"Brown fat"; *cf*. Adipose tissue

Brunner's glands
    ← albumen i.p. + DHT, 89, 255
    ← albumen i.v. + DHT, 86
    ← CrCl₃ i.v. + DHT, 100, *Fig. 66*
    ← CrCl₃ i.v. + DHT (in rabbit), 297
    ← DHT + FeCl₂ i.v., 112
    ← DHT + Fe-Din i.v., 135
    ← DHT + Fe (ferric) albuminate i.p., 112
    ← DHT + Fe-OS i.v., 139
    ← DHT + yolk i.v., 198

Buccal mucous membranes and conjunctivas, in dermatomyositis, 352

Buccal scleroderma, among habitual betel-nut chewers in Taiwan, 427

Buerger's disease, 326
    combined with Raynaud's phenomenon, 326
    as disease of adaptation, 326
    giant cells in the thrombi of vessels, 326
    ⇄ scleroderma, 326

Burnett's syndrome; *cf*. Milk-alkali syndrome of Burnett *et al*.

Burns → calcification, 433

Bursae, calcinosis of, 327

Buschke-Ollendorff syndrome; *cf*. Scleredema adultorum Buschke

"Butterfly and Sleeves" syndrome, 126

Ca(CH₃COO)₂, 27, 50

CaCl₂, 27, 50
    as direct calcifier, 311

CaCl₂ s.c. → calciphylaxis, 314, *Fig. 251*

Cadmium chloride, 27

"Café au lait" patches, in neurofibromatosis, 386

Calcamin®; *cf*. DHT

Calcareous arthritis, in calciphylactic scleroderma with esophageal calcinosis and arthritis, 135

Calcareous chondrodystrophy, 342

Calcification
    direct, 441
    dystrophic, 3
    incrustation of elastic fibers in, 327
    of necrotic fat tissue, in sclerema neonatorum, 406

Calcification—*Continued*
  role of topical tissue injury in, 433
  in scars resulting from mechanical trauma or
    burns, 433
  systemogenic, 16
  in tissues; *cf.* under individual target organs and
    Calcinosis
  topogenic, 16
  in tumors, 434
  ← burns, 433
  ← foreign-body granulomas, infarcts, insect bite,
    lithopedions, tissue necrosis, tubercles, 434
  ← frost bite, 434
  ← trauma, 433
  ⇄ iron deposition, 327
Calcified plate formation, in topical calciphylaxis,
  37
Calcifier (systemic sensitizing agent), 2
  action of, 440
  definition of, 13
  direct, 13, 298, 441
  direct systemic, 3
  endogenous, 47
  indirect, 13, 441
  indirect systemic, 3
Calcinoscleroses, 318, 343
  concept of, 464
  definition of, 13
Calcinosis, 326
  acute soft-tissue, 327
  circumscripta, 327
  cutaneous, 15, 328
  definition of, 14
  in collagen diseases, 327
  induced by tumors, 436
Calcinosis cutis, 328
  ← EDTA, 330
  ← stress, 329
  ⇄ dermatomyositis, 330
Calcinosis of
  adrenals, 327
  biliary system, *Fig. 316*
  bursae, 327
  cardiovascular system ⇄ hyperparathyroidism,
    357
  choroid plexus, 328, *Fig. 257*
  ear, 330
  gallbladder, 331
  intervertebral discs, 331, *Fig. 259*
  intestines ⇄ hyperparathyroidism, 357
  joints, 331, *Fig. 260*
  kidney; *cf.* Renal diseases
  lung, 334, *Figs. 261–63*
  lung ⇄ hyperparathyroidism, 357
  nose, 336
  ovary, 338, *Fig. 264*
  pancreas, 338, 357, *Fig. 265*
  pericardium, 338

pineal body, 338
pleura, 339
salivary glands (excluding the parotid), 149,
  Figs. 107–19
salivary glands (including the parotid), 159, *Fig.
  120*
scrotum, 339
spleen, 340
stomach ⇄ hyperparathyroidism, 357
thyroid, 340
uterus, 341, *Fig. 266*
Calcinosis, nonspecific, 15
  ← age + DHT + FeCl₃ s.c., plucking, 289
  ← Ag₂SO₄ i.v. + DHT, 85
  ← AlK(SO₄)₂, AlNH₄(SO₄)₂ i.v. + DHT, 97
  ← As-acetate, BiCl₃, CdCl₂ i.v. + DHT, 98
  ← CoCl₂ i.v. + DHT, 100
  ← CuCl, Din i.v. + DHT, 111
  ← CuCl₂ i.v. + DHT, 104
  ← DHT + FeCl₃ i.v., 114
  ← DHT + Ga₂(SO₄)₃ i.v., 145
  ← DHT + gelatin s.c., 145
  ← DHT + KMnO₄, LaCl₃ i.v., 168
  ← DHT + Na₂SnO₃ i.v., 170, *Fig. 126*
  ← DHT + PVP i.p., reserpine i.v., 176
  ← DHT + PVP i.v., 174
  ← DHT + SnCl₂, ThCl₄, Th(NO₃)₄, TiCl₃,
    TiCl₄ i.v., 177
  ← DHT + VOSO₄ i.v., 194
  ← DHT + ZrOCl₂ i.v., 211
  ← NaAST i.p., 235, *Fig. 193*
Calcinosis, postphlebitic subcutaneous, 330, *Fig.
  258*
Calcinosis Segmentalis Congenita, 340
Calcinosis universalis, 327, 340
  ← EDTA, 341
  ← thyroparathyroidectomy (partial), 341
  ⇄ myositis ossificans, 384
  ⇄ rheumatic fever, 400

Calciphylaxis
Calciphylactic "annular scleroderma," *Fig. 91*
  dermatomyositis, 14, 127, 171, 208, 212, 255,
    265, 281, 288, 290, *Figs. 128–31*
  prevention by restraint, *Fig. 217*
  lesions, produced after sensitization with
    NaAST, 235
Calciphylactic muscular dystrophy, 14, 213, 223,
  Figs. 173, 182–85
  periarteritis nodosa, 8
  psoriasis, definition of, 14
    produced by DHT + Fe-Dex i.p., 120, *Figs.
      77–80*
  reactions, noncalcifying, 465
  scleroderma, 14, *Fig. 89*
    with arthritis, 83
    atypical, 145
    with esophageal calcinosis, 236, *Fig. 195*

with esophageal calcinosis and arthritis, 134, 177, 231, 239, *Figs. 90–94, 132–46, 186–92, 197*

sensitizers, site of action of, 444

syndromes, 83

 produced after sensitization by esophageal and gastric fistulas, 239

 by nephrectomy, 227

 by parathyroid hormone, 213

 with vitamin D_3, 212

 by other means, 240

wheal, 58

 with central "overchallenge," *Fig. 12*

Calciphylaxis, **1**

auriculo-biliary, 138, 215, 230, 236, *Figs. 95–98, 176–81, 196*

auriculo-cutaneous, 86

biologic significance of, 460

chemical observations, 36

clinical implications, **318**

definitions and terminology, 13, **14**

direct calcifiers, **298**

evaluation of lesions, **30**

factors influencing susceptibility to, **250**

hepato-splenic, 209, *Figs. 169, 170*

histologic observations and technique, 33

history, 8

hyalinization in, 242

inflammatory changes, 241

local factors, 455

macroscopic observations, 30

metacalciphylactic syndromes, 241

methodology, **17**

omental, thymic, and RES-type, 203, *Figs. 161–66*

pancreatic and psoriasiform, 115, 117

pancreatic and RES-type, 167

pancreatico-cutaneous, 87

peritoneal, 111, 143, 168, 190, *Fig. 148*

peritoneo-pleural, 168

phylactic value of, 461

physiologic significance of, 466

production of, 19

 in kidney, liver, peritoneum, pleura, 73, 74

 in lung, 76

renal (cortico-medullary), 192, *Figs. 149, 150*

RES-type, 98, 170, 194, *Figs. 127, 127a, 151–60*

salivary gland, 212

sclerosis in, 242

sensitizers, role of, 257

site of challenge, **250**

systemic, 1, **14**

thymic, 145, *Figs. 103–5*

thyroid-parathyroid-carotid-body, 100, 112, 145, 213, 227, *Figs. 102, 171, 172, 188*

topical, 1, **14**

uterine and psoriasiform, 118

← AAN + DHT + plucking, 284

← ACTH, glucocorticoids, hypophysectomy + DHT + Fe-Dex i.v. + PMX s.c., 278

← adrenalectomy, 278

← adrenalectomy + DHT + triamcinolone + FeCl₃, plucking, 278

← age, 20, 289

← age + DHT + FeCl₃ s.c., plucking, 289

← age + DHT + Fe-Dex i.p., i.v., Thorotrast® i.v., 291

← age + KMnO₄ s.c., 303, *Fig. 242*

← Ag₂SO₄ i.v. + DHT, 85

← albumen i.p. + DHT, 87, 255, *Figs. 43–54*

← albumen i.p. + DHT + PMX s.c., 285

← albumen i.p. + DHT + restraint, 265, *Figs. 214, 215*

← albumen i.p., i.v. + DHT, *Fig. 41*

← albumen i.p., i.v., CrCl₂, CrCl₃, FeCl₂, FeCl₃, Fe-Dex, Fe-Din i.v., + DHT + PMX s.c., 290

← albumen i.v. + DHT, 86, *Figs. 39, 40, 42*

← albumen, chromium, Fe-Dex, Fe-OS, 5HT, thorium i.v. + DHT, 12

← albumen s.c. + DHT, 242, *Figs. 198, 202, 205, 206*

← albumen s.c. + DHT + FeCl₃ s.c. + PMX s.c., 287

← albumen s.c. + DHT + Fe-Dex s.c. + PMX s.c., 285

← albumen s.c. + DHT + hypophysectomy + plucking, 276, *Fig. 225*

← albumen s.c. + DHT + restraint + Thorotrast® s.c., 263

← albumen, FeCl₃, Fe-Dex, yolk s.c. + DHT (in cat, dog, hamster, monkey, mouse), 292, 293

← albumen, Fe-Dex s.c. + DHT + parathyroidectomy, 246

← albumen, Fe-Dex, 5HT, Thorotrast® s.c., 79

← alizarin red s.c. + DHT, *Fig. 5*

← AlK(SO₄)₂ i.p., i.v. + DHT, 97

← AlNH₄(SO₄)₂ i.p., i.v. + DHT, 97

← As-acetate i.v., BiCl₃ i.v., CdCl₂ i.v., CeCl₃ i.p., i.v., chondroitin sulfuric acid i.p. + DHT, 98

← Ca-acetate, Na-acetate, Na₃-citrate, NaCl, NaH₂PO₄, Na₂HPO₄ + Tl-acetate, 240

← CaCl₂ s.c., 314, *Fig. 251*

← calcium (dietary intake), 257

← calcium acetate p.o. + DHT, 258, *Fig. 211*

← CrCl₂ i.v. + DHT, 104, *Figs. 67–70*

← CrCl₂ s.c. + DHT, 302

← CrCl₂, CrCl₃, FeCl₂, FeCl₃, Fe-Dex, Fe-Din, Fe-OS, Fe-Sol i.v. + DHT + PMX s.c., 288

← CrCl₃ intracarotid + DHT, *Figs. 20–26, 35*

← CrCl₃ intra-iliac + DHT, *Figs. 27–29, 36*

← CrCl₃ intraportal + DHT, *Fig. 32*

← CrCl₃ i.v. + DHT, 255, *Figs. 55, 57–66*

Calciphylaxis—*Continued*

← CrCl₃ i.v. + DHT (in cat), 293, *Figs. 233, 234*

← CrCl₃ i.v. + DHT (in dog), 297

← CrCl₃ i.v. + DHT (in guinea pig), 297, *Fig. 235*

← CrCl₃ i.v. + DHT (in hamster), 297

← CrCl₃ i.v. + DHT (in rabbit), 297, *Fig. 236*

← CrCl₃ i.v. + DHT + extirpation of superior cervical sympathetic ganglion, 282, *Fig. 230*

← CrCl₃ i.v. + DHT + PMX s.c., 287

← CrCl₃ i.v. + DHT + restraint, 265, *Fig. 216*

← CrCl₃ s.c. + DHT + FeCl₃ s.c., 254

← CrCl₃ s.c. + DHT + Fe-Dex s.c. + restraint, 263

← CrCl₃ s.c. + DHT + hemostat + PMX s.c., 285

← CrCl₃ i.v. + nephrectomy, *Fig. 188*

← CrCl₃ i.v. + parathyroid hormone s.c., 213, *Figs. 171, 172*

← CrCl₃, FeCl₂ intracarotid, intra-iliac, i.v. + DHT, 64

← critical period, **252**

← CuCl, Din i.v. + DHT, 111

← CuCl₂ i.v. + DHT, 104

← DHT + DOC s.c. + Fe-Dex i.v. + PMX s.c. + triamcinolone s.c., 281

← DHT + egg white, egg yolk i.v., 4

← DHT + estradiol, methyltestosterone + plucking, 281

← DHT + F-COL, triamcinolone, 281

← DHT + FeCl₂ intracarotid, *Fig. 37*

← DHT + FeCl₂ intraportal, *Figs. 31, 33*

← DHT + FeCl₂ i.v., 112, 255, *Figs. 71–73*

← DHT + FeCl₃ i.v., 114

← DHT + FeCl₃ s.c. + plucking + PMX s.c., 285

← DHT + FeCl₃ s.c. + restraint + yolk s.c., 263

← DHT + FeCl₃ s.c., Fe-OS i.v., 1

← DHT + Fe-Dex intrapedal, *Fig. 208*

← DHT + Fe-Dex i.p., 5, 117, *Figs. 77–83, 318*

← DHT + Fe-Dex i.p. + ovariectomy, 281, *Fig. 229*

← DHT + Fe-Dex i.p., i.v., 255

← DHT + Fe-Dex i.v., 249, *Fig. 207*

← DHT + Fe-Dex intratumoral, 82, *Fig. 38*

← DHT + Fe-Dex i.v., 115, *Figs. 74, 75*

← DHT + Fe-Dex i.v. + glucocorticoids + PMX s.c., 242

← DHT + Fe-Dex i.v. + hypophysectomy + PMX s.c., 277, *Fig. 226*

← DHT + Fe-Dex i.v. + insulin s.c., 126, *Fig. 83a*

← DHT + Fe-Dex i.v. + PMX s.c., 127, 255, 287, *Figs. 84–89, 209*

← DHT + Fe-Dex i.v. + PMX s.c. + restraint, 265, *Fig. 217*

← DHT + Fe-Dex i.v. + PMX s.c. + triamcinolone s.c., 280

← DHT + Fe-Dex s.c., 242, 254, *Figs. 199–203*

← DHT + Fe-Dex s.c. (in hamster), *Fig. 231*

← DHT + Fe-Dex s.c. (in mouse), *Fig. 232*

← DHT + Fe-Dex s.c. + albumen s.c., 254

← DHT + Fe-Din i.v., 134, *Figs. 90–94*

← DHT + Fe-Din i.v. + PMX s.c., 287

← DHT + Fe-Din i.v. + restraint, 265, *Fig. 218*

← DHT + Fe (ferric) albuminate i.p., 111

← DHT + Fe-OS, 5HT intratumoral, 82

← DHT + Fe-OS i.p., 143, *Fig. 83*

← DHT + Fe-OS i.v., 5, 138, 256, *Figs. 95–98, 101*

← DHT + Fe-OS s.c., 254

← DHT + Fe-OS i.v. + PMX s.c., 287, 291

← DHT + FeSO₄ i.v., 145, *Fig. 102*

← DHT + Fe-Sol i.v., 145

← DHT + Fe-Sol, yolk i.v. + PMX s.c., 291

← DHT + Ga₂(SO₄)₃ i.v., 145

← DHT + gelatin s.c., 145

← DHT + glucocorticoids s.c., 145, *Figs. 103–5*

← DHT + hematoporphyrin, HgCl₂ i.v., 166

← DHT + histamine liberators i.v., s.c., 4

← DHT + 5HT i.p., s.c., 149, *Figs. 106–19*

← DHT + 5HT s.c. + IPR i.p., 159, *Figs. 120–23*

← DHT + 5HT + nerve lesion, 282

← DHT + 5HT i.p. + PMX s.c., 285

← DHT + 5HT s.c. + restraint, 265

← DHT + hypophysectomy, *Fig. 227*

← DHT + InCl₃ i.v., 167

← DHT + IPR i.p., 167, 256, *Fig. 124*

← DHT + KCl, MgCl₂, NaCl, NaClO₄, Na₂SO₄ + plucking, 259

← DHT + KMnO₄ i.p., i.v., 168

← DHT + LaCl₃ i.p., i.v., 168

← DHT + LAP s.c., 278, *Fig. 228*

← DHT + LTH, STH, vasopressin + plucking, 278

← DHT + MgH₄(PO₄)₂ p.o., 168

← DHT + NaClO₄ p.o., s.c., 169

← DHT + Na₂HPO₄ p.o., *Fig. 212*

← DHT + NaH₂PO₄ p.o., 170, *Fig. 213*

← DHT + Na₂SnO₃ i.v., 170, *Fig. 126*

← DHT + nephrotoxic substances, thallium acetate + plucking, 283

← DHT + Pb-acetate i.v., 170, *Figs. 127, 127a*

← DHT + plucking + restraint + Tl-acetate s.c., *Fig. 149*

← DHT + PMX s.c., 171, *Figs. 128–31, 252, 253*

← DHT + PMX s.c. + Thorotrast® i.v., 287

← DHT + PMX s.c. + yolk i.v., 208, 285, 287, *Fig. 168*

← DHT + PVP i.v., 174

← DHT + PVP i.p., reserpine i.v., 176

← DHT + restraint + Thorotrast® i.v., 266, *Figs. 219–21*

← DHT + SnCl₂, ThCl₄, Th(NO₃)₄, TiCl₃, TiCl₄ i.v., 177

← DHT + thallium salts, 284

← DHT + thallium salts + plucking, 284

← DHT + Thorotrast®, 340

← DHT + Thorotrast® i.p., 190, *Fig. 148*

← DHT + Thorotrast® i.v., 177, 246, 256, *Figs. 132–46*

← DHT + Tl-acetate s.c., 192, *Figs. 149, 150*

← DHT + trauma, 10, 74, 82

← DHT + VOSO₄ i.v., 194

← DHT + Walker tumor transplant, *Fig. 317*

← DHT + yolk i.p., 203, *Figs. 161–67*

← DHT + yolk i.v., 194, 246, *Figs. 151–60, 204*

← DHT + ZnCl₂ i.v., 209, *Figs. 169, 170*

← DHT + ZrOCl₂ i.v., 211

← DHT, NaAST, parathyroid hormone, surgical interventions, vitamin D₂, vitamin D₃, 26

← DHT, parathyroid hormone + parathyroidectomy, 281

← 2:4-dinitrophenol, lathyrogenic compounds, thallium salts, mastocyte dischargers, 284

← direct calcifiers + glucocorticoids, hypophysectomy, stress, 302

← drugs, **284**

← electrolytes, Fe-Dex, Fe-Din, Fe-OS, Fe-Sol, Thorotrast®, 26, 27

← electrolytes (various) + Tl-acetate, 240

← F-COL s.c. + Fe-OS i.v. + Na₂HPO₄ p.o., 240

← Fe-Dex i.v. + NaAST i.p., 236, *Fig. 194*

← Fe-Dex i.v. + parathyroid hormone s.c. + PMX s.c., 213, *Figs. 173–75*

← Fe-Dex i.v. + PMX s.c. + restraint + vitamin D₃ i.v., 266, *Fig. 222*

← Fe-Dex i.v. + PMX s.c. + vitamin D₃ i.v., 212

← Fe-Din i.v. + NaAST i.p., 236, *Fig. 195*

← Fe-OS i.v. + NaAST i.p., 236, *Fig. 196*

← Fe-OS i.v. + nephrectomy, 230

← Fe-OS i.v. + parathyroid hormone s.c., 215, *Figs. 176–81*

← Fe-OS, Thorotrast® i.v. + nephrectomy + parathyroidectomy, 281

← gastric and esophageal fistulas, 283

← glucocorticoids, 281

← glucocorticoids, 5HT, PMX, 48/80, 29, 30

← glucocorticoids, stress + KMnO₄ s.c., 302

← hormones, **274**

← 5HT s.c. + parathyroid hormone s.c., 223, 256, *Figs. 182–85*

← 5HT s.c. + restraint + vitamin D₃ i.v., 266, *Figs. 223, 224*

← 5HT s.c. + vitamin D₃ i.v., 212

← hypophyseal hormones, 277

← hypophysectomy + KMnO₄ s.c., 302, *Fig. 241*

← KMnO₄ intra-iliac, 304, *Figs. 243–50*

← KMnO₄ s.c., 298, *Figs. 237, 238, 248–50*

← KMnO₄ s.c. + parathyroidectomy, 303

← NaAST i.p., 235, *Fig. 193*

← NaAST i.p. + Thorotrast® i.v., 239, *Fig. 197*

← NaH₂PO₄ p.o. + vitamin D₂, 258, *Fig. 210*

← nephrectomy, 282

← nephrectomy + Thorotrast® i.v., 231, *Figs. 189–92*

← nerves of the thyro-parathyroid apparatus, 282

← nervous stimuli, 282

← neurohumoral substances, 282

← parathyroid hormone s.c. + Thorotrast® i.v., 226, *Figs. 186, 187*

← phosphate (dietary intake), 257

← renal lesions, 282

← sex, **291**

← species, 18, **292**

← stress, **261**

← surgical interventions, 3

← Thorotrast® i.v., *Fig. 147*

← yolk i.v., 200, *Fig. 160*

← ZnCl₂ s.c., *Fig. 240*

⇄ allergic reactions, 6

⇄ collagen diseases, 7, 449, 464

⇄ infectious diseases, 463

⇄ inflammation, 6

⇄ neoplasia, 465

⇄ other connective-tissue reactions, 6

⇄ stress, 468

⇄ wound healing, 7

Calcium in

adrenals ← albumen i.v. + DHT, 87

biliary passages ← DHT + Fe-OS, 83

blood, in calcinosis cutis, 329

    in calcinosis universalis, 340

    in Dupuytren's contracture, 354

    in keloids, 367

    in osteitis deformans, 387

    in rheumatoid arthritis, 399

blood, urine, in dermatomyositis, 351

carotid body ← CrCl₃, KMnO₄ intracarotid + DHT, 79

ciliary body ← 5HT subconjunctival, 79

connective tissue ← DHT + FeCl₂ intracarotid, *Fig. 37*

duodenum ← DHT + Fe-OS, 83

eyelids ← CrCl₃, FeCl₃, 5HT, Thorotrast® subconjunctival, 79

heart ← albumen i.v. + DHT, 86

    ← cutaneous calcinosis, 330

    ← DHT, 85

    ← DHT + FeCl₂ i.v., *Fig. 73*

kidney ← DHT, 85

    ← DHT + Fe-OS, 83

Calcium in—*Continued*
 kidney—*Continued*
  ← HgCl₂, PMX s.c., trauma, vessel ligature, 317
 lacrimal gland ← albumen, Fe-Dex, 5HT, Thorotrast® s.c., 79
 lung ← DHT + KMnO₄ intratracheal, *Fig. 34*
  ← cutaneous calcinosis, 330
 muscle ← albumen, Fe-Dex i.p. + DHT, 75
  ← histamine liberators, PMX, 48/80, 77
 muscle, tongue ← CrCl₃ intracarotid, intra-iliac + DHT, 79
 pancreas ← albumen i.v. + DHT, 87
 pancreas, peritoneum, stomach ← chondroitin sulfuric acid i.p., i.v. + DHT, 98
 salivary glands ← albumen i.v. + DHT, *Fig. 40*
  ← albumen, Fe-Dex, 5HT, Thorotrast® s.c., 79
 sclerematous subcutis, 406
 spleen ← CeCl₃ i.v. + DHT, *Fig. 55*
 stomach ← DHT, 85
  ← DHT + FeCl₂ i.v., *Fig. 71*
 submaxillary gland ← albumen, Fe-Dex, 5HT, Thorotrast® s.c., 79
 thymus ← albumen i.v. + DHT, 87
  ← cutaneous calcinosis, 330
  ← DHT, 85
 thyroid ← cutaneous calcinosis, 330
 tissues; *cf. also* Calcinosis, nonspecific, and under individual target organs
  ← albumen i.v. + DHT, 86
  ← bismuth, calcium, copper, 434
  ← CaCl₂ s.c., 314, *Fig. 251*
  ← CrCl₂ i.v. + DHT, *Fig. 70*
  ← DHT + Fe (ferric) albuminate i.p., 112
  ← glucocorticoids, stress + KMnO₄ s.c., 302
  ← hypophysectomy + KMnO₄ s.c., 302, *Fig. 241*
  ← KMnO₄ s.c., 298, *Figs. 237, 238*
  ← KMnO₄ s.c. + parathyroidectomy, 303
  ← scleroderma, 425
  ← ZnCl₂ s.c., *Fig. 240*
Walker tumor transplant ← DHT + Fe-Dex intratumoral, *Fig. 38*

Calcium acetate, 27
 as direct calcifier, 311
 → calciphylaxis ← Tl-acetate, 240

Calcium acetate p.o. → calciphylaxis ← DHT, 258, *Fig. 211*

Calcium chloride anhydrous, dihydrate, 27

Calcium gout, 340

Calcium incrustated collagen fibers and fat cells, in topical calciphylaxis, 37

Calcium salts, as direct calcifiers, 314

Calculi, 341, 397

Carapace, 40

Carbohydrates and related compounds, cutaneous calciphylactic challenging effect of, 49

Carboxymethylcellulose, 49

Carcinoma psammosum, 436

Carcinomas of the thyroid, calcification in, 436

Cardiac and muscular lesions
 produced by DHT + glucocorticoids s.c. + NaH₂PO₄ p.o., 147
 produced by DHT + NaClO₄ p.o., s.c., 169

Carotid body
 ← CrCl₃ i.v. + DHT, 100, *Figs. 56, 57*
 ← CrCl₃ i.v. + DHT (in cat), 293, *Figs. 233, 234*
 ← CrCl₃ i.v. + DHT (in guinea pig), 297, *Fig. 235*
 ← CrCl₃ i.v. + DHT (in rabbit), 297, *Fig. 236*
 ← CrCl₃ i.v. + DHT + extirpation of superior cervical sympathetic ganglion, 282, *Fig. 230*
 ← CrCl₃ i.v. + DHT + PMX s.c., 287, 290
 ← CrCl₃ i.v. + DHT + restraint, 265
 ← CrCl₃ i.v. + nephrectomy, 227, *Fig. 188*
 ← CrCl₃ i.v. + parathyroid hormone s.c., 213, *Fig. 171*
 ← CrCl₃, KMnO₄ intracarotid + DHT, 78
 ← DHT + FeCl₂ i.v., 112
 ← DHT + FeCl₂ i.v. + PMX s.c., 290

Carrageenin, 49

Carrier substance, 23

Cartilage extract, 49

CdCl₂, 27, 50
 as direct calcifier, 311

CeCl₃, 27, 50
 as direct calcifier, 311

CeCl₃ i.p., i.v. → calciphylaxis ← DHT, 98

CeCl₃ i.v. → calcium in spleen ← DHT, *Fig. 55*

Celestin blue, 53
 technique of, 33, 35

Cerebral; *cf.* Brain

Cerium, as challenger, 4

Cerous chloride, 27

Cesium chloride, 27

Challenge, 444

Challenger (vital mordant), **4**, 441
 action of, 440
 adjuvants, 13, 57, 441, 453
 classification, 25
 definition, **14**
 direct, 4, **14**, 441
 endogenous, 451
 indirect, 4, **14**
 inhibitors of, **15**
 route of administration, 23, 445

Chemical observations, of calciphylactic lesions, 36

Chloriodized oil, 52

Chlorophyll, 52

Cholesterol
in blood, in calcinosis universalis, 340
in sclerematous subcutis, 406

Cholografin®, 52

Chondroangiopathia calcarea, 342
punctata, 342

Chondrocalcinosis polyarticularis (familiaris), 332

Chondrodystrophia calcificans congenita punctata, 342, *Fig. 268*
fetalis calcarea, 342
fetalis hypoplastica, 342

Chondroitin sulfate A, B, C, 51

Chondroitin sulfuric acid; *cf.* C.S.A.

Chondroma ossificans, 436

Choroid plexus
calcinosis of, 328, *Fig. 257*
← CrCl₂ i.v. + DHT, *Fig. 69*
← CrCl₃ intracarotid + DHT, *Fig. 26*
← CrCl₃ i.v. + parathyroid hormone s.c., 213, *Fig. 172*
← DHT + Fe-Din i.v., 136

Chromium, as challenger, 4

Chromium i.v. → calciphylaxis ← DHT, 12

Chromium chloride, -nitrate, -oxide, -sulfate, chromous chloride, 27

Circinate cutaneous calcinosis, 44, *Fig. 12*
produced by DHT around a Walker tumor transplant, *Fig. 317*

Circumscribed myositis ossificans, 382

Classification, of sensitizers, challengers, and adjuvants, 25

Clinical implications, **318**

Cobalt chloride, 27

Coccidoides immitis, 334

CoCl₂, 27, 50

CoCl₂, as direct calcifier, 311

Cold; *cf. also* Stress
(local), cutaneous calciphylactic challenging, effect of, 52
→ scleroderma, 427

Collagen diseases, 319, 343
← EDTA, 343
⇄ calciphylaxis, 7, 449, 464

Colloidal carbon, 52

Conditioning, hormonal, 319

Congenital ectodermal defect, 345

Congenital stippled epiphyses, 342

Congo red, 53

Connective tissue
reactions ⇄ calciphylaxis, 6

← albumen, Fe-Dex, Thorotrast® + DHT, 64
← Thorotrast® intracarotid, 65

Copper → calcium in tissue, 434

Cornea; *cf.* Eye

Corticoids; *cf.* Glucocorticoids

Cortico-medullary nephrocalcinosis, 240

CrCl₂, 27, 50
as topical challenger, 57
→ calciphylaxis ← albumen, C.S.A., dextran, dextrin, gelatin, KMnO₄, pectin, plasma, PMX, PVP, yolk, 48/80 + DHT, 62
→ calciphylaxis ← DHT, 62, 302, *Figs. 67–69*

CrCl₂ i.v.
→ calcium in tissues ← DHT, *Fig. 70*
→ calciphylaxis ← DHT + PMX s.c., 288

CrCl₃, 27, 50
as direct calcifier, 311

CrCl₃ intracarotid
→ calciphylaxis ← DHT, *Figs. 19–26, 35*
→ carotid body ← DHT, 78

CrCl₃ intracarotid, intra-iliac → calcium in muscle ← DHT, 77, 79

CrCl₃ intracarotid, intra-iliac, i.v. → calciphylaxis ← DHT, 64

CrCl₃ intra-iliac → calciphylaxis ← DHT, *Figs. 27–29, 36*

CrCl₃ intraportal → calciphylaxis ← DHT, 65, *Fig. 32*

CrCl₃ i.v.
→ calciphylaxis ← DHT, 47, 255, *Figs. 55–66, 70*
← DHT (in cat), 293, *Figs. 233, 234*
← DHT (in dog), 297
← DHT (in guinea pig), 297, *Fig. 235*
← DHT (in hamster), 297
← DHT (in rabbit), 297, *Fig. 236*
← DHT + extirpation of superior cervical sympathetic ganglion, 282, *Fig. 230*
← DHT + PMX s.c., 287, 290
← DHT + restraint, 265, *Fig. 216*
← nephrectomy, 227, *Fig. 188*
← parathyroid hormone s.c., 213, *Figs. 171, 172*

CrCl₃ s.c.
→ calciphylaxis ← DHT + FeCl₃ s.c., 254
← DHT + Fe-Dex s.c. + restraint, 263
← DHT + hemostat + PMX s.c., 285

CrCl₃ subconjunctival → eye, 78

CrCl₃ (topically) → granuloma pouch ← DHT, *Fig. 30*

Critical period, 5, 22, 252, 454
definition of, **14**
in systemic calciphylaxis, **253**
in topical calciphylaxis, **252**

Cr(NO₃)₃·9H₂O, 27

CrO₃, 50

CrO_3, 50
Cr_2O_3, 27
Croton oil, 49, 52
$Cr_2(SO_4)_3 \cdot 15H_2O$, 27
Crushing of skin (hemostat), cutaneous calciphylactic challenging effect of, 52
C.S.A. (chondroitin sulfuric acid), 51
  as adjuvant, 30
  → calciphylaxis ← $CrCl_2$ + DHT, 62, 98
    ← DHT, 59, 62
    ← DHT + $FeCl_3$, Fe-Dex, 59
CsCl, 27, 50
Csillag's disease; *cf.* Lichen sclerosus
$Cu(CH_3COO)_2$, 50
CuCl, 27, 50
Cupric chloride, -nitrate, -sulfate, cuprous chloride, 27
$CuSO_4$, 27, 50
  as direct calcifier, 311
Cutaneous; *cf. also* Skin
Cutaneous calcinosis, 328; *cf. also* Calcinosis cutis
  definition, 15
  forms of, 37
  histology, 37
  produced by DHT + plucking of scalp hair, *Fig. 7*
  with sclerosis, produced by parathyroid hormone, 9
Cutaneous calcinosis ⇄ hyperparathyroidism, 357, *Fig. 273*
Cutaneous calciphylactic challenging effect of
  body constituents and tissue extracts, 49
  carbohydrates and related compounds, 49
  dyes, 53
  eggs and egg constituents, 53
  enzymes, 53
  exudates collected from granuloma pouches, 49
  hormones, 49
  metallic compounds and electrolytes, 50
  microbial products, 51
  mucilages, 51
  mucopolysaccharides, 51
  physical agents, 52
  radiopaque substances, 52
Cutaneous incision, cutaneous calciphylactic challenging effect of, 52
Cutaneous molt
  production of, 40
  production by DHT + albumen s.c., *Fig. 11*
Cutaneous rashes ⇄ myositis ossificans, 384
Cutis hyperelastica; *cf.* Ehlers-Danlos syndrome
Cytosteatonecrosis of the subcutaneous tissue of the newborn; *cf.* Sclerema neonatorum

Dacryosialoadenopathia atrophicans; *cf.* Sjögren's syndrome
Definition of
  adjuvants of challengers, 13
  adjuvants of indirect calcifiers, 13
  albumen, 13
  calcifiers, 13
  calcinoscleroses, 13
  calcinosis, 14
  calciphylactic dermatomyositis, 14
  calciphylactic muscular dystrophy, 14
  calciphylactic psoriasis, 14
  calciphylactic scleroderma, 14
  calciphylaxis, 14
  challengers, 14
  critical period, 14
  cutaneous calcinosis, 15
  direct calcifiers, 13
  indirect calcifiers, 13
  direct challengers, 14
  indirect challengers, 14
  inhibitors of challengers, 15
  inhibitors of indirect calcifiers, 15
  metacalciphylactic changes, 15
  nonspecific calcinosis, 15
  overchallenge, 16
  physical agents, 29
  siderocalciphylaxis, 16
  stromal depot system, 16
  systemic calciphylaxis, 14
  systemogenic calcification, 16
  topical calciphylaxis, 14
  topogenic calcification, 16
Degeneration, basophilic, mucinous, fuchsinophilic, 36
Dens, dental; *cf.* Tooth
Dermatitis atrophicans maculosa lipoidea diabetica; *cf.* Necrobiosis lipoidica diabeticorum
Dermatitis atrophicans reticularis; *cf.* Poikiloderma vascular atrophicans
Dermatitis herpetiformis, 367
Dermatitis lichenoides chronica atrophicans; *cf.* Lichen sclerosus
Dermatofibrosis lenticularis disseminata, 345
Dermatomucomyositis; *cf.* Dermatomyositis
Dermatomyositis, 7, 343, 346, *Figs. 269–72*
  buccal mucous membranes and conjunctivas in, 352
  calciphylactic, **14**, 127, 171, 208, 212, 255, 265, 281, 288, *Figs. 128–31*
  calciphylactic, prevention by restraint, *Fig. 217*
  as hypersensitivity reaction, 353
  induced by calciphylaxis, definition of, **15**
  muscle changes in, 352
  nervous complications, 353
  ocular lesions in, 352
  ← ACTH, 354, *Fig. 272*

← EDTA, 354
← irradiation of the diencephalon, 354
← penicillin, 353
← vitamin E, 354
⇄ calcinosis cutis, 330
⇄ infection, 352
⇄ rheumatic fever, 400
⇄ rheumatism, 353
⇄ Rothmund's disease, 401
⇄ sclerema neonatorum, 406
⇄ scleroderma, 351, 426
⇄ status thymicolymphaticus, 353
⇄ tumors, 353

Dermatosclerosis; *cf.* Scleroderma

Dermatosis, superficial, macular, scaly form of, 47

Dermoids, calcification in, 436

Desiccation, local (high frequency current), cutaneous calciphylactic challenging effect of, 52

Desoxycorticosterone (acetate); *cf.* DOC

Dextran, 49
    as adjuvant, 30, 56, *Figs. 17, 18*
    → calciphylaxis ← CrCl$_2$ + DHT, 62
    → calciphylaxis ← DHT, 59
    → calciphylaxis ← DHT + FeCl$_3$ s.c., *Figs. 17, 18*
    → calciphylaxis ← DHT + FeCl$_3$, Fe-Dex, 59

Dextrin
    as adjuvant, 30
    → calciphylaxis ← CrCl$_2$ + DHT, 62
    → calciphylaxis ← DHT, 59, 62
    → calciphylaxis ← DHT + FeCl$_3$, Fe-Dex, 59

DHT, 15
    mechanism of action, 3
    as sensitizer, 26
    solvent, route of administration, 2, 84
    → calciphylaxis, 26
        ← AAN + plucking, 284
        ← ACTH, glucocorticoids, hypophysectomy + Fe-Dex i.v. + PMX s.c., 278
        ← adrenalectomy + triamcinolone + FeCl$_3$, plucking, 278
        ← age + FeCl$_3$ s.c., plucking, 289
        ← age + Fe-Dex i.p., i.v., Thorotrast® i.v., 291
        ← Ag$_2$SO$_4$, 85
        ← albumen i.p., 87, 255, *Figs. 43–54*
        ← albumen i.p. + PMX s.c., 285
        ← albumen i.p. + restraint, 265, *Figs. 214, 215*
        ← albumen i.p., i.v., *Fig. 41*
        ← albumen i.p., i.v., CrCl$_2$, CrCl$_3$, FeCl$_2$, FeCl$_3$, Fe-Dex, Fe-Din i.v. + PMX s.c., 290
        ← albumen i.v., 12, 86, *Figs. 39, 40, 42*
        ← albumen, Fe-Dex, Thorotrast®, 64
        ← albumen s.c., 242, *Figs. 198, 202, 205, 206*
        ← albumen s.c. + FeCl$_3$ s.c. + PMX s.c., 287

← albumen, FeCl$_3$, Fe-Dex, yolk s.c. (in cat, dog, hamster, monkey, mouse), 292, 293
← albumen s.c. + Fe-Dex s.c., 254
← albumen s.c. + Fe-Dex s.c. + PMX s.c., 285
← albumen s.c. + hypophysectomy + plucking, 276, *Fig. 225*
← albumen s.c. + restraint + Thorotrast® s.c., 263
← albumen, Fe-Dex s.c. + parathyroidectomy, 246
← albumen, C.S.A., dextran, dextrin, gelatin, pectin, plasma, PMX, yolk s.c. + FeCl$_3$, Fe-Dex, 59
← albumen, C.S.A., dextran, dextrin, gelatin, KMnO$_4$, pectin, plasma, PMX, PVP, yolk, 48/80 s.c. + CrCl$_2$, 62
← alizarin red s.c., *Fig. 5*
← AlK(SO$_4$)$_2$ i.p., i.v., 97
← AlNH$_4$(SO$_4$)$_2$ i.p., i.v., 97
← As-acetate i.v., BiCl$_3$ i.v., CdCl$_2$ i.v., CeCl$_3$ i.p., i.v., chondroitin sulfuric acid i.p., 98
← calcium acetate p.o., 258, *Fig. 211*
← chromium, Fe-Dex, Fe-OS, 5HT, thorium i.v., 12
← CrCl$_2$ i.v., 104, *Figs. 67–70*
← CrCl$_2$ s.c., 302
← CrCl$_2$, FeCl$_2$, FeCl$_3$, Fe-Dex, Fe-Din, Fe-OS, Fe-Sol i.v. + PMX, 288
← CrCl$_3$ intracarotid, *Figs. 19, 20, 22–26*
← CrCl$_3$, FeCl$_2$ intracarotid, intra-iliac, i.v., 64
← CrCl$_3$ intra-iliac, *Figs. 27–29, 36*
← CrCl$_3$ intraportal, 65, *Fig. 32*
← CrCl$_3$ i.v., 47, 100, 255, 288, 297, *Figs. 55–66*
← CrCl$_3$ i.v. (in cat), 293, *Figs. 233, 234*
← CrCl$_3$ i.v. (in guinea pig), 297, *Fig. 235*
← CrCl$_3$ i.v. (in rabbit), 297, *Fig. 236*
← CrCl$_3$ i.v. + extirpation of superior cervical sympathetic ganglion, 282, *Fig. 230*
← CrCl$_3$ s.c. + Fe-Dex s.c. + restraint, 263
← CrCl$_3$ s.c. + hemostat + PMX s.c., 285
← CrCl$_3$ i.v. + PMX s.c., 287
← CrCl$_3$ i.v. + restraint, 265, *Fig. 216*
← CuCl$_2$ i.v., 104, 111
← Dextran + FeCl$_3$ s.c., *Fig. 18*
← dextrin i.v., 111
← DOC s.c. + Fe-Dex i.v. + PMX s.c. + triamcinolone s.c., 281
← egg white, yolk, i.v., 4
← estradiol, methyltestosterone + plucking, 281
← F-COL, triamcinolone, 281
← Fe(ferric) albuminate i.p., 111
← FeCl$_2$ intracarotid, *Fig. 37*
← FeCl$_2$ intraportal, 65, *Figs. 31, 33*

DHT—*Continued*
→ calciphylaxis—*Continued*
← FeCl₂ i.v., 112, 255, *Figs. 71–73*
← FeCl₃, Fe-Dex + KMnO₄, 48/80, PVP, 60
← FeCl₃ i.v., 114
← FeCl₃ s.c., *Figs. 9, 17*
← FeCl₃ s.c. + CrCl₃ s.c., 254
← FeCl₃ s.c., Fe-OS i.v., 1
← FeCl₃ s.c. + plucking + PMX s.c., 285
← FeCl₃ s.c. + restraint + yolk s.c., 263
← Fe-Dex intrapedal, *Fig. 208*
← Fe-Dex intratumoral, 82, *Fig. 38*
← Fe-Dex i.p., 5, 117, *Figs. 13, 77–83, 318*
← Fe-Dex i.p. + ovariectomy, 281, *Fig. 229*
← Fe-Dex i.p., i.v., 255
← Fe-Dex i.v., 115, 249, *Figs. 74, 75, 207*
← Fe-Dex i.v. + glucocorticoids + PMX s.c.,
    242
← Fe-Dex i.v. + hypophysectomy + PMX
    s.c., 277, *Fig. 226*
← Fe-Dex i.v. + insulin s.c., 126, *Fig. 83a*
← Fe-Dex i.v. + PMX s.c., 217, 255, 287,
    Fig. 209
← Fe-Dex i.v. + PMX s.c. + restraint, 265,
    Fig. 217
← Fe-Dex i.v. + PMX s.c. + triamcinolone
    s.c., 280
← Fe-Dex s.c., 242, 254, *Figs. 199–203*
← Fe-Dex s.c. (in hamster), *Fig. 231*
← Fe-Dex s.c. (in mouse), *Fig. 232*
← Fe-Din i.v., 134, *Figs. 90–94*
← Fe-Din i.v. + PMX s.c., 287
← Fe-Din i.v. + restraint, 265, *Fig. 218*
← Fe-OS, 83
← Fe-OS, 5HT intratumoral, 82
← Fe-OS i.p., 143, *Fig. 83*
← Fe-OS i.v., 1, 5, 138, *Figs. 95–98*
← Fe-OS i.v., 141, 256, *Fig. 101*
← Fe-OS i.v. + PMX s.c., 287, 291
← Fe-OS s.c., 254
← FeSO₄ i.v., 145, *Fig. 102*
← Fe-Sol i.v., 145
← Fe-Sol, yolk i.v. + PMX s.c., 291
← Ga₂(SO₄)₃ i.v., 145
← gelatin s.c., 145
← glucocorticoids s.c., 145, *Figs. 103–5*
← hematoporphyrin, HgCl₂ i.v., 166
← histamine liberators i.v., s.c., 4
← 5HT + nerve lesion, 282
← 5HT i.p. + PMX s.c., 285
← 5HT i.p., s.c., 149, *Figs. 107–19*
← 5HT s.c. + IPR i.p., 159, *Figs. 120–23*
← 5HT s.c. + restraint, 265
← hypophysectomy, *Fig. 227*
← InCl₃ i.v., 167
← IPR i.p., 167, 256, *Fig. 124*
← KCl, MgCl₂, NaCl, NaClO₄, Na₂SO₄ +
    plucking, 259
← MnO₄ i.p., 168

← KMnO₄, PVP, 48/80, 60
← LaCl₃ i.p., 168
← LAP s.c., 278, *Fig. 228*
← LTH, STH, vasopressin + plucking, 278
← MgH₄(PO₄)₂ p.o., 168
← NaClO₄ p.o., s.c., 169
← Na₂HPO₄ p.o., *Fig. 212*
← NaH₂PO₄ p.o., 179, *Fig. 213*
← Na₂SnO₃ i.v., 170, *Fig. 126*
← nephrotoxic substances, thallium acetate
    + plucking, 283
← parathyroidectomy, 281
← Pb-acetate i.v., 170, *Figs. 127, 127a*
← pectin s.c., *Fig. 14*
← plucking (of scalp hair), *Figs. 7, 8, 10*
← plucking + restraint + thallium acetate
    s.c., *Fig. 149*
← PMX s.c., 171, *Figs. 128–31, 252, 253*
← PMX s.c. + Thorotrast® i.v., 287
← PMX s.c. + yolk i.v., 208, 285, 287, *Fig.
    168*
← PVP i.p., reserpine i.v., 176
← PVP i.v., 174
← restraint + Thorotrast® i.v., 266, *Figs.
    219–21*
← skin traction, *Fig. 16*
← SnCl₂, ThCl₄, Th(NO₃)₄, TiCl₃, TiCl₄, i.v.,
    177
← thallium acetate s.c., 192, *Figs. 149, 150*
← thallium salts, 284
← thallium salts + plucking, 284
← Thorotrast®, 340
← Thorotrast®, i.p., 190, *Fig. 148*
← Thorotrast® i.v., 177, 246, 256, *Figs. 132–
    46*
← trauma, 10, 74, 82
← VOSO₄ i.v., 194
← Walker tumor, *Fig. 317*
← yolk i.p., 203, *Figs. 161–67*
← yolk i.v., 194, 246, *Figs. 151–60, 204*
← ZnCl₂ i.v., 209, *Figs. 169, 170*
← ZrOCl₂ i.v., 211
→ calcium in heart, kidney, stomach, thymus,
    85
→ calcium in muscle ← albumen, Fe-Dex i.p.,
    75
    ← CrCl₃ intracarotid, intra-iliac, 77, 79
→ calcium in spleen ← CeCl₃ i.v., *Fig. 55*
→ calcium in tissues ← albumen i.v., 86, 87
    ← Chondroitin sulfuric acid i.p., i.v., 98
    ← CrCl₂ i.v., *Fig. 70*
    ← FeCl₂ i.v., *Figs. 71–73*
    ← Fe (ferric) albuminate i.p., 112
→ cardiac and skeletal-muscle ← glucocorti-
    coids s.c. + NaH₂PO₄ p.o., 147
→ carotid body ← CrCl₃, KMnO₄ intracarotid,
    79
→ granuloma pouch ← CrCl₃ topically, *Fig. 30*

→ heart, muscle ← Me-Cl-COL s.c. + NaH₂PO₄ p.o. + species, 147

→ lung ← KMnO₄ intratracheal, *Fig. 34*

→ muscle ← KCl, MgCl₂ + Me-Cl-COL s.c. + NaH₂PO₄ p.o., 147

→ scleroderma, 430

Diabetes, calcinosis and ossification of the skin in, 330

Diaphragm; *cf. also* Muscle
← albumen i.p + DHT, *Fig. 53*
← CrCl₃ i.v. + DHT, *Figs. 63, 64*
← DHT + FeCl₂ i.v., 112

Diatrizoate methylglucamine, 52

Diet, **257**

Dihydrotachysterol; *cf.* DHT

2:4-dinitrophenol → calciphylaxis, 284

Dionosil®, 52

Direct calcification, 441

Direct calcifiers, **298**; *cf. also* Calcifiers
definition, **13**
→ calciphylaxis ← glucocorticoids, hypophysectomy, stress, 302

Direct calcifying effect ⇌ calciphylaxis, 300

Direct challenger, 4; *cf. also* Challengers
definition, **14**
route of administration, 445
valency of elements, 446

Direct systemic calcifier, 3

Disc, calcinosis of, 331, *Fig. 259*

Discoid lupus erythematosus, *Fig. 282; cf. also* Lupus erythematosus

Diseases of adaptation, 326

Disseminated lupus erythematosus, 374, *Fig. 283*

Disseminated necrotizing periarteritis; *cf.* Periarteritis nodosa

DOC (desoxycorticosterone), 15, 49

DOC s.c. → calciphylaxis ← DHT + Fe-Dex i.v. + PMX s.c. + triamcinolone s.c., 281

Drugs → calciphylaxis, **284**

Dry vitamin D₂; *cf.* Vitamin D₂

Duhring's disease, 367

Duodenal extract, 49

Duodenum
← albumen i.p. + DHT, 89
← CrCl₃ i.v. + DHT (in hamster), 297
← DHT + Fe (ferric) albuminate i.p., 112
← DHT + Fe-Dex i.p., 117, 118
← DHT + Fe-Dex i.v., 115

Dupuytren's contracture, 354
← EDTA, 354
⇌ myocardial infarction, 354

Dyes, cutaneous calciphylactic challenging effect of, 53

Dysplasia epiphysiaria punctata, 342

Dystrophic calcification, **3**

Ear
calcinosis of, 330
← albumen, Fe-Dex, Thorotrast® + DHT, 64
← scleroderma, 421

Ectopic osteogenesis, 242

Eczema, chronic, 330

Edematous polymyositis, 352

Edematous scleroderma of Hardy; *cf.* Scleredema adultorum Buschke

EDTA
→ calcinosis universalis, 341
→ dermatomyositis, 354
→ keloid, 370
→ sarcoidosis, 404
→ scleroderma, 430

Egg, egg constituents, cutaneous calciphylactic challenging effect of, 53

Egg white, as challenger, 4

Egg white i.v. → calciphylaxis ← DHT, 4

Egg yolk; *cf. also* Yolk
as challenger, 4

Egg yolk i.v. → calciphylaxis ← DHT, 4

Ehlers-Danlos syndrome, 354

Elastic fibers, tendency to undergo calcification of, 456

Electrolytes
cutaneous calciphylactic challenging effect of, 50
as direct challengers, 27
→ calciphylaxis, 27
→ calciphylaxis ← thallium acetate, 240

Embryo extract, 49

Encephalopathy ⇌ lupus erythematosus, 374

Endogenous calcifiers, 47

Endogenous challengers, 451

Enzymes, cutaneous calciphylactic challenging effect of, 53

Eosinophilia
in dermatomyositis, 353
in scleredema adultorum Buschke, 405
in scleroderma, 427

Epidermal cell, ingrowth under the calcified necrotic plate, 40

Epilation; *cf.* Plucking

Epiphysis ← KMnO₄ intra-iliac, 305, *Fig. 247*

Epitheliomas, calcifying cutaneous, 436

Ertron®, intoxication, 361

Erythema multiforme, 404

Erythema nodosum, 404

Escherichia coli lipopolysaccharide (Difco), 51

Esophageal fistulas → calciphylaxis, 283

Esophagus
    ← DHT + Fe-Dex i.v. + PMX s.c., *Fig. 87*
    ← DHT + Fe-Din i.v., 135
    ← DHT + Fe-Din i.v. + PMX s.c., 287, 290
    ← DHT + Fe-Din i.v. + restraint, 265, *Fig. 218*
    ← DHT + PMX s.c. + Thorotrast® i.v., 287
    ← DHT + restraint + Thorotrast® i.v., 266
    ← DHT + thorium i.v., 12
    ← DHT + Thorotrast® i.v., 246, 256, *Figs. 132–44*
    ← Fe-Din i.v. + NaAST i.p., 236, *Fig. 195*
    ← parathyroid hormone s.c. + Thorotrast® i.v., *Fig. 186*
    ← Thorotrast® i.v., *Fig. 147*
    ← scleroderma, 409, *Figs. 305, 306*
Estradiol, 49
    → calciphylaxis ← DHT + plucking, 281
Ethanol, 52
Ethiodol®, 52
Ethiodized oil, 52
Ethyl iodophenylundecylate, 52
17α-Ethyl-19 nortestosterone, 49
Exanthematous erythematosus; *cf.* Disseminated lupus erythematosus
External lacrimal gland; *cf.* Lacrimal gland
Extrusion of calcified skin masses, following treatment with DHT + Fe-Dex i.p., *Fig. 318*
Exudates collected from granuloma pouches, cutaneous calciphylactic challenging effect of, 49
Eye
    ← CrCl₃ intracarotid + DHT, *Fig. 23*
    ← CrCl₃, FeCl₃, 5HT, Thorotrast® subconjunctival, 78
    ← DHT + Fe-Din i.v., 136
    ← DHT + 5HT s.c., 151, *Figs. 109, 115–19*
    ← DHT + 5HT s.c. + IPR i.p., *Fig. 123*
    ← hyperparathyroidism, 357
    ← sarcoidosis, 404
    ← scleredema adultorum Buschke, 405
    ← scleroderma, 421

Face
    ← DHT + Fe-Din i.v. + restraint, *Fig. 218*
    ← DHT + Fe-Din i.v. + restraint, 265
    ← DHT + restraint + Thorotrast® i.v., *Figs. 220, 221*
    ← DHT + restraint + Thorotrast® i.v., 266
    ← DHT + Thorotrast® i.v., *Figs. 134, 143, 144*
    ← nephrectomy + Thorotrast® i.v., *Figs. 189, 191*
Facial desmoids, 354
Facial hemiatrophy, in scleroderma, 423
Factors influencing susceptibility to calciphylaxis, **250**
Fat; *cf.* Adipose tissue

F-COL (9α-fluorocortisol), 15, 49
    → calciphylaxis ← DHT, 281
F-COL s.c.
    → calciphylaxis ← DHT, *Fig. 103*
        ← Fe-OS i.v. + Na₂HPO₄ p.o., 240
Fe (ferric) albuminate i.p. → calciphylaxis ← DHT, 111
Febrile panniculitis; *cf.* Panniculitis
Fe[CH₂OH(CHOH)₄CO₂]₂·2H₂O, 28
Fe(C₃H₅O₃)₂·3H₂O, 28
FeCl₂, 27, 50
    as direct calcifier, 311
FeCl₂ intracarotid → calciphylaxis ← DHT, 255, *Fig. 37*
FeCl₂ intracarotid, intra-iliac, i.v. → calciphylaxis ← DHT, 64
FeCl₂ intraportal → calciphylaxis ← DHT, 65, *Figs. 31, 33*
FeCl₂ i.v.
    → calciphylaxis ← DHT, 112, *Figs. 71–73*
    ← DHT + PMX s.c., 288, 290
FeCl₃, 50
    as direct calcifier, 311
    as topical challenger, 57
    topical effect upon subcutaneous tissue in the nonsensitized rat, *Fig. 6*
    → calciphylaxis ← adrenalectomy + DHT + triamcinolone, 278
        ← albumen, C.S.A., dextran, dextrin, gelatin, pectin, plasma, PMX, yolk + DHT, 59
        ← DHT, 59
        ← DHT + KMnO₄, PVP, 48/80. 60
    → skin, *Fig. 6*
FeCl₃ i.v.
    → calciphylaxis ← DHT, 114
        ← DHT + PMX s.c., 288, 290
FeCl₃ s.c.
    → calciphylaxis ← dextran + DHT, *Figs. 17, 18*
        ← age + DHT, 289
        ← albumen s.c. + DHT + PMX s.c., 287
        ← DHT, 1, *Fig. 9*
        ← DHT (in cat, dog, hamster, monkey, mouse), 292, 293
        ← DHT + CrCl₃ s.c., 254
        ← DHT + plucking + PMX s.c., 285
        ← DHT + restraint + yolk s.c., 263
FeCl₃ subconjunctival → eye, 78
Fe-Dex (ferric dextran), 15
    as direct challenger, 26
    as systemic challenger, 57
    → calciphylaxis, 26
        ← albumen, C.S.A., dextran, dextrin, gelatin, pectin, plasma, PMX, yolk + DHT, 59
        ← DHT, 64

← DHT + $KMnO_4$, PVP, 48/80, 60
← DHT + PMX, *Fig. 209*
Fe-Dex i.p.
→ calciphylaxis ← *Figs. 77–82*
← DHT, 5, 6, 117, 118, *Figs. 13, 83, 318*
← DHT + ovariectomy, 281, *Fig. 229*
→ calcium in muscle ← DHT, 75
Fe-Dex i.p., i.v.
→ calciphylaxis ← age + DHT, 291
← DHT, 255
Fe-Dex intrapedal → calciphylaxis ← DHT, *Fig. 208*
Fe-Dex intratumoral → calciphylaxis ← DHT, *Fig. 38, 82*
Fe-Dex i.v.
→ calciphylaxis ← ACTH, glucocorticoids, hypophysectomy + DHT + PMX s.c., 278
← DHT, 12, 115, 249, *Figs. 74, 75, 207*
← DHT + DOC s.c. + PMX s.c. + triamcinolone s.c., 281
← DHT + glucocorticoids + PMX s.c., 242
← DHT + hypophysectomy + PMX s.c., 277, *Fig. 226*
← DHT + insulin s.c., 126, *Fig. 83a*
← DHT + PMX s.c., 127, 255, 287, 288, 290, *Figs. 84–89*
← DHT + PMX s.c. + restraint, 265, *Fig. 217*
← DHT + PMX s.c. + triamcinolone s.c., 280
← NaAST i.p., 236, *Fig. 194*
← parathyroid hormone s.c. + PMX s.c., 213, *Figs. 173–75*
← PMX s.c. + vitamin D_3 i.v., 212
← PMX s.c. + restraint + vitamin D_3 i.v., 266, *Fig. 222*
← albumen s.c. + DHT + PMX s.c., 285
← $CrCl_3$ s.c. + DHT + restraint, 263
← DHT, 242, 254, *Figs. 199–203*
← DHT (in cat, dog, monkey), 292, 293
← DHT (in hamster), 292, *Fig. 231*
← DHT (in mouse), 292, *Fig. 232*
Fe-Dex s.c.
→ calciphylaxis ← DHT + albumen s.c., 254
← DHT + parathyroidectomy, 246
→ lacrimal gland, 78
→ salivary gland, 78
→ submaxillary gland, 79
Fe-Din (ferric dextrin), 15, 27
as direct challenger, 27
Fe-Din i.v.
→ calciphylaxis, 134, *Figs. 90–94*
← DHT + PMX s.c., 287, 290
← DHT + restraint, 265, *Fig. 218*
← NaAST i.p., 236, *Fig. 195*
$Fe(NH_4)(SO_4)_2$, 27, 50
$Fe(NO_3)_3$, 27, 50
Fe_2O_3, 27
Fe-OS (ferric oxide saccharate), 15
as direct challenger, 26
→ calciphylaxis, 26
← DHT, 83
← parathyroid hormone, 83
Fe-OS intratumoral → calciphylaxis ← DHT, 82
Fe-OS i.p. → calciphylaxis ← DHT, 143, *Fig. 83*
Fe-OS i.v.
→ biliary tract, pancreas, *Figs. 99, 100*
→ calciphylaxis ← DHT, 1, 5, 12, 138, 141, 256, *Figs. 95–98, 101*
← DHT + PMX s.c., 287, 288, 291
← F-COL s.c. + Na_2HPO_4 p.o., 240
← NaAST i.p., 236, *Fig. 196*
← nephrectomy, 230
← nephrectomy + parathyroidectomy, 281
← parathyroid hormone s.c., 215, *Figs. 176–81*
Fe-OS s.c. → calciphylaxis ← DHT, 254
Ferric ammonium sulfate, ferric chloride, -nitrate, -oxide, 27
Ferric dextran; *cf.* Fe-Dex
Ferric dextrin; *cf.* Fe-Din
Ferric oxide saccharate; *cf.* Fe-OS
Ferric sorbitol; *cf.* Fe-Sol
Ferrigen®; *cf.* Fe-Din
Ferritin, 50
Ferrous ammonium sulfate, ferrous chloride, -gluconate, -lactate, -sulfate, 27, 28, 50
$FeSO_4$, 28, 50
$FeSO_4$ i.v. → calciphylaxis ← DHT, 145, *Fig. 102*
Fe-Sol (ferric sorbitol), 15
as direct challenger, 27
→ calciphylaxis, 27
Fe-Sol i.v.
→ calciphylaxis ← DHT + PMX s.c., 288
← DHT, 145
← DHT + PMX s.c., 291
Fibroma molluscum; *cf.* Neurofibromatosis
Fibroma petrificans, 436
9α-fluorocortisol; *cf.* F-COL
Formalin, 52
Fracture → scleroderma, 427
Frostbite → calcification, 434
Fuchsinophilic degeneration, 36

Gallbladder, calcinosis of, 331
Gallium nitrate, -sulfate, 28
Gamna corpuscles, in sideroscleroses, 431
$Ga(NO_3)_3$, as direct calcifier, 311
$Ga_2(SO_4)_3$, 50
as direct calcifier, 311
$Ga_2(SO_4)_3$ i.v. → calciphylaxis ← DHT, 145

Gasserian ganglion ← CrCl₃ intracarotid + DHT, *Fig. 26*

Gastric and esophageal fistulas → calciphylaxis, 283

Gastric extracts, 49

Gastric mucin, 51

Gastric mucosa
   ← albumen i.p. + DHT, 89
   ← DHT + yolk i.v., *Fig. 157*

Gastrointestinal system; *cf. also* under individual organs
   ← scleroderma, 412

Gavage, technique of, *Fig. 1*

Gelatin, 52
   as adjuvant, 30
   → calciphylaxis ← CrCl₂ + DHT, 62
      ← DHT, 59, 62, 145
      ← DHT + FeCl₃, Fe-Dex, 59

Generalized myositis ossificans, 7

Generalized ("nonspecific") calcinosis, 334

Giant-cell formation
   in Buerger's disease, 326
   ← DHT + Thorotrast® i.v., *Fig. 135*

Globin, 49

α-, β-, γ-Globulin, 52

Glomus
   ← CrCl₃ i.v. + DHT, 255
   ← DHT + FeCl₂ i.v., 255

Glucocorticoids; *cf. also* Adrenal hormones
   as indirect challenger, 30
   → calciphylaxis, 30, 281
      ← DHT, 145, *Figs. 103–5*
      ← DHT + Fe-Dex i.v. + PMX s.c., 242, 278
      ← direct calcifiers, 302
      ← KMnO₄ s.c., 302
   → calcium in tissue ← KMnO₄ s.c., 302
   → cardiac and skeletal-muscle ← DHT + NaH₂PO₄ p.o., 147
   → scleroderma, 431

Glucose, 49

Glycerides, in sclerematous subcutis, 406

Glycerin, 52

Glycogen, 49

Gold sodium thiomalate, 28

Granular form, of topical calciphylaxis, 46

Granuloma pouch
   calcification by Fe-Dex or CrCl₃ (into a pneumodermal pouch of the DHT-sensitized rat), 72
   exudates, cutaneous calciphylactic challenging effect of, 49
   ← CrCl₃, Fe-Dex (into a pneumodermal pouch) + DHT, 72
   ← DHT + CrCl₃ topically, *Fig. 30*

Granulomas (foreign body) → calcification, 434

Growth hormone; *cf.* STH (somatotrophic hormone)

Gum Arabic, British, Indian (ghatti), kino, tragacanth, 51

Hair plucking; *cf.* Plucking

Harder gland ← CrCl₃, FeCl₃, 5HT, Thorotrast® subconjunctival, 78

Heart
   ← AAN + DHT, 284
   ← albumen i.v. + DHT, 86, *Fig. 39*
   ← albumen s.c. + DHT, *Figs. 205, 206*
   ← AlK(SO₄)₂ i.v. + DHT, 97
   ← AlNH₄(SO₄)₂ i.p. + DHT, 97
   ← CrCl₂ i.v. + DHT, *Fig. 70*
   ← CrCl₂ i.v. + DHT + PMX s.c., 290
   ← CrCl₃ i.v. + DHT, 100, 255, *Fig. 65*
   ← CrCl₃ i.v. + DHT (in hamster), 297
   ← CrCl₃ i.v. + DHT (in rabbit), 297
   ← CrCl₃ i.v. + DHT + PMX s.c., 287, 288, 290
   ← CrCl₃ i.v. + parathyroid hormone s.c., 213, *Fig. 171*
   ← DHT + Fe (ferric) albuminate i.p., 112
   ← DHT + FeCl₂ i.v., 112, *Fig. 73*
   ← DHT + FeCl₂ i.v. + PMX s.c., 127, 290, *Fig. 86*
   ← DHT + Fe-Din i.v., 135
   ← DHT + Fe-OS, 83
   ← DHT + Fe-OS i.v., 1, 5, 12, 141, 256, *Fig. 101*
   ← DHT + Fe-OS i.v. + PMX s.c., 287, 291
   ← DHT + glucocorticoids s.c. + NaH₂PO₄ p.o., 147
   ← DHT + 5HT i.p., s.c., 151
   ← DHT + IPR i.p., 167, 256, *Fig. 124*
   ← DHT + KMnO₄ i.p., 168
   ← DHT + Me-Cl-COL s.c. + NaH₂PO₄ p.o. + species, 147
   ← DHT + NaClO₄ p.o., s.c., 169
   ← DHT + NaH₂PO₄ p.o., 170
   ← DHT + trauma, 82
   ← DHT + yolk i.v., 198
   ← F-COL s.c. + FeOS i.v. + Na₂HPO₄ p.o., 240
   ← Fe-OS + parathyroid hormone, 83
   ← Fe-OS i.v. + NaAST i.p., *Fig. 196*
   ← Fe-OS i.v. + parathyroid hormone s.c., 215, *Fig. 176*
   ← 5HT s.c. + parathyroid hormone s.c., *Fig. 185*
   ← NaAST i.p., *Fig. 193*
   ← scleroderma, 415, *Fig. 310*

Heat; *cf. also* Stress
   cutaneous calciphylactic challenging effect of, 52
   → scleroderma, 427

Heberden's nodules, 356

Heerfordt's syndrome, 431

Hematomas ⇄ myositis ossificans, 382

Hematoporphyrin, 52
→ scleroderma, 430

Hematoporphyrin i.v. → calciphylaxis ← DHT, 166

Hematoxylin, 35

Hemiatrophy, facial, in scleroderma, 423

Hemiscleroderma, 423

Hemochromatosis, 356

Hemoglobin, 49

Hemosiderosis, 356

Hemostat → calciphylaxis ← $CrCl_3$ s.c. + DHT + PMX s.c., 285

Heparin, 49

Heparitin sulfate, 51

Hepatic; *cf.* Liver

Hepato-splenic calciphylaxis, 209, *Figs. 169, 170*

Hereditary hemorrhagic telangiectasis; *cf.* Osler-Rendu-Weber's syndrome

Hg-acetate, as direct calcifier, 311

$HgCl_2$ → kidney, 3

$HgCl_2$ i.v. → calciphylaxis ← DHT, 166

$HgCl_2$ s.c. → calcium in kidney, 317, *Fig. 254*

Hg-sulfide, 28, 50

Hibernating gland
← albumen, Fe-Dex, Thorotrast® + DHT, 64
← DHT + 5HT s.c., *Fig. 113*

Histamine, 49

Histamine liberators; *cf. also* 48/80
route of administration, 4
→ calcium in muscle, 75

Histamine liberators i.v., s.c. → calciphylaxis ← DHT, 4

Histology, of calciphylaxis, 33, 37

Histoplasma capsulatum, 334

Histoplasmosis, 334, *Figs. 261–63*

History, of calciphylaxis, 8

Hives; *cf.* Urticaria

H_2O_2, as direct calcifier, 311

Hormonal conditioning, 319

Hormones
cutaneous calciphylactic challenging effect of, 49
participation in calciphylaxis, 459
→ calciphylaxis, **274**

5HT (5-hydroxytryptamine, serotonin), 49
as indirect challenger, 30
→ calciphylaxis, 30
← DHT + nerve lesion, 282

5HT intratumoral → calciphylaxis ← DHT, 82

5HT i.p. → calciphylaxis ← DHT + PMX s.c., 285

5HT i.p., s.c. → calciphylaxis ← DHT, 149, *Figs. 107–19*

5HT i.v. → calciphylaxis ← DHT, 12

5HT s.c.
→ calciphylaxis ← DHT + IPR i.p., 159, *Figs. 120–23*
← DHT + restraint, 265
← parathyroid hormone s.c., 223, 256, *Figs. 182–85*
← restraint + vitamin D_3 i.v., 266, *Figs. 223, 224*
← vitamin D_3 i.v., 212
→ lacrimal gland, 78
→ salivary gland, 78

5HT subconjunctival
→ calcium in ciliary body, 78
→ eyes, 78

Hutchinson-Gilford syndrome; *cf.* Progeria

Hyalinization, in calciphylaxis, 242

Hyaluronidase, 53

Hydrosol®; *cf.* Vitamin D_3

5-hydroxytryptamine; *cf.* 5HT

Hygromatosis lipocalcinogranulomatosa progrediens; *cf.* Lipocalcinogranulomatosis

Hypaque®, 52

Hypercalcemia
in scleroderma, 425
⇄ sarcoidosis, 402
⇄ scleredema adultorum Buschke, 405

Hyperkeratosis, types of, 367

Hyperparathyroidism, 334, 356, 366
"masked," 360
ocular lesions, 357
in a pregnant woman with discoid lupus erythematosus, 357
secondary, 360
→ mucopolysaccharides, 361
⇄ cutaneous calcinosis, 357, *Fig. 273*
⇄ milk-alkali syndrome of Burnett *et al.*, *Fig. 287*
⇄ nephrocalcinosis, *Fig. 275*
⇄ nephrocalcinosis, urolithiasis, calcinosis of the cardiovascular system, lung, stomach, intestines, and other soft tissues, pancreatitis and pancreatic calcification with sclerosis, 357
⇄ parathyroid carcinoma, *Fig. 274*
⇄ peptic ulcers, 360
⇄ sarcoidosis, 402
⇄ scleroderma, 357, 366

Hyperproteinemia, in sarcoidosis, 403

Hypersensitivity reaction, in lupus erythematosus, 374

Hypertension, pulmonary, in dermatomyositis, 352

Hyperthyroidism ⇄ scleroderma, 426

Hypertrichosis and pigmentation, in dermatomyositis, 352
Hypervitaminosis D, 334, 361, *Figs. 277–79*
  calcium deposition in tissues, 362
  with calcinosis universalis and scleroderma, *Fig. 277*
  ⇄ sarcoidosis, 403
Hypocalcemia
  in sclerema neonatorum, 406
  ⇄ sarcoidosis, 402
Hypoparathyroid tetany, complicated by Raynaud's syndrome, 396
Hypoparathyroidism
  ← stress, 366
  ⇄ Raynaud's phenomenon, 366
Hypophyseal hormones → calciphylaxis, 277
Hypophysectomy
  → calciphylaxis ← albumen s.c. + DHT + plucking, 276, *Fig. 255*
  ← DHT, *Fig. 227*
  ← DHT + Fe-Dex i.v. + PMX s.c., 277, *Fig. 226*
  ← direct calcifiers, 302
  ← KMnO₄ s.c., 302, *Fig. 241*
  → calcium in tissue ← KMnO₄ s.c., 302, *Fig. 241*
  → topical calciphylaxis, 276
Hypothyroidism ⇄ scleroderma, 426

Ichthyosis ⇄ scleroderma, 427
Ichthyosis and other types of hyperkeratosis, 367
Imferon®; *cf.* Fe-Dex
Immunologic reactions; *cf.* Allergic reactions
Impetigo herpetiformis, 367
  with parathyroid tetany after strumectomy, *Fig. 280*
  ⇄ parathyroid insufficiency, 367
  ⇄ pregnancy, 367
Imposil®; *cf.* Fe-Dex
InCl₃, 28, 50
  as direct calcifier, 311
InCl₃ i.v. → calciphylaxis ← DHT, 167
India ink, 53
Indian gum (ghatti), 51
Indirect calcifiers, 441; *cf. also* Calcifier
  adjuvants of, 13
  definition, **13**
  inhibitors of, **15**
Indirect challengers, 4; *cf. also* Challengers
  definition, **14**
  route of administration, 4
Indirect systemic calcifier, 3
Indium chloride, 28
Induratio penis plastica, 354
Infarcts → calcification, 434

Infection
  ⇄ dermatomyositis, 352
  ⇄ scleroderma, 427
Infectious diseases, and calciphylaxis, 463
Inflammation
  ⇄ calciphylaxis, 6
  ⇄ scleroderma, 426
Inflammatory changes, in calciphylaxis, 241
Inhibitors of challengers
  definition of, **15**
  of indirect calcifiers, definition of, **15**
Injury, topical, 433
Insect bite → calcification, 434
Insulin s.c. → calciphylaxis ← DHT + Fe-Dex i.v., 126, *Fig. 83a*
Interstitial polymyositis; *cf.* Myositis fibrosa
Intervertebral discs, calcinosis of, 331, *Fig. 259*
Intestine ← DHT + FeSO₄ i.v., *Fig. 102*
Intrapedal injection, technique of, 23, *Fig. 3*
Intraperitoneal injection, technique of, 23
Intravenous injection, technique of, 24, *Fig. 4*
Iodipamine methylglucamine, 52
Iodochlorol®, 52
IPR (Isoproterenol), 15
IPR i.p.
  → calciphylaxis ← DHT, 167, 256, *Fig. 124*
  ← DHT + 5HT s.c., *Figs. 121–23*
  ← DHT + 5HT s.c., 159, *Fig. 120*
IrCl₄, 28, 50
Iron; *cf. also* Fe
  as challenger, 4
  deposition ⇄ calcification, 327
  in muscle, in poikiloderma vasculare atrophicans, 393
  salts, role in calciphylactic challenge, 446
  in skin, in scleroderma, 409
Iron-calcium incrustations; *cf.* Sideroscleroses
Irradiation → scleroderma, 430
Isamine blue, 53
Isoproterenol; *cf.* IPR
Ivalon sponge, 49

Jectofer®; *cf.* Fe-Sol
Joints
  calcinosis of, 331, *Fig. 260*
  ← age + DHT + Thorotrast® i.v., 291
  ← DHT + Fe-Din i.v. + PMX s.c., 287
  ← DHT + PMX s.c. + Thorotrast® i.v., 287
  ← DHT + Thorotrast® i.v., 246, 256, *Figs. 139, 140, 145, 146*
  ← parathyroid hormone s.c. + Thorotrast® i.v., 226, *Fig. 187*
Juvenile spondylitis; *cf.* Rheumatoid spondylitis

Kalkpanzerhaut, 357

Kaolin, 49, 52

KBr, 28, 50

KCl, 28, 50
  → calciphylaxis ← DHT + plucking, 259
  → muscle ← DHT + Me-Cl-COL s.c. + NaH$_2$PO$_4$ p.o., 147

KClO$_3$, KClO$_4$, 28, 50

K$_2$CrO$_4$, 28, 50
  as direct calcifier, 311

K$_2$Cr$_2$O$_7$, as direct calcifier, 311

Keloids, 354, 367
  ← EDTA, 370
  ⇌ scleroderma, 367, 427

Kernechtrot, 53

Keratosulfate, 51

K$_3$Fe(CN)$_6$, K$_4$Fe(CN)$_6$, 28, 50

KI, 28, 50

Kidney
  calciphylaxis in, 74
  ← albumen i.p. + DHT, 89
  ← albumen i.v. + DHT, 86
  ← albumen s.c. + DHT, *Figs. 205, 206*
  ← AlNH$_4$(SO$_4$)$_2$ i.p. + DHT, 97
  ← calcium acetate p.o. + DHT, 258, *Fig. 211*
  ← Ca-acetate, Na-acetate, Na$_3$-citrate, NaCl, NaH$_2$PO$_4$, Na$_2$HPO$_4$ + thallium acetate, 240
  ← CrCl$_4$ i.v. + DHT, 100, *Fig. 61*
  ← CrCl$_3$ i.v. + DHT (in hamster), 297
  ← CrCl$_3$ i.v. + DHT (in rabbit), 297
  ← DHT + Fe (ferric) albuminate i.p., 112
  ← DHT + FeCl$_2$ i.v., 112
  ← DHT + Fe-Din i.v., 135
  ← DHT + Fe-OS i.v., 1, 5, *Fig. 95*
  ← DHT + HgCl$_2$ i.v., 166
  ← DHT + 5HT s.c., 150, *Fig. 110*
  ← DHT + hypophysectomy, *Fig. 227*
  ← DHT + IPR i.p., 168, 256
  ← DHT + KMnO$_4$ i.p., 168
  ← DHT + MgH$_4$(PO$_4$)$_2$ p.o., 168, *Fig. 125*
  ← DHT + Na$_2$HPO$_4$ p.o., *Fig. 212*
  ← DHT + thallium acetate s.c., 192, *Fig. 150*
  ← DHT + thallium salts, 284
  ← DHT + yolk i.v., *Figs. 154, 155, 158, 159*
  ← Fe-OS i.v. + parathyroid hormone s.c. 215, *Fig. 178*
  ← HgCl$_2$, 3
  ← 5HT s.c. + restraint + vitamin D$_3$ i.v., *Fig. 223*
  ← KMnO$_4$ intra-iliac, 305
  ← NaAST i.p., *Fig. 193*
  ← Scleroderma, 418

Kidney diseases; *cf.* Renal diseases

KIO$_3$, KIO$_4$, 28, 50

KMnO$_4$, 50
  as direct calcifier, 298, 311
  → calciphylaxis ← CrCl$_2$ + DHT, 62
    ← DHT, 60, 62
    ← DHT + FeCl$_3$, Fe-Dex, 60

KMnO$_4$ intracarotid → carotid body ← DHT, 78

KMnO$_4$ intra-iliac → calciphylaxis, 304, *Figs. 243–50*

KMnO$_4$ intratracheal → lung ← DHT, *Fig. 34*

KMnO$_4$ i.p., i.v. → calciphylaxis ← DHT, 168

KMnO$_4$ s.c.
  → calciphylaxis, *Figs. 248–50*
    ← age, 303, *Fig. 242*
    ← glucocorticoids, stress, 302
    ← hypophysectomy, 302, *Fig. 241*
    ← parathyroidectomy, 303
  → calcium in tissue, 298, *Figs. 237, 238*
    ← glucocorticoids, stress, 302
    ← hypophysectomy, 302, *Fig. 241*
    ← parathyroidectomy, 303

K$_2$MnO$_4$, as direct calcifier, 311

von Kóssa
  plus van Gieson technique, 34
  plus methylene blue technique, 34
  plus PAS technique, 34

Kraurosis vulvae, 370

KSCN, 28, 50

Kupffer cells; *cf. also* RES
  ← DHT + egg yolk i.v., 4, *Figs. 158, 160*
  ← Fe-OS i.v. + parathyroid hormone s.c., 215

LaCl$_3$, 50
  as direct calcifier, 311

LaCl$_3$ i.p., i.v. → calciphylaxis ← DHT, 168

Lacrimal gland
  ← CrCl$_2$ i.v. + DHT, *Fig. 68*
  ← CrCl$_3$ intracarotid + DHT, *Fig. 21*
  ← DHT + 5HT s.c., 150, *Fig. 106*
  ← DHT + 5HT s.c. + IPR i.p., 163

Langerhans' islets ← albumen i.p. + DHT, *Fig. 46*

Lanthanum chloride, 28

LAP (lyophilized anterior-pituitary powder), 278

LAP s.c. → calciphylaxis ← DHT, 278, *Fig. 228*

Larynx ← parathyroid hormone s.c. + Thorotrast® i.v., *Fig. 186*

Latency period, 455

Lathyrogenic compounds; *cf. also* AAN
  → calciphylaxis, 284

Lead; *cf. also* Pb
  as challenger, 4, 28

Leiomyomas of the esophagus, calcification in, 436

Leontiasis ossea; *cf.* Osteitis deformans

Lesions, evaluation of, 30

Leucodermie atrophique ponctuée of Millian; *cf.* Lichen sclerosus

Leukemia ⇄ scleroderma, 427

Leukoplakia, and kraurosis vulvae, 370

Libman-Sacks syndrome; *cf.* Lupus erythematosus disseminatus

Lichen albus of Zumbusch; *cf.* Lichen sclerosus

Lichen myxedematosus, 409

Lichen sclerosus, 370
   ⇄ scleroderma, 370

LiCl, 28, 50

Ligature → calcium in kidney, 317

Limb ← CrCl₃ intra-iliac + DHT, *Fig. 27*

Lingual; *cf.* Tongue

Lipocalcinogranulomatosis, 371, *Fig. 281*

Lipo-fibro-calcareous myopathy, 371

Lipoma petrificans, 436

Lipophagic granuloma, 321; *cf. also* Sclerema neonatorum

Lips
   ← DHT + Fe-Din i.v. + PMX s.c., 287, 290
   ← DHT + Fe-OS i.v. + PMX s.c., 288, 291
   ← DHT + Thorotrast® i.v., 256

Lithium chloride, 28

Lithopedion, 434, *Fig. 267*

Liver
   calciphylaxis in, 74
   ← CrCl₃, FeCl₂ intraportal + DHT, 65
   ← DHT + egg yolk i.v., 4, *Figs. 153, 158*
   ← DHT + FeCl₂ intraportal, *Figs. 31, 33*
   ← DHT + Fe-OS i.v., 139
   ← DHT + InCl₃ i.v., 167
   ← DHT + PMX s.c. + yolk i.v., 285
   ← DHT + ZnCl₂ i.v., *Fig. 169*
   ← Fe-OS i.v. + parathyroid hormone s.c., 215, *Figs. 177–80*
   ← KMnO₄ s.c., *Figs. 249, 250*
   ← scleroderma, 418

Lobstein's syndrome; *cf.* Osteogenesis imperfecta

Local factors in calciphylaxis, 455

Localizing adjuvation, 57

LTH (luteotrophic hormone) → calciphylaxis ← DHT + plucking, 278

Lung
   calcinosis of, 74, 334, *Figs. 261–63*
   ossification of, 334
   ← Albumen i.p., i.v. + DHT, *Fig. 41*
   ← albumen i.v. + DHT, 86
   ← CrCl₂ i.v. + DHT, *Fig. 70*
   ← CrCl₃ i.v. + DHT, 100, 255, *Fig. 65*
   ← CrCl₃ i.v. + DHT (in cat), 293, *Figs. 233, 234*
   ← CrCl₃ i.v. + DHT (in guinea pig), 297
   ← CrCl₃ i.v. + DHT (in rabbit), 297
   ← CrCl₃ i.v. + DHT + PMX s.c., 287, 288, 290

← DHT + FeCl₂ i.v., 112, *Fig. 72*
← DHT + FeCl₂ i.v. + PMX s.c., 290
← DHT + Fe-Dex i.v., 249, *Fig. 207*
← DHT + Fe-Din i.v., *Fig. 93*
← DHT + Fe-OS i.v., 138
← DHT + KMnO₄ intratracheal, *Fig. 34*
← DHT + egg yolk i.p., *Fig. 167*
← DHT + egg yolk i.v., *Fig. 158*
← periarteritis nodosa, *Fig. 295*
← scleroderma, 412, *Figs. 308, 309*
← systemic lupus erythematosus, *Fig. 284*

Lupus erythematosus (discoid and disseminated), 7, 343, 373, *Figs. 282–84; cf. also* Discoid lupus erythematosus; Disseminated lupus erythematosus
   hypersensitivity reactions in, 374
   in a pregnant woman with hyperparathyroidism, 357
   ← antimalarial compounds, vitamin E, 377
   ⇄ encephalopathy, rheumatoid arthritis, scleroderma, 374
   ⇄ scleroderma, 426

Lupus pernio of Besnier; *cf.* Sarcoidosis

Lupus sebaceous; *cf.* Lupus erythematosus

Lupus superficialis; *cf.* Lupus erythematosus

Lycopodium, 52

Lymph nodes ← DHT + Fe-Din i.v., 136

Lymphadenitis, in dermatomyositis, 353

Lymphogranulomatosis of Schaumann (benign); *cf.* Sarcoidosis

Macroscopic observations, of calciphylactic lesions, 30

Macular dermatosis, 47

Magnesium chloride, 28

Malpighian follicles (spleen) ← CeCl₃ i.v. + DHT, 98

Manganese, as challenger, 4

Marble-bone disease; *cf.* Osteopetrosis

Masked hyperparathyroidism, 360

Mast cells ← DHT + Fe-Dex i.v. + PMX s.c., *Fig. 88*

Mastocyte dischargers → calciphylaxis, 284

Mastocyte granules, 447

Mastocyte tumors; *cf.* under individual mastocytomas

Mastocytes
   in dermatomyositis, 351
   in sarcoid granulomas, 402
   in scleredema adultorum Buschke, 405
   in scleroderma, 409
   in urticaria pigmentosa, 377

Mechanism of action
   of DHT, 3
   of NaAST, 3

Me-Cl-COL s.c.
→ heart, muscle ← DHT + NaH₂PO₄ p.o. + species, 147
→ muscle ← DHT + KCl, MgCl₂ + NaH₂PO₄ p.o., 147

Mediastinum
← DHT + Fe-Dex i.v. + PMX s.c., *Fig. 87*
← DHT + Fe-Din i.v., 135
← Thorotrast® i.v., *Fig. 147*

Mercuric acetate, sulfide, 28

Mesenteric vessels ← albumen i.p. + DHT, *Fig. 48*

Metacalciphylactic changes, definition of, **15**

Metacalciphylactic syndromes, 241

Metachromatic substance, 351
intercellular accumulations of (in scleredema adultorum Buschke), 405

Metallic compounds and electrolytes, cutaneous calciphylactic challenging effect of, 50

Metaplastic ossification, 351

Methodology, of calciphylaxis, **17**

Methyl-testosterone, 49
→ calciphylaxis ← DHT + plucking, 281

MgCl₂, 50
→ calciphylaxis ← DHT + plucking, 259
→ muscle ← DHT + Me-Cl-COL s.c. + NaH₂PO₄ p.o., 147

MgH₄(PO₄)₂ p.o. → calciphylaxis ← DHT, 168

Microbial products, cutaneous calciphylactic challenging effect of, 51

Mikulicz's disease, 431

Milia and epidermal inclusion cysts, 377

Milk-alkali syndrome of Burnett *et al.*, 377, *Figs. 286, 287*
bone, parathyroid, skin lesions in, 379
⇄ hyperparathyroidism, *Fig. 287*

Milk-drinker's syndrome; *cf.* Milk-alkali syndrome of Burnett *et al.*

Miokon®, 52

MnCl₂, 50

MnCl₂, as direct calcifier, 311

Mn(NO₃)₂, as direct calcifier, 311

MnSO₄(NH₄)₂SO₄, as direct calcifier, 311

MRLS tumor, 49

Mucilages, cutaneous calciphylactic challenging effect of, 51

Mucinous degeneration, 36

Mucopolysaccharides, cutaneous calciphylactic challenging effect of, 51
in scleroderma, 409
← hyperparathyroidism, 361

Mucoproteins, in sarcoidosis, 402

Multinuclear giant cells, 38

Multiple neurofibromatosis; *cf.* Neurofibromatosis

Murphy rat lymphosarcoma ← DHT + Fe-Dex, Fe-OS, 5HT intratumoral, 82

Muscle
← albumen i.p. + DHT, *Figs. 53, 54*
← CrCl₃ intracarotid + DHT, 79, *Fig. 21*
← CrCl₃ intra-iliac + DHT, 79, *Fig. 36*
← CrCl₃ i.v. + DHT, 100, *Fig. 63*
← CrCl₃ i.v. + DHT (in rabbit), 297
← DHT + FeCl₂ i.v., 112
← DHT + Fe-Dex i.v. + PMX s.c., 127, *Fig. 85*
← DHT + glucocorticoids s.c. + NaH₂PO₄ p.o., 147
← DHT + 5HT + nerve lesion, 282
← DHT + 5HT i.p. + PMX s.c., 285
← DHT + 5HT s.c., *Figs. 111, 112*
← DHT + 5HT s.c. + IPR i.p., 163, *Fig. 121*
← DHT + 5HT s.c. + restraint, 265
← DHT + KCl, MgCl₂ + Me-Cl-COL s.c. + NaH₂PO₄ p.o., 147
← DHT + KMnO₄ i.p., 168
← DHT + Me-Cl-COL s.c. + NaH₂PO₄ p.o. + species, 147
← DHT + NaClO₄ p.o., s.c., 169
← DHT + PMX s.c., *Figs. 252, 253*
← DHT + Thorotrast® i.v., *Figs. 136, 140*
← DHT + trauma, 74
← Fe-Dex i.v. + parathyroid hormone s.c. + PMX s.c., 213, *Fig. 173*
← Fe-Dex i.v. + PMX s.c. + restraint + vitamin D₃ i.v., *Fig. 222*
← 5HT s.c. + parathyroid hormone s.c., 223, 256, *Figs. 183, 184*
← KMnO₄ intra-iliac, 305, *Figs. 243–45*
← scleroderma, 415

Muscular dystrophy, calciphylactic, **14**, 213, 223, *Figs. 173, 182–85*

Muscular exercise; *cf.* Stress

Mustard oil, powder of, 52

Myocardial infarction
⇄ Dupuytren's contracture, 354
⇄ scleroderma, 430

Myocarditis, suppurating, 170

Myocardium; *cf.* Heart

Myodil®, 52

Myositis, traumatic, 351

Myositis fibrosa, 382

Myositis ossificans
circumscribed and progressive, 382, *Figs. 288–90*
generalized, 7
⇄ calcinosis universalis, cutaneous rashes, scleroderma, 384
⇄ hematomas, 382

Myxedema ⇌ scleredema adultorum Buschke, 405

Myxomatosis cutis papulosa, 409

Na-acetate → calciphylaxis ← thallium acetate, 240

NaAsO₂, 29, 50

NaAST (sodium acetylsulfathiazole), 15
  mechanism of action, 3
  as sensitizer, 3, 26
  → calciphylaxis, 26

NaAST i.p.
  → calciphylaxis, 235, *Fig. 193*
  ← albumen s.c., *Fig. 15*
  ← Fe-Dex i.v., 236, *Fig. 194*
  ← Fe-Din i.v., 236, *Fig. 195*
  ← Fe-OS i.v., 236, *Fig. 196*
  ← Thorotrast® i.v., 239, *Fig. 197*

Na₃-citrate → calciphylaxis ← thallium acetate, 240

NaCl, 29, 51
  → calciphylaxis ← DHT + plucking, 259
  ← thallium acetate, 240

NaClO₄, 29
  as direct calcifier, 311
  → calciphylaxis ← DHT + plucking, 259
  ← DHT, 169

NaH₂PO₄, 51

NaH₂PO₄ p.o.
  → calciphylaxis ← DHT, 170, *Fig. 213*
  ← thallium acetate, 240
  ← vitamin D₂, 258, *Fig. 210*
  → cardiac and skeletal muscle ← DHT + glucocorticoids s.c., 147
  ← DHT + Me-Cl-COL s.c. + species, 147
  ← DHT + KCl, MgCl₂ + Me-Cl-COL s.c., 147

Na₂HPO₄, 29

Na₂HPO₄ p.o.
  → calciphylaxis ← DHT, *Fig. 212*
  ← F-COL s.c. + Fe-OS i.v., 240
  ← thallium acetate, 240

NaMnO₄, 29, 51
  as direct calcifier, 311

Na₂MoO₄, NaNO₂, NaNO₃, Na-oxalate, -pyruvate, 29, 51

Nasal cavity ← scleroderma, 412

Na₂SnO₃, 51
  as direct calcifier, 311

Na₂SnO₃ i.v. → calciphylaxis ← DHT, 170, *Fig. 126*

Na₂SO₄, 29, 51
  → calciphylaxis ← DHT + plucking, 259

NaVO₃, Na₂WO₄, 51

NbCl₅, 28
  as direct calcifier, 311

Necrobiosis lipoidica diabeticorum, 386

Necrosis → calcification, 434

Neoplasia ⇌ calciphylaxis, 465

Neoplasma; *cf.* Tumors

Nephrectomy
  → calciphylaxis, 282
  ← CrCl₃ i.v., 227, *Fig. 188*
  ← Fe-OS i.v., 230
  ← Fe-OS, Thorotrast® i.v. + parathyroidectomy, 281
  ← Thorotrast® i.v., 231, *Figs. 189–92*

Nephrocalcinosis, 397
  cortico-medullary, 240
  with osteomalacia, *Fig. 296*
  papillary, 168, *Fig. 125*
  in sclerema neonatorum, 406
  ⇌ hyperparathyroidism, 357, *Fig. 275*
  ⇌ osteitis deformans, 287

Nephrotoxic substances → calciphylaxis ← DHT + plucking, 283

Nerve lesion
  → calciphylaxis ← CrCl₃ i.v. + DHT, 282, *Fig. 230*
  ← DHT + 5HT, 282

Nerves
  ← scleredema adultorum Buschke, 405
  ← scleroderma, 421

Nervous stimuli → calciphylaxis, 282

Nettle rash; *cf.* Urticaria

Neurofibromatosis, 386

Neurohumoral substances → calciphylaxis, 282

Neuromyositis; *cf.* Dermatomyositis

(NH₄)₂SO₄, 51

NiCl₂, 51

Niobium pentachloride, 28

Nodular panniculitis; *cf.* Panniculitis

Nodular polymyositis; *cf.* Myositis fibrosa

Noncalcifying calciphylactic reactions, 465

Nonspecific calcinoses; *cf.* Calcinosis, nonspecific

Nonsuppurating panniculitis; *cf.* Panniculitis

Noradrenaline, 49

Nose, calcinosis of, 336

Nucleus pulposus extract, 49

Occlusive coronary lesions, 240
  produced by DHT + Fe-OS i.v., 141, *Fig. 101*

Ocular; *cf.* Eye

Oculo-urethro-synovial syndrome of Fiessinger-Leroy-Reiter; *cf.* Reiter's syndrome

Omental, thymic, and RES-type of calciphylaxis, 203, *Figs. 161–66*

Omentum ← DHT + yolk i.p., 203, *Fig. 161*

Oral cavity ← scleroderma, 412

Organ-specific calcifiers, 317

Osler-Rendu-Weber's syndrome, 386, *Figs. 291–94*
  with calcinosis of the finger tips, *Fig. 294*
  with cutaneous amyloidosis, *Figs. 291, 292*
  with cutaneous calcinosis, *Fig. 292*
  with flat angioma-like formations on toes, *Fig. 293*

OsO₄, 51

Ossification of the lung, 334

Osteitis
  syphilitic, 325
  deformans, 387
  deformans ⇄ nephrocalcinosis, 387
  fibrosa, 93, 325
  fibrosa and osteosclerosis, 242, *Figs. 198–205*

Osteogenesis
  ectopic, 242
  imperfecta, 387, 390

Osteomalacia, with nephrocalcinosis, *Fig. 296*

Osteomyelitis, 325

Osteopetrosis, 391

Osteoporosis, 351, 391, 402
  senile, 325

Osteopsathyrosis; *cf.* Osteogenesis imperfecta

Osteosis cutis, 391

Ovariectomy → calciphylaxis ← DHT + Fe-Dex
  i.p., 281, *Fig. 229*

Ovary
  calcinosis of, 338, *Fig. 264*
  ← albumen i.p. + DHT, 93, *Fig. 49*

Overchallenge, 252
  calciphylactic wheal, *Fig. 12*
  definition, **16**

Oviduct ← albumen i.p. + DHT, 93, *Fig. 50*

Ovomucoid, 53
  in NaCl, 53

Oxytocin, 49

Paget's disease; *cf.* Osteitis deformans

Palladium chloride, nitrate, 28

Panarteritis nodosa; *cf.* Periarteritis nodosa

Pancreas
  calcinosis of, 338, *Fig. 265*
  ← albumen i.p. + DHT, 87, 88, 255, *Figs. 44–46, 51*
  ← albumen i.p. + DHT + restraint, 265, *Figs. 214, 215*
  ← albumen i.p., i.v. + DHT + PMX s.c., 285, 290
  ← albumen, Fe-Dex i.v. + DHT, 12
  ← chondroitin sulfuric acid i.p., i.v. + DHT, 98
  ← CrCl₃ i.v. + DHT, 100

← DHT + egg white i.v., 4
← DHT + Fe (ferric) albuminate i.p., 112
← DHT + FeCl₂ i.v., 112
← DHT + Fe-Dex i.p., 5, 117, 118, *Fig. 76*
← DHT + Fe-Dex i.p., i.v., 255
← DHT + Fe-Dex i.v., 115, *Figs. 74, 75*
← DHT + Fe-Dex i.v. + PMX s.c., 287
← DHT + InCl₃ i.v., 167
← DHT + KMnO₄ i.p., 168
← DHT + Thorotrast® i.p., *Fig. 148*
← DHT + Thorotrast® i.v., *Fig. 137*
← DHT + egg yolk i.v., 198
← Fe-Dex i.v. + NaAST i.p., 236, *Fig. 194*
← Fe-OS i.v., *Fig. 100*
← KMnO₄ intra-iliac, 305
← scleroderma, 426

Pancreatic calciphylaxis, 236, *Fig. 194*

Pancreatic and psoriasiform calciphylaxis, 115, 117

Pancreatic and RES-type of calciphylaxis, 167

Pancreatic stroma, in pancreatico-cutaneous calciphylaxis, 88

Pancreatico-cutaneous calciphylaxis, 87

Pancreatitis ⇄ hyperparathyroidism, 357

Panniculitis, 392

Panniculus adiposus; *cf.* Adipose tissue

Papain, 53

Papillary nephrocalcinosis, produced by DHT +
  magnesium phosphate, 168, *Fig. 125*

Para-Thor-Mone®; *cf.* Parathyroid hormone

Parathyroid
  ← chromium i.v. + DHT, 12
  ← CrCl₂ i.v. + DHT + PMX s.c., 290
  ← CrCl₃ i.v. + DHT, 100, 255, *Figs. 58, 59, 62*
  ← CrCl₃ i.v. + DHT (in dog), 297
  ← CrCl₃ i.v. + DHT (in hamster), 297
  ← CrCl₃ i.v. + DHT (in rabbit), 297, *Fig. 236*
  ← CrCl₃ i.v. + DHT + PMX s.c., 287, 288, 290
  ← CrCl₃ i.v. + DHT + restraint, 265, *Fig. 216*
  ← CrCl₃ i.v. + nephrectomy, 227, *Fig. 188*
  ← CrCl₃ i.v. + parathyroid hormone s.c., 213
  ← DHT + FeCl₂ i.v., 112, 255
  ← DHT + FeCl₂ i.v. + PMX s.c., 290
  ← DHT + FeCl₃, 82
  ← KMnO₄ intra-iliac, 305
  ← scleroderma, 425

Parathyroid carcinoma ⇄ hyperparathyroidism,
  Fig. 274

Parathyroid hormone, 49
  in production of cutaneous calcinosis with sclerosis, 9
  as sensitizer, 3, 26
  → calciphylaxis, 26
    ← CrCl₃ i.v., 213, *Figs. 171, 172*
    ← Fe-Dex i.v. + PMX s.c., 213, *Figs. 173–75*
    ← Fe-OS, 83, 215, *Figs. 176–81*

Parathyroid hormone s.c.
  → calciphylaxis ← 5HT s.c., 223, 256, *Figs. 182–85*
  ← parathyroidectomy, 281
  ← Thorotrast® i.v., 226, *Figs. 186, 187*

Parathyroid insufficiency ⇄ impetigo herpetiformis, 367

Parathyroidectomy
  → calciphylaxis ← albumen,   Fe-Dex s.c. + DHT, 246
  ← DHT, parathyroid hormone, 281
  ← Fe-OS, Thorotrast® i.v. + nephrectomy, 281

Parotid gland
  calciphylactic reaction of, 80
  ← DHT + 5HT s.c. + IPR i.p., 159

PAS-positive matrix, 38

Paws ← albumen, Fe-Dex, Thorotrast® + DHT, 64

Pb (lead), 51

Pb-acetate i.v. → calciphylaxis ← DHT, 170, *Figs. 127, 127a*

PbCl₂, 28, 51
  as direct calcifier, 311

PdCl₂·2KCl, as direct calcifier, 311

Pectin, 49
  as adjuvant, 30
  → calciphylaxis ← CrCl₂ + DHT, 62
  ← DHT, 59, 62, *Fig. 14*
  ← DHT + FeCl₃, Fe-Dex, 59

Pemphigus, 392
  as a stress disease, 392

Penicillin → dermatomyositis, 353

Pepsin, 53

Peptic ulcer ⇄ hyperparathyroidism, 360

Periadrenal fat ← albumen i.p. + DHT, *Fig. 47*

Periarteritis nodosa, 7, 392
  calciphylactic, 8
  production by parathyroid hormone and Fe-OS i.v., 7
  as a stress disease, 393
  ⇄ scleroderma, 393, 427

Pericardium, calcinosis of, 338

Peritoneal calciphylaxis, 111, 143, 168, 190, *Fig. 148*

Peritoneo-pleural calciphylaxis, 168

Peritoneum
  calciphylaxis in, 73
  ← AlK(SO₄)₂ i.p. + DHT, 97
  ← AlNH₄(SO₄)₂ i.p. + DHT, 97
  ← CeCl₃ i.p. + DHT, 98
  ← chondroitin sulfuric acid i.p., i.v. + DHT, 98
  ← DHT + Fe(ferric) albuminate i.p., 111
  ← DHT + Fe-OS i.p., 143
  ← DHT + KMnO₄ i.p., 168

← DHT + LaCl₃ i.p., 168
← DHT + Thorotrast® i.p., 190, *Fig. 148*

Peyer's patches ← DHT + PMX s.c., *Fig. 129*

Peyronie's disease, 354; *cf. also* Scleroderma

Pharynx ← DHT + Thorotrast® i.v., *Fig. 132*

Phenylbutazone, 52

Phosphomolybdic acid, 52

Phosphorus
  in blood, in calcinosis cutis, 329
    in calcinosis universalis, 340
    in osteitis deformans, 387
    in sclerematous subcutis, 406

Phosphotungstic acid, 52

Phyltone, 52

Physical agents
  cutaneous calciphylactic challenging effect, 52
  definition of, **29**
  role in determining the challenging activity of metals, 446

Pigmentation and hypertrichosis, in dermatomyositis, 352

Pigmented villonodular synovitis; *cf.* Villonodular synovitis

Pineal body, calcinosis of, 338

Pituitary; *cf. also* Hypophysis

Pituitary hemorrhage ⇄ scleroderma, 426

Planimetric measurements, 31

Plasma, 49
  as adjuvant, 30
  → calciphylaxis ← CrCl₂ + DHT, 62
  ← DHT, 59, 62
  ← DHT + FeCl₃, Fe-Dex, 59

Platinic potassium chloride, 28

Pleura
  calcinosis of, 339
  calciphylaxis in, 73
  ← albumen i.p. + DHT, 93
  ← CrCl₃ i.v. + DHT, 100
  ← DHT + FeCl₂ i.v., 112
  ← DHT + KMnO₄ i.p., 168

Plucking
  cutaneous calciphylactic challenging effect, 52
  → calciphylaxis ← AAN + DHT, 284
  ← adrenalectomy + DHT + triamcinolone, 278
  ← age + DHT, 289
  ← albumen s.c. + DHT + hypophysectomy, 276, *Fig. 225*
  ← DHT, *Figs. 7, 8, 10*
  ← DHT + estradiol, methyltestosterone, 281
  ← DHT + FeCl₃ s.c. + PMX s.c., 285
  ← DHT + KCl,   MgCl₂,   NaCl,   NaClO₄, Na₂SO₄, 259
  ← DHT + LTH, STH, vasopressin, 278

← DHT + nephrotoxic substances, thallium acetate, 283
← DHT + restraint + thallium acetate s.c., *Fig. 149*
← DHT + thallium salts, 284
Pluricausal diseases, 319
PMX (polymyxin), 16, 52, 58
as indirect challenger, 29
as organ-specific calcifier, 317
→ calciphylaxis, 29
← CrCl₂ + DHT, 62
← CrCl₂, CrCl₃, FeCl₂, FeCl₃, Fe-Dex, Fe-Din, Fe-OS, Fe-Sol i.v. + DHT, 288
← DHT, 59, 62
← DHT + FeCl₃, Fe-Dex, 59
← DHT + Fe-Dex, *Fig. 209*
→ calcium in muscle, 75
PMX s.c.
→ calciphylaxis ← ACTH, glucocorticoids, hypophysectomy + DHT + Fe-Dex i.v., 278
← albumen i.p., i.v., CrCl₂, CrCl₃, FeCl₂, FeCl₃, Fe-Dex, Fe-Din i.v. + DHT, 290
← albumen i.p. + DHT, 285
← albumen s.c. + DHT + FeCl₃ s.c., 287
← albumen s.c. + DHT + Fe-Dex s.c., 285
← CrCl₃ i.v. + DHT, 287
← CrCl₃ s.c. + DHT + hemostat, 285
← DHT, 171, *Figs. 128–31, 252, 253*
← DHT + DOC s.c. + Fe-Dex i.v. + triamcinolone s.c., 281
← DHT + egg yolk i.v., 208, 285, 287, *Fig. 168*
← DHT + FeCl₃ s.c. + plucking, 285
← DHT + Fe-Dex i.v., 127, 255, 287, *Figs. 84–89*
← DHT + Fe-Dex i.v. + glucocorticoids, 242
← DHT + Fe-Dex i.v. + hypophysectomy, 277, *Fig. 226*
← DHT + Fe-Dex i.v. + restraint, 265, *Fig. 217*
← DHT + Fe-Dex i.v. + triamcinolone s.c., 280
← DHT + Fe-Din i.v., 287
← DHT + Fe-OS i.v., 287, 291
← DHT + Fe-Sol, yolk i.v., 291
← DHT + 5HT i.p., 285
← DHT + Thorotrast® i.v., 287
← Fe-Dex i.v. + parathyroid hormone s.c., 213, *Figs. 173–75*
← Fe-Dex i.v. + restraint + vitamin D₃ i.v., 266
← Fe-Dex i.v. + restraint + vitamin D₃ i.v., *Fig. 222*
← Fe-Dex i.v. + vitamin D₃ i.v., 212
→ calcium in kidney, 317
Poikiloderma; *cf. also* Dermatomyositis

of Jacobi; *cf.* Poikiloderma vasculare atrophicans
vasculare atrophicans, 393
Poikilodermatitis; *cf.* Poikiloderma vasculare atrophicans
Poikilodermatomyositis, 393; *cf. also* Dermatomyositis
Polyarteritis nodosa; *cf.* Periarteritis nodosa
Polyarthritis, in sarcoidosis, 404
Polymyositis; *cf. also* Dermatomyositis
ossificans, 351; *cf. also* Progressive myositis ossificans
in sarcoidosis, 404
Polymyxin; *cf.* PMX
Polyvinylpyrrolidone; *cf.* PVP
Portal vein ← CrCl₃ intraportal + DHT, *Fig. 32*
Postphlebitic subcutaneous calcinosis, 330, *Fig. 258*
Potassium; *cf. also* K
bromide, 28
salts, 28
thiocyanate, 28
Pregnancy
⇄ impetigo herpetiformis, 367
⇄ scleroderma, 430
Preosseous spicules, 38
Preputial gland ← DHT + LAP s.c., 278, *Fig. 228*
Pressure → scleroderma, 427
Production
of calciphylaxis, **19**
of sensitization, 23
of systemic calciphylaxis, 20
of topical calciphylaxis, 19
Proferrin®; *cf.* Fe-OS
Progeria, 393
of the adult; *cf.* Werner's disease
Progesterone, 49
Progressive myositis ossificans, 383
Progressive systemic sclerosis; *cf.* Scleroderma
Propyliodone, 52
Prostatic tumors, calcification in, 436
Pseudohypoparathyroidism, 366, 395
Pseudomonas polysaccharide (Piromen), 51
Pseudotrichinosis; *cf.* Dermatomyositis
Pseudoxanthoma elasticum, 395
Psoriasis, 367, 395
calciphylactic, **14**, 120, *Figs. 77–80*
⇄ scleroderma, 396, 427
Puhr's disease, 334

Pulmonary; *cf. also* Lung
  changes, in periarteritis nodosa, *Fig. 295*
    in systemic lupus erythematosus, *Fig. 284*
  fibrosis, acute, diffuse, interstitial, 334
  infarct $\rightleftarrows$ scleroderma, 430
  stasis, 334

Puncticularis, 342

Pure adjuvants, 453
  in topical calciphylaxis, 56

PVP (polyvinylpyrrolidone), 16, 52
  as adjuvant, 30
  $\rightarrow$ calciphylaxis $\leftarrow$ CrCl$_2$ + DHT, 62
    $\leftarrow$ DHT, 60, 62
    $\leftarrow$ DHT + FeCl$_3$, Fe-Dex, 60

PVP i.p. $\rightarrow$ calciphylaxis $\leftarrow$ DHT, 176

PVP i.v. $\rightarrow$ calciphylaxis $\leftarrow$ DHT, 174

Quadriplegia; *cf.* Stress

Radiopaque substances, cutaneous calciphylactic
  challenging effect of, 52

"Rat bite defects" in scleroderma, *Fig. 299*

Raynaud's syndrome, 343, 354, 396
  in combination with Buerger's disease, 326
  $\rightleftarrows$ hypoparathyroidism, 366
  $\rightleftarrows$ scleroderma, 396

RbCl, 28, 51

von Recklinghausen's disease; *cf.* Neurofibromatosis

Rectum $\leftarrow$ CrCl$_3$ intra-iliac + DHT, *Fig. 29*

Reiter's syndrome, 396

Relapsing panniculitis; *cf.* Panniculitis

Renal; *cf. also* Kidney
  (cortico-medullary) calciphylaxis, 192, *Figs. 149, 150*
  diseases, 283, 397
  insufficiency, with severe calcinosis due to exces-
    sive alkali-intake, *Fig. 276*
  lesions $\rightarrow$ calciphylaxis, 282

Renografin®, 52

RES; *cf. also* Kupffer cells
  $\leftarrow$ CeCl$_3$ i.v. + DHT, 98

RES-type of calciphylaxis, 98, 170, 194, *Figs. 127, 127a, 151–60*

Reserpine i.v. $\rightarrow$ calciphylaxis $\leftarrow$ DHT, 176

Resistance, 456

Restraint; *cf. also* Stress
  $\rightarrow$ calciphylaxis $\leftarrow$ albumen i.p. + DHT, 265, *Figs. 214, 215*
    $\leftarrow$ albumen s.c. + DHT + Thorotrast® s.c., 263
    $\leftarrow$ CrCl$_3$ i.v. + DHT, 265, *Fig. 216*
    $\leftarrow$ CrCl$_3$ s.c. + DHT + Fe-Dex s.c., 263
    $\leftarrow$ DHT + FeCl$_3$ s.c. + yolk s.c., 263

$\leftarrow$ DHT + Fe-Dex i.v. + PMX s.c., 265, *Fig. 217*
$\leftarrow$ DHT + Fe-Din i.v., 265, *Fig. 218*
$\leftarrow$ DHT + 5HT s.c., 265
$\leftarrow$ DHT + plucking + thallium acetate s.c., *Fig. 149*
$\leftarrow$ DHT + Thorotrast® i.v., 266, *Figs. 219–21*
$\leftarrow$ Fe-Dex i.v. + PMX s.c. + vitamin D$_3$ i.v., 266, *Fig. 222*

Restraint $\rightarrow$ calciphylaxis $\leftarrow$ 5HT s.c. + vitamin D$_3$ i.v., 266, *Figs. 223, 224*

Reticuloendothelial system; *cf.* RES

Reticular form, of topical calciphylaxis, 45

Retroperitoneal fat; *cf. also* Adipose tissue
  $\leftarrow$ albumen i.p. + DHT, *Fig 52*

Rheumatic fever, 400
  $\rightleftarrows$ calcinosis universalis, dermatomyositis, 400

Rheumatism $\rightleftarrows$ dermatomyositis, 353

Rheumatoid arthritis, 398
  $\rightleftarrows$ lupus erythematosus, 374
  $\rightleftarrows$ scleroderma, 399, 427

Rheumatoid spondylitis, 400

Rhinoscleroma, 336

Rhizomelic spondylitis; *cf.* Rheumatoid spondylitis

Romberg's disease, 401

Rothmund's disease, 401
  $\rightleftarrows$ dermatomyositis, 401

Rothmund-Thomson syndrome; *cf.* Rothmund's disease

Route of administration
  of DHT, 2
  of histamine liberators, 4
  of indirect challengers, 4
  of sensitizers, challengers, adjuvants, 23

Rubber-man syndrome; *cf.* Ehlers-Danlos syndrome

Salicylic acid, 52

Salivary glands
  calcinosis of (including the parotid), 159, *Fig. 120*
  calciphylaxis, 212
    $\leftarrow$ albumen i.v. + DHT, 86, *Fig. 40*
    $\leftarrow$ albumen, Fe-Dex, 5HT, Thorotrast® s.c., 78
    $\leftarrow$ CrCl$_2$ i.v. + DHT, *Fig. 67*
    $\leftarrow$ CrCl$_3$ i.v. + DHT, 100
    $\leftarrow$ DHT + FeCl$_2$ i.v., 112
    $\leftarrow$ DHT + 5HT i.p., s.c., 149, *Figs. 107–19*
    $\leftarrow$ DHT + 5HT i.v., 12
    $\leftarrow$ DHT + 5HT s.c. + IPR i.p., 159, *Figs. 120, 122*
    $\leftarrow$ DHT + 5HT i.p. + PMX s.c., 285
    $\leftarrow$ DHT + PMX intrapedal, s.c., *Figs. 130, 131*

← 5HT s.c. + restraint + vitamin D₃ i.v., 212, *Figs. 223, 224*
← KMnO₄ intra-iliac, 305
Sarcoidosis, 7, 401
  massive soft-tissue calcification in, 402
  with chronic polymyositis, *Fig. 297*
  ← EDTA, 404
  → eye, 404
  ⇌ erythema multiforme, erythema nodosum, scleroderma, subcutaneous steatonecrosis, 404
  ⇌ hypercalcemia, hypocalcemia, 402
  ⇌ hyperparathyroidism, 402
  ⇌ hypervitaminosis D, 403
Scaly dermatosis, 47
  ← CrCl₃ i.v. + DHT, 100
Schaumann bodies, 402
Scleredema adultorum Buschke, 405; *cf. also* Scleroderma
  ← stress, 406
  ⇌ hypercalcemia, myxedema, scleroderma, 405
Sclerema; *cf.* Sclerema neonatorum
Sclerema adiposum; *cf.* Sclerema neonatorum
Sclerema neonatorum, 352, 406
  calcium, cholesterol, glycerides, phosphorus in scleromatous subcutis, 406
  ⇌ dermatomyositis, 406
  ⇌ scleroderma, 406
Scleriasis; *cf.* Scleroderma
Sclerodactyly; *cf.* Scleroderma
Scleroderma, 7, 343, 354, 404, 406, *Figs. 298–315*
  "annular," calciphylactic, *Fig. 91*
  atypical, calciphylactic, 145
  buccal, among habitual betel-nut chewers in Taiwan, 427
  calciphylactic, 14, *Fig. 89*
    with esophageal calcinosis, 236, *Fig. 195*
    with esophageal calcinosis and arthritis, 134, 177, 226, 231, *Figs. 90–94, 132–46, 186–92*
    with esophageal calcinosis and calcareous arthritis, 239, *Fig. 197*
  characteristics, 407
  factors influencing, 427
  histology, 407
  linear, 421, *Fig. 314*
  nervous factors in, 430
  occurrence in stonemasons, 427
  patches in the vaginal or rectal mucosa and in the larynx and trachea, 412
  skin transplantation in, 425
  systemic, 407
  tonsils and fauces, dental changes in, 412
  with cataracts; *cf.* Werner's disease
  ← ACTH, glucocorticoids, vitamin E, 431
  ← cold, fracture, heat, pressure, silver polish, trichloroethylene, vaccination, 427

  ← DHT, EDTA, parathyroidectomy, 430
  ← hematoporphyrin, solar-, ultraviolet irradiation, 430
  ← parathyroidectomy, 10, 426
  ← stress, 430
  → adrenal, 426
  → bone, 418
  → brain, 423
  → calcium in tissue, 425
  → ear, 421
  → esophagus, 409, *Fig. 306*
  → eye, 421
  → gastrointestinal system, 412
  → heart, *Fig. 310*
  → heart, muscle, thorax, vessels, 415
  → kidney, liver, 418
  → lung, 412, *Figs. 308, 309*
  → nerves, 421
  → oral and nasal cavities, 412
  → pancreas, submaxillary gland, 426
  → parathyroid, 425
  → spleen, 427
  → vessel, *Fig. 311*
  ⇌ acromegaly, hypo-, hyperthyroidism, inflammation, pituitary hemorrhage, 426
  ⇌ Addison's disease, 426
  ⇌ Buerger's disease, 326
  ⇌ dermatomyositis, 351
  ⇌ dermatomyositis, ichthyosis, infections, leukemia, lupus erythematosus, periarteritis nodosa, psoriasis, psychic and nervous diseases, Sjögren's syndrome, 427
  ⇌ hyperparathyroidism, 357, 366
  ⇌ keloids, 367
  ⇌ lichen sclerosus, 370
  ⇌ lupus erythematosus, 374
  ⇌ myocardial infarction, pregnancy, pulmonary infarct, stress, 430
  ⇌ myositis ossificans, 384
  ⇌ periarteritis nodosa, 393
  ⇌ psoriasis, 396
  ⇌ Raynaud's syndrome, 396
  ⇌ rheumatoid arthritis, 399
  ⇌ scleredema adultorum Buschke, 405
  ⇌ sclerema neonatorum, 406
  ⇌ Sjögren's syndrome, *Fig. 315*
Sclérodermie calcaire; *cf.* Scleroderma
Sclerofascia of Blaschko; *cf.* Scleredema adultorum Buschke
Scleromyxedema, *Fig. 314a*
Sclerosis
  in calciphylaxis, 242
  systemic, 407
Scrotum, calcinosis of, 339
SDS (stromal depot system), 16
  concept of, 462
  definition, **16**

Seabright-Bantam syndrome; *cf.* Pseudohypoparathyroidism

Secondary hyperparathyroidism, 360

Senile osteoporosis, 325

Sensitization, production of, 23

Sensitizers
classification of, 25
role of, 257
route of administration, 23

Serotonin; *cf.* 5HT

Sex → calciphylaxis, **291**

Shoulder-hand syndrome of Steinbrocker, 354

Siderocalciphylactic sensitization, 57, 447

Siderocalciphylaxis
definition of, **16**
mechanism of, 448

Siderofibroses; *cf.* Sideroscleroses

Sideroscleroses, 7, 431
Gamna corpuscles in, 431

Silver polish → scleroderma, 427

Site of challenge, **250**

Sjögren's disease; *cf.* Sjögren's syndrome

Sjögren's syndrome, 431
⇄ scleroderma, 427, *Fig. 315*

Skeletal muscles; *cf.* Muscles

Skin; *cf. also* Cutaneous
topical calciphylaxis in, **37**
← AAN + DHT + plucking, 284
← ACTH, glucocorticoids, hypophysectomy +
DHT + Fe-Dex i.v. + PMX s.c., 278
← age + DHT + FeCl₃ s.c., plucking, 289
← age + KMnO₄ s.c., 303, *Fig. 242*
← albumen i.p. + DHT, 88, 255
← albumen i.p. + DHT + PMX s.c., 285
← albumen i.p. + DHT + restraint, *Fig. 215*
← albumen i.p., i.v. + DHT + PMX s.c., 290
← albumen i.v. + DHT, 86, *Fig. 42*
← albumen s.c. + DHT, *Fig. 11*
← albumen s.c. + DHT + FeCl₃ s.c. + PMX
s.c., 287
← albumen s.c. + DHT + Fe-Dex s.c., 254
← albumen s.c. + DHT + hypophysectomy +
plucking, 276, *Fig. 225*
← albumen s.c. + DHT + restraint + Thoro-
trast® s.c., 263
← albumen s.c. + Fe-Dex s.c. + DHT + PMX
s.c., 285
← albumen, C.S.A., dextran, dextrin, gelatin,
KMnO₄, pectin, plasma, PMX, PVP, yolk,
48/80 + CrCl₂ + DHT, 62
← albumen, C.S.A., dextran, dextrin, FeCl₃,
gelatin, pectin, plasma, PMX, yolk +
DHT, 59
← albumen, CrCl₂, C.S.A., dextran, dextrin, gel-

atin, KMnO₄, pectin, plasma, PMX, PVP,
yolk, 48/80 + DHT, 62
← albumen, FeCl₃, Fe-Dex, yolk s.c. + DHT
(in cat, dog, hamster, monkey, mouse), 292,
293
← albumen, C.S.A., dextran, dextrin, gelatin,
pectin, plasma, PMX, yolk + DHT +
FeCl₃, Fe-Dex, 59
← albumen s.c. + NaAST, *Fig. 15*
← CrCl₂ i.v. + DHT + PMX s.c., 288, 290
← CrCl₂ s.c. + DHT, 302
← CrCl₃ i.v. + DHT, 100
← CrCl₃ s.c. + DHT + Fe-Dex s.c. + restraint,
263
← CrCl₃ s.c. + DHT + hemostat + PMX s.c.,
285
← Dextran + DHT + FeCl₃ s.c., *Figs. 17, 18*
← DHT + CrCl₃ i.v., 47
← DHT + DOC s.c. + Fe-Dex i.v. + PMX
s.c., + triamcinolone s.c., 281
← DHT + egg yolk i.v. + PMX s.c., 291
← DHT + estradiol, methyltestosterone +
plucking, 281
← DHT + FeCl₂, FeCl₃ i.v. + PMX s.c., 288,
290
← DHT + FeCl₃ s.c. + CrCl₃ s.c., 254
← DHT + FeCl₃ s.c. + plucking + PMX s.c.,
285
← DHT + FeCl₃ s.c. + restraint + yolk s.c.,
263
← DHT + FeCl₃, Fe-Dex + KMnO₄, PVP,
48/80, 60
← DHT + Fe-Dex intrapedal, *Fig. 208*
← DHT + Fe-Dex i.p., 118, *Figs. 13, 77–80, 318*
← DHT + Fe-Dex i.p., i.v., 255
← DHT + Fe-Dex i.v., 115
← DHT + Fe-Dex i.v. + glucocorticoids +
PMX s.c., 242
← DHT + Fe-Dex i.v. + hypophysectomy +
PMX s.c., 277, *Fig. 226*
← DHT + Fe-Dex i.v. + PMX s.c., 127, 255,
287–90, *Figs. 84, 88, 89*
← DHT + Fe-Dex i.v. + PMX s.c. + re-
straint, 265, *Fig. 217*
← DHT + Fe-Dex i.v. + PMX s.c. + triam-
cinolone s.c., 280
← DHT + Fe-Dex s.c., 254
← DHT + Fe-Dex s.c. (in hamster), *Fig. 231*
← DHT + Fe-Dex s.c. (in mouse), *Fig. 232*
← DHT + Fe-Din i.v., 134, *Figs. 90–92*
← DHT + Fe-Din i.v. + PMX s.c., 287, 288,
290
← DHT + Fe-OS i.v. + PMX s.c., 288, 291
← DHT + Fe-OS s.c , 254
← DHT + Fe-Sol i.v. + PMX s.c., 288, 291
← DHT + 5HT i.p., s.c., 151
← DHT + KCl, MgCl₂, NaCl, NaClO₄,
Na₂SO₄ + plucking, 259
← DHT + KMnO₄, PVP, 48/80, 60

← DHT + LTH, STH, vasopressin + plucking, 278

← DHT + nephrotoxic substances, thallium
acetate + plucking, 283

← DHT + pectin s.c., *Fig. 14*

← DHT + plucking (of scalp hair), *Figs. 7, 8, 10*

← DHT + plucking + restraint + thallium
acetate s.c., *Fig. 149*

← DHT + PMX intrapedal, *Fig. 128*

← DHT + PMX s.c. + Thorotrast® i.v., 287

← DHT + PMX s.c. + yolk i.v., 208, *Fig. 168*

← DHT + restraint + Thorotrast® i.v., *Figs.
219–21*

← DHT + skin traction, *Fig. 16*

← DHT + thallium salts + plucking, 284

← DHT + Thorotrast® i.v., 246, 256, *Figs.
132–47*

← DHT + Walker tumor, *Fig. 317*

← FeCl₃, *Fig. 6*

← Fe-Dex i.v. + parathyroid hormone s.c. +
PMX s.c., *Figs. 174, 175*

← Fe-Dex i.v. + PMX s.c. + restraint + vitamin D₃ i.v., 266, *Fig. 222*

← Fe-Dex i.v. + PMX s.c. + Vitamin D₃ i.v.,
212

← Fe-Din i.v. + NaAST i.p., 236

← KMnO₄ s.c., *Fig. 249*

← NaAST i.p. + Thorotrast® i.v., 239, *Fig. 197*

← NaH₂PO₄ p.o. + vitamin D₂, 258, *Fig. 210*

← nephrectomy + Thorotrast® i.v., 231, *Figs.
189, 191*

← parathyroid hormone s.c. + Thorotrast®
i.v., 226, *Figs. 186, 187*

← Thorotrast® i.v., *Fig. 147*

Skin reaction

production of, *Fig. 16*

→ calciphylaxis ← DHT, *Fig. 16*

Sn (tin), 51

SnCl₂, as direct calcifier, 311

SnCl₂ i.v. → calciphylaxis ← DHT, 177

Sodium; *cf. also* Na

salts, 28, 29, 51

acetylsulfathiazole; *cf.* NaAST

Solid form, of topical calciphylaxis, 37

Solvent, of DHT, 2

Somatotrophic hormone; *cf.* STH

Species

→ calciphylaxis, 18, 292

→ heart, muscle ← DHT + Me-Cl-COL s.c. +
NaH₂PO₄ p.o., 147

Speculations, 439

Spleen

calcinosis of, 340

← CeCl₃ i.v. + DHT, 98

← DHT + InCl₃ i.v., 167

← DHT + Pb-acetate i.v., 170, *Figs. 127, 127a*

← DHT + PMX s.c. + yolk i.v., 285

← DHT + Thorotrast® i.v., *Fig. 138*

← DHT + yolk i.p., 203, *Figs. 165, 166*

← DHT + yolk i.v., 41, 195, *Figs. 151, 152, 158*

← DHT + ZnCl₂ i.v., 209

← egg yolk i.v., 200, *Fig. 160*

← nephrectomy + Thorotrast® i.v., *Fig. 190*

← scleroderma, 427

Spondylarthritis ankylopoietica; *cf.* Rheumatoid
spondylitis

Spondylitis deformans; *cf.* Rheumatoid spondylitis

Spondylitis ossificans ligamentosa; *cf.* Rheumatoid
spondylitis

SrCl₂, 51

Staining, of calcified tissue, 31

Stannous chloride, 29

Status thymicolymphaticus ⇌ dermatomyositis,
353

Steatonecrosis, subcutaneous, 404

STH (somatotrophic hormone), 16

→ calciphylaxis ← DHT + plucking, 278

Stiff-man syndrome, and the "stiffness syndrome"
of guinea pigs, 431

← stigmasterol, 431

Stigmasterol → stiff-man syndrome, 431

Stomach

← albumen i.v. + DHT, 86

← Chondroitin sulfuric acid i.p., i.v. + DHT, 98

← CrCl₃ i.v. + DHT (in hamster), 297

← DHT + Fe (ferric) albuminate i.p., 112

← DHT + FeCl₂ i.v., *Fig. 71*

← DHT + Fe-Dex i.v., 115

← DHT + Fe-Din i.v., 135

← DHT + Fe-OS i.v., 138, *Fig. 96*

← DHT + 5HT i.p., s.c., 151

← DHT + yolk i.v., *Figs. 156, 157*

Stress; *cf.* under individual stressors (Restraint,
Quadriplegia, Muscular exercise, Cold, Heat,
etc.)

role in calciphylaxis, 457, 459, 468

→ calciphylaxis, **261**

← direct calcifiers, 302

← KMnO₄ s.c., 302

→ calcium in tissue ← KMnO₄ s.c., 302

→ hypoparathyroidism, 366

→ scleredema adultorum Buschke, 406

→ scleroderma, 430

→ systemic calciphylaxis, 264

→ topical calciphylaxis, 262

Stress dermatoses, 376

Stromal depot system; *cf.* SDS

Subcutaneous fat necrosis; *cf.* Sclerema neonatorum

Subcutaneous injection, technique, 23, *Fig. 2*

Subcutaneous steatonecrosis, 404

Sublingual gland, calciphylactic reaction of, 80

Submaxillary gland
  ← albumen, Fe-Dex, 5HT, Thorotrast® s.c., 79
  ← DHT + FeCl₂ intracarotid, *Fig. 37*
  ← DHT + 5HT s.c. + restraint, 265
  ← 5HT s.c. + restraint + vitamin D₃ i.v., 266
  ← scleroderma, 426
Subtosan®; *cf.* PVP
Superficial dermatosis, 47
Suppurating myocarditis, produced by DHT +
  NaH₂PO₄ p.o., 170
Surgical interventions
  → calciphylaxis, 3, 26
  as sensitizers, 26
Syphilitic osteitis, 325
Systemic calciphylaxis, **1**
  characterization, 83
  critical period, 253
  definition, **14**
  production of, 20
  ← age, 291
Systemic scleroderma, 407
Systemic sclerosis, 407
Systemic sensitizing agent; *cf.* Calcifier
Systemogenic calcification, definition of, **16**

Tail ← albumen, Fe-Dex, Thorotrast® + DHT,
  64
Tannic acid, 52
Technique
  celestin blue, 35
  of gavage, *Fig. 1*
  intravenous injection, *Fig. 4*
  von Kóssa plus van Gieson, 34
  von Kóssa plus methylene blue, 34
  von Kóssa plus PAS, 34
  of subcutaneous injection, *Fig. 2*
  of subcutaneous, intraperitoneal, intrapedal, in-
    travenous injection, 23, 24
Tendinitis, calcareous, following local infection,
  434
Tendovaginitis, calcareous, following local infection, 434
Teratomas, calcification in, 436
Thallium acetate, 29; *cf. also* Nephrotoxic substances
  → calciphylaxis ← Ca-acetate, Na-acetate, Na₃-
    citrate, NaCl, NaH₂PO₄, Na₂HPO₄, 240
  ← DHT + plucking, 283
  ← electrolytes (various), 240
Thallium acetate s.c.
  → calciphylaxis ← DHT, 192, *Figs. 149, 150*
  ← DHT + plucking + restraint, *Fig. 149*
Thallium salts
  → calciphylaxis, 284
  ← DHT, 284
  ← DHT + plucking, 284

ThCl₄ i.v. → calciphylaxis ← DHT, 177
4′ -(2-thiazolylsulfamoyl); *cf.* NaAST
Th(NO₃)₄ i.v. → calciphylaxis ← DHT, 177
Thomson's disease; *cf.* Rothmund's disease
Thorax ← scleroderma, 415
Thorium,
  as challenger, 4
Thorium i.v. → calciphylaxis ← DHT, 12
Thorotrast®, 52
  as direct challenger, 26
  storage, in phagocytes of bristle roots, *Fig. 147*
  → calciphylaxis, 26
  ← DHT, 64, 340
Thorotrast® intracarotid → calciphylaxis, 65
Thorotrast® intrathoracic, s.c. → lacrimal, sali-
  vary, submaxillary gland, 79
Thorotrast® i.p. → calciphylaxis ← DHT, 190,
  Fig. 148
Thorotrast® i.v.
  → calciphylaxis, *Fig. 147*
  ← age + DHT, 291
  ← DHT, 177, 246, 256, *Figs. 132–46*
  ← DHT + PMX s.c., 287
  ← DHT + restraint, 266, *Figs. 219–21*
  ← NaAST i.p., 239, *Fig. 197*
  ← nephrectomy, 231, *Figs. 189–92*
  ← nephrectomy + parathyroidectomy, 281
  ← parathyroid hormone s.c., 226, *Figs. 186,
    187*
Thorotrast® s.c. → calciphylaxis ← albumen s.c.
  + DHT + restraint, 263
Thorotrast® subconjunctival → eye, 78
Thromboangiitis obliterans; *cf.* Buerger's disease
Thrombotic thrombocytopenic purpura, 433
Thymic calciphylaxis, 145, *Figs. 103–5*
Thymus
  ← albumen i.v. + DHT, 86
  ← CrCl₂ i.v. + DHT, *Fig. 70*
  ← DHT + egg yolk i.p., 203, *Figs. 162–64*
  ← DHT + egg yolk i.v., 198
  ← DHT + F-COL s.c., *Fig. 103*
  ← DHT + F-COL, triamcinolone, 281
  ← DHT + Fe (ferric) albuminate i.p., 112
  ← DHT + triamcinolone s.c., 145, *Figs. 104,
    105*
Thyroid
  calcinosis of, 340, 436
  ← chromium i.v. + DHT, 12
  ← CrCl₂ i.v. + DHT + PMX s.c., 290
  ← CrCl₃ i.v. + DHT, 255
  ← CrCl₃ i.v. + DHT (in dog), 297
  ← CrCl₃ i.v. + DHT (in hamster), 297
  ← CrCl₃ i.v. + DHT + PMX s.c., 287, 288,
    290
  ← CrCl₃ i.v. + DHT + restraint, 265, *Fig. 216*

← CrCl₃ i.v. + nephrectomy, 227, *Fig. 188*
← CrCl₃ i.v. + parathyroid hormone s.c., 213, *Fig. 171*
← DHT + FeCl₂ i.v., 112, 255
← DHT + FeCl₂ i.v. + PMX s.c., 290
← DHT + FeCl₃, 82
← KMnO₄ intra-iliac, 305
Thyroid-parathyroid-carotid-body calciphylaxis, 100
  produced by CrCl₂ i.v. + DHT, 104
  produced by CrCl₃ i.v. + DHT, 100
  produced by CrCl₃ i.v. + parathyroid hormone s.c., 213, *Figs. 171, 172*
  produced by DHT + FeCl₂ i.v., 112
  produced by DHT + FeSO₄ i.v., 145, *Fig. 102*
  produced by DHT + other chromium salts i.v., 104
  produced by nephrectomy + CrCl₃ i.v., 227, *Fig. 188*
Thyro-parathyroid apparatus (nerves of) → calciphylaxis, 282
Thyroparathyroidectomy → calcinosis universalis, 341
TiCl₃, 29, 51
  as direct calcifier, 311
TiCl₃ i.v. → calciphylaxis ← DHT, 177
TiCl₄, 29, 51
TiCl₄ i.v. → calciphylaxis ← DHT, 177
Tissue scaffolding, 39
Titanium, as challenger, 4, 29
Tongue
  ← CrCl₃ intracarotid + DHT, *Figs. 21, 22, 35*
  ← DHT + 5HT s.c., *Fig. 114*
  ← DHT + NaH₂PO₄ p.o., *Fig. 213*
  ← DHT + Thorotrast® i.v., *Figs. 132, 142, 143*
  ← nephrectomy + Thorotrast® i.v., *Fig. 192*
  ← parathyroid hormone s.c. + Thorotrast® i.v., *Fig. 186*
Tonsil ← scleroderma, 412
Tooth ← CrCl₃ intracarotid + DHT, *Figs. 19, 20*
Topical activator of challenger; *cf.* Adjuvant
Topical calciphylaxis, 1
  adjuvants, 55
  calcified plate formation, 37
  calcium incrustation of collagen fibers and fat cells, 37
  characterization, 37
  critical period, 54, 252
  definition, 14
  granular form, 46
  histology, 37
  in the skin, 37
  in tissues other than the skin, 63
  production of, 19
  production by intra-arterial injection of challengers, 79

reticular form, 45
solid form, 37
← hypophysectomy, 276
Topical tissue injury, 433
Topical trauma; *cf.* Trauma
Topogenic calcification, definition of, 16
Toxoplasma, 332
Trachea
  ← CrCl₂ i.v. + DHT, *Fig. 70*
  ← CrCl₃ i.v. + DHT (in hamster), 297
  ← CrCl₃ i.v. + nephrectomy, *Fig. 188*
  ← DHT + FeCl₂ i.v., 112
Tracheal epithelium ← CrCl₃ i.v. + DHT, *Fig. 60*
Traction on skin, cutaneous calciphylactic challenging effect of, 52
Tragacanth gum, 51
Transplantable tumors; *cf.* under individual names (Walker, Murphy, etc.)
Trauma
  → calcification, 433
  → calciphylaxis ← DHT, 10, 74, 82
  → calcium in kidney, 317
Traumatic myositis, 351
Triamcinolone
  → calciphylaxis ← DHT, 281
  ← adrenalectomy + DHT + FeCl₃, plucking, 278
Triamcinolone s.c.
  → calciphylaxis ← DHT, 145, *Figs. 104, 105*
  ← DHT + DOC s.c. + Fe-Dex i.v. + PMX s.c., 281
  ← DHT + Fe-Dex i.v. + PMX s.c., 280
Trichloroethylene → scleroderma, 427
Triple wheal test, 31, 48, *Fig. 5*
Trypan blue, 53
Trypsin, 53
TTP; *cf.* Thrombotic thrombocytopenic purpura
Tubercle → calcification, 434
Tuberculosis, 334
  of the skin, in scleroderma, 427
Tumors
  calcification in, 434, 436
  ⇌ dermatomyositis, 353
Tween 80, 52

Ulerythema centrifugum; *cf.* Lupus erythematosus
Ultraviolet rays (general), cutaneous calciphylactic challenging effect of, 52
Ureter ← CrCl₃ intra-iliac + DHT, *Figs. 28, 29*
Urinary calculi, 397
Urinary bladder ← CrCl₃ intra-iliac + DHT, *Fig. 28*
Urokon®, 52

Urolithiasis ⇄ hyperparathyroidism, 357

Urticaria, 437

Urticaria factitia, in scleroderma, 427

Urticaria pigmentosa, 377, *Fig. 285*

Uterine and psoriasiform calciphylaxis, 118

Uterus
  calcinosis of, 341, *Fig. 266*
  ← age + DHT + Fe-Dex i.p., i.v., 291
  ← CrCl₃ intra-iliac + DHT, *Fig. 28*
  ← DHT + Fe-Dex i.p., 5, 6, 117, 118, *Figs. 81–83*
  ← DHT + Fe-Dex i.p. + ovariectomy, 281, *Fig. 229*
  ← DHT + Fe-Dex i.p., i.v., 255
  ← DHT + Fe-OS i.p., *Fig. 83*

Vaccination → scleroderma, 427

Vagina
  ← CrCl₃ intra-iliac + DHT, *Fig. 29*
  ← scleroderma, 412

Vasopressin, 49
  → calciphylaxis ← DHT + plucking, 278

Vessels
  ← DHT + FeCl₃, 82
  ← DHT + ZnCl₂ i.v., *Fig. 170*
  ← KMnO₄ intra-iliac, 305
  ← scleroderma, 415, *Fig. 311*

Villonodular synovitis, 437

Vital mordant; *cf.* Challenger

Vitamin D₂
  as sensitizer, 3, 26
  → calciphylaxis, 26
    ← NaH₂PO₄ p.o., 258, *Fig. 210*

Vitamin D₃
  as sensitizer, 3, 26
  → calciphylaxis, 26

Vitamin D₃ i.v.
  → calciphylaxis ← Fe-Dex i.v. + PMX s.c., 212
    ← Fe-Dex i.v. + PMX s.c., + restraint, 266, *Fig. 22*
    ← 5HT s.c., 212
    ← 5HT s.c. + restraint, 266, *Figs. 223, 224*

Vitamin E
  → dermatomyositis, 354
  → lupus erythematosus, 377
  → scleroderma, 431

VOSO₄, 51

VOSO₄ i.v. → calciphylaxis ← DHT, 194

Walker tumor, 49
  → calciphylaxis ← DHT, *Fig. 317*

transplant ← DHT + Fe-Dex intratumoral, *Fig. 38*

Werner's disease, 401, 437

Werner's syndrome; *cf.* Werner's disease

Westphal. lipopolysaccharide, 51

Wharton's jelly, lyophilized, 49

Wound healing ⇄ calciphylaxis, 7

X-rays
  cutaneous calciphylactic challenging effect of, 52

Yolk, **16**, 53; *cf. also* Egg yolk
  definition, **16**
  → calciphylaxis ← CrCl₂ + DHT, 62
  ← DHT, 59, 62
  ← DHT + FeCl₃, Fe-Dex, 59

Yolk i.p. → calciphylaxis ← DHT, 203, *Figs. 161–67*

Yolk i.v.
  → calciphylaxis, 200, *Fig. 160*
    ← DHT, 194, 246, *Figs. 151–60, 204*
    ← DHT + PMX s.c., 208, 285, 287, 291, *Fig. 168*
  → Kupffer cells, *Fig. 160*

Yolk s.c.
  → calciphylaxis ← DHT (in cat, dog, hamster, monkey, mouse), 292, 293
  ← DHT + FeCl₃ s.c. + restraint, 263

Zirconium, as challenger, 4, 29

ZnCl₂, 29, 51
  as direct calcifier, 311

ZnCl₂ i.v. → calciphylaxis ← DHT, 209, *Figs. 169, 170*

ZnCl₂ s.c.
  as direct calcifier, 303, *Fig. 240*
  → calciphylaxis, *Fig. 240*

ZnCl₂ s.c. → calcium in tissue, *Fig. 240*

ZrOCl₂, 29, 51
  as direct calcifier, 311

ZrOCl₂ i.v. → calciphylaxis ← DHT, 211

Zymosan, 51

48/80, 52, 58; *cf. also* Histamine liberators
  composition, **16**
  as indirect challenger, 29
  → calciphylaxis, 29
    ← CrCl₂ + DHT, 62
    ← DHT, 60, 62
    ← DHT + FeCl₃, Fe-Dex, 60
  → calcium in muscle, 75